Cultured Human Keratinocytes and Tissue Engineered Skin Substitutes

Editors
Raymund E. Horch, Andrew M. Munster, Bruce M. Achauer

With forewords by
C. Vacanti and I. V. Yannas

Georg Thieme Verlag Stuttgart

Library of Congress Cataloging-in-Publication Data

Cultured human keratinocytes and tissue
engineered skin substitutes /
ed. Raymund E. Horch ...
With forew. by C. Vacanti and I. V. Yannas. –
Stuttgart ; New York : Thieme, 2001
    ISBN 3-13-130161-9

Important Note: Medicine is an ever-changing
science undergoing continual development. Research and clinical experience are continually
expanding our knowledge, in particular our
knowledge of proper treatment and drug therapy. Insofar as this book mentions any dosage or
application, readers may rest assured that the
authors, editors, and publishers have made every effort to ensure that such references are in ac-
cordance with the state of knowledge at the time
of production of the book.

Nevertheless, this does not involve, imply, or
express any guarantee or responsibility on the
part of the publishers in respect of any dosage
instructions and forms of application stated in
the book. Every user is requested to examine
carefully the manufacturer's leaflets accompa-
nying each drug and to check, if necessary in
consultation with a physician or specialist,
whether the dosage schedules mentioned
therein or the contraindications stated by the
manufacturers differ from the statements
made in the present book. Such examination is
particularly important with drugs that are either rarely used or have been newly released
on the market. Every dosage schedule or every
form of application used is entirely at the user's own risk and responsibility. The authors
and publishers request every user to report to
the publishers any discrepancies or inaccura-
cies noticed.

© 2001 Georg Thieme Verlag
Rüdigerstraße 14, D-70469 Stuttgart
Printed in Germany
http://www.thieme.de

Cover: Thieme-Marketing, Stuttgart
Typesetting: SATZPUNKT Bayreuth GmbH,
typeset on Adobe FrameMaker
Printed by Gulde Druck, Tübingen
ISBN 3-13-130161-9

This book is dedicated to my wife Andrea Johanna and to my sons Mark Alexander and Christian, who made it hard to be at work since it is so great to be at home, for her love and support, during the time spent with this book.

Raymund E. Horch

Acknowledgements

We want to thank all those who developed the cell culture techniques and who proceeded with the experimental and clinical experiences to advance the art of tissue engineering skin substitutes and bringing them into patient care, as well as all the authors for their fine contributions to this work.

We also want to thank Dr. Elizabeth Marczell for her great engagement and help during the whole process of the edition of this book. She made many fruitful contacts possible which were necessary to bring this book into existence and helped us keeping the milestones.

Further on we want to thank Dr. Johann Odar. He always stimulated and engaged research efforts towards the development of new skin substitution techniques using biological carriers. His continuous support of new ideas over the years finally resulted in unforeseen developments in skin substitution with physiological matrices.

Last but not least we want to thank Greg Bosch from Vienna, who unrestrictedly supported this work, for his fruitful comments and personal engagement in the future development of tissue engineered products. His commitment is based on the awareness that scientific progress and economic trends are strongly interrelated to stay abreast of changes and to promote future developments.

Raymund E. Horch
Andrew M. Munster
Bruce M. Achauer

Preface

The technique of culturing human keratinocytes in defined media and the exciting possibility to multiply epithelial cells up to ten thousand fold the amount of the original skin sample has been available for more than two decades by now. Many scientific pioneers in the field of biology, surgery and other disciplines have added their efforts with enormous creativity and ambition to further improve this method.

The introduction of this technique into burn treatment in the early eighties of the past century was followed by initial enthusiasm about the prospect of saving the lifes of many extensively burned patients. In addition it opened new dimensions in the possible survival of such severe injuries, that had previously been unthought.

However, after the first experiences had been gained a variety of considerable drawbacks was noted, including the fragility of the cultured epithelial autografts (CEA), the long time until enough epithelia were grown in the laboratory, the difficulty of handling the material, the uncertain take rates of grafts as well as mechanical instability, blistering of healed areas and excessive scarring as well as high costs. One way to produce a more reliable clinical outcome was the introduction of a pre-treatment of full thickness wounds with allograft skin as a preliminary step before the allogenic epidermis is secondarily removed and the CEA are grafted on this bed. This approach has become a standard in the clinical care of burn wounds being treated with CEA.

New ideas arise steadily to optimize cultured epithelial grafting procedures and to enhance the quality of cultured skin or skin substitutes. Among the latest developments is the use of biomaterials such as human fibrin sealant to carry the cultured cells and to allow safer fixation of cells on a recipient wound bed. Another new step is the use of monolayers of cultured keratinocytes on various membrane like materials instead of grafting multilayered skin resembling sheets of epithelia.

A variety of more or less critical single center experiences have been reported until now but no comprehensive review of the results obtained in the leading centers over the world has been carried out yet.

We feel that after the successful clinical introduction of CEA the time has come to summarize the efforts of producing and grafting cultured skin substitutes in order to resume the state of the art and to show where the next steps in the development might go.

This book brings together the specific experiences of the scientific community in this field as well as the clinical experiences of the most renowned experts in the field from all over the world. The editors are especially proud of bringing together the leading biologists and material scientists together with burn surgeons, dermatologists, and surgeons of all specialities from all continets of the world. Taken together this unique collection of world wide expert opinions and experiences represents the current spectrum of possibilities in artificial, tissue engineered skin subsitution.

Raymund E. Horch
Department of Plastic and
Hand Surgery
Albert-Ludwigs-University,
Freiburg, Germany

Andrew M. Munster
Baltimore Regional Burn Center,
Francis Scott Key Medical Center,
Johns Hopkins Bayview Medical
Center Baltimore, MD USA

Bruce M. Achauer
Division of Plastic Surgery
University of California
Irvine, CA
USA

Foreword

C. Vacanti

As we enter into a new millenium we hope to look toward the future and imagine what is possible. To effectively accomplish this, however, one must reflect on the past, and consider what has already been achieved. This is especially true in Tissue Engineering, which has been defined as "the use of biological and/or synthetic materials in conjunction with cells to create biologic substitutes to serve as functional tissue replacements" [1].

Retrospectively, many events can be perceived as descriptions of "Tissue Engineering". Dating back to biblical times, "The Lord God, cast a deep sleep on the man, and while he was asleep, he took out one of his ribs and closed up its place with flesh. The Lord God then built up into a woman the rib that he had taken from the man" [2].

In modern times, as early as 1908, Lexer [3] described early attempts at engineering of tissue in his report of the use of freshly amputated or cadaver allografts for joint reconstruction.

Modern efforts to generate new tissue and restore lost function have been dependent on advances in associated fields of cell biology, and material sciences. It has now seems clear that the use of living cells will result in a higher degree of tissue function than the use of endogenous, or exogenous chemicals to stimulate development.

Early approaches to reintroduce cells into a host were quite simplistic and usually unsuccessful. Cells were injected as free suspensions in hope that they would randomly engraft.

During the last two decades, synthetic and naturally occurring polymer scaffolds have been used to provide cell anchorage sites and intrinsic structure when implanting cells. The use of a template enables precise engineering of a multitude of characteristics, such as surface area and exposure of the attached cells to nutrients. The porosity of synthetic scaffolds can be varied to alter the intrinsic strength and elasticity of the matrix, as well as other characteristics, such as the degradation rate and the environment into which the cells are implanted. It is conceivable to correct a variety of hormonal and enzymatic deficiencies using this approach in combination with gene therapy.

Successful application of this technology requires the identification of key features of scaffoldings that are important for maintaining cell function.

Initial studies focused on scaffolds composed of the naturally occurring polymer, collagen, and the synthetic polymers polylactic and polyglycolic acid. The matrix to which cells are attached in vitro proved to be a crucial variable in this technology. Numerous natural and synthetic polymer fibers, foams and hydrogels have now been identified to serve as suitable substrates for cell delivery.

An equally important aspect is the immunologic barrier. Improvements in the understanding of immunology and the ability to fool mother nature into thinking foreign cells are "self" may allow for implantation of allogeneic or even xengeneic cells to generate functional tissue in the future. Unfortunately, at this time in history, the development of a universal donor cell type that can be used in the construction of a commercially available cell/polymer construct that will meet the needs of any recipient is still a dream.

Another critical factor, which is only now being fully explored, is the source of the cells to be utilized. Several studies have suggested that immature cells, as compared to the fully differentiated cells of specialized tissues, are better able to multiply. Immature or progenitor cells can be induced to differentiate after several generations, in contrast to fully differentiated cells, which tend to dedifferentiate and do not function as well. Implantation of progenitor cells may be advantageous in that they require significantly less oxygen, as compared to their more mature, fully differentiated counterpart. Hence, they are much more likely to survive the transplantation into a less vascularized bed. This very likely mimics what occurs in nature, in that undifferentiated progenitor cells seem to multiply in an injured area, and may very well be responsible for efforts by the body to restore lost tissue function.

The parallel to nature is extremely important, as many efforts have reported the highest degree of success when mimicking nature. What is known scientifically represents only a miniscule degree of the organization and function of living systems. Although numerous theories have been proposed and then replaced by more "modern hypotheses", most of the biologic processes remain "a black box".

The basic premise in health care is to enable the body to heal itself. Physicians do nothing more than optimize an environment most conducive to healing. Hostile environments are minimized at the same time that the supply of oxygen and nutrients, necessary for healing, is maximized. Basic principles of surgery are to debride dead tissue, which removes the source of unfavorable chemical agents, to approximate tissue, and to optimize the vascular supply and delivery of nutrients to the injured site.

In Tissue Engineering, we strive to accomplish the same goals. Dead tissue and scar is excised. Rather than approximating the remaining tissue to eliminate the dead space, living cells that belong in the damaged area, are implanted in a configuration that will prevent them from dissociating. The use of a scaffolding or template provides this configuration and dictates shape and function of the new tissue by providing structural cues. Under ideal conditions, this will enable the body to heal itself.

Application of these principles has enabled scientists to successfully generate several new function tissue equivalents.

Conclusion

We learned that if cell anchorage sites and reasonable structural cues are provided in an appropriate environment, the intrinsic ability of cells to reorganize and generate new tissue is enhanced. It is our belief that advances in material sciences and the life sciences will enable physicians and scientists to help humankind in the future by being able to replace a multitude of diseased or damaged tissues.

References

[1] Tissue Engineering: 1(1):1, 1995.
[2] Genesis. 2: 21–22.
[3] Lexer E: Die Verwendung der freien Knochenplastik nebst Versuchen über Gelenkversteifung und Gelenktransplantation. Arch Klin Chir 86: 939 54, 1908.

Foreword

I. V. Yannas

Future trends in tissue-engineered skin substitute developments: in vitro or in vivo?

The skin is a versatile organ functioning at the interface between man and the environment. This organ can be repaired naturally when damaged (say, by fire) as long as roughly 40 % of it continues to function; otherwise, death often ensues.

Efforts to replace nonfunctional organs have been relying on formation of the desired tissues and organs either in vitro or in vivo. In vitro processes rely extensively on formation of the desired organ in the laboratory, based on a series of culture steps, followed by implantation in the host. In vivo methods make minimal use of cell culture; they rely instead on identification of the appropriate nondiffusible regulator. An example is the dermis regeneration template, a biologically active analog of the extracellular matrix, seeded with keratinocytes, which induces simultaneous regeneration of the epidermis and the dermis following implantation in a dermis-free wound in the host (Yannas et al., 1989; Compton et al., 1998).

It is possible to simplify the presentation of the complex protocols used by different investigators for formation of organs by using the systematics of synthetic chemistry (Yannas, 2000a). Presented in this simple code, the data from a large number of independent investigators can be analyzed simply and directly. In the area of synthesis of skin, for example, the analysis leads to a few *conclusions:*

1. The epidermis and the basement membrane can both be synthesized in vitro. The synthesis requires simply keratinocyte culture; no serum or dermal elements are required.
2. A physiological dermis (lacking appendages) has not been synthesized in vitro. Its synthesis in vivo requires the presence of a nondiffusible regulator; exogenous keratinocytes are not required in the dermis-free defect.
3. Synthesis of a physiological skin, complete with an epidermis, basement membrane and a neodermis (no appendages), requires that the keratinocyte-seeded nondiffusible regulator be implanted. Exogenous fibroblasts are not required.

These findings agree with independent data on the conditions required for synthesis of peripheral nerves and their tissue components. The data support the overall conclusion that extension of the synthetic process for skin from the epithelia (epidermis) to the basement membrane and, finally, to the stroma (dermis) requires a gradual transition from in vitro to in vivo protocols (Yannas, 2000b). It is suggested that this transition is necessary in order to accommodate the requirements for stroma synthesis: not only endogenous fibroblasts but also the appropriate concentration of soluble regulators (cytokines and growth factors), supplied by the exudate inside the dermis-free wound, are required.

References

[1] *Compton, CC, CE Butler, IV Yannas, G Warland, DP Orgill:* Organized skin structure is regenerated *in vivo* from collagen-GAG matrices seeded with autologous keratinocytes. J. Invest. Dermatol. 110:908–916 1998.

[2] *Yannas, IV, Lee, E, Orgill, DP, Skrabut, EM, Murphy, GF:* Synthesis and characterization of a model extracellular matrix which induces partial regeneration of adult mammalian skin, Proc. Natl. Acad. Sci. USA, 86:933–937 1989.

[3] *Yannas, IV:* Tissue and Organ Regeneration in Adults. New York: Springer, in the press, 2000a.

[4] *Yannas, IV:* Synthesis of organs: in vitro or in vivo? Proc. Natl. Acad. Sci. USA, in the press, 2000b.

Contents

Contents

List of Contributors

Achauer, B.M., MD
Division of Plastic Surgery
University of California Irvine
1140 W. La Veta, Suite 810
Orange, CA 92868, **USA**
Fax: 714-836-4477, Phone: 714-836-4466
Email: BAchauer@aol.com

Adler, J., PhD
Tissue Bank, Burns & Reconstructive
Surgery Centre
University Hospital Brno-Bohunice
Jihlavska 20
639 00 Brno, **Czech Republic**
Tel: +420 5 4319 3004,
Fax: +420 5 4321 5250
Email: pbrychta@fnbrno.cz

Ainaud, P., MD
Burn Center, Centre de Traitement des Brules,
Hopital d'Instruction des Armees Percy
Avenue henri Barbusse 101
F–92140 Paris (Clamart), **France**
Tel.: +33-1-41-46-62-11
Fax: +33-1-40-95-08-72
Email: c/o jmriv1@aol.com

Andree, C., MD
Department of Plastic and Hand Surgery,
Albert-Ludwigs-University
Hugstetter Str. 55
D–79106 Freiburg i.Br., **Germany**
Tel: ++49-761-270-2817
Fax: ++49-761-270-2501
Email: andree@ch11.ukl.uni-freiburg.de

Argenta, L.C., MD
Department of Plastic and Reconstructive
Surgery
Wake Forest University School of Medicine
Medical Center Boulevard
Winston-Salem, North Carolina 27157, **USA**
Tel: (336) 716-5848, Fax: (336) 716-6642
Email: largenta@wfubmc.edu

Auger, F.A., MD, FRCP
LOEX Laboratoire de Recherche des
Grands Brules
Hopital du Saint-Sacrement
Quebec, Qc G1S 4L8, **Canada**
Tel: (418) 682-7662, Fax: (418) 682-8000
Email: www.loex.ulaval.ca

Bahoric, A., DVM, MSc
Department of Surgery at the Hospital for
Sick Children, Suit 1524
555 University Avenue
Toronto, Ontario, M5G IX8, **Canada**
Tel: (416)-204-9565
Email: bahoric@look.ca

Barbul, A., MD, FACS
Johns Hopkins University School of Medicine
Sinai Hospital of Baltimore
Hofberger Professional Building
2435 W. Belvedere Ave. Suite 46
Baltimore, MD 21215, **USA**
001-410-601-5843
Fax: 410-601-5835
abarbul@welchlink.welch.jhu.edu

Barrandon, Y., PhD
Laboratoire de Differenciation Epitheliale
Dept. Biologie, Ecole Normale Superieur
46, rue d´Ulm
F-75230 Paris cedex 05, **France**
Tel: ++33 144 32 3630/39
fax: ++33 144 32 39 10
Email: barrand@biologie.ens.fr

Barret, J.P., MD
Shriners Burns Hospital-Galveston
UTMB at Galveston
815 Market Street
Galveston, TX 77550-2725, **USA**
Phone: 409 772-2222, fax: 409-770-6919
Email: tavila@utmb.edu

Bayer, G.S., MD
Department of Reconstructive and Plastic
Surgery and Burn Unit, University of Vienna
Austria, Universitätsklinik für Chirurgie
Währinger Gürtel 18-20
A-1090 Wien, **Austria**
Tel.: +43-1-40400-5620
Fax: +43-1-40400-5640
Email: http://www.vu-wien.ac.at

Berthod, F., PhD
LOEX Laboratoire de Recherche des Grands
Brules
Hopital du Saint-Sacrement,
Quebec, G1S 4L8, **Canada**
Tel: (418) 682-7662, Fax: (418) 682-8000
Email: http://www.loex.ulaval.ca

Bormann, J., MB CHB FRCS
Blond McIndoe Research Centre
Queen Victoria Hospital
East Grinstead, West Sussex, RH19 3DZ, **UK**
Tel: 44-1342-313088, Fax: 44-1342-301701
http://www.dialspace.dial.pipex.com/mcindoe

Bevan, S., BSC, PhD
Blond McIndoe Research Centre
Queen Victoria Hospital
East Grinstead, West Sussex, RH19 3DZ, **UK**
Tel: 44-1342-313088, Fax: 44-1342-301701
http://www.dialspace.dial.pipex.com/mcindoe

Bierochs, B., MD
Department of Reconstructive and Plastic
Surgery and Burn Unit
University of Vienna, Austria,
Universitätsklinik für Chirurgie
Währinger Gürtel 18-20
A-1090 Wien, **Austria**
Tel.: +43-1-40400-5620
Fax: +43-1-40400-5640
Email: http://www.vu-wien.ac.at

Black, A., PhD
Laboratoire des Substituts Cutanés
Pavillon I5, Hôpital E. Herriot
Place d'Arsonval
F–69437 Lyon CEDEX 03, **France**
Tel.: (33) 04.72.11.75.92
Fax: (33) 04.72.11.74.99
Email: a.black@chu-lyon.fr

Böhlen, L.M., MD
University of Bern
Department of Dermatology, Inselspital
CH-3010 Bern, **Switzerland**
Tel.: ++41 (31) 632 21 11
Email: lorenz.boehlen@insel.ch

Boyce, S.T., PhD
Research Department, Shriners Hospitals
for Children, Shriners Burns Hospital
3229 Burnet Ave.
Cincinnati, OH 45229, **USA**
Tel.: 513-872-6000, Fax 513-872-6999
Email: http://www.shrinershq.org

Boyle, J.C., MD, FRCS (C)
University of British Columbia
Plastic Surgery & Burn Unit
2nd Floor, Laurel Street Pavillon
899 West 12th Avenue
Vancouver,B.C., V5Z 1M9, **Canada**
Tel.: 604-875-4084, Fax: 604-875-5614
E-mail: jcboyle@interchange.ubc.ca

Braye, F., MD
Centre des brûlés
Pavillon I5, Hôpital E. Herriot
Place d'Arsonval
F–69003 Lyon CEDEX 03, **France**
Email: francois.braye@chu-lyon.fr

Breitkreuz, D., MD
DKFZ Heidelberg
Abteilung Differenzierung und
Carcinogenese in vitro
Im Neuenheimer Feld 280
D-69120 Heidelberg, **Germany**
Tel: 06221-42 4507, Fax: 06221-42 45 51
Email: c/o: N.Fusenig@dkfz-heidelberg.de

Broz, L., MD
Burns Center, Charles University Hospital
Prague
Srobarova str. 50
100 34 Prague 10, **Czech Republic**
Phone: +420-2-6716 3365
Fax: +420-2-6731 3374
Email: burnsec@fnkv.cz

Brychta, P., MD
Masaryk University
Burns & Reconstructive Surgery Centre
University Hospital Brno-Bohunice
Jihlavska 20
639 00 Brno, **Czech Republic**
Tel: +420 5 4319 3004, Fax: +420 5 4321 5250
Email: pbrychta@fnbrno.cz

Burd, A., MD, FRCSEd, FHKCS
Plastic, Reconstructive and Burns Surgery
Department of Surgery
Prince of Wales Hospital
30-32 Ngan Shing Street
Sha Tin, N.T., **Hong Kong**
Tel:(852).2632.2639, Fax:(852).2632.5008
Email: andrewburd@cuhk.edu.hk

Butler, C.E., MD
Harvard Medical School
Brigham and Women's Hospital
75 Francis Street
Boston, MA 02115, **USA**
Phone: (617) 732-5456, Fax: (617) 732-6387
Email: cebutlerl@bics.bwh.harvard.edu

Cantaloube, D., MD
Service de Chirurgie Plastique et de Chirurgie
Maxillo-faciale
Hopital d'Instruction des Armees Percy
Avenue henri Barbusse 101
F–92140 Paris (Clamart), **France**
Tel.: +33 –1-4645 2104 Fax: +33-1-4638
2006
Email: c/o jmriv1@aol.com

Carlos, A., PhD
LOEX Laboratoire de Recherche des Grands
Brules
Hopital du Saint-Sacrement
Quebec, Qc, G1S 4L8, **Canada**
Tel.: (418) 682-7662, Fax: (418) 682-8000

Carsin, H., MD
Burn Center, Centre de Traitement des
Brules
Hopital d'Instruction des Armees Percy
Avenue henri Barbusse 101
F–92140 Paris (Clamart), **France**
Tel.: +33 –1-41-46-62-11
Fax: +33-1-40-95-08-72
Email: c/o jmriv1@aol.com

Chan, E.S.Y., MD
Department of Surgery
Regional Medical Center of San Jose
225 North Jackson Avenue
San Jose, California 95116, **USA**
Tel: (408)259-5000
http://www.regionalmedicalsanjose.com

Clark, H.M., MD PhD, FRCS (C), FACS
Department of Surgery at the Hospital for
Sick Children, Suit 1524
555 University Avenue
Toronto, Ontario, M5G IX8, **Canada**
Tel: (416)-204-9565
Email: howard.clarke@utoronto.ca

Clugston, P.A., MD, FRCS (C)
University of British Columbia
Plastic Surgery & Burn Unit
2nd Floor, Laurel Street Pavillon
899 West 12th Avenue
Vancouver, B.C., V5Z 1M9, **Canada**
Tel.: 604-875-4084, Fax: 604-875-5614
Email: pac@interchange.ubc.ca

Cohen, M., MD, MPs
Department of Surgery at the Hospital for
Sick Children
Suit 1524, 555 University Avenue
Toronto, Ontario, M5G IX8, **Canada**
Tel: (416)-204-9565
Email: drcohen@netvision.net.il

Damour, O., PhD
Laboratoire des Substituts Cutanés
Pavillon I5, Hôpital E. Herriot
Place d'Arsonval
F–69437 Lyon CEDEX 03, **France**
Tel.: (33) 04.72.11.75.92
Fax: (33) 04.72.11.74.99
Email: odile.damour@chu-lyon.fr

DeLuca, M., PhD
Istituto Dermopatice dell'immacolata,
Laboratorio di Ingegneria dei Tessuti
Lab Tiss. Eng. JDJ
Via die Casteli Romani 83185
I-00040 Pomezia Roma, **Italy**
Tel.:06.91.12.192-3,Fax:06.91.06.765
Email: m.deluca@idi.it

Dellambra, E., PhD
Istituto Dermopatice dell'immacolata
Laboratorio di Ingegneria dei Tessuti
Lab Tiss. Eng. JDJ
Via die Casteli Romani 83185
I-00040 Pomezia Roma, **Italy**
Email: tissutale@sinergia.it

Dobozy, A., MD
University of Szeged
Department of Dermatology
Nagyerdei krt. 98
H-4012 Debrecen P.O.B. 34, **Hungary**
Tel.: (36-52) 442-204, Fax: (36-52) 414 632
Email: dermatol@privat.dote

Donati, L., MD
Istituto di Chirurgia Plastica
Facolta' di Medicina E Chirurgia
University of Milano
Pza Ospedale Maggiore, 3
I-20162 Milano, **Italy**
tel. 02-64442443, fax. 02-6425215
Email: Luigi.Donati@unimi.it

Duinslaeger, L., MD
Burn Center Brussels and Military Hospital
De Ring 5
B-9220 Hamme, **Belgium**
Tel.: 00-32-2-264 48 54,
Fax: 00-32-2-264 48 33
Email: luc.duinslaeger@ping.be

Eriksson, E., MD
Harvard Medical School
Brigham and Women's Hospital
75 Francis Street
Boston, MA 02115, **USA**
Phone: (617) 732-5093 Fax: (617) 732-6387
Email: eeriksson@bics.bwh.harvard.edu

Ehrlich, H.P., PhD
Division of Plastic and Reconstructive
Surgery H071
Hershey Medical Center
500 University Dr.
Hershey, PA 17033-0850, **USA**
Phone:717-531-1019, Fax 717-531-4339
Email: pehrlich@psu.edu

Farkas, B., MD
University of Debrecen
Department of Dermatology
DOTE-Börklinika
Nagyerdei krt. 98
H-4012 Debrecen P.O.B. 34, **Hungary**
Tel.: (36-52) 442-204, Fax: (36-52) 414 632
Email: dermatol@privat.dote

Fratianne, R.B., MD
Case Western Reserve University at
MetroHealth Medical Center
Cleveland, Ohio 2500 MetroHealth
Drive Cleveland,
Ohio 44109-1998, **USA**
Tel.: (216) 778-5627
Email: http://www.cwru.edu/med

Freising, C., MD
Department of Anaesthesiology
Albert-Ludwigs-University
Hugstetter Str. 55
D- 79106 Freiburg i.Br., **Germany**
Tel.: ++49-761-270-2817
Fax: ++49-761-270-2501
Email: freising@ana1.ukl.uni-freiburg.de

Frey, M., MD
Department of Reconstructive and Plastic
Surgery and Burn Unit
University of Vienna, Austria
Universitätsklinik für Chirurgie
Währinger Gürtel 18-20
A-1090 Wien, **Austria**
Tel.: +43-1-40400-56986
Fax: +43-1-40400-56988
Email: http://www.vu-wien.ac.at

Fusenig, N.E., MD
DKFZ Heidelberg
Abteilung Differenzierung und
Carcinogenese in vitro
Im Neuenheimer Feld 280
D-69120 Heidelberg, **Germany**
Tel.: 06221-42 4507, Fax: 06221-42 45 51
Email: N.Fusenig@dkfz-heidelberg.de

Germann, E., MSc
University of British Columbia,
Plastic Surgery & Burn Unit
2nd Floor, Laurel Street Pavillon
899 West 12th Avenue
Vancouver,B.C., V5Z 1M9, **Canada**
Tel.: 604-875-4084, Fax: 604-875-5614
Email: http://www.ubc.ca

Goulet, F., PhD
LOEX Laboratoire de Recherche des Grands
Brules
Hopital du Saint-Sacrement
Quebec, Qc, G1S 4L8, **Canada**
Tel.: (418) 682-7662, Fax: (418) 682-8000
Email: lucieg@mlink.net

Guignard, R., PhD
LOEX Laboratoire de Recherche des Grands
Brules
Hopital du Saint-Sacrement
Quebec, Qc, G1S 4L8, **Canada**
Tel.: (418) 682-7662, Fax: (418) 682-8000
Email: http://www.loex.ulaval.ca

Guerra, L., PhD
Istituto Dermopatice dell'ìmmacolata
Laboratorio di Ingegneria dei Tessuti
Lab Tiss. Eng. JDJ
Via die Casteli Romani 83185
I-00040 Pomezia Roma, **Italy**
Email: tissutale@sinergia.it

Gorodetsky, R., PhD
Kiryat Hadassah Sharett Institute of Oncology
Radiobiology & Biotechnology Laboratories
Hadassah University Hospital
P.O.B. 12000
Jerusalem 91120, **Israel**
Tel.: 972-2-6778395, Fax: 972-2-6411128
Email: rafi@hadassah.org.il

Grant, I., MA BM BCh FRCS
Blond McIndoe Research Centre
Queen Victoria Hospital
East Grinstead, West Sussex, RH19 3DZ, **UK**
Tel.: 44-1342-313088, Fax: 44-1342-301701
Email: http://www.dialspace.di-
al.pipex.com/mcindoe

Hayward, C.J., PhD
LOEX Laboratoire de Recherche des Grands
Brules
Hopital du Saint-Sacrement
Quebec, Qc, G1S 4L8, **Canada**
Tel.: (418) 682-7662, Fax: (418) 682-8000
Email: http://www.loex.ulaval.ca

Hansbrough, J.F., MD
Regional Burn Center & Regional Tissue Bank
University of California
San Diego Medical Center
8896 San Diego, California, **USA**
Tel.: (619) 294-6042, Fax: (619) 293-0923
Email: http://www-surgery.ucsd.edu/Trau-
ma.htm

Hata, K.I., MD
Nagoya University, Postgraduate School of
Medicine
Dep. Oral and Maxillofacial Surgery
65 Tsurumai-Cho, Showa-Ku
Nagoya, 466-8550, **Japan**
T: +81-52-744-2345, F: +81-52-744-2352
Email: http://www.med.nagoya-u.ac.jp

Hayward, C.J., MD
LOEX Laboratoire de Recherche des Grands
Brules
Hopital du Saint-Sacrement
Quebec, Qc, G1S 4L8, **Canada**
Tel.: (418) 682-7662, Fax: (418) 682-8000
Email: http://www.loex.ulaval.ca

Herndon, D.N., MD
Shriners Burns Hospital-Galveston
UTMB at Galveston
815 Market Street
Galveston, TX 77550-2725, **USA**
Phone: 409 772-2222, fax: 409-770-6919
Email: tavila@utmb.edu

Hibino, Y., MD
Nagoya University, Postgraduate School
of Medicine
Dep. Oral and Maxillofacial Surgery
65 Tsurumai-Cho, Showa-Ku
Nagoya, 466-8550, **Japan**
T: +81-52-744-2345, F: +81-52-744-2352
Email: http://www.med.nagoya-u.ac.jp

Hickerson, W.L., MD
Firefighters Regional Burn Center
Plastic and Reconstructive Surgery
910 Madison Avbenue Suite 525
Memphis Tennessee, TN 38103, **USA**
Phone: 901-448-1259, fax: 901-448-2973
Email: bhickerson@med1.the-med.org

Horch, R.E., MD
Department of Plastic and Hand Surgery
Albert-Ludwigs-University
Hugstetter Str. 55
D-79106 Freiburg i.Br., **Germany**
Tel: ++49-761-270-2354
Fax: ++49-761-270-2501
Email: horch@ch11.ukl.uni-freiburg.de

Hori K., MD
Nagoya University, Postgraduate School
of Medicine
Dep. Oral and Maxillofacial Surgery
65 Tsurumai-Cho, Showa-Ku,
Nagoya, 466-8550, **Japan**
T: +81-52-744-2345, F: +81-52-744-2352
Email: http://www.med.nagoya-u.ac.jp

Hunyadi, J., MD
University of Debrecen
Department of Dermatology
DOTE-Börklinika
Nagyerdei krt. 98
H-4012 Debrecen P.O.B. 34, **Hungary**
Tel.: (36-52) 442-204, Fax: (36-52) 414 632
Email: dermatol@privat.dote

Hunziker, T., MD
University of Bern
Department of Dermatology, Inselspital
CH-3010 Bern, **Switzerland**
Tel.: ++41 (31) 632 21 11
Email: thomas.hunziker@insel.ch

James. E., BSc PhD
Blond McIndoe Research Centre
Queen Victoria Hospital
East Grinstead, West Sussex, RH19 3DZ, **UK**
Tel: 44-1342-313088, Fax: 44-1342-301701
Email: http://www.dialspace.di-
al.pipex.com/mcindoe

Jones. E., MB BS FRCS
Blond McIndoe Research Centre
Queen Victoria Hospital
East Grinstead, West Sussex, RH19 3DZ, **UK**
Tel.: 44-1342-313088, Fax: 44-1342-301701
Email: http://www.dialspace.di-
al.pipex.com/mcindoe

Kaloudova, Y., MD
Burns & Reconstructive Surgery Centre
University Hospital Brno-Bohunice
Jihlavska 20
639 00 Brno, **Czech Republic**
Tel: +420 5 4319 3004
Fax: +420 5 4321 5250
Email: pbrychta@fnbrno.cz

King, W.W.K., MD
Plastic & Reconstractive Surgery Center
Hong Kong Sanatorium & Hospital, **Hong Kong**
Tel.: 852 5632 2200, Fax (852) 2645 1931
http://www.ha.org.hk/pwh

King, S.R., MD
Firefighters Regional Burn Center
Plastic and Reconstructive Surgery
910 Madison Avbenue Suite 525
Memphis Tennessee, TN 38103, **USA**
Phone: 901-448-1259, fax: 901-448-2973
Email: root@med1.the-med.org

Königova, R., MD, PhD
Burns Center, Charles University Hospital
Prague
Srobarova str. 50
100 34 Prague 10, **Czech Republic**
Phone: +420-2-6716 3365
Fax: +420-2-6731 3374
Email: burnsec@fnkv.cz

Koller, R., MD
Department. of Reconstructive and Plastic
Surgery and Burn Unit
University of Vienna, Austria
Universitätsklinik für Chirurgie
Währinger Gürtel 18-20
A-1090 Wien, **Austria**
Tel.: +43-1-40400-5620
Fax: +43-1-40400-5640
Email: Rupert.Koller@univie.ac.at

Koupil, J., MD
Burns & Reconstructive Surgery Centre
University Hospital Brno-Bohunice
Jihlavska 20
639 00 Brno, **Czech Republic**
Tel.: +420 5 4319 3004
Fax: +420 5 4321 5250
Email: jkoupil@fnbrno.cz

Lakhel, A., MD
Service de Chirurgie Plastique et de Chirurgie
Maxillo-faciale
Hopital d'Instruction des Armees Percy
Avenue henri Barbusse 101
F-92140 Paris (Clamart), **France**
Tel.: +33 –1-4645 2104
Fax: +33-1-4638 2006
Email: c/o jmriv1@aol.com

Lambert, F., MD
Service de Chirurgie Plastique et de Chirurgie
Maxillo-faciale
Hopital d'Instruction des Armees Percy
Avenue henri Barbusse 101
F-92140 Paris (Clamart), **France**
Tel.: +33 –1-4645 2104
Fax: +33-1-4638 2006
Email: c/o jmriv1@aol.com

Lam. PK., PhD, FIBMS
The Hong Kong Skin Bank, Department of
Surgery, The Chinese University of Hong
Kong, Prince of Wales Hospital, **Hong Kong**
Tel.: 852 5632 2200
Fax (852) 2645 1931
Email: pklam@cuhk.edu.hk

Le Bever, H., MD
Burn Center
Centre de Traitement des Brules
Hopital d'Instruction des Armees Percy
Avenue henri Barbusse 101
F-92140 Paris (Clamart), **France**
Tel.: +33 –1-41-46-62-11
Fax: +33-1-40-95-08-72
Email: c/o jmriv1@aol.com

Leigh, I.M., PhD
Centre for Cutaneous Research
St Bartholomew's & The Royal London Hospital Medical & Dental School
Queen Mary & Westfield College
2 Newark St.,
London E1 2AT, **UK**
Tel: 0207 882 7173/7163, Fax: 0207 882 7171
Email: h.navsaria@icrf.icnet.uk

Limat, A., MD
University of Bern
Department of Dermatology, Inselspital
CH-3010 Bern, **Switzerland**
Tel.: ++41 (31) 632 21 11
Email: alain.limat@insel.ch

Liew, C.T., MD
Department of Anatomical &
Cellular Pathology
The Chinese University of Hong Kong
Prince of Wales Hospital, **Hong Kong**
Tel.: 852 5632 2200, Fax (852) 2645 1931
Email: http://www.ha.org.hk/pwh

Lopez-Valle, C.A., PhD
LOEX Laboratoire de Recherche des Grands
Brules
Hopital du Saint-Sacrement
Quebec, Qc, G1S 4L8 **Canada**
Tel.: (418) 682-7662
Fax: (418) 682-8000
Email: www.loex.ulaval.ca

Maas-Szabowski, N., PhD
DKFZ Heidelberg
Abteilung Differenzierung und
Carcinogenese in vitro
Im Neuenheimer Feld 280
D-69120 Heidelberg, **Germany**
Tel: 06221–42 4507, Fax: 06221–42 45 51
Email: c/o N.Fusenig@dkfz-heidelberg.de

Macdonald, I., MSc
University of British Columbia
Plastic Surgery & Burn Unit
2nd Floor, Laurel Street Pavillon
899 West 12th Avenue
Vancouver,B.C., V5Z 1M9, **Canada**
Tel.: 604-875-4084, Fax: 604-875-5614
Email: http://www.ubc.ca

Martin, R., BSc, PhD
Blond McIndoe Research Centre
Queen Victoria Hospital
East Grinstead, West Sussex, RH19 3DZ, **UK**
Tel: 44-1342-313088, Fax: 44-1342-301701
Email: http://dialspace.dial.pipex.com/mcindoe

Marx, G., MD
Hapto Biotech and Kiryat Hadassah Sharett
Institute of Oncology
Radiobiology & Biotechnology Laboratories
Hadassah University Hospital
P.O.B. 12000
Jerusalem, **Israel** 91120
Tel: 972-2-6778395 Fax: 972-2-6411128
http://www.koldoon.com/complist_h_n.htm

Matouskova, E., PhD
Institute of Molecular Genetics, ASCR
Flemingovo nam. 2
166 37 Prague 6, **Czech Republic**
Phone: +420-2-201 83 111
Fax: +420-2-24 31 09 55
Email: matous@img.cas.cz

Meissl, G., MD
Department of Reconstructive and
Plastic Surgery and Burn Unit
University of Vienna, Austria
Universitätsklinik für Chirurgie
Währinger Gürtel 18–20
A-1090 Wien, **Austria**
Tel.: +43-1-40400-5620
Fax: +43-1-40400-5640
Email: http://www.vu-wien.ac.at

Mirancea, N., PhD
DKFZ Heidelberg
Abteilung Differenzierung und
Carcinogenese in vitro
Im Neuenheimer Feld 280
D-69120 Heidelberg, **Germany**
Tel.: 06221-42 4507, Fax: 06221-42 45 51
Email: c/o: N.Fusenig@dkfz-heidelberg.de

Moulin, V., PhD
LOEX Laboratoire de Recherche des Grands
Brules
Hopital du Saint-Sacrement,
Quebec, Qc, G1S 4L8, **Canada**
Tel.: (418) 682-7662
Fax: (418) 682-8000
Email: http://www.loex.ulaval.ca

Morykwas, M.J., PhD
Department of Plastic and Reconstructive
Surgery
Wake Forest University School of Medicine
Medical Center Boulevard
Winston-Salem, North Carolina 27157, **USA**
Tel.: (336) 716-5848, Fax: (336) 716-6642
Email: mmorykwa@wfubmc.edu

Munster A.M., MD
Baltimore Regional Burn Center
Francis Scott Key Medical Center
Johns Hopkins Bayview Medical Center
4940 Eastern Avenue
Baltimore, MD 21224, **USA**
Phone: 410-550-0886, Fax: 410-550-1165
Email: amunster@welchlink.welch.jhu.edu

Navsaria, H., PhD
Centre for Cutaneous Research
St Bartholomew's & The Royal London
Hospital Medical & Dental School
Queen Mary & Westfield College
2 Newark St.
London E1 2AT, **UK**
Tel: 0207 882 7173/7163
Fax: 0207 882 7171
Email: h.navsaria@icrf.icnet.uk

Ng, R., MA BM BCh MD FRCS
Blond McIndoe Research Centre
Queen Victoria Hospital
East Grinstead, West Sussex, RH19 3DZ, **UK**
Tel: 44-1342-313088, Fax: 44-1342-301701
Email: http://www.dialspace.di-
al.pipex.com/mcindoe

Orgill, D.P., MD
Harvard University
Brigham and Women's Hospital
75 Francis Street
Boston, MA 02115, **USA**
Phone: (617) 732-5456, Fax: (617) 732-6387
Email: dporgill@bics.bwh.harvard.edu

Parkhouse, N., DM MCh, FRCS
McIndoe Burns Centre
Queen Victoria Hospital
East Grinstead, West Sussex, RH19 3DZ, **UK**
Tel: 44-1342-313088, Fax: 44-1342-301701
Email: http://dialspace.dial.pipex.com/mcin-
doe

Pascal, P., PhD
Laboratoire des Substituts Cutanés
Pavillon I5, Hôpital E. Herriot
Place d'Arsonval
F-69437 Lyon CEDEX 03, **France**
Tel.: (33) 04.72.11.75.92
Fax: (33) 04.72.11.74.99
Email: p.pascal@chu-lyon.fr

Pellegrini, G., PhD
Istituto Dermopatice dell'immacolata
Laboratorio di Ingegneria dei Tessuti
Lab Tiss. Eng. JDJ
Via die Casteli Romani 83185
I-00040 Pomezia Roma, **Italy**
Email: tissutale@sinergia.it

Perrot, J., MD
Burn Center
Centre de Traitement des Brules
Hopital d'Instruction des Armees Percy
Avenue henri Barbusse 101
F-92140 Paris (Clamart), **France**
Tel.: +33 –1-41-46-62-11
Fax: +33-1-40-95-08-72
Email: c/o jmriv1@aol.com

Price, R.D., MD
St Andrews Centre for Plastic &
Reconstructive Surgery, Broomfield Hospital
Court Road
Chelmsford, Essex, UK
Tel.: 0207 882 7173/7163
Fax: 0207 882 7171
Email: h.navsaria@icrf.icnet.uk

Putland, M., MSc MD
University of British Columbia
Plastic Surgery & Burn Unit
2nd Floor, Laurel Street Pavillon
899 West 12th Avenue
Vancouver,B.C., V5Z 1M9, **Canada**
Tel.: 604-875-4084, Fax: 604-875-5614
Email: http://www.ubc.ca

Putnins, E.E., PhD
University of British Columbia
Faculty of Dentistry
Department of Oral Biological and
Medical Sciences
Rm 320-2199 Wesbrook Mall
Vancouver, B.C. V6T 1Z3, **Canada**
Email: putnins@unixg.ubc.ca

Rennekampf, H.O., MD
Department of Hand – Plastic and
Burn Surgery
BG Unfallklinik – Eberhard Karls Universität
Schnarrenbergstraße 95
D-72076 Tübingen, **Germany**
Tel.:07071-606-71, Fax: 07071-606-1002
Email: http://www.bgu-tuebingen.de/hand-
chir.htm

Rihova, H., MD
Burns & Reconstructive Surgery Centre
University Hospital Brno-Bohunice
Jihlavska 20
639 00 Brno, **Czech Republic**
Tel: +420 5 4319 3004, Fax: +420 5 4321 5250
Email: pbrychta@fnbrno.cz

Rives, J.M., MD
Plastic, Reconstructive and Aesthetic Surgery
2, reue des Capucins
F-92190 Meudon, **France**
++33-1 46 23 87 80, Fax: ++33- 1 46 23 10 06
Email: jmriv1@aol.com

Ronfard, V., PhD
Organogenesis Inc.,
150 Dan Road
Canton, Massachusetts 02021, **USA**
Tel: ++1-781-575-0775, Fax: ++1-781-575-
0440
Email: vronfard@organo.com

Rubin, P., MB ChB FRCS
Blond McIndoe Research Centre,
Queen Victoria Hospital
East Grinstead, West Sussex, RH19 3DZ, **UK**
Tel: 44-1342-313088, Fax: 44-1342-301701
Email: http://www.dialspace.di-
al.pipex.com/mcindoe

Schafer, I.A., MD
Case Western Reserve University at
MetroHealth Medical Center
2500 MetroHealth Drive
Cleveland, Ohio 44109-1998, **USA**
Tel.: (216) 778-5627
Email: http://www.cwru.edu/med

Schaefer, D., MD
Department of Plastic and Hand Surgery
Albert-Ludwigs-University
Hugstetter Str. 55
D–79106 Freiburg i.Br., **Germany**
Tel: ++49-761-270-2817
Fax: ++49-761-270-2501
Email: schaefer@ch11.ukl.uni-freiburg.de

Sheridan, R.L., MD
Shriners Burns Hospital and Department of
Surgery
Massachusetts General Hospital and Harvard
Medical School
Boston, MA 02114, **USA**
Email: sheridan.robert@mgh.harvard.edu

Smola, H., MD
DKFZ Heidelberg
Abteilung Differenzierung und
Carcinogenese in vitro
Im Neuenheimer Feld 280
D-69120 Heidelberg, **Germany**
Tel.: 06221-42 4507, Fax: 06221-42 45 51
Email: c/o N.Fusenig@dkfz-heidelberg.de

Snelling, C.F.T., MD, FRCSC
University of British Columbia
Plastic Surgery & Burn Unit
2nd Floor, Laurel Street Pavillon
899 West 12th Avenue
Vancouver, B.C., V5Z 1M9, **Canada**
Tel.: 604-875-4084, Fax: 604-875-5614
Email: **snelling@interchange.ubc.ca**

Spence, R.J., MD
Baltimore Regional Burn Center
Francis Scott Key Medical Center
Johns Hopkins Bayview Medical Center
4940 Eastern Avenue
Baltimore, MD 21224, **USA**
Phone: 410-550-0886, Fax: 410-550-1165
Email: amunster@welchlink.welch.jhu.edu

Spies, M., MD
Shriners Burns Hospital-Galveston,
UTMB at Galveston,
815 Market Street
Galveston, TX 77550-2725, **USA**
Phone: 409 772-2222, fax: 409-770-6919
Email: maspies@UTMB.EDU

Staiano-Coico, L., PhD
Department of Surgery, Cornell Univ.
Joan and Sanford I. Weill Medical College
Cornell University
1300 York Avenue Room A131
New York, NY 10021, **USA**
Telephone (212) 746-6020
Fax (212) 746-6938
Email: lisasc@med.cornell.edu

Stark, G.B., MD
Department of Plastic and Hand Surgery
Albert-Ludwigs-University
Hugstetter Str. 55
D- 79106 Freiburg i.Br., **Germany**
Tel: ++49-761-270-2817
Fax: ++49-761-270-2501
Email: stark@ch11.ukl.uni-freiburg.de

Stark, H.J., PhD
DKFZ Heidelberg
Abteilung Differenzierung und
Carcinogenese in vitro
Im Neuenheimer Feld 280
D-69120 Heidelberg, **Germany**
Tel.: 06221-42 4507, Fax: 06221-42 45 51
Email: HJ.Stark@DKFZ-Heidelberg.de

Stephanazzi, H., MD
Burn Center
Centre de Traitement des Brules
Hopital d'Instruction des Armees Percy
Avenue henri Barbusse 101
F-92140 Paris (Clamart), **France**
Tel.: +33 –1-41-46-62-11
Fax: +33-1-40-95-08-72
Email: c/o jmriv1@aol.com

Schwartz, S., MD
Department of Surgery, Cornell Univ.
Joan and Sanford I. Weill Medical College
Cornell University
1300 York Avenue Room A131
New York, NY 10021 **USA**
Telephone (212) 746-6020
Fax: (212) 746-6938
Email: sus2003@med.cornell.edu

Suchanek, I., MD
Burns & Reconstructive Surgery Centre
University Hospital Brno-Bohunice
Jihlavska 20
639 00 Brno, **Czech Republic**
Tel.: +420 5 4319 3004
Fax: +420 5 4321 5250
Email: isuchanek@fnbrno.cz

Sugimura, Y., MD
Nagoya University
Postgraduate School of Medicine
Dep. Oral and Maxillofacial Surgery
65 Tsurumai-Cho, Showa-Ku
Nagoya, 466-8550, **Japan**
T: +81-52-744-2345, F: +81-52-744-2352
Email: http://www.med.nagoya-u.ac.jp

Supp, D., PhD
Research Department
Shriners Hospitals for Children
Shriners Burns Hospital
3229 Burnet Ave.
Cincinnati, OH 45229, **USA**
Tel: 513-872-6346, Fax: 513-872-6072
Email: dsupp@shrinenet.org

Torii, S., MD
Nagoya University
Postgraduate School of Medicine
Dep. Plastic Surgery
65 Tsurumai-Cho, Showa-Ku
Nagoya, 466-8550, **Japan**
T: +81-52-744-2345, F: +81-52-744-2352
Email: http://www.med.nagoya-u.ac.jp

Toriyama, K., MD
Nagoya University
Postgraduate School of Medicine
Dep. Plastic Surgery
65 Tsurumai-Cho, Showa-Ku
Nagoya, 466-8550, **Japan**
T: +81-52-744-2345, F: +81-52-744-2352
Email: http://www.med.nagoya-u.ac.jp

Tsai, C.Y., DDS, PhD
21-1 Alley 16, Lane 559,
Chung-Hsiao East Road, Sec.4
Taipei, **Taiwan**
Email: dentaltsai@tomail.com.tw

Tron, V., PhD, MD, FRCP(C)
University of British Columbia
Plastic Surgery & Burn Unit
2nd Floor, Laurel Street Pavillon
899 West 12th Avenue
Vancouver,B.C., V5Z 1M9, **Canada**
Tel.: 604-875-4084, Fax: 604-875-5614
Email: http://www.ubc.ca

Ueda, M., D.D.S., PhD
Nagoya University
Postgraduate School of Medicine
Dep. Oral and Maxillofacial Surgery
65 Tsurumai-Cho, Showa-Ku
Nagoya, 466-8550, **Japan**
T: +81-52-744-2345, F: +81-52-744-2352
Email: mueda@tsuru.med.nagoya-u.ac.jp

Vacanti, Ch., MD
Dep Anaesthesiology
University of Massachusetts Medical Center,
S-2, Room 751
55 Lake Avenue North
Worcester, MA 01655, **USA**
tel.: 508-856-5259, fax: 508-856-5911
Email: Charles.Vacanti@banyan.ummed.edu

Van der Kam, V.M., RN BS CPSN
Division of Plastic Surgery
University of California Irvine
1140 W. La Veta, Suite 810
Orange, CA 92868, **USA**
Phone (714) 456-5755, Fax: (714) 456-7718
Email: vbvander@uci.edu

Venet, E., PhD
Laboratoire des Substituts Cutanés
Pavillon I5, Hôpital E. Herriot
Place d'Arsonval
F-69437 Lyon CEDEX 03, **France**
Tel.: (33) 04.72.11.75.92
Fax: (33) 04.72.11.74.99
Email: e.venet@chu-lyon.fr

Vesely, P., MD
Burns Center
Charles University Hospital Prague
Srobarova str. 50
100 34 Prague 10 **Czech Republic**
Phone: +420-2-6716 3365
Fax: +420-2-6731 3374
Email: burnsec@fnkv.cz

Vexler, A., MD, PhD
Kiryat Hadassah Sharett Institute
of Oncology,
Radiobiology & Biotechnology Laboratories
Hadassah University Hospital
P.O.B. 12000
Jerusalem, **Israel** 91120
Tel.: 972-2-6778395, Fax: 972-2-6411128
Email: c/o rafi@hadassah.org.il

Voigt, M., MD
Gemeinschaftspraxis
Münsterplatz
D-79105 Freiburg i.Br., **Germany**
Tel.: ++49-761-270-2817
Fax: ++49-761-270-2501
Email: voigt@ch11.ukl.uni-freiburg.de

Walgenbach, K.J., MD
Department of Plastic and Hand Surgery
Albert-Ludwigs-University
Hugstetter Str. 55
D-79106 Freiburg i.Br., **Germany**
Tel.: ++49-761-270-2817
Fax: ++49-761-270-2501
Email: walgenbach@ch11.ukl.uni-
freiburg.de

Wasif, N., MD
Department of Surgery
Joan and Sanford I. Weill Medical College
Cornell University
1300 York Avenue Room A131
New York, NY 10021, **USA**
Telephone (212) 746-6020
Fax (212) 746-6938

Williamson, J.S., M.D., FRCS(C)
University of British Columbia
Plastic Surgery & Burn Unit
2nd Floor, Laurel Street Pavillon
899 West 12th Avenue
Vancouver,B.C., V5Z 1M9, **Canada**
Tel.: 604-875-4084, Fax: 604-875-5614
Email: **snelling@interchange.ubc.ca**

Wood, F., MD
Subiaco Rooms - FM Wood & T Kierath
Med Co Pty. Ltd.
36 Richardson Street
West Perth 6005, **Western Australia**
Tel.: (08) 9321-0007, Fax: (08) 9321 0059
Email: fionawood@thelanddownunder.com

Woodward, B., BSc PhD
Blond McIndoe Research Centre
Queen Victoria Hospital
East Grinstead, West Sussex, RH19 3DZ, **UK**
Tel: 44-1342-313088, Fax: 44-1342-301701
Email: http://www.dialspace.di-
al.pipex.com/mcindoe

Yannas, I.V., PhD
Massachusetts Institute of Technology
Department of Materials Science
and Engineering
Room 3-332, 77 Mass. Ave.
Cambridge, MA 02139, **USA**
Tel.: 617-253-4469
Email: yannas@mit.edu

Section I

Basic Principles, Basic Research

Tissue Engineering and the Skin: Development of Cultured Skin Substitutes from Sheets and Composites to Suspensions and Monolayers on Biological Carrier Materials

R. E. Horch

Summary

Replacement of skin has long been the ultimate task for surgeons facing skin-resurfacing challenges such as thermal burns and chronic ulcerations. In recent years, skin grafting has evolved from the initial autograft and allograft preparations to biosynthetic and tissue-engineered living skin replacements. Autologous skin grafts have been the "gold standard" for wound closure, but in patients who are massively burned, the availability of normal skin is the limiting factor. The pioneering work of numerous investigators led to the following precursors of tissue-engineered skin replacements: cultured autologous keratinocyte grafts, cultured allogeneic keratinocyte grafts, autologous/allogeneic composites, acellular collagen matrices, and cellular matrices including such biological substances like fibrin sealant and various types of collagen. Although the technique is costly and arduous, grafting patients who are severely burned with cultured epidermal autografts has proved itself to be a life-saving measure where few alternatives exist. Although a longer follow-up is necessary, recent evidence suggests that under appropriate circumstances cultured epidermis may provide a wound cover that could be just as durable and esthetically acceptable as conventional split-thickness skin grafts. This article reviews aspects of the historical evolution and applications of epidermal cell culture. The rationale for the development of the newer products and the technical advances leading to the production of new tissue-engineered human skin products utilizing various biomaterials as a matrix and cell carrier will be pointed out with regard to the history of skin cell culture and future prospects.

Introduction

Life on earth is made possible by the evolution of systems which enable organisms to survive various and potentially detrimental physical, chemical, or biological influences of their environment. Survival of the individual organism is definitely influenced by the ability, to regain lost functions after wounding. Skin is the appropriate interface between the organism and its environment. Although it is adapted to withstand several physical, chemical, microbial and other variables, in all organisms protected by an epidermis, skin is permanently exposed to multiple minor or major injuries. Skin wound healing allows for an adequate reaction to such injuries. This involves a complex cascade of strongly related mechanisms to reestablish homoeostasis. It may therefore well be regarded as the prototype of a defense mechanism against environmental lesions.

In primitive animals like amphibians reconstitution of lost functions relies on regenerative processes [70]. Amphibians exhibit phenomenal regenerative ability of limbs. A lost limb is replaced by a new one. Once the pattern of gene expression responsible for amphibian limb development and regeneration will be detected this might be a promising way to apply these principles to differentiated cells and organs. However, with increasing complexity of evolution, defense mechanisms have become more complex. At the other end of the evolutionary scale regenerative processes do not reach significant success. Less valuable scar tissue replaces the defect. Despite this fact, in most cases a high amount of function can be regained. Besides the mere amount of scar tissue, the complex specific three-dimensinal organization of tissue is crucial for its integrity and stability.

The process of wound healing shows regularities in the temporal sequence, tissue–cell specifity and a complex reticule from signalling and regulatory substances. This means that a variety of origins is possible to induce wound healing disorders. The wounded part of the body has to repeat evolutionarily long past processes of organ formation within a short time. Connective tissue cells have to change from an undifferentiated status into a well balanced cascade of proliferation and differentiation steps (locomotion). According to the lost three dimensional tissue structure these processes must lead to defect closure and tissue reorganization.

Mutual interactions among keratinocytes, cell-cell interactions, growth factors and extracellular matrix are required to achieve the primary destination of wound healing, the reepithelialization of the wound surface [191, 26]. Cytokines are known to orchestrate different biochemical mediators resulting in the restoration of the healing phases. Growth factors may play a significant role in stimulating wound repair by stimulating growth and proliferation [170].

Keratinocyte migration over the wound bed is the single most important parameter for wound epithelialization. Migration itself is independent from epithelial proliferation [50]. However, it has been demonstrated experimentally that wounds which are unable to support keratinocyte migration can undergo epithelialization if a conductive substrate, supplying appropriate extracellular matrix and/or matrix-bound growth factors (such as collagen IV, a promoter of keratinocyte migration) is applied [134].

Wounds heal by the development of a scar in which a new cell population settles in a newly constructed connective tissue matrix. Although the chemical composition of a skin scar closely resembles the composition of normal skin, the structural composition differs significantly. The disability to connect collagen in the same patterns like normal skin is a specific feature of scars [70].

Specific Problems of the Burn Wound

Extensive burns represent probably the most devastating injuriy to the human body. In burn wounds the reparation is slowed down compared to excisional wounds as long as necrotic tissue is persistent. A prolonged inflammatory reaction decelerates the progress of repair. The surgical removal of heat denaturated proteins from a wound turns the burn into an excisional wound which can heal faster [39, 69, 70]. This perception lead to modern treatment concepts in burn surgery. Improved understandings of the burn disease, advances in intensive care and aggressive surgical concepts. Surgical principles of early excision of devitalized tissue and prompt wound closure which govern the management of all traumatic injuries have been developed in the primary treatment of burns. Following initial evaluation, wound excision is carried beyond the deepest level of injured tissue. Excision to the level of muscle fascia is used for full-thickness injury and sequential excision in or below the dermis for deep dermal injury. Early necrectomy (= staged serial debridement) – if possible between the second and tenth day after the burn – nowadays allows to save the lifes of extremely burned patients after survival of the initial shock period [73, 89, 94, 103, 104, 106, 107, 108, 201].

Techniques of skin grafting and subsequent care of the graft including the use of human allografts have been steadily refined in the past decades. Primary excision has reduced mortality, morbidity and later reconstructive measures by a factor of 50% when compared to results obtained by awaiting spontaneous separation of eschar with later grafting. The number of necessary operations and the rate of septic complications can be minimized and hospital stay can be shortened. Early excision leads to a better wound healing with improved functional results. With massive burns the use of allografts from familial donors of close immunologic type and immunosuppression of the patient may even prolong the period before allograft rejection and permit repeated harvest of the patient's donor sites for permanent wound closure. Over 60% of young burn victims with greater than 70% full-thickness burn injury have survived with this method of treatment [106]. Essentially it may be regarded as a common sense in burn treatment today that the early removal of the burned areas in extensive burn injuries and the early reconstitution of a functional skin as early as possible is crucial for the further course and for the patient's survival [39, 40–43, 73, 82, 89, 94, 103, 104, 106, 107, 108].

Conventional autologous split thickness skin autografts still represent the "gold standard" to resurface large wounds. However, depending on the extent of lost skin the donor sites may be limited. In these cases a temporary allogeneic or alloplastic coverage is necessary until definitive cover can be achieved [4, 145, 175, 202, 218, 220, 221]. By such means the problem of definitive coverage is only temporarily delayed. In patients with a wounded body surface of more than 50% (TBSA = Total Body Surface Area) the harvesting of split skin creates additional wounds which in turn may lead to a critical enlargement of the wound surface and an amplification of the mortality rate [4, 5]. Allogenic skin grafts may be completely integrated into the healing wound initially and bridge the critical time gap in the early phase of burn treatment, but in the further course irrevocably undergo immunogenic rejection [1, 3, 4, 112, 117, 118, 163, 216, 217, 221]. Theoretically the aplication of in vitro cultivated skin substitutes could circumvent this specific deficit of today's burn treatment and reconstructive surgery.

Historical Developments in Skin Cell Culture

The technical possibility to successfully culture autologous epidermal cells under controlled in vitro culture conditions has greatly inspired research developments in the field of wound healing during the past decades.

Historically the development of skin cell cultures followed different pathways. One approach based on the discovery of Ljunggren in 1898 [8, 152], that skin fragments could be kept vital over a prolonged period of time in ascites and could be successfully retransplanted to the donors. Other researchers showed that skin fragments on a substrate could be incubated in a suitable medium to produce an outgrowth of epithelial and connective cells [47, 95, 132]. The media used in these first experiments consisted of simple saline solutions with or without glucose, enriched with biological fluids like serum or ascites which seemed to be necessary for the success of the culture.

Subsequent modification of these saline solutions through the addition of amino acids or peptides opened the way for the development of standardized media [211]. Such cultures were able to demonstrate that epithelial outgrowth from explant cultures mainly depends on the migration of keratinocytes and that such cells tend to form consistent membranes or cell strains and that cultured epidermal growth is positively influenced by the presence of a dermal substrate [181]. Further on these experiements already showed that epithelial growth is only mediated by basal cells, whereas most of the differentiated epidermal parts are lost. Medawar was the first one to succeed in isolating proliferating epidermal cells in 1944 [161]. By continuous shaking of skin explants in culture he could demonstrate that the keratinocytes were never found far from the fragment but moved about on the explant dermis which was completely coated by epithelium after a few days. In addition he was able to show that such cultivated keratinocytes could be transplanted back to the original donor successfully.

Despite these advantages it became evident that with the explant technique no sufficient gain in cell number could be obtained and that the therapeutic use would therefore be only limited. Further on considerable fibroblasts overgrowth over the keratinocytes in such culture systems limited the culture time [176].

By further modifying the culture techniques it became possible to grow multilayered epithelial grafts, closely resembling the human epidermis. Since no further subcultivations were possible these epithelial laminae were only used as models for in-vitro dermatological research purposes [81]. Transplantation of such autologous epithelial cultures were then effectively demonstrated to give rise to a well-stratified epidermis experimentally in rabbit wounds. But after 6 weeks this epithelium deteriorated for unknown reasons [127]. Under the assumption that a dermal matrix was responsible for a permanent take, epithelial explant cultures using pig skin as a support were then used to obtain transplantable epidermis and were clinically applied [85]. Although this technique was not largely adopted it may be regarded as a basis for recent developments [157, 158, 223].

In 1952 Billingham and Reynolds were able to show that keratinocytes treated with trypsin maintained their vitality and could be used for cell culture [25]. The differentiation of keratinocytes, which can be notified by polystratification and the advent of epidermal differentiation markers, made it virtually impossible to multiply cell populations by successive replications [54]. A definitive improvement of this method was finally achieved, when epithelial cells after their dissociation with trypsin were cultivated on an acid-soluble collagen gel in plastic flasks [127]. This feature greatly increased the proliferative pool of keratinocytes, which were then able to reach confluence and could be subcultured for two to three times [8]. These results were still modest, but gave rise to the assumption that the presence of dermal elements is necessary for the development of epithelial cultures. The search for a suitable carrier-layer finally resulted in the use of lethally irradiated mouse fibroblasts after testing different substrates, also known as 3T3 cells, which proved to be beneficial for the growth of keratinocytes, while at the same time hindering the out- and overgrowth of fibroblasts.

The pioneering work of Green opened the way to possible therapeutic applications [92, 198] but the critical impulse was given by the introduction of epidermal growth factor (= EGF) [52]. The breakthrough for further progress was laid by the technique published by Rheinwald and Green in 1975 that allowed keratinocytes to be successfully cultured and subcultured in clonal cell densities on a "feeder-layer" of lethally irradiated mouse fibroblasts [184]. Further modifications led to standardized techniques to culture epithelial cells reproducibly [16, 17, 23, 210]. By these efforts it became possible to multiply keratinocytes in a clinically relevant number and to utilize them for therapeutic purposes.

The possibility to rapidly multiply a large number of epithelial cells under culture conditions with intervals of cell-multiplication lesser than 24 hours renders the chance to grow epidermis in the quantity of the complete body´s surface within three to four weeks out of a single small skin biopsy. Numerous and outstanding research efforts of various groups led to the formulation of perfectly defined commercially available media, which enable keratinocytes to be cultured without a feeder layer and serum free [141]. The use of defined media is one of the latest but certainly not the last step in the history of keratinocyte culture. The combination of the concepts of early staged burn debridement with temporary skin cover and the technique of keratinocyte multiplication in culture gave rise to the hope that each burn wound no matter how extensive it is may be covered within 3 to 4 weeks [53, 86, 173].

The further development of in-vitro cultured skin substitutes can ever since the first clinical applications mainly been characterized by two different strands:

- the construction of multilayered epiethelial transplants (so called "sheet grafts") (Fig. 1a, 1b) [14, 60, 61, 63, 67, 72, 74, 87, 93, 110, 131, 136, 140, 154, 155, 165, 167, 169, 173, 174, 180, 195]

- and the construction of composite dermal-epidermal analogues [19, 22, 24, 28, 31, 33, 37, 42, 46, 49, 55–57, 68, 76, 91, 97–99, 102, 119, 124, 135, 137, 138, 151, 153, 157, 159, 160, 175, 183, 203, 209, 215, 218, 219]

An overview over the most well known techniques to produce and apply cultured skin substitutes and of the most currently available methods and research directions can be found in table 1 (Table 1). Regarding these different approaches some implications for the further development and research can be deduced which are mainly based on clinical problems with cultured skin.

Problems of Standard "Sheet Grafts" (CEA)

"Sheet grafts" have been commercially available for now more than two decades. According to the main maufacturer over 600 patients have been treated worldwide since the product was introduced. Despite the fascinating feasibility of grafting cultured sheets of epithelium controversies exist about the optimal indications and the pros and cons of this exciting technique [66]. Among the disadvantages especially the high costs have tempered

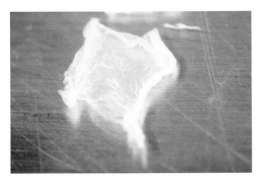

Fig. 1a: Cultured human epithelial multilayered "sheet graft" (CEA).

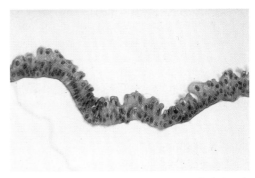

Fig. 1b: Histology of cultured human epithelial multilayered "sheet graft" (CEA) showing basal cell layer and 3 to 4 layers of epithelial cells.

Table 1: Overview over some of the most popular currently used cultured skin substitutes and experimental developments using cultured keratinocytes

I.	**AUTOLOGOUS KERATINOCYTES**
1.	*Autologous epidermal sheet transplants* [53, 86]
2.	*In-vitro cultured and constructed dermo-epidermal autologous transplants:*
2.1.	Keratinocytes on a collagen gel + fibroblasts [9, 20]
2.2.	Keratinocyte sheets + Kollagen-Glykosaminoglykan-Membrane + Fibroblasts [56, 97]
2.3.	Keratinocyte sheets on a layer of fibrin-gel [186]
2.4.	Keratinocyte sheets on cell free pig dermis [158]
2.5.	Keratinocyte sheets on cell free human dermis [71, 118, 182]
2.6.	Keratinocytes on bovine or equine collagen matrices [116]
2.7.	Keratinocyte sheets on micro-perforated hyaluronic acid membranes [7, 100]
2.8.	Keratinocyte sheets on collagen + Chondroitin-6-sulfate with silicon membrane coverage (living skin equivalent) [44]
3.	*Combination of allogenic dermis (in vivo) with epidermal sheets* [58, 110, 185, 208]
4.	*non-confluent keratinozyte suspensions*
	as a spray in saline solutions [13, 197, 213]
	in a fibrin matrix [118, 125, 194]
4.1.	exclusively [118]
4.2.	in combination with fresh or preserved allogenic skin [112, 194]
4.4.	in combination with bovine collagen matrices or hyaluronic acid membranes [111, 114]
4.6.	in combination with collagen coated nylon on silicone backing [129]
4.7.	dissociated keratinocytes without culture [88, 122]
4.8.	Outer root sheath cells non-cultured [162]
4.8.	Outer root sheath cells cultured [143, 144]
5.	*Three dimentional cell cluster cultures (spherocytes)*
5.1.	Cultured on microspheres as carrier systems (dextrane, collagen, hyaluronic acid) [101, 166, 206]
5.2.	Cell seeded microspheres + allografts/biomaterials (under development [206])
II.	**ALLOGENEIC KERATINOCYTES**
	Allogeneic Keratinocytes
6.1.	Keratinocyte -sheets – temporary cover [11, 35, 48, 62, 74, 84, 96, 121, 175, 179, 200]
6.2.	Allogeneic keratinocyte suspensions (experimentally]
6.3.	Syngenic-allofeneic keratinocytes [188, 199]
	In-vitro constructed dermo-epidermal composites/analogues
6.4.	Keratinocytes and Fibroblasts in collagen matrices [75, 77, 120, 175]

a more widespread use. In a clinical trial conventional meshed autografts were found to be superior to CEA for containing hospital cost, diminishing length of hospital stay, and decreasing the number of readmissions for reconstruction of contractures [18]. In a survey of burn survival costs after treating a patient with 88 % TBSA burn with CEA an amount of 850.000 German Marks (currently 403,751.49 USD) has been specified for the successful primary care of this patient [130]. According to the literature the cost for the successful treatment of 1 % of TBSA

with CEA accounted for 13.000 USD in 1995. Reported take rates of CEA and the necessity to repeatedly graft the areas again are extremely variable and differ considerably [10, 66, 106].

Wound infection, that is, clinically significant bacterial contamination, is the main cause of graft failure. Particularly in the first few days following grafting, the fragile noncornified epithelium and dermoepidermal junction are much more susceptible to the damaging effects of bacterial infection than a meshed graft.

Single center experiences with a larger number of CEA grafted patients report lower take rates (between 15% and 65%) than the other earlier literature data of multicenter trials revealed [10, 83, 109, 110, 174, 165, 212]. The true "take rate" from the cumulative literature data may therefore reach an average value of 50% or less. This is consistent with the original data of the pioneering works which varied considerably between 0% and more than 80% take in adults and 50% take in children [53, 190].

The sheet graft consists of cultured epidermal cells attached with surgical clips to a backing of petrolatum gauze. They are usually available with a timely delay of some three to five weeks after the initial biopsy until enough surface has been created in vitro. The grafts consist of 3 to 5 cell layers and the surgical handling with secondary devices is delicate [165, 212] . One more problem is the lack of adherence and the tendency to form blisters even months after the engraftment when exhibited to shearing forces. Mechanical stress, with its resultant potential for injury and infection, therefore has to be avoided in CEA grafted areas.

Take may be adversely influenced by the degree of systemic or localized infection as well as by the patient's nutrition and general medical condition. One of the reasons for the poor take rates may be related to the abnormal structure of the anchoring fibrils [214]. Until now predominantly only parts of the body have been successfully covered with sheet grafts in extensive burns. CEA are not suitable on posterior surfaces, face or hands or over joints, respectively areas subject to mechanical shearing forces. The true mechanisms of intra- and extracellular adherence processes are not yet completely understood [214] and are subject to ongoing investigations [34, 50, 65, 90, 204].

The lack of dermis represents one critical problem in resurfacing third degree burn and chronic wounds. Several research efforts therefore aim towards the development of dermal equivalents or combinations of keratinocytes and dermal analogues or matrix cells such as fibroblasts [44, 22, 29, 32, 57, 68, 98, 102, 215].

Alternatively the temporary coverage of debrided wounds has been propagated and relies on the engraftment of at least parts of the allograft dermis that remain after the immunogenic rejection process or after surgical removal of the allogenic epidermis. This is supposed to present a better attachment zone for the cultured keratinocytes and a more natural remodelling of the wound. In burn patients, clinical experience has shown that early excision and covering with cadaver allograft that temporarily engrafts may keep the wound bed clean and well vascularized and enhance the likelihood of sheet graft take [110, 59, 91, 105, 158, 126, 18, 35, 182].

The combination of smallest skin particles or islands with allogenic skin graft overlays, known as so called "sandwich technique" or its counterpart known as "chinese" or "intermingled technique" makes use of conventional extreme mechanical expansion of autologous skin as mesh grafts or island grafts covered with allogenic skin [4, 112, 116, 133].

It represents the successful application of conventional surgical tools, to utilize the proliferative capacity of epidermal cells in vivo. The allogenic skin serves as an optimal biological and infection preventing in-vivo-culture environment after debridement until the allogenic epidermis is rejected [71]. The fate of the allogenic dermis after this type of transplantation remains unclear und deserves further investigations [128, 149]. The allograft allow for a safe and stable temporary wound cover until further harvesting of the already used donor sites is possible. The autologous split skin is then subsequently mechanically expanded by different means. Thus even with limited donor sites extensive burn areas may sequentially be covered with a definite result. Among other reasons the limited resources in various health systems have recently favoured the further development of these conventional techniques to circumvent cultured skin substitutes whenever possible, leading to the propagation of "microskin grafting" [6, 11, 38, 78, 147, 148, 216, 217, 220, 222].

Using various technical modalities to reduce harvested split skin grafts to small pieces, the yield of expansion may result in expansion rates of 50:1 up to 100:1 or even more regarding the original skin graft [88, 133, 150, 148, 189, 217]. In addition to the coverage with allografts alloplastic materials such as Biobrane dressings have been utilized to hatch such small skin particles until epithelial outgrowth has resurfaced the excisional wounds [5, 18, 146].

Development of Single Cell Suspensions

In 1895 von Mangoldt described his technique of "epithelial cell seeding" to chronic wounds and wound cavities with good clinical results [156]. He harvested epithelial cell or cell clusters by scraping off superficial epithelium from a patient's forearm with a surgical blade "until fibrin was exudated from the wound". The cells which were dissolved in natural serum or blood components were successfully used for what he called "epithelial seeding" to wounds. He believed that the advantages of his approach compared to the method of Reverdin – which was the common method at this time [51] – were the reduction of the donor site morbidity and a more regular aspect of the resurfaced wounds. Due to his exact clinical and histological observations he noted that single cells or cell clusters "better stick to the wound bed" than pieces of skin.

At the beginning of the 19th century Pels-Leusden further modified this technique. He described that he scraped off epithelial cells from the skin surface until serum and blood exudated. But he mixed the cell-serum/blood suspension and injected it into the wound bed of chronic wounds. Other surgeons feared the induction of epithelial cell cysts and the method was not widely adopted for this reason [178].

Epidermal cell-suspensions which have not been enzymatically dissociated trans-plantated without a binding matrix, such as fibrin sealant, have been applied during the fifties of the last century [168, 172]. However it did not win broader recognition due to the inconsistent clinical results. The trypsinization of epithelial cells and successful transplantation was first described by Moscona in 1961 [164]. Experimentally Worst and coworkers were able to demonstrate the ability of epithelial cell suspensions to reconstitute the epidermis in 1982 [215]. In 1988 Hunyadi and coworkers reported upon the successful application of non-cultured keratinocytes gained by trypsinization from biopsies and suspended in a fibrin matrix to heal chronic venous leg ulcers, while at the same time trypsinized keratinocytes suspensions without fibrin sealant did not lead to reepithelialization in a control group [122]. Fibrin, as a naturally occuring substrate leads to hemostasis and plays a key role in wound healing. The use of fibrin sealant to fix skin grafts on burn and other wounds has been shown by various authors [2, 27, 36, 80, 123, 192, 205].

In clinical trials our group could successfully demonstrate for the first time that extensive burned areas up to 88% TBSA can be covered with a cultured keratinocyte-fibrin-sealant-suspension in 6 patients and 14 transplantations using a commercially available two component fibrin sealant [118, 125, 194]. Although it is difficult ot estimate the "take rate" healed wound surfaces were estimated with a take between 70 and 100% on the leg of a patient with 88% TBSA, while at the same time standard CEA covered areas were incompletely healed to an extend of only 30% at the other leg, requiring repeated CEA transplantations. Both legs had been equally prepared with temporary allogenic skin grafts to provide an adequate recipient bed. The KFGS (= Keratinocyte-Fibrin-Glue-Suspension) was available after 10 days since no epidermal differentaition was needed for the single cell suspensions, while the CEA were available after 3 weeks only. The initial attempts of KFGS grafting without meshed allograft overlays led to reepithelialization within one week when applied to long lasting and non-spontaneously healing wounds, but showed mechanical instability similar to CEA grafted areas.

The technique was therefore modified by preliminary wound bed preparation with allograft skin and subsequent KFGS transplantation together with meshed splith thickness allograft skin overlays. While the allografts healed initially showing signs of revascularization like autologus skin grafts a slight and progressive immunogenic rejection period was noted after 12 to 14 days and was followed by stable wound coverage within two more weeks. It seems notable that a stable wound closure was achieved even over stress prone areas like knees and elbow joint regions without signs of mechanical instability as was seen after simple epithelial grafting without allografts [193, 125, 194].

In a further modification of this new technique we performed additional transplantation of an autologous cultured fibroblast-keratinocyte-fibrin-sealant-suspension (FKFGS) with allogenic skin coverage to a freshly debrided third degree burn wound on the muscular fascial layer in an extensively burned patient with 95% TBSA (Fig. 2). This lead to a complete reepithelialization in the transplanted area with a multilayered epithelium after 12 days. Further investigations of this procedure impossible since the patient deceased due to a secondary septic shock. These preliminary observations are in congruency with principally similar experimental approaches of other groups who use cultured fibroblasts [32, 56].

Other groups try to provide readily available sources of cultured epithelium using allogenic keratinocytes, which are of special interest for large burns. In extensive burns superficial wounds are thought to be immediately covered or third degree wounds may be covered with a biological skin substitute until enough autologous grafts are available. Skin donor sites are described to heal faster and thus repeated harvest of thin skin grafts may be facilitated. However, the duration of persistance of such allogenic cells or substitutes in the wound and the timely course of rejection is unclear and controversely discussed [35, 45, 61, 72, 74, 79, 84, 139, 142, 155, 166, 167, 169, 187, 188, 200, 224].

Stem Cells and Biological Carriers

During the adult life, stem cells are responsible for tissue homeostasis; they proliferate to maintain the number of differentiated cells at a constant level and replace dead cells or cells lost through injury. The skin is a tissue with permanently renewing epithelial cell populations giving rise to the epidermis and the hairs. The stem cells are expected to possess the following properties: they are relatively undifferentiated, both ultrastructurally and biochemically; they retain a high capacity for self renewal throughout adult life and have a large proliferative potential; they are normally slow-cycling, but can be stimulated to proliferate in response to injuries and to certain growth stimuli; and finally, they are usually found in well protected, highly vascularized and innervated areas [12, 64, 177]. The main epithelial cells of the epidermis, the keratinocytes, are organized into multiple layers and undergo terminal differentiation as they move through the su prabasal layers toward the skin surface. The capacity to form holoclones of highly proliferating basal keratinocytes has influenced recent developments in skin cell culture and

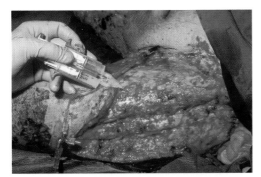

Fig. 2: Cultured Autologous Keratinocyte-Fibroblast-Fibrin-Sealant Suspension grafted on muscle fascia after debridement for third degree burn wounds.

Fig. 3a Transplantation of cultured autologous Keratinocyte-Fibrin-Sealant Suspension simultaneously with overgrafted meshed allogenic preserved split thickness donor skin.

Fig. 3b Healing of third degree burn after debridement and transplantation of cultured autologous Keratinocyte-Fibrin-Sealant Suspension simultaneously with overgrafted meshed allogenic preserved split thickness donor skin.

tion in the laboratory and to bring cultured epidermal cells back to the more natural wound healing environment as early as possible. The combination of allografting with simultaneously delivered cultured human keratinocytes in fibrin sealant as a carrier and matrix vehicle both clinically and experimentally is feasible [155, 194] (Fig. 3a, 3b) (Fig. 4a, 4b).

One of the unsolved problems is the constant and reliable delivery of cultured cells to the recipient wound bed [15]. Using fibrin sealant as a biological cell carrier, some groups now have introduced spray techniques. This enables the dispersion and distribution of cultured cells to a maximum

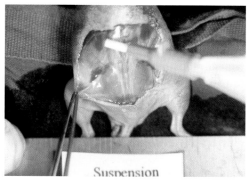

Fig. 4a: Grafting of cultured Keratinocyte-Fibrin-Sealant-Suspensions on full thickness standard nude mice wound.

possible new approaches to tissue engineered skin substitutes [64].

Since only the proliferating basal cells are responsible for the initial reconstitution of an epithelium it seems logical that only these cells may be needed to resurface wounds. Differentiation of cells in vitro has not been proved to be necessary for reepithelialization. Differentiated cells are not likely to actively contribute to the process of reepithelialization since they do not divide themselves any longer. From our previous studies and clinical trials the concept was delineated that it is more natural to shorten the time of skin substitute produc-

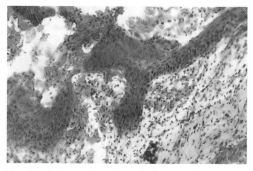

Fig. 4b: Reformation of epithelium at day 7 after grafting of keratinocyte-fibrin sealant cell suspensions on nude mice wounds within the matrix and with still visible remnants of fibrin sealant (orange).

surface compared to our initial traditional approach without spray systems. The fact that cultured keratinocytes do survive this procedure has recently been shown in vitro by our group [111, 207] and experimentally as well as clinically by others [13, 196]. Another way to optimize keratinocyte growth and delivery is the method of Ronfard and coworkers who cultured keratinocytes on a stabilized fibrin sealant in the gel phase. After sufficient multiplication the whole fibrin-keratinocyte graft can be mechanically removed from the culture systems and be transplanted to the recipient. By this elegant technique a reliable and simple delivery of keratinocytes is enabled, as was shown experimentally and clinically [186].

Especially the enzymatic detachment from the culture dishes necessary in the delivery of CEA sheets is potentially harmful to the cultured cells and may well be related to the lack of adherence of sheets to the wound. As has been pointed out earlier the attempts of mounting cultured epithelia on dermal matrices has been a possible way to facilitate handling, avoid enzymatic treatment before grafting and at the same time delivering a dermal analogue. Various templates have been used and are discussed by several authors in this book. One of the most common material has been collagen in combination glycosaminoglycane attempt has (C-GAG), with or without a cover of a gas permeable silastic membrane, that serves as a barrier to fluid loss [21]. The question whether dermal fibroblasts seeded into such composites are necessary or not has not been clearly answered up to now [30, 57, 171, 183].

However, questions of survival of such grafts in wounds remained open due to a possible barrier function of the matrix material towards nutrients necessary for keratinocyte survival on top of such composites and the clinical long term success will have to be clearly shown. The insights into the potential stem cell capacity of keratinocyte holoclones, the need to avoid enzymatic detachment of cultured cells and the need for an appropriate biological matrix for the ke-

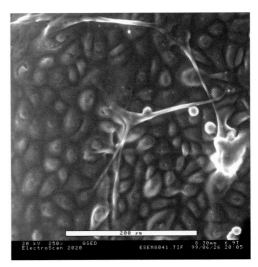

Fig. 5: Monolayer of cultured keratinocytes on equine collagen type I membrane (TissuFoil E, Baxter) after 3 days of culture in serum free medium, showing an almost confluent cell layer.

ratinocytes led to new approaches. Firstly, to avoid any barrier function we transplanted composite grafts with the keratinocyte layer in an "upside-down" direction towards the wound bed, so that the collagen component serves as a carrier and as a biological dressing on top. Secondly we used subconfluent monolayers of cultured human keratinocytes (Fig. 5) instead of multilayered sheet grafts. Collagen and collagen peptide fragments are a normal part of the wound healing mechanism. Collagen therefore seems to be an obvious material for use in fabrication of dermal substitutes and has been used in various forms to resurface full thickness wounds as a cell-carrier material or dermal template. To evaluate the potential use of this technique we transplanted these KCMG "upside-down" grafts onto full thickness nude mice wounds to test the feasibility of this hypothesis and were able to show the feasibility of this combined new approach [114]. Contrary to standard composite grafts this new technique does not attempt direct dermal regeneration but makes use of the collagen membrane as an effective carrier and biological dressing mate-

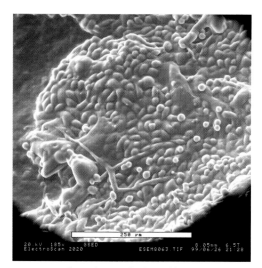

Fig. 6: Confluent layers of cultured keratinocytes on equine collagen type I membrane (TissuFoil E, Baxter) after 7 days of culture in serum free medium.

rial (Fig. 6). In contrast to known standard composite grafts there is no time required until revascularization is established and nourishment is reestablished so that a high number of transplanted cells can survive in the natural wound environment, similar to buried chip skin grafting [113]. However, it may be speculated that parts of this biological carrier might be integrated into the remodelling process of the newly reconstituted skin due to the collagen degradation and turnover rate in early wound healing. This method combines the in vitro expansion of graftable cells with advantages of the transplantation of actively proliferating cell populations on an appropriate biological carrier, and may become a valuable tool in burn or chronic wound treatment.

Future Prospects

Socio-econonomic impacts may well afflict the treatment modalities of severely burned patients in the future. Althoug at the moment research as well as clinical application of cultured human skin substitutes seems to be ex-

pensive further progress is necessary. It may lead to improvements in skin reconstitution while at the same time overcoming nowadays limits of donor site morbidity. Improved cosmesis and the ultimate regaining of lost skin functions including sensitivity, elasticity, normal physiological sweat gland and dermal appendage function, as well as normal pigmentation with invisible scars are the goals of future endeavors in this field. There will be major improvements in the understanding and ability to effectively deal with the problems of wound healing and truly functional skin replacement with dermal appendages through basic and clinical research; but perhaps the major improvement will come through the ability to replace worn out, defective or damaged body parts through technologies that resemble regeneration. Here the concepts of Tissue Engineering have much to contribute and it is worth exploring the donation of Tissue Engineering to dermal replacement following burn injury to serve as an example of what types of additions to treatment Tissue Engineering can make.

References

[1] *Achauer BM, Hewitt CW, Black KS, Martinez SE, Waxman KS, Ott RA and Furnas DW:* Long-term allograft survival after short term cyclosporin treatment in a patient with massive burns. Lancet 4(8471), 14–15, 1986.

[2] *Adant JP, Detroz B, D'Silva M, Matowitz L, Ledoux M, Pestiaux B, and LeClercq P:* Skin grafting with fibrin glue in burns. Eur J Plast Surg 16, 292–296, 1993.

[3] *Alexander JW, Craycraft TK:* Prolongation of allogeneic skin survival by in vitro treatment with fluocinolone acetonide: effect of incubation time and length of storage. J Trauma 14, 836–840, 1974.

[4] *Alexander JW, MacMillan BG, Law E, Kittur DS:* Treatment of severe burns with widly meshed skin autograft and meshed skin allograft overlay. J Trauma 21, 433–438, 1981.

[5] *Alexander JW, Wheeler LM, Rooney RC, McDonald JJ, MacMillan BG:* Clinical evaluation of Epigard, a new synthetic substitute for homograft and heterograft skin. J Trauma 13, 374–383, 1973.

[6] *Alsbjorn BF:* Clinical results of grafting burns with epidermal Langerhans' cell depleted allograft overlay. Scand J Plast Reconstr Surg Hand Surg 25, 35–39, 1991.

[7] *Andreassi L, Casini L, Trabucchi E, Diamantini S, Rastrelli A, Donati L, Tenchini ML, Malcovati M:* Human keratinocytes cultured on membranes composed of benzyl ester of hyaluronic acid and suitable for grafting. Wounds 3, 116–126, 1991.

[8] *Andreassi L:* History of keratinocyte cultivation. Burns 18, S2–S4, 1992.

[9] *Archambault M, Yaar M, Gilchrest BA:* Keratinocytes and fibroblasts in a human skin equivalent model enhance melanocyte survival and melanin synthesis after ultraviolet irradiation. J Invest Dermatol 104, 859–867, 1995.

[10] *Arons JA, Wainwright DJ, Jordon RE:* The surgical applications and implications of cultured human epidermis: a comprehensive review. Surgery 111, 4–11, 1992.

[11] *Aubock J, Irschick E, Romani N et al.:* Rejection, after a slightly prolonged survival time, of Langerhans cell-free allogeneic cultured epidermis used for wound coverage in humans. Transplantation 45, 730–737, 1988.

[12] *Auger FA, Pouliot R, Tremblay N et al.:* Multistep production of bioengineered skin substitutes: sequential modulation of culture conditions. In Vitro Cell Dev Biol Anim 36, 96–103, 2000:

[13] *Bahoric A, Harrop AR, Clarke HM, Zuker A:* Aerosol vehicle for delivery of epidermal cells – an in vitro study. Can J Plast Surg 5, 153–156, 1997.

[14] *Banks-Schlegel S, Green H:* Formation of epidermis by serially cultivated human epidermal cells transplanted as an epithelium to athymic mice. Transplantation 29, 308–313, 1980.

[15] *Bannasch H, Horch RE, Tanczos E, Stark GB:* Treatment of chronic wounds with cultivated autologous keratinocytes as suspension in fibrin glue. Zentralbl Chir 125, 79–81, 2000.

[16] *Barrandon Y, Li V, Green H:* New techniques for the grafting of cultured human epidermal cells onto athymic animals. J Invest Dermatol 91, 315–318, 1988.

[17] *Barreca A, De Luca M, Del Monte P et al.:* In vitro paracrine regulation of human keratinocyte growth by fibroblast-derived insulin-like growth factors. J Cell Physiol 151, 262–268, 1992.

[18] *Barret JP, Wolf SE, Desai MH, Herndon DN:* Cost-efficacy of cultured epidermal autografts in massive pediatric burns. Ann Surg 231, 869–876, 2000.

[19] *Bell E, Ehrlich HP, Buttle DJ, Nakatsui T:* Living tissue formed in vitro and accepted as skin-equivalent tissue of full thickness. Science 211, 1052–1054, 1981.

[20] *Bell E, Sher S, Hull B et al.:* The reconstitution of living skin. J Invest Dermatol 81, 2s–10s, 1983.

[21] *Bell E, Ehrlich HP, Sher S et al.:* Development and use of a living skin equivalent. Plast Reconstr Surg 67, 386–392, 1981.

[22] *Bell E, Sher S, Hull B et al.:* The reconstitution of living skin. J Invest Dermatol 81, 2s–10s, 1983.

[23] *Bettger WJ, Boyce ST, Walthall BJ, Ham RG:* Rapid clonal growth and serial passage of human diploid fibroblasts in a lipid-enriched synthetic medium supplemented with epidermal growth factor, insulin, and dexamethasone. Proc Natl Acad Sci U S A 78, 5588–5592, 1981.

[24] *Bideaux JC , Echinard C , Damour O:* Experimental study on a skin substitute. Artificial dermis epidermised by human keratinocytes. Chirurgie 118, 411–415, 1992.

[25] *Billingham R E, Reynolds J:* Transplantation studies on sheet of pure epidermal epithelium and of epidermal cell suspensions. Br J Plast Surg 23, 25–32, 1952.

[26] *Blitstein-Willinger E:* The role of growth factors in wound healing. Skin Pharmacol 4, 175–182, 1991.

[27] *Boeckx W, Vandevoort M, Blondeel P, Van Raemdonck D, Vandekerckhove E:* Fibrin glue in the treatment of dorsal hand burns. Burns 18, 395–400, 1992.

[28] *Bosca AR, Tinois E, Faure M, Kanitakis J, Roche P, Thivolet J:* Epithelial differentiation of human skin equivalents after grafting onto nude mice. J Invest Dermatol 91, 136–141, 1988.

[29] *Boyce ST, Supp AP, Harringer MD, Greenhaalgh DG, Warden GD:* Topical nutrients promote engraftment and inhibit wound contraction of cultured skin substitutes in aathymic mice. J Invest Dermatol 104, 345–349, 1995.

[30] *Boyce ST, Christianson DJ, Hansbrough JF:* Structure of a collagen-GAG dermal skin substitute optimized for cultured human epidermal keratinocytes. J Biomed Mater Res 22, 939–957, 1988.

[31] *Boyce ST, Goretsky MJ, Greenhalgh DG et al.:* Comparative Assessment of Cultured Skin Substitutes and Native Skin Autograft for Treatment of Full-Thickness Burns. Ann Surg 222, 743–752, 1995.

[32] *Boyce ST, Hansbrough JF:* Biologic attachment, growth, and differentiation of cultured human epidermal keratinocytes on a graftable collagen and chondroitin-6-sulfate substrate. Surgery 103, 421–431, 1988.

[33] *Boyce ST, Supp AP, Harriger MD, Greenhalgh DG, Warden GD:* Topical nutrients promote engraftment and inhibit wound contraction of cultured skin substitutes in athymic mice. J Invest Dermatol 104, 345–349, 1995.

[34] *Boyce ST, Warden GD, Holder IA:* Cytotoxicity testing of topical antimicrobial agents on human keratinocytes and fibroblasts for cultured skin grafts. J Burn Care Rehabil 16, 97–103, 1995.

[35] *Brain A, Purkis P, Coates P, Hackett M, Navsaria H, Leigh I:* Survival of cultured allogeneic keratinocytes transplanted to deep dermal bed assessed with probe specific for Y chromosome. BMJ 298, 917–919, 1989.

[36] *Brown DM, Barton BR, Young VL, Pruitt BA:* Decreased wound contraction with fibrin glue – treated skin grafts. Arch Surg 127, 404–406, 1992.

[37] *Burke JF:* Observations on the development of an artificial skin: Presidential Address, 1982 American Burn Association Meeting. J Trauma 23, 543–551, 1983.

[38] *Burke JF, Bondoc CC:* Combined burn therapy utilizing immediate skin allografts and 0.5 percent AgNO3. Arch Surg 97, 716–721, 1968.

[39] *Burke JF, Bondoc CC, Quinby WC:* Primary burn excision and immediate grafting: a method shortening illness. J Trauma 14, 389–395, 1974.

[40] *Burke JF, May JW, Jr., Albright N, Quinby WC, Russell PS:* Temporary skin transplantation and immunosuppression for extensive burns. N Engl J Med 290, 269–271, 1974.

[41] *Burke JF, Quinby WC, Bondoc CC, Cosimi AB, Russell PS, Szyfelbein SK:* Immunosuppression and temporary skin transplantation in the treatment of massive third degree burns. Ann Surg 182, 183–197, 1975.

[42] *Burke JF, Quinby WC, Jr., Behringer GE, Bondoc CC:* 1981 – approach to burn therapy. Surg Annu 13, 1–14: 1–14, 1981.

[43] *Burke JF, Quinby WC, Jr., Bondoc CC:* Primary excision and prompt grafting as routine therapy for the treatment of thermal burns in children. Surg Clin North Am 56, 477–494, 1976.

[44] *Burke JF, Yannas IV, Quinby WC, Jr., Bondoc CC, Jung WK:* Successful use of a physiologically acceptable artificial skin in the treatment of extensive burn injury. Ann Surg 194, 413–428, 1981.

[45] *Burt AM, Pallett CD, Sloane JP et al.:* Survival of cultured allografts in patients with burns assessed with probe specific for Y chromosome. BMJ 298, 915–917, 1989.

[46] *Butler CE, Yannas IV, Compton C, Correia CA, Orgill DP:* Comparison of cultured and uncultured keratinocytes seeded into a collagen-GAG matrix for skin replacements. Br J Plast Surg 52, 127–132, 1999.

[47] *Carrel A, Burrows MT:* Cultivation of adult tissues and organs outside the body. JAMA 1379–1384, 1910.

[48] *Carter DM, Lin AN, Varghese MC, Caldwell D, Pratt LA, Eisinger M:* Treatment of junctional epidermolysis bullosa with epidermal autografts. J Am Acad Dermatol 17, 246–250, 1987.

[49] *Chang DW, Sanchez LA, Veith FJ, Wain RA, Okhi T, Suggs WD:* Can a tissue-engineered skin graft improve healing of lower extremity foot wounds after revascularization? Ann Vasc Surg 14, 44–49, 2000.

[50] *Chen JD, Kim JP, Zhang K et al.:* Epidermal growth factor (EGF) promotes human keratinocyte locomotion on collagen by increasing the alpha 2 integrin subunit. Exp Cell Res 209, 216–223, 1993.

[51] *Chick LR:* Brief history and biology of skin grafting. Ann Plast Surg 1988:21: 358–365.

[52] *Cohen S:* The stimulation of epidermal proliferation by a specific protein. Develop Biol 12, 394–399, 1965.

[53] *Compton CC, Gill JM, Bradford DA, Regauer S, Gallico GG, O'Connor NE:* Skin regenerated from cultured epithelial autografts on full-thickness burn wounds from 6 days to 5 years after grafting. A light, electron microscopic and immunohistochemical study. Lab Invest 60, 600–612, 1989.

[54] Constable H, Cooper JR, Cruickshank CN, Mann PR. Keratinization in dispersed cell cultures of adult guinea-pig ear skin. Br J Dermatol 91, 39–48, 1974.

[55] *Contard P, Bartel RL, Jacobs L et al.:* Culturing keratinocytes and fibroblasts in a three-dimensional mesh results in epidermal differentiation and formation of a basal lamina-anchoring zone. J Invest Dermatol 100, 35–39, 1993.

[56] *Cooper ML, Andree C, Hansbrough JF, Zapata-Sirvent RL, Spielvogel RL:* Direct comparison of a cultured composite skin substitute containing human keratinocytes and fibroblasts to an epidermal sheet graft containing human keratinocytes on athymic mice. J Invest Dermatol 101, 811–819, 1993.

[57] *Cooper ML, Hansbrough JF:* Use of a composite skin graft composed of cultured human keratinocytes and fibroblasts and a collagen-GAG matrix to cover full-thickness wounds on athymic mice. Surgery 109, 198–207, 1991.

[58] *Cuono C, Langdon R, Mc Guire J:* Use of cultured epidermal autografts and dermal allografts as skin replacement after burn injury. Lancet 1, 1124, 1986.

[59] *Cuono CB, Langdon R, Birchall N, Barttelbort S, McGuire J:* Composite autologous-allogeneic skin replacement: development and clinical application. Plast Reconstr Surg 80, 626–637, 1987.

[60] *Damour O, Braye F, Foyatier JL et al.:* Cultured Autologous Epidermis for Massiv Burn Wounds: 15 Years of Practice. In: Rouabhia M, ed. Skin Substitute Production by Tissue

Engineering: Clinical and Fundamental applications. New York: Chapman & Hall, 47–74, 1997.

[61] De Luca M, Albanese E, Bondanza S et al.: Multicentre experience in the treatment of burns with autologous and allogenic cultured epithelium, fresh or preserved in a frozen state. Burns 15, 303–309, 1989.

[62] De Luca M, Albanese E, Cancedda R et al.: Treatment fo leg ulcers with cryopreserved allogenic cultured epithelium. Arch Dermatol 128, 633–638, 1992.

[63] De Luca M, Bondanza S, Cancedda R et al.: Permanent coverage of full skin thickness burns with autologous cultured epidermis and reepithelialization of partial skin thickness lesions induced by allogenic cultured epidermis: a multicentre study in the treatment of children. Burns 18, S16–S19, 1992.

[64] De Luca M, Pellegrini G: The importance of epidermal stem cells in keratinocyte-mediated gene therapy [editorial]. Gene Ther 4, 381–383, 1997.

[65] Dellambra E, Vailly J, Pellegrini G et al.: Corrective transduction of human epidermal stem cells in laminin-5-dependent junctional epidermolysis bullosa. Hum Gene Ther 9, 1359–1370, 1998.

[66] Desai MH, Mlakar JM, McCauley RL et al.: Lack of long-term durability of cultured keratinocyte burn-wound coverage: a case report. J Burn Care Rehabil 12, 540–545, 1991.

[67] Donati, L: The Growth and Clinical Use of Cultured Keratinocytes. Burns 18 (Supplement 1), 1992.

[68] Dubertret L, Coulomb B: In vitro cutaneous organogenesis (application to skin grafts). Bull Acad Natl Med 179, 1121–1130, 1995.

[69] Ehrlich HP: The physiology of wound healing. A summary of normal and abnormal wound healing processes. Adv Wound Care 11, 326–328, 1998.

[70] Ehrlich HP: The role of connective tissue matrix in wound healing. Prog Clin Biol Res 266, 243–258, 1998.

[71] Eldad A, Benmeir P, Weinberg A et al.: Cyclosporin A treatment failed to extend skin allograft survival in two burn patients. Burns 20, 262–264, 1994.

[72] Eldad A, Burt A, Clarke JA, Gusterson B: Cultured epithelium as a skin substitute. Burns Incl Therm Inj 13, 173–180, 1987.

[73] Engrav LH, Heimbach DM, Reus JL, Harnar TJ, Marvin JA: Early excision and grafting vs. nonoperative treatment of burns of indeterminant depth: a randomized prospective study. J Trauma 23, 1001–1004, 1983.

[74] Fabre JW: Epidermal allografts. Immunol Lett 29, 161–165, 1991.

[75] Falanga V, Margolis D, Alvarez O et al.: Rapid healing of venous ulcers and lack of clinical rejection with an allogeneic cultured human skin equivalent. Human Skin Equivalent Investigators Group [see comments]. Arch Dermatol 134, 293–300, 1998.

[76] Falanga V, Margolis D, Alvarez O et al.: Rapid Healing of venous ulcers and lack of clinical rejection with an allogenic cultured human skin equivalent. Arch Dermatol 134, 293–300, 1998.

[77] Falanga V, Sabolinski M: A bilayered living skin construct (APLIGRAF) accelerates complete closure of hard-to-heal venous ulcers. Wound Repair Regen 7, 201–207, 1999.

[78] Fang CH, Yu GS, Fan YF, Wang K, Alexander JW: A preliminary report on transplantation of microskin autografts overlaid with sheet allograft in the treatment of large burns. J Burn Care Rehabil 9, 629–633, 1988.

[79] Faure M, Mauduit G, Schmitt D, Kanitakis J, Demidem A, Thivolet J: Growth and differentiation of human epidermal cultures used as auto- and allografts in humans. Br J Dermatol 116, 161–170, 1987.

[80] Fisseler-Eckhoff A, Muller KM: Lendrum (-MSB) staining for fibrin identification in sealed skin grafts. Pathol Res Pract 190, 444–448, 1994.

[81] Flaxman B A, Lutzner M A, Van Scott E J: Cell maturation and tissue organization in epithelial outgrowths from skin and buccal mucosa in vitro. J Invest Dermatol 49, 322–325, 1967.

[82] Foy HM, Pavlin ED, Heimbach DM: Excision and grafting of large burns: operation length not related to increased morbidity. J Trauma 26, 51–53, 1986.

[83] Foyatier JL, Faure M, Hezez G et al.: [Clinical application of grafts of cultured epidermis in burn patients. Apropos of 16 patients]. Ann Chir Plast Esthet 35, 39–46, 1990.

[84] Fratianne R, Papay F, Housini I, Lang C, Schafer IA: Keratinocyte allografts accelerate healing of split-thickness donor sites: applications for improved treatment of burns. J Burn Care Rehabil 14, 148–154, 1993.

[85] Freeman AE, Igel HJ, Herrman BJ, Kleinfeld KL: Growth and characterization of human skin epithelial cell cultures. In Vitro 12, 352–362, 1976.

[86] Gallico GG, O'Connor NE, Compton C, Kehinde O, Green H: Permanent coverage of large burn wounds with autologous cultured human epithelium. N Engl J Med 331, 448–451, 1984.

[87] Gao ZR: [Treatment of full-thickness burns with autologous epidermal cell grafting]. Chung Hua I Hsueh Tsa Chih 65, 278–280, 1985.

[88] Gao ZR, Hao ZQ, Nie LJ, Liu GF: Coverage of full skin thickness burns with allograft inoculat-

ed with autogenous epithelial cells. Burns Incl Therm Inj 12, 220–224, 1986.

[89] *Garrison JL, Thomas F, Cunningham P:* Improved large burn therapy with reduced mortality following an associated septic challenge by early excision and skin allografting using donor-specific tolerance. Transplant Proc 27, 1416–1418, 1995.

[90] *Germain L, Guignard R, Rouabhia M, Auger FA:* Early basement membrane formation following the grafting of cultured epidermal sheets detached with thermolysin or Dispase. Burns 21, 175–180, 1995.

[91] *Ghosh MM, Boyce S, Layton C, Freedlander E, Mac NS:* A comparison of methodologies for the preparation of human epidermal-dermal composites. Ann Plast Surg 39, 390–404, 1997.

[92] *Green H:* Cell culture for the study of epithelial cells. Natl Cancer Inst Monogr 259–262, 1978.

[93] *Green H, Kehinde O, Thomas J:* Growth of cultured human epidermal cells into multiple epithelia suitable for grafting. Proc Natl Acad Sci U S A 76, 5665–5668, 1979.

[94] *Greenleaf G, Hansbrough JF:* Current trends in the use of allograft skin for patients with burns and reflections on the future of skin banking in the United States. J Burn Care Rehabil 15, 428–431, 1994.

[95] *Hadda S:* Die Kultur lebender Zellen. Klin Wschr 49, 11–19, 1912.

[96] *Hammond EJ, Ng RL, Stanley MA, Munro AJ:* Prolonged survival of cultured keratinocyte allografts in the nonimmunosuppressed mouse. Transplantation 44, 106–112, 1987.

[97] *Hansbrough JF, Boyce ST, Cooper ML, Foreman TJ:* Burn wound closure with cultured autologous keratinocytes and fibroblasts attached to a collagen-glycosaminoglycan substrate. JAMA 262, 2125–2130, 1989.

[98] *Hansbrough JF, Morgan JL, Greenleaf GE, Bartel R:* Composite grafts of human keratinocytes grown on a polyglactin mesh-cultured fibroblast dermal substitute function as a bilayer skin replacement in full-thickness wounds on athymic mice. J Burn Care Rehabil 14, 485–494, 1993.

[99] *Harriger MD, Warden GD, Greenhalgh DG, Kagan RJ, Boyce ST:* Pigmentation and microanatomy of skin regenerated from composite grafts of cultured cells and biopolymers applied to full-thickness burn wounds. Transplantation 59, 702–707, 1995.

[100] *Harris PA, di Francesco F, Barisoni D, Leigh IM, Navsaria HA:* Use of hyaluronic acid and cultured autologous keratinocytes and fibroblasts in extensive burns. Lancet 353, 35–36, 1999.

[101] *Hecht J, Hoefter EA, Hecht J et al.* [Cultivated keratinocytes on micro-carriers: in vitro studies of a new carrier system]. Handchir Mikrochir Plast Chir 29, 101–106, 1997.

[102] *Heck EL, Bergstresser PR, Baxter CR:* Composite skin graft: Frozen dermal allografts support the engraftment and expansion of autologous epidermis. J Trauma 25, 106–112, 1985.

[103] *Heimbach D, Herndon D, Luterman A et al.:* Early excision of thermal burns – an international round-table discussion, Geneva, June 22, 1987. J Burn Care Rehabil 9, 549–561, 1988.

[104] *Heimbach DM:* Early burn excision and grafting. Surg Clin North Am 67, 93–107, 1987.

[105] *Herndon D, Rutan RL:* Comparision of cultured epidermal autograft and massive excision with serial autografting plus homograft overlay. J Burn Care Rehabil 13, 154–157, 1992.

[106] *Herndon DN, Barrow RE, Rutan RL, Rutan TC, Desai MH, Abston S:* A comparison of conservative versus early excision. Therapies in severely burned patients. Ann Surg 209, 547–552, 1989.

[107] *Herndon DN, Parks DH:* Comparison of serial debridement and autografting and early massive excision with cadaver skin overlay in the treatment of large burns in children. J Trauma 26, 149–152, 1986.

[108] *Herndon DN, Rutan RL:* Comparison of cultured epidermal autograft and massive excision with serial autografting plus homograft overlay. J Burn Care Rehabil 13, 154–157, 1992.

[109] *Hickerson WL, Bishop JF. Discussion:* Combined Use of Allograft and Autograft Epidermal Cultures in Therapy of Burns. Discussion 98 6, 940–941, 1998.

[110] *Hickerson WL, Compton C, Fletchall S, Smith LR:* Cultured epidermal autografts and allodermis combination for permanent burn wound coverage. Burns 20, S52–S56, 1994.

[111] *Horch RE, Wagner G, Debus M, Stark GB:* Kultivierte humane Keratinozyten auf esterifizierten Hyaluronsäure-Membranen zur Deckung von Vollhautwunden bei athymischen Nacktmäusen. Hefte zur Zeitschrift Unfallchirurg 278, 107–113, 2000.

[112] *Horch RE, Stark GB, Kopp J, Spilker G:* Cologne Burn Centre experiences with glycerol-preserved allogeneic skin: Part I: Clinical experiences and histological findings (overgraft and sandwich technique). Burns 20 Suppl 1, S23–6, S23–S26, 1994.

[113] *Horch RE, Stark GB, Spilker G:* [Treatment of perianal burns with submerged skin particles]. Zentralbl Chir 119, 722–725, 1994.

[114] *Horch RE, Debus M, Wagner G, Stark GB:* Cultured human keratinocytes on type I colagen membranes to reconstitute the epidermis. Tissue Engineering 6, 53–67, 2000.

[115] *Horch RE, Bannasch H, Kopp J, Andree C, Stark GB:* Single-cell suspensions of cultured human keratinocytes in fibrin-glue reconstitute the epidermis. Cell Transplant 7, 309–317, 1998.

[116] *Horch RE, Corbei O, Formanek-Corbei B, Brand-Saberi B, Vanscheidt W, Stark GB:* Reconstitution of basement membrane after 'sandwich-technique' skin grafting for severe burns demonstrated by immunohistochemistry. J Burn Care Rehabil 19, 189–202, 1998.

[117] *Horch RE, Corbei O, Formanek-Corbei B, Brand-Saberi B, Vanscheidt W, Stark GB:* Reconstitution of Basement Menbrane after "Sandwich-Technique" Skin Grafting for Severe Burns Demonstrated by Immunhistochemistry. J Burn Care Rehabil 19, 189–202, 1998.

[118] *Horch RE, Stark GB, Kopp J, Andree C:* Dermisersatz nach drittgradigen Verbrennungen und bei chronischen Wunden-Neue Erkenntnisse zur Morphologie nach Fremdheuttransplantation in Kombination mit kultivierten autologen Keratinocyten. Transplantationsmedizin 7, 99–103, 1995.

[119] *Hull BE, Finley RK, Miller SF:* Coverage of full-thickness burns with bilayered skin equivalents: A preliminary clinical trail. Surg 107, 496–502, 1990.

[120] *Hultman CS, Brinson GM, Siltharm S et al.:* Allogeneic fibroblasts used to grow cultured epidermal autografts persist in vivo and sensitize the graft recipient for accelerated second-set rejection. J Trauma 41, 51–58, 1996.

[121] *Hultman CS, Hunt JP, Yamamoto H et al.:* Immunogenicity of cultured keratinocyte allografts deficient in major histocompatibility complex antigens. J Trauma 45, 25–33, 1998.

[122] *Hunyadi J, Farkas B, Bertenyl C, Olah J, Dobozy A:* Keratinocyte Grafting: a new means of transplantation for full-thickness wounds. J Dermatol Surg Oncol 1988:14: 75–78.

[123] *Jabs AD Jr, Wider TM, DeBellis J, Hugo NE:* The effect of fibrin glue on skin grafts in infected sites. Plast Reconstr Surg 89, 268–271, 1992.

[124] *Kagan RJ:* Skin substitutes: implications for burns and chronic wounds. Adv Wound Care 12, 94–95, 1999.

[125] *Kaiser HW, Stark GB, Kopp J, Balcerkiewicz A, Spilker G, Kreysel HW:* Cultured autologous keratinocytes in fibrin glue suspension, exclusively and combined with STS-allograft (preliminary clinical and histological report of a new technique). Burns 20, 23–29, 1994.

[126] *Kangesu T, Navsaria H, Menek S, Fryer PR, Leigh IM, Green C:* Kerato-dermal grafts: the importance of dermis for the in vivo growth of cultured keratinocytes. Br J Plast Surg 46, 401–409, 1993.

[127] *Karasek MA:* Culture of human keratinocytes in liquid medium. J Invest Dermatol 81, 24s–28s, 1983.

[128] *Kistler D, Hafemann B, Hettich R:* Cytogenetic investigations of the allodermis after intermingled skin grafting. Burns 15, 82–84, 1989.

[129] *Kopp J, Jiao XY, Bannasch H et al.:* Membrane cell grafts (MCG), fresh and frozen, to cover full thickness wounds in athymic nude mice. Eur J Plast Surg 22, 213–219, 1999.

[130] *Kovacs L, Horch RE, Grandel S, Spilker G:* Versuch der Kostenanalyse bei erfolgreicher Behandlung eines Schwerstverbrannten. In: Schmelzle R, ed. Plastische und Wiederherstellungschirurgie – ein Jahrbuch. Lorch: Uni-Med, 355–357, 1996.

[131] *Königová R, Kapounková Z, Vogtová D, Vesely P, Matousková E:* First experiences with clinical application of cultured auto-epithelium grafts. Acta Chirurgiae Plasticae 31, 193–200, 1989.

[132] *Kreibich K:* Kultur erwachsener Haut auf festem Nährboden. Arch Dermatol Syph 120, 168–178, 1914.

[133] *Kreis RW, Mackie DP, Vloemans AW, Hermans RP, Hoekstra MJ:* Widely expanded postage stamp skin grafts using a modified Meek technique in combination with an allograft overlay. Burns 19, 142–145, 1993.

[134] *Krejci-Papa NC, Cardon WR, Hoang A, Tenenhaus M, Hansbrough JF:* A comparison of the outgrowth potentials of split-thickness skin grafts sectioned by scalpel, mechanical mesher, and CO2 laser. J Burn Care Rehabil 20, 400–405, 1999.

[135] *Krejci NC, McGuire J:* Treatment of burns with skin substitutes. J Dermatol Sci 4, 149–155, 1992.

[136] *Krupp S, Benathan M, Meuli M et al.:* Current concepts in pediatric burn care: Management of burn wounds with cultured epidermal autografts. Eur J Pediatr Surg 2, 210–215, 1992.

[137] *Kuroyanagi Y, Kenmochi M, Ishihara S et al.:* A cultured skin substitute composed of fibroblasts and keratinocytes with a collagen matrix: preliminary results of clinical trials. Ann Plast Surg 31, 340–349, 1993.

[138] *Lam PK, Chan ES, Liew CT, Lau CH, Yen SC, King WW:* The efficacy of collagen dermis membrane and fibrin on cultured epidermal graft using an athymic mouse model. Ann Plast Surg 43, 523–528, 1999.

[139] *Larochelle F, Ross G, Rouabhia M:* Permanent skin replacement using engineered epidermis containing fewer than 5% syngeneic keratinocytes. Lab Invest 78, 1089–1099, 1998.

[140] *Latarjet J, Gangolphe M, Hezez G et al.:* The grafting of burns with cultured epidermis as autografts in man. Two case reports. Scand

J Plast Reconstr Surg Hand Surg 21, 241–244, 1987.

[141] *Lechner JF, Haugen A, McClendon IA, Shamsuddin AM:* Induction of squamous differentiation of normal human bronchial epithelial cells by small amounts of serum. Differentiation 25, 229–237, 1984.

[142] *Leigh IM, Purkis PE, Navsaria H, Phillips TJ:* Treatment of chronic venous ulcers with sheets of cultured allogenic keratinocytes. Br J Dermatol 117, 591–597, 1987.

[143] *Limat A, Breitkreutz D, Thiekoetter G et al.:* Formation of a regular neo-epidermis by cultured human outer root sheath cells grafted on nude mice. Transplantation 59, 1032–1038, 1995.

[144] *Limat A, Mauri D, Hunziker T:* Successful treatment of chronic leg ulcers with epidermal equivalents generated from cultured autologous outer root sheath cells. J Invest Dermatol 107, 128–135, 1996:

[145] *Lin SD, Chou CK, Lai CS, Yang CC:* Microskin grafting of rabbits with pigskin xenograft overlay. Burns 17, 473–477, 1991.

[146] *Lin SD, Lai CS, Chou CK, Tsai CW:* Microskin grafting of rabbit skin wounds with Biobrane overlay. Burns 18, 390–394, 1992.

[147] *Lin SD, Lai CS, Chou CK, Tsai CW, Wu KF, Chang CW:* Microskin autograft with pigskin xenograft overlay: a preliminary report of studies on patients. Burns 18, 321–325, 1992.

[148] *Lin TW:* The algebraic view-point in microskin grafting in burned patients. Burns 20, 347–350, 1994.

[149] *Lin TW:* An alternative method of skin grafting: the scalp microdermis graft. Burns 21, 374–378, 1995.

[150] *Lin TW, Horng SY:* A new method of microskin mincing. Burns 20, 526–528, 1994.

[151] *Livesey SA, Herndon DN, Hollyoak MA, Atkinson YH, Nag A:* Transplanted acellular allograft dermal matrix. Potential as a template for the reconstruction of viable dermis. Transplantation 60, 1–9, 1995.

[152] *Ljunggren C A:* Von der Fähigkeit des Hautepithels, ausserhalb des Organismus sein Leben zu erhalten, mit Berücksichtigung der Transplantation. Deutsch Z Chir 47, 608–615, 1898.

[153] *Lopez Valle CA, Germain L, Rouabhia M et al.:* Grafting on nude mice of living skin equivalents produced using human collagens. Transplantation 62, 317–323, 1996.

[154] *López Gutiérrez JC, Ros Z, Vallejo D, Perdiguero M, Soto C, Tovar J:* Cultured epidermal autograft in the management of critical pediatric burn patients. Eur J Pediatr Surg 5, 174–176, 1995.

[155] *Madden MR, Finkelstein JL, Staiano-Coico L et al.:* Grafting of cultured allogeneic epidermis on second- and third-degree burn wounds on 26 patients. J Trauma 26, 955–962, 1986.

[156] *Mangoldt v. F:* Die Überhäutung von Wundflächen und Wundhöhlen durch Epithelausaat, eine neue Methode der Transplantation. Deut Med Wschr 798–799, 1895.

[157] *Matouskova E, Bucek S, Vogtova D et al.:* Treatment of burns and donor sites with human allogeneic keratinocytes grown on acellular pig dermis. Br J Dermatol 136, 901–907, 1997.

[158] *Matouskova E, Vogtova D, Konigova R:* A recombined skin composed of human keratinocytes cultured on cell-free pig dermis. Burns 19, 118–123, 1993.

[159] *McKay I, Woodward B, Wood K, Navsaria H, Hoekstra H, Green C:* Reconstruction of human skin from glycerol-preserved allodermis and cultured keratinocyte sheets. Burns 20, S19–S22, 1994.

[160] *Medalie DA, Eming SA, Collins SA, Tompkins RG, Yarmush ML, Morgan JR:* Differences in dermal analogs influence subsequent pigmentation, epidermal differentiation, basement membrane, and rete ridge formation of transplanted composite skin grafts. Transpl 64, 454–465, 1997.

[161] *Medawar PB:* The behaviour and fate of skin autografts and skin homografts in rabbits. J Anat 78, 176–184, 1944.

[162] *Meichlböck A, Fleischer S, Moll I:* Autologous ORS- Keratinocytes in the therapy of chronic leg ulcers. In: Stark GB, Horch R, Tanczos E, eds. Biological matrices and tissue reconstruction. Berlin Heidelberg New York: Springer Verlag, 105–110, 1998.

[163] *Mindikoglu AN, Cetinkale O:* Prolonged allograft survival in a patient with extensive burns using cyclosporin. Burns 19, 70–72, 1993.

[164] *Moscona A:* Rotation-mediated histogenic aggreagtion of dissociated cell Exp Cell Res 22, 455–460, 1984.

[165] *Munster AM, Weiner SH, Spence RJ:* Cultured epidermis for the coverage of massive burn wounds – A single center experience. Ann Surg 211, 676–680, 1990.

[166] *Mühlbauer W, Henkel v.Donnersmark G, Hoefter E, Hartinger A:* Keratinozytenzüchtung und -transplantation bei Verbrennungen. Chirurg 66, 271–276, 1995.

[167] *Myers SR, Navsaria HA, Brain AN, Purkis PE, Leigh IM:* Epidermal differentiation and dermal changes in healing following treatment of surgical wounds with sheets of cultured allogeneic keratinocytes. J Clin Pathol 48, 1087–1092, 1995.

[168] *Najarian JS, McCorkle HJ:* An experimental study on the grafting of a suspension of epithelial particles. Surgery 42, 218–227, 1957.

[169] Nakano M, Yoshida T, Ohura T, Azami K, Senoo A, Fuse Y: Clinicopathologic studies on human epithelial autografts and allografts. Plast Reconstr Surg 90, 899–909, 1992.

[170] Nath C, Gulati SC: Role of cytokines in healing chronic skin wounds. Acta Haematol 99, 175–179, 1998.

[171] Nolte CJ, Oleson MA, Hansbrough JF, Morgan J, Greenleaf G, Wilkins L: Ultrastructural features of composite skin cultures grafted onto athymic mice. J Anat 185, 325–333, 1994.

[172] Nyström G: Sewing of small skin particles for epithelialisation especially of extensive wound surfaces. Plast Reconstr Surg 23, 226–239, 1959.

[173] O'Connor NE, Mulliken JB: Grafting of burns with cultured epithelium prepared from autologous epidermal cells. Lancet 75–78, 1981.

[174] Odessey R: Addendum: Multicenter Experience with Cultured Epidermal Autograft for Treatment of Burns. J Burn Care Rehabil 13, 174–180, 1992.

[175] Otto WR, Nanchahal J, Lu QL, Boddy N, Dover R: Survival of allogeneic cells in cultured organotypic skin grafts. Plast Reconstr Surg 96, 166–176, 1995.

[176] Parshley M S, Simm H S: Cultivation of adult skin epithelial cells (chicken and human) in vitro. Am J Anat 86, 163–169, 1950.

[177] Pellegrini G, Ranno R, Stracuzzi G et al.: The control of epidermal stem cells (holoclones) in the treatment of massive full-thickness burns with autologous keratinocytes cultured on fibrin. Transplantation 68, 868–879, 1999.

[178] Pels-Leusden F: Die Anwendung des Spalthautlappens in der Chirurgie. Deut Med Wschr 31, 99–102, 1905.

[179] Phillips TJ: Cultured epidermal allografts a temporary or permanent solution? Transplantation 51, 937–941, 1991.

[180] Phillips TJ, Bhawan J, Leigh IM, Baum HJ, Gilchrest BA: Cultured epidermal autografts and allografts: a study of differentiation and allograft survival. J Am Acad Dermatol 23, 189–198, 1990.

[181] Pinkus H: Über Gewebekulturen menschlicher Epoidermis. Arch Dermatol Syph 165, 53–59, 1932.

[182] Rennekampff HO, Kiessig V, Griffey S, Greenleaf G, Hansbrough JF: Acellular human dermis promotes cultured keratinocyte engraftment. J Burn Care Rehabil 18, 535–544, 1997

[183] Rennekampff HO, Kiessig V, Hansbrough JF: Current concepts in the development of cultured skin replacements. J Surg Res 62, 288–295, 1996.

[184] Rheinwald JG, Green H: Serial Cultivation of Stains of Human Epidermal Keratinocytes: the Formation of Keratinizing Colonies from Single Cells. Cell 6, 331–344, 1975.

[185] Rives JM, Cantaloube D, Ainaud P, Barandon Y, Carsin H: [Role of autografts of cultured epidermis in the treatment of deep burns of the face. Preliminary results]. Ann Chir Plast Esthet 40, 286–292, 1995.

[186] Ronfard V, Broly H, Mitchell V et al.: Use of human keratinocytes cultured on fibrin glue in the treatment of burn wounds. Burns 17, 181–184, 1991.

[187] Rouabhia M, Germain L, Belanger F, Auger FA: Cultured epithelium allografts: Langerhans cell and Thy-1+ dendritic epidermal cell depletion effects on allograft rejection. Transplantation 56, 259–264, 1993.

[188] Rouabhia M, Germain L, Bergeron J, Auger FA: Allogeneic-syngeneic cultured epithelia. A successful therapeutic option for skin regeneration. Transplantation 59, 1229–1235, 1995.

[189] Sawada Y: Survival of an extensively burned child following use of fragments of autograft skin overlain with meshed allograft skin. Burns Incl Therm Inj 11, 429–433, 1985.

[190] Siwy BK, Compton CC: Cultured epidermis: Indiana University Medical Center's experience. J Burn Care Rehabil 13, 130–137, 1992.

[191] Slavin J: The role of cytokines in wound healing. J Pathol 178, 5–10, 1996.

[192] Stark GB, Horch RE, Voigt M, Tanczos E: [Biological wound tissue glue systems in wound healing]. Langenbecks Arch Chir Suppl Kongressbd 115, 683-8, 683–688, 1998.

[193] Stark GB, Kaiser HW: Cologne Burn Centre experience with glycerol-preserved allogeneic skin: Part II: Combination with autologous cultured keratinocytes. Burns 20, S34–S38, 1994.

[194] Stark GB, Kaiser HW, Horch RE, Kopp J, Spilker G: Cultured autologous keratinocytes suspended in fibrin glue (KFGS) with allogenic overgraft for definitive burn wound coverage. Eur J Plast Surg 18, 267–271, 1995.

[195] Still J, Orlet HK, Law EJ: Use of cultured epidermal autografts in the treatment of large burns. Burns 20, 539–541, 1994.

[196] Stoner ML, Wood FM: Systemic factors influencing the growth of cultured epithelial autograft. Burns 22, 197–199, 1996.

[197] Stoner ML, Wood FM: Cultured epithelial autograft take confirmed by the presence of cytokeratin 9 [letter]. J Invest Dermatol 112, 391–392, 1999.

[198] Sun TT, Green H: Differentiation of the epidermal keratinocyte in cell culture: formation of the cornified envelope. Cell 9, 511–521, 1976.

[199] *Suzuki T, Ui K, Shioya N, Ihara S:* Mixed cultures comprising syngeneic and allogeneic mouse keratinocytes as a graftable skin substitute. Transplantation 59, 1236–1241, 1995.

[200] *Thivolet J, Faure M, Demidem A, Mauduit G:* Long-term survival and immunological tolerance of human epidermal allografts produced in culture. Transplantation 42, 274–280, 1986.

[201] *Tompkins RG, Hilton JF, Burke JF et al.:* Increased survival after massive thermal injuries in adults: Preliminary report using artificial skin. Crit Care Med 17, 734–740, 1989.

[202] *Tompkins RG, Burke JF:* Progress in burn treatment and the use of artificial skin. World J Surg 14, 819–824, 1990.

[203] *Tompkins RG, Burke JF:* Burn wound closure using permanent skin replacement materials. World J Surg 16, 47–52, 1992.

[204] *van Dorp AG, Verhoeven MC, Nat-Van Der Meij TH, Koerten HK, Ponec M:* A modified culture system for epidermal cells for grafting purposes: an in vitro and in vivo study. Wound Repair Regen 7, 214–225, 1999.

[205] *Vedung S, Hedlung A:* Fibrin glue: its use for skin grafting of contaminated burn wounds in areas difficult to immobilize. J Burn Care Rehabil 14, 356–358, 1993.

[206] *Voigt M, Schauer M, Schaefer DJ, Andree C, Horch RE, Stark GB:* Cultured epidermal keratinocytes on a microspherical transport system are feasible to reconstitute the epidermis in full-thickness wounds. Tissue Eng 5, 563–572, 1999.

[207] *Wagner G, Debus M, Stark GB, Horch RE:* Esterifizierte Hyaluronsäure-Membranen als Wachstumssubstrat für humane Keratinozyten. Hefte zur Zeitschrift Unfallchirurg 278, 91–96, 2000.

[208] *Wainwright DJ:* Use of an acellular allograft dermal matrix (AlloDerm) in the management of full-thickness burns. Burns 21, 243–248, 1995.

[209] *Wang X, Wang J, Wu J:* [Manufacture and application of a new composite allograft]. Chung Kuo Hsiu Fu Chung Chien Wai Ko Tsa Chih 11, 100–102, 1997.

[210] *Watt FM:* Proliferation and terminal differentiation of human epidermal keratinocytes in culture. Biochem Soc Trans 16, 666–668, 1988.

[211] *Waymouth C:* Construction and use of synthetic media. In: Wilmer EN (ed.), ed. Cells and Tissues in Culture. London: Academic Press, 99–110, 1965.

[212] *Williamson JS, Snelling CFT, Clugston P, Macdonalds IB, Germann E:* Cultured Epithelial Autograft: Five Years of Clinical Experience with Twenty-Eight Patients. J Trauma 39, 309–319, 1995.

[213] *Wood F, Liddiard K, Skinner A, Ballentyne J:* Scar management of cultured epithelial autograft. Burns 22, 451–454, 1996.

[214] *Woodley DT, Peterson HD, Herzog SR et al.:* Burn wounds resurfaced by cultured epidermal autografts show abnormal reconstitution of anchoring fibrils. JAMA 259, 2566–2571, 1988.

[215] *Worst PK, Mackenzie IC, Fusenig NE:* Reformation of organized epidermal structure by transplantation of suspensions and cultures of epidermal and dermal cells. Cell Tissue Res 225, 65–77, 1982.

[216] *Wu J, Barisoni D, Armato U:* Prolongation of survival of alloskin grafts with no concurrent general suppression of the burned patient's immune system: a preliminary clinical investigation. Burns 22, 353–358, 1996.

[217] *Xie WG:* [Use of microskin grafting for burn wound coverage]. Chung Hua Cheng Hsing Shao Shang Wai Ko Tsa Chih 6, 275–277, 1990.

[218] *Yannas IV, Burke JF, Orgill DP, Skrabut EM:* Wound tissue can utilize a polymeric template to synthesize a functional extension of skin. Science 215, 174–176, 1982.

[219] *Zacchi V, Soranzo C, Cortivo R, Radice M, Brun P, Abatangelo G:* In vitro engineering of human skin-like tissue. J Biomed Mater Res 40, 187–194, 1998.

[220] *Zhang ML, Chang ZD, Wang CY, Fang CH:* Microskin grafting in the treatment of extensive burns: a preliminary report. J Trauma 28, 804–807, 1988.

[221] *Zhang ML, Wang CY, Chang ZD:* [Microskin grafting in animal experiments and clinical practice]. Chung Hua Wai Ko Tsa Chih 24, 219–4, 1986.

[222] *Zhang ML, Wang CY, Chang ZD, Cao DX, Han X:* Microskin grafting. II. Clinical report. Burns Incl Therm Inj 12, 544–548, 1986.

[223] *Zhao CA:* Clinical use of irradiated allogeneic dermis in the coverage of burn wounds. Chung Hua Cheng Hsing Shao Shang Wai Ko Tsa Chih 9, 257–258, 1993.

[224] *Zhao YB:* [Primary observation of prolonged survival of cultured epidermal allografts]. Chung Hua Wai Ko Tsa Chih 30, 104–106, 1992.

Wound Healing:
Physiology and Possible Role of Skin Substitutes

A. Barbul

Summary

This article Wound healing is characterized by a number of events until the final remodelling state is reached. Various growth factors and cytokines produced locally and systemically in response to the injury govern this complex cascade. Disturbances of this process can occur on various levels during the different healing phases. One of the critical steps is the restoration of epithelial integrity taking place while granulation tissue and collagen synthesis is procedding deep in the wound. This article summarozes the potential usefulness of the currently available different types of tissue engineered skin substitutes in the treatment of problem wounds. Desired features of such products are outliend and future developments are discussed.

Wound healing is an organized cascade of cellular and biochemical events that occurs in a timely, predictable and limited fashion. An important feature of normal wound healing is its regulated transition from an exuberant cellular and mainly inflammatory response to a quiescent, acellular, remodelling phase. Progression through the phases of healing is governed by various growth factors and cytokines produced locally and systemically in response to the injury. For didactic purposes the wound healing response can be divided into three distinct but overlapping phases:

1. hemostasis and inflammation,
2. proliferation and
3. maturation or remodeling [1].

The populations of cells that participate in the timely healing of wounds are the same implicated in causing and participating in global inflammatory responses such as systemic inflammatory response syndrome (Fig. 1). As such, altered, prolonged, delayed or imbalanced production of cytokines and growth factors will disrupt or delay the wound healing process. Failure or prolongation in one phase may result in delay of healing or non-closure of the wound. Wound healing failures remain a significant clinical problem with large impact on health care costs. A better grasp of the fundamental physiology of healing will result in a clearer understanding of the pathophysiologic processes that impair healing.

When wounds fail, the process may be characterized as globally impaired, as observed in diabetes or chronic steroid use, or delayed, as noted with infections or malnutrition (Fig. 2). In the first instance, the wound will never achieve the mechanical characteristics of a normally healed wound; with delayed healing such mechanical integrity is achieved but belatedly. Clinically, acute wound failure and chronic wounds are two pathophysiologically distinct entities requiring different therapeutic strategies. A better understanding of the pathophysiology of wound healing will inevitably help in the prevention and treatment of wound failure.

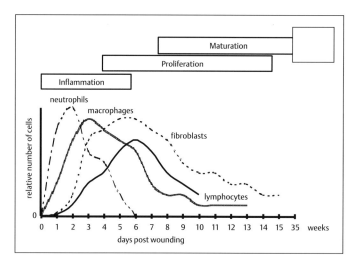

Fig. 1: Cellular events during wound healing.

Phases of Healing

Although the different cellular and biochemical phases of the wound healing process occur in a continuous, integrated manner it is convenient to divide the overall process into three overlapping but somewhat distinct steps for descriptive purposes

1-Inflammatory Phase: (Day 0–5)

The healing response is initiated at the moment of injury. Surgical or traumatic wounds disrupt the tissue architecture and cause hemorrhage. Initially blood fills the wound defect and its contact with exposed tissue collagen leads to platelet degranulation and activation of Hageman factor [2]. This in turn sets into motion a number of biological amplification systems including the complement, kinin and clotting cascades and plasmin generation. These serve to amplify the original injury signal and lead not only to clot formation, which unites the wound edges, but also to the accumulation of a number of mitogens and chemoattractants at the site of wounding [3]. Production of both kinins and prostaglandins results in vasodilatation and increased small vessel permeability in the region of wound [4]. This contributes to the formation of edema in the area of the injury which is responsible for the pain and swelling.

Platelets trapped within the clot become activated in response to thrombin and release the contents of their alpha granules. Al-

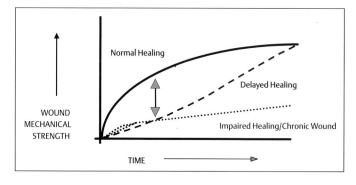

Fig. 2: The relationship between nornal, delayed and impaired healing.

though not completely characterized these granules contain locally acting growth factors, most notably platelet-derived growth factor (PDGF), platelet-derived angiogenesis factor (PDAF), transforming growth factor-b (TGF-b), platelet-derived epidermal growth factor (PDEGF) and platelet factor-4 (PF-4). All of these factors have been shown to stimulate the migration, replication and function of various cellular elements critical to wound healing [5].

Within six hours of injury circulating immune cells start to appear in the wound. Polymorphonuclear leucocytes (PMN) are the first blood leukocytes to enter the wound site and their numbers increase steadily, peaking at 24–48 hours [6]. The main function of the PMN's appears to be phagocytosis of the bacteria which have been introduced into the wound during injury. The presence of PMNs does not appear to the essential in order for normal wound healing to take place, provided that bacterial contamination has not occurred [7, 8]. However, recent studies suggest that leukocytes are a major source of cytokines early during inflammation, especially tumor necrosis factor (TNF)-α [9]. Neutrophils thus may have a potential role in subsequent angiogenesis and collagen synthesis. Neutrophils also release proteases such as collagenases and participate in matrix and ground substance degradation in the early phase of wound healing [10]. In the absence of infection PMNs have a relatively short life span in the wound and their numbers decrease rapidly after the third day [11].

Different subpopulations of polymorphonuclear leukocytes, albeit low in numbers, may exert distinct functions. A recently established leukocyte subpopulation are the fibrocytes. These fibroblast-like cells have some leukocyte specific features: they are found at the site of injury shortly after trauma, they synthesize matrix (collagen types I and III), and display the spindle shape form of fibroblasts. The fibrocytes also express leukocyte associated antigenic structures such as CD34 and can act as an antigen presenting cells during T-cell proliferation [12–14].

Mast cells are known to participate in inflammation. Recent work suggests that mast cells may have a role in wound healing as a major source of cytokines such as fibroblast growth factor (FGF), IL-1, -3, -4, PDGF, TNF-ß and tumor growth factor (TGF)-β as well as heparin, histamine, leukotrienes and other factors [15]. Mast cells can regulate vascular tone and permeability, coagulation and chemoattraction of other cells in the early phase of wound healing. In vitro work has shown that mast cells stimulate fibroblast proliferation probably via histamine release [16]. Mast cell derived TGF-β, FGF and IL-4 are potent stimulators of extracellular matrix synthesis [17, 18], but the exact contribution of mast cell derived cytokines to wound healing remains to be fully elucidated.

The next cellular immune elements to enter the wound are the macrophages. These cells, derived from circulating monocytes, migrate within the wound at 48–96 hours post-injury and reach a peak around the third day post injury. Wound macrophages have a much longer lifespan than the PMNs and persist in the wound until healing is complete. Their appearance is followed somewhat later by lymphocytes which appear in significant numbers around the fifth day post-injury, with peak numbers occurring about the seventh day after injury. In contrast to PMNs, the presence and activation of both macrophages and lymphocytes in the wound is critical to the progress of the normal healing process [19, 20]

The Role of the Macrophage

The macrophage appears to have a dual role at the wound site. Initially they participate in the inflammatory and debridement process, superceding the PMN as the major wound phagocyte and later play a regulatory role in the mediation of the fibroblastic phase of healing. It is this latter role which is crucial to the success of the wound healing process (Fig. 3).

Activation of macrophages leads to release of cytokines mediating angiogenesis and

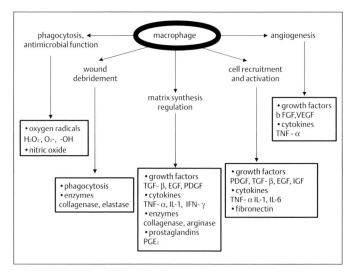

Fig. 3: Multiple functions of macrophages during wound healing.

fibroplasias. Evidence for macrophage involvement in the regulation of wound healing is provided by the findings that intradermal injection of allogeneic macrophages increases both collagen synthesis and wound breaking strength in eight day old rat skin wounds [21], while injection of wound macrophages into rabbit corneas induces angiogenesis and scar formation [22, 23].

Activated macrophages are capable of influencing many aspects of wound healing including the proliferative and synthetic activities of fibroblasts and induction of neovascularization [23–25].

Activation of wound macrophages also results in the synthesis of nitric oxide, which has many functions including antimicrobial properties [26, 27]. Albina showed that macrophages are activated during the early phase of healing to synthesize nitric oxide and that the hypoxic wound environment further enhances its expression [28]. Many other cells participating in wound healing including endothelial cells [29], fibroblasts [30], monocytes [31] and lymphocytes [32] can be activated in vitro to produce nitric oxide. Recent studies demonstrated that nitric oxide synthesis is reduced in impaired wound healing models [33–35]; conversely in vivo inhibition of nitric oxide synthesis in mice impairs wound healing [36].

It is clear that numerous macrophage derived cytokines influence the function of various wound cells. What is unknown is the temporal sequence of the appearance of these cytokine at the wound site, how the various up- and down-regulatory factors interact and what are the the control mechanism for the generation of these factors.

The Role of the Lymphocyte

Evidence supporting a role for T lymphocytes in the control of wound healing is provided by studies which examine the in vivo effects of alternate forms of T cell manipulation on various parameters of healing. T-lymphocytes are essential to wound healing, although their role is not fully defined. Depletion of wound T-lymphocytes decreases wound strength and collagen content [37]. Selective depletion of the CD8+ suppressor subset of T-lymphocytes enhances wound healing; depletion of the CD4+ helper subset has no effect [38]. This suggests that an incompletely characterized T cell population, bearing the T cell marker but neither the T helper nor the T suppressor antigenic determinant is responsible for the promotion of wound healing, since its deletion impairs wound healing.

Modification of T lymphocyte function by adult thymectomy, which prevents the induction of T suppressor cells, causes an increase in wound maturation. This effect could be reversed by intraperitoneal placement of autologous thymic grafts in millipore chambers in thymectomized rats [39]. Congenitally athymic nude mice, which have an impaired T-cell system, demonstrate better breaking strength and increased wound collagen deposition when compared to normal animals [40]. Conversely administration of purified thymic hormones, thymulin, thymopoietin and thymosin fraction V, results in impaired wound healing, as assessed by wound breaking strength and wound collagen deposition [41]. The data suggests that the thymus exerts an inhibitory effect on normal wound healing, possibly by enhancing T suppressor cell activation following injury. Although the thymus appears to exert a down-regulating effect on wound healing, administration of Interleukin-2 or thymosin-α_1, both potent stimulators of lymphocyte proliferation and differentiation, improves wound healing [42, 43]. Lymphocytes can exert a direct down-regulating effect on fibroblast collagen synthesis by cell-associated interferon (IFN)-γ, TNF-α and IL-1α [44]. This effect is abrogated if the cells are physically separated, demonstrating that extracellular matrix synthesis is regulated not only via soluble factors but also via direct cell-cell contact between lymphocytes and fibroblasts.

2. Proliferative Phase: (Day 3–14)

In the absence of significant infection or contamination, the inflammatory phase is short and leads to the proliferative phase of healing. This phase is characterized by the formation of granulation tissue in the wound. Granulation tissue consists of a combination of cellular elements, including fibroblasts and inflammatory cells, along with new capillaries, all embedded in a loose extra cellular matrix of collagen, fibronectin and hyaluronic acid.

Angiogenesis

Revascularization of the wound proceeds in parallel with fibroplasia. Capillary buds sprout from blood vessels adjacent to the wound and extend into the wound space. On the second day post injury endothelial cells from the side of the venule closest to the wound begin to migrate in response to angiogenic stimuli. These capillary sprouts eventually branch at their tips and join to form capillary loops through which blood begins to flow. New sprouts then extend from these loops to form a capillary plexus [45, 46]. The soluble factors responsible for angiogenesis remain incompletely defined. It appears that angiogenesis occurs by a combination of proliferation and migration. Putative mediators for endothelial cell growth and chemotaxis include include cytokines produced by platelets, macrophages and lymphocytes in the wound [47, 48] low oxygen tension [49], lactic acid [50] and biogenic amines [51]. Of the potential cytokine mediators of neovascularization basic fibroblast growth factor (bFGF), acidic fibroblast growth factor (aFGF), TGF-α, EGF, and TGF-β have all been shown to be potent stimuli for new vessel formation [52–55].

The Fibroblast

Fibroblasts first appear in significant numbers in the wound on the third day post injury and achieve peak numbers around the seventh day [6]. This rapid expansion in the fibroblast population at the wound site occurs via a combination of proliferation and migration [56]. Fibroblasts are derived from local mesenchymal cells, particularly those associated with blood vessel adventitia [57], and are attracted to the wound and induced to proliferate by cytokines released initially from platelets and subsequently from macrophages and lymphocytes. The strongest chemotactic factor for fibroblasts is PDGF [58, 59]. Recruited fibroblasts need to become activated from a quiescent state prior to participation in healing. This activation is partially induced by the cytokines released from macrophages. The primary functions of wound fibroblasts are matrix synthesis and remodeling. Fibroblasts isolated from wounds differ significantly from non-wound fibroblasts in that they have higher contractile and matrix synthesizing capacity [60]. The contractile property of fibroblasts is due to their expression of alpha-smooth muscle actin which is organized into stress fibers within the cell; alpha-smooth muscle actin can be induced in vitro by TGF-β [61] or by the addition of wound fluid to cultured fibroblasts [60]. This contractile phenotype is not permanent since myofibroblasts undergo apoptosis during the repair process [62].

Wound derived fibroblasts also synthesize more collagen than non-wound derived fibroblasts [60]. The mechanism that induces high collagen production is not well understood. The cytokine-rich wound environment plays a signficant role as exposure of fibroblasts to wound fluid induces increased collagen synthesis [63, 64]. Additionally, lactate accumulates in wound fluid over time (10 to 15 mM) and it regulates collagen synthesis through a mechanism involving ADP-ribosylation [65].

Recently wound fibroblasts have been shown to produce nitric oxide which in turn influences their collagen metabolism [66]. Normal dermal fibroblasts do not produce nitric oxide spontaneously. Upon exposure to wound fluid dermal fibroblasts can be induced to synthesize nitric oxide [67] and this may be at least partially responsible for the switch to a wound fibroblast phenotype. Similarly, induction of nitric oxide synthesis in epithelial cells and keratinocytes correlates with a switch in phenotype [68, 69].

In vivo administration of nitric oxide donors as well as direct in vivo transfection of the iNOS synthase gene enhances wound strength and collagen deposition under experimental conditions [70, 71]. iNOS knockout mice exhibit delayed healing of excisional wounds, an effect reversible by in vivo transfection of the iNOS gene [72]. These data provide further support for a significant role of nitric oxide in wound healing, although the exact mechanism of action remains to be defined fully.

Fibroblasts are the primary synthetic element in the repair process and are responsible for production of the majority of structural proteins necessary for tissue reconstruction. The main protein product of fibroblasts is collagen, a family of triple chain glycoproteins, which forms the main constituent of the extra cellular wound matrix and which is ultimately responsible for imparting tensile strength to the scar. Collagen is first detected in the wound around the third day post injury [73, 74] and thereafter the levels increase rapidly for approximately three weeks. It then continues to accumulate at a more gradual pace for up to three months post wounding. The collagen is initially deposited in a seemingly haphazard fashion and subsequently these individual collagen fibrils are reorganized, by crosslinking, into regularly aligned bundles oriented along the lines of stress in the healing wound. Fibroblasts are also responsible for the production of other matrix constituents including fibronectin, hyaluronic acid and the glycosaminoglycans [75]. The process of fibroblast proliferation and synthetic activity is known as fibroplasia.

Biochemistry of Collagen

Collagen, the most abundant protein in the body, plays a critical role in the successful completion of wound healing. Its deposition, maturation and subsequent remodelling are critical to the functional integrity of the wound.

Although there are at least 13 types of collagen described, the main ones of interest to wound repair are types I and III. Type I collagen is the major component of extracellular matrix in skin. Type III, which is also normally present in skin, becomes a more prominent component during the repair process.

Biochemically, each chain of collagen is composed of a glycine residue in every third position. The second position in the triplet is

Table 1: Major steps in the synthesis of collagen and their cellular localization.

Transcription	Nucleus
Translation	Cytoplasm/RER
Hydroxylation of Proline and Lysine	RER lumen
Glycosylation	RER lumen
a-chain association	RER lumen
helix formation	RER lumen
secretion	–
registration peptide cleavage	extracellular
polymerization	extracellular
crosslinking	extracellular

registration peptides are cleaved by a procollagen peptidase. Extracellularly the procollagen strands undergo further polymerization and crosslinking. The resulting collagen monomer is further polymerized and cross linked by the formation of intra- and intermolecular covalent bonds.

Collagen biosynthesis and its post-translational modification are highly complex biochemical events (Table 1). Each step in this process requires its own set of enzymes, cofactors and substrate for successful completion.

made up of proline or lysine during the translation process. The polypeptide chain that is translated from mRNA contains approximately 1,000 amino acid residues and is called protocollagen. Release of protocollagen into the endoplasmic reticulum results in the hydroxylation of proline to hydroxyproline and of lysine to hydroxylysine by specific hydroxylases. Prolyl hydroxylase requires oxygen and iron as cofactors, a-ketoglutarate as co-substrate and ascorbic acid (vitamin C) as an electron donor. In the endoplasmic reticulum the protocollagen chainis glycosylated by the linking of galactose and glucose at specific hydroxylysine residues. These steps of hydroxylation and glycosylation alter the hydrogen bonding forces within the chain which imposes steric changes so that the protocollagen chain assumes an a-helical configuration. Three a-helical chains then entwine to form a right-handed superhelical structure called procollagen. This structure contains at both ends non-helical peptide domains named "registration peptides". Although initially joined by weak ionic bonds, the procollagen molecule becomes much stronger by the covalent crosslinking of lysine residues.

Prior to the procollagen molecule being extruded extra-cellularly, the non-helical

Proteoglycans

Glycosaminoglycans comprise a large portion of the "ground substance" which makes up the granulation tissue. Rarely found free, they are coupled with proteins thus forming proteoglycans. The polysaccharide chain is made up of repeating disaccharide units composed of glucuronic or iduronic acid and a hexosamine which is usually sulfated. The disaccharide composition of proteoglycans vary from about 10 units in the case of heparin sulfate to as much as 2,000 units in the case of hyaluronic acid.

In wounds the major glycosaminoglycans are dermatan and chondroitin sulfate. Fibroblasts synthesize these compounds and their concentration in wounds increases greatly during the first three weeks of healing. The interaction between collagen and proteoglycans is being actively studied. It is thought that the assembly of collagen subunits into fibrils and fibers is dependent on the lattice provided by the sulfated proteoglycans. Furthermore, it appears that the extent of sulfation is critical in determining the configuration of the collagen fibrils. As the scar collagen is deposited, the proteoglycans are incorporated into the collagen scaffolding. However, with scar maturation and collagen remodelling, the content of proteoglycan gradually diminishes.

Epithelialization

While granulation tissue and collagen synthesis is proceeding deep in the wound, restoration of epithelial integrity is taking place at the wound surface. Re-epithelialization of the wound begins within a couple of hours of the injury. Epithelial cells, arising from either the wound margins or residual dermal epithelial appendages within the wound bed, begin to migrate under the scab and over the underlying viable connective tissue. The epidermis immediately adjacent to the wound edge begins thickening within twenty four hours after injury. Marginal basal cells at the edge of the wound loose their firm attachment to the underlying dermis, enlarge and begin to migrate across the surface of the provisional matrix filling the wound. Fixed basal cells in a zone near the cut edge undergo a series of rapid mitotic divisions and these cells appear to migrate by moving over one another in a leapfrog fashion until the defect is covered [76, 77]. Once the defect is bridged the migrating epithelial cells loose their flattened appearance, become more columnar in shape and increase in mitotic activity. Layering of the epithelium is re-established and the surface layer eventually keratinized [78]. Re-epithelialization is complete in less than forty eight hours in the case of approximated incised wounds but may take substantially longer in the case of larger wounds where there is a significant tissue defect. If only the epithelium is damaged, such as occurs in split thickness skin graft donor sites or in superficial second degree burns, then repair consists primarily of re-epithelialization with minimal or absent fibroplasia and granulation tissue formation. The stimuli for re-epithelialization remain incompletely defined but it appears that the process is mediated by a combination of loss of contact inhibition, exposure of constituents of the extracellular matrix, particularly fibronectin [79] and by cytokines produced by immune mononuclear cells [80]. In particular EGF, TGF-b, bFGF, PDGF and IGF-1 have been shown to promote epithelialization. Although the mechanisms by which these factors enhance epithelialization are not clear, they all possess in vitro mitogenic and/or chemotactic properties toward epithelial cells.

Maturation Phase: (Day 7–1 Year)

Almost as soon as the extracellular matrix is laid down its reorganization begins. Initially the extracellular matrix is rich in fibronectin, which forms a provisional fiber network. This serves not only as a substratum for migration and ingrowth of cells but also as a template for collagen deposition by fibroblasts [81]. There are also significant quantities of hyaluronic acid and large molecular weight proteoglycans present which contribute to the gel like consistency of the extra cellular matrix and aid cellular infiltration. Collagen rapidly becomes the predominant constituent of the matrix. The initially randomly distributed collagen fibers become crosslinked and aggregated into fibrillar bundles, which gradually provide the healing tissue with increasing stiffness and tensile strength [82]. After a five day lag period, which corresponds to early granulation tissue formation and a matrix largely composed of fibronectin and hyaluronic acid, there is a rapid increase in wound breaking strength due to collagen fibrogenesis. The subsequent rate of gain in wound tensile strength is slow, with the wound having gained only 20% of its final strength after three weeks. The final strength of the wound remains less than that of uninjured skin, with the maximum breaking strength of the scar reaching only 70% of that of the intact skin.

This gradual gain in tensile strength is due not only to continuing collagen deposition but also to collagen remodeling, with formation of larger collagen bundles and alteration of intermolecular cross linking [83]. Collagen remodeling during scar formation is dependent on both continued collagen synthesis and collagen catabolism. The degradation of wound collagen is controlled by a variety of collagenase enzymes and the net increase in wound collagen is determined by the balance of these opposing mechanisms. The high rate of collagen synthesis within the wound returns to normal levels by six to twelve months [84], while active remodeling of the scar continues for up one year after injury and indeed appears to continue at a very slow rate for life.

As remodeling progresses there is a gradual reduction in the cellularity and vascularity of the reparative tissue which results in the formation of a relatively avascular and acellular collagen scar. Grossly this can be observed as a reduction in erythema associated with the earlier scar and some reduction in the scar volume resulting in a pale thin scar. This is normally a desirable feature of healing however in some cases shrinkage of the scar may give rise to an undesirable reduction in skin mobility resulting in contracture.

Contraction

Wound contraction, i.e. inward movement of the wound edge, is a further important element in the healing process and should be distinguished from contracture. Sharply incised and sutured wounds heal rapidly without the need for significant reduction in the wound volume. Such wounds are described as having healed by primary intention. Large wounds, particularly those associated with significant tissue loss, heal by secondary intention, with granulation tissue gradually filling the defect and epithelialization proceeding slowly from the wound edges. Contraction of the wound edges can lead to a significant reduction in the quantity of granulation tissue required to fill the wound defect and a reduction in the area requiring re-epithelization, with a consequent reduction in scar volume. Contraction is only undesirable where it leads to unacceptable tissue distortion and an unsatisfactory cosmetic result. Although contraction normally accounts for a larger portion of overall wound closure in loose skinned animals, it still accounts for a significant proportion of the healing process in man, particularly in areas where the skin is not tightly bound down to underlying structures, such as on the back,

neck and forearms. Initially there is a slight retraction of the wound edges due to the release of normal elastic tension in the skin, with a resultant increase in wound volume. The wound area starts to decrease rapidly from the third day onwards. While this is due in part to re-epithelization the main reason is an inward movement of the uninjured skin edges. Wound contraction usually begins around the fifth day post-wounding and is complete by twelve to fifteen days after wounding [85, 86]. Fibroblasts within the wound appear to be responsible for providing the force for this contractile activity [87]. It was initially felt that specialized fibroblasts called myofibroblasts provided the motive force for wound contraction via a muscle cell-like contraction [88–90]. More recent studies reveal that wound contraction occurs as a result of the interaction between fibroblast locomotion and collagen re-organization [87, 91]. The contraction is thought to be mediated by the attachment of collagen fibrils to cell surface receptors [92], with the resulting tractional forces generated by cell motility bringing the attached collagen fibrils closer together and eventually compacting them [93].

Chronic Wounds

Chronic wounds are generally defined as those that fail to heal following three months of conservative wound therapy. Upon examination, these wounds demonstrate failure of central migration of epithelial tissue, leaving a central eschar or moist, fluid-losing center. The etiology of the development and maintenance of the chronic wound is multifactorial, involving bacterial contamination, ongoing tissue ischemia, inadequate inflammatory response, and failure of wound protein synthesis. Advanced age, immobility, and malnutrition are further contributors to this process.

Chronic wounds represent significant morbidity to patients and add tremendously to costs in medical care. Many chronic wounds may be avoidable, and clinicians should be attentive to these issues with patients who

Table 2: Desired Features of Tissue Engineered Skin.

- Rapid reestablishment of functional skin (epidermis/dermis)
- Receptive to body's own cells (eg, rapid "take" and integration)
- Graftable by a single, simple procedure
- Graftable on chronic or acute wounds
- Engraftment without use of extraordinary clinical intervention (ie, immunosuppression)
  - Alleviate wound pain
  - Sterilizable/free of infection
  - Cost:benefit ratio
  - Effective shelf life

susceptible to their development. Treatment requires a multi-system approach, and can frequently bring relief to the patient and ultimate healing of the wound.

One hypothesis for the chronicity of non-healing wounds invokes a paucity of growth factors in the wound environment [94, 95]. Enhanced bacterial degradation, entrapment in fibrin clots or decreased overall synthesis are all factors contributing to diminished growth factor concentration in chronic wounds. Interestingly, most current formulations for clinical application of growth factors to chronic wounds deliver concentrations $\sim 10^3$ higher than those observed physiologically.

Tissue Engineered Skin Substitutes

All wounds require coverage in order to prevent evaporative losses, prevent infection and provide an environment that promotes healing. Skin substitutes, originally devised to provide coverage of extensive wounds with limited availability of autografts, have now gained acceptance also as natural dressings. Manufactured by tissue engineering, they combine novel materials with living cells to provide functional skin substitutes. This has caused the differences between dressings and skin substitutes to become less and less clear.

Skin substitutes have the theoretical advantage of being readily available, not requiring painful harvest and may be used with free or surgical application. In addition they promote healing, either by stimulating host cytokine generation or by providing cells that may also produce growth factors locally. The disadvantages include limited survival, high cost, and need for multiple applications; sometimes allografting, albeit with a very thin graft may be required for complete coverage to occur [96–99].

The ideal skin substitute is still not available. The development of the newer composite substitutes, by providing both the dermal and epidermal components essential for permanent skin replacement, may represent an advance toward that goal. The acellular (eg, native collagen or synthetic material) component acts as a scaffold, promotes cell migration and growth, and activates tissue regeneration and remodeling. The cellular elements reestablish lost tissue and associated function, synthesize extracellular matrix components, produce essential media-

Table 3: Types of Skin Substitutes.

	Components	Approved Uses
Epidermal		
– Epicel	cultured autologous epidermal cells	burns, leg ulcers
Dermal		
– Integra	bovine collagen + chondroitin 6 sulfate+ Silastic polymers	burns, ulcers
– Alloderm	Acellular cadaveric skin matrix	burns, scar revision
– Dermagraft	Fibroblasts + nylon mesh	burns, diabetic foot ulcers
Composites		
– Apligraf	bovine collagen + human fibroblasts + keratinocytes	venous ulcers, diabetic ulcers
– Composite Cultured Skin	collagen matrix + fibroblasts +keratinocytes	burns, chronic wounds

tors such as cytokines and growth factors and promote proliferation and migration.

The function and development of such skin substitutes is dealt with in much more detail in this volume. It is clear however, that a solid understanding of the fundamentals of wound healing represents an important first step toward developing better functional skin substitutes.

References

[1] *Schilling J A:* Wound healing. Surg Clin North Am 56:859,1976

[2] *Kaplan, A P:* Hageman factor dependent pathways: Mechanism of initiation and bradykinin formation. Fed. Proc. 42: 3123–3127, 1983.

[3] *Knighton, D R, Ciresi, K and Fiegel, V D:* Stimulation of repair in chronic nonhealing, cutaneous ulcers using platelet derived wound healing formula. Surg. Gynecol. Obstet. 170: 56–60, 1990.

[4] *Gorman, R R:* Prostaglandins, thromboxanes and prostacyclins. Int. Rev. Biochem. 48: 81, 1978.

[5] *Knighton, D R, Doucette, M, Fiegel, V D, Ciresi, K, Butler, E, and Austin, L:* The use of platelet derived wound healing formula in human clinical trials. In A. Barbul, E. Pines, M. Caldwell and T. K. Hunt. (Eds): Growth Factors and Other Aspects of Wound Healing: Biological and Clinical Implications., Alan R. Liss, Inc., Pp. 319–329, 1988.

[6] *Ross, R and Benditt, E P:* Wound healing and collagen formation. I. Sequential changes in components of guinea pig skin wounds observed in the electron microscope. J. Biophysiol. Biochem. Cytol. 11: 677–700, 1961.

[7] *Simpson, D M and Ross, R:* Effects of heterologous antineutrophil serum in ginea pigs: hematological and ultrastructural observations. Am. J. Pathol. 65: 49–102, 1971.

[8] *Simpson, D M and Ross, R:* The neutrophilic leucocyte in wound repair. A study with antineutrophil serum. J Clin Invest 51: 2009–2023, 1972.

[9] *Feiken E, Romer J, Eriksen J, et al.:* Neutrophils express tumor necrosis factor-alpha during mouse skin wound healing. J.Invest.Dermatol.; 105:120–123, 1995.

[10] *Welgus H G, Senior R M, Parks W C, et al.:* Neutral proteinase expression by human mononuclear phagocytes: a prominent role of cellular differentiation. Matrix Suppl.; 1:363–367, 1992.

[11] *Willoughby, D A:* Some views on the pathogenesis of inflammation. In W. Montagna, J. P. Bently and R. Dobson. (Eds): The dermis, Advances in the biology of skin., Vol X, Appleton-Century-Crofts, Pp. 221–230, 1970.

[12] *Bucala R, Spiegel L A, Chesney J, et al.:* Circulating fibrocytes define a new leukocyte subpopulation that mediates tissue repair. Mol.Med.; 1:71–81, 1994.

[13] *Chesney J, Bacher M, Bender A, et al.:* The peripheral blood fibrocyte is a potent antigenpresenting cell capable of priming naive T cells in situ. Proc.Natl.Acad.Sci.U.S.A.; 94:6307–6312, 1997.

[14] *Chesney J, Metz C, Stavitsky A B, et al.:* Regulated production of type I collagen and inflammatory cytokines by peripheral blood fibrocytes. J.Immunol.; 160:419–425, 1998.

[15] *Gottwald T, Coerper S, Schäffer M, et al.:* The mast cell-nerve axis in wound healing: a hypothesis. WOUND REP REG; 6:8–20, 1998.

[16] *Kupietzky A, Levi S F:* The role of mast cell-derived histamine in the closure of an in vitro wound. Inflamm.Res.; 45:176–180, 1996.

[17] *Postlethwaite A E, Holness M A, Katai H, et al.:* Human fibroblasts synthesize elevated levels of extracellular matrix proteins in response to interleukin 4. J.Clin.Invest.; 90: 1479–1485, 1992.

[18] *Levi S F, Rubinchik E:* Activated mast cells are fibrogenic for 3T3 fibroblasts. J.Invest.Dermatol.; 104:999–1003, 1995.

[19] *Leibovich, S J and Ross, R:* The role of the macrophage in wound repair. A study with hydrocortisone and antimacrophage serum. Am. J. Pathol. 78: 71–100, 1975.

[20] *Barbul, A, Breslin, J R, Woodyard, J P, Wasserkrug, H L and Efron, G:* The effect of in vivo T helper and T suppressor lymphocyte depletion on wound healing. Ann. Surg. 209: 479–483, 1989.

[21] *Casey, W, Peacock, E J and Chvapil, M:* Induction of collagen synthesis in rats by transplantation of allogeneic macrophages. Surg. Forum. 27: 53, 1976.

[22] *Hunt, T, K, Knighton, D R, Thakral, K K, Goodson, W H and Andrews, W S:* Studies on inflammation and wound healing: Angiogenesis and collagen synthesis stimulated in vivo by resident and activated wound macrophages. Surgery 96: 48–54, 1984.

[23] *Clarke, R A F, Stone, R D, Leung, D Y K, Silver, I, Hohn, D C and Hunt, T K:* Role of macrophages in wound healing. Surg. Forum. 27: 16–18, 1976.

[24] *Greenberg, G B and Hunt, T K:* The proliferation response in vitro of vascular endothelial and smooth muscle cells exposed to wound

fluid and macrophages. J. Cell. Physiol. 97: 353–360, 1978.

[25] *Polverini, P J, Cotran, R S, Gimbrone, M A and Unanue, E R:* Activated macrophages induce vascular proliferation. Nature 269: 804–806, 1977.

[26] *Buchmuller-Rouiller Y Mauel J:* Macrophage activation for intracellular killing as induced by calcium ionophore. Correlation with biologic and biochemical events. J. Immunol. 146:217, 1991.

[27] *Malawista S E, Montgomery R R, van Blaricom G:* Evidence for reactive nitrogen intermediates in killing of staphylococci by human neutrophil cytoplasts. A new microbicidal pathway for polymorphonuclear leukocytes. J. Clin. Invest. 90:631,1992

[28] *Albina J E, Henry W L, Jr, Mastrofrancesco B, et al.:* Macrophage activation by culture in an anoxic environment. J. Immunol. 155:4391,1995.

[29] *Schmidt H H, Zernikow B, Baeblich S, et al.:* Basal and stimulated formation and release of L-arginine-derived nitrogen oxides from cultured endothelial cells. J. Pharmacol. Exp. Ther. 254:591,1990.

[30] *Werner-Felmayer G, Werner E R, Fuchs D, et al.:* Tetrahydrobiopterin-dependent formation of nitrite and nitrate in murine fibroblasts. J. Exp. Med. 172:1599,1990.

[31] *Mautino G, Paul-Eugene N, Chanez P, et al.:* Heterogeneous spontaneous and interleukin-4-induced nitric oxide production by human monocytes. J. Leukoc. Biol. 56:15,1994.

[32] *Xiao L, Eneroth P H E, Qureshi G A:* Nitric oxide synthase pathway may mediate human natural killer cell cytotoxicity. Scan. J. Immunol. 42:505, 1995.

[33] *Bulgrin J P, Shabani M, Chakravarthy D, et al.:* Nitric Oxide synthesis is suppressed in steroid-impaired and diabetic wound healing. Wounds 7:48,1995.

[34] *Schäffer M R, Tantry U, Ahrendt G M, Wasserkrug H L, Barbul A:* Acute protein-calorie malnutrition impairs wound healing: A possible role of decreased wound nitric oxide synthesis. JACS 184:37–43, 1997.

[35] *Schäffer M R, Tantry U, Efron P A, Ahrendt G M, Wasserkrug H L, Barbul A:* Diabetes-impaired wound healing and reduced wound nitric oxide synthesis: A possible pathophysiologic correlation. Surgery 121:513–519, 1997

[36] *Schäffer M R, Tantry U, Gross S S, Wasserkrug H L, Barbul A:* Nitric oxide regulates wound healing. J Surg Res 63:237–240, 1996.

[37] *Efron J E, Frankel H L, Lazarou S A, et al.:* Wound healing and T-lymphocytes. J.Surg.Res.; 48:460–463, 1990.

[38] *Barbul A, Breslin R J, Woodyard J P, et al.:* The effect of in vivo T helper and T suppressor lymphocyte depletion on wound healing. Ann.Surg.; 209:479–483, 1989.

[39] *Barbul, A, Sisto, D, Rettura, G, Levenson, S M, Seifter, E and Efron, G:* Thymic inhibition of wound healing: Abrogation by adult thymectomy. J Surg Res. 32: 338–342, 1982.

[40] *Barbul A, Shawe T, Rotter SM, et al.:* Wound healing in nude mice: a study on the regulatory role of lymphocytes in fibroplasia. Surgery; 105:764–769, 1989.

[41] *Barbul, A, Shawe, T, Frankel, H, Efron, J E and Wasserkrug, H L:* Inhibition of wound repair by thymic hormones. Surgery 106: 373–377, 1989.

[42] *Barbul, A, Knud-Hansen, J, Wasserkrug, H L and Efron, G:* Interleukin 2 enhances wound healing in rats. J. Surg. Res. 40: 315–319, 1986.

[43] *Malinda K M, Sidhu G S, Banaudha K K, et al.:* Thymosin alpha 1 stimulates endothelial cell migration, angiogenesis, and wound healing. J.Immunol.; 160:1001–1006, 1998.

[44] *Rezzonico R, Burger D, Dayer J M:* Direct contact between T lymphocytes and human dermal fibroblasts or synoviocytes down-regulates types I and III collagen production via cell-associated cytokines. J.Biol.Chem.; 273: 18720–18728, 1998.

[45] *Ausprunk, D H and Folkman, J:* Migration and proliferation of endothelial cells in preformed and newly formed blood vessels during tumor angiogenesis. Microvasc. Res. 14: 53–65, 1977.

[46] *Burger, P C, Chandler, D B and Klintworth, O K:* Corneal neovascularization as studied by scaning electron microscopy of vascular casts. Lab. Invest. 48: 169–180, 1983.

[47] *Knighton, D R, Silver, I A and Hunt, T K:* Regulation of wound healing angiogenesis: Effect of oxygen gradient and inspired oxygen concentration. Surgery 90: 262–270, 1981.

[48] *Harlan, J A:* Consequences of leucocyte vessel wall interactions in inflammatory and immune reactions. Sem. Thrombosis Hemostasis 13: 434–444, 1987.

[49] *Remensnyder, J P and Majno, G:* Oxygen gradients in healing wounds. Am. J. Pathol. **52**: 301–319, 1969.

[50] *Imre, G:* Role of lactic acid. Br. J. Ophthalmol. 48: 75–82, 1964.

[51] *Zauberman, H, Michaelson, I C, Bergmann, F and Mauric, D M:* Stimulation of neovascularization in the cornea by biogenic amines. Exp. Eye Res. 8: 77–83, 1969.

[52] *Schreiber, A B, Winkler, M E and Derynck, R:* Transforming growth factor alpha: a more potent angiogenic mediator than epidermal growth factor. Science 232: 1250–1253, 1986.

[53] *Lynch, S E, Colvin, R B and Antoniades, H N:* Growth factors in wound healing. Single and synergistic effects on partial thickness porcine skin wounds. J. Clin. Invest. 84: 640–646, 1989.

[54] Gospodarowicz, D., Cheng, J., Lui, G. M., Baird, A., Esch, F. and Bohlen, P. Angiogenic factor is related to fibroblast growth factor. Endocrinol. 117: 2383–2391, 1985.

[55] *Gospodarowicz, D, Ferrara, N, Schweigerer, L and Neufeld, G:* Structural characterization and biological function of fibroblast growth factor. Endocrinol. Rev. 8: 95–114, 1987.

[56] *Clarke, R A F:* Overview and general considerations of wound repair. In R. A. F. Clarke and P. M. Henson. (Eds): The molecular and cellular biology of wound repair., New York, Plenum Press, Pp. 3–23, 1988.

[57] *Ross, R, Everett, N B and Tyler, R:* Wound healing and collagen formation. VI. The origin of the wound fibroblast studied in parabiosis. J. Cell Biol. 44: 645–650, 1970.

[58] *Grotendorst G R:* Chemoattractants and Growth Factors. In: Cohen K, Diegelmann RF, Lindblad WJ, editors. Wound Healing, Biochemical and Clinical Aspects. WB Saunders, Philadelphia. 237–247, 1992.

[59] *Bonner J C, Osornio-Vargas A R, et al.:* Differential proliferation of rat lung fibroblasts induced by the platelet-derived growth factor-AA, -AB, and -BB isoforms secreted by rat alveolar macrophages. Am.J.Respir.Cell Mol.Biol.; 5:539–547, 1991.

[60] *Regan M C, Kirk S J, Wasserkrug H L, et al.:* The wound environment as a regulator of fibroblast phenotype. J Surg Res; 50:442–448, 1991.

[61] *Serini G, Gabbiani G:* Modulation of a-smooth muscle actin expression in fibroblasts by transforming growth factor-b isoforms: an in vivo and in vitro study. WOUND REP REG; 4:278–287, 1996.

[62] *Desmouliere A, Redard M, Darby I, et al.:* Apoptosis mediates the decrease in cellularity during the transition between granulation tissue and scar. Am.J.Pathol.; 146:56–66, 1995.

[63] *Pricolo V E, Caldwell M D, Mastrofrancesco B, et al.:* Modulatory activities of wound fluid on fibroblast proliferation and collagen synthesis. J Surg Res; 48:534–538, 1990.

[64] *Schäffer M R, Tantry U, Ahrendt G M, Wasserkrug H L, Barbul A:* Stimulation of fibroblast proliferation and matrix contraction by wound fluid. Int J Biochem Cell Biol 29:231–239, 1997.

[65] *Hussain M Z, Ghani Q P, Hunt T K:* Inhibition of prolyl hydroxylase by poly(ADP-ribose) and phosphoribosyl-AMP. Possible role of ADP-ribosylation in intracellular

prolyl hydroxylase regulation. J.Biol.Chem.; 264:7850–7855, 1989.

[66] *Schaffer M R, Efron P A, Thornton F J, et al.:* Nitric Oxide, an Autocrine Regulator of Wound Fibroblast Synthetic Function. J.Immunol.; 158:2375–2381, 1997.

[67] Witte MB, Efron DT, Kiyama T, et al. Wound fluid regulates nitric oxide expression in fibroblasts. Surg.Forum. XLIX:623–624, 1998.

[68] *Paulsen S M, Wurster S H, Nanney L B:* Expression of inducible nitric oxide syntase in human burn wounds. WOUND REP REG; 6:142–148, 1998.

[69] *Noiri E, Peresleni T, Srivastava N, et al.:* Nitric oxide is necessary for a switch from stationary to locomoting phenotype in epithelial cells. Am.J.Physiol.; 270:C794–C802, 1996.

[70] *Witte M B, Thornton F J, Kiyama T, et al.:* Nitric oxide enhances wound collagen deposition in diabetic rats. Surg.Forum.; (XLVIII)665–667, 1997.

[71] *Thornton F J, Schaffer M R, Witte M B, et al.:* Enhanced collagen accumulation following direct transfection of the inducible nitric oxide synthase gene in cutaneous wounds. Biochem.Biophys.Res.Commun.; 246: 654–659, 1998.

[72] *Yamasaki K, Edington H D J, McClosky C, et al.:* Reversal of impaired wound repair in iNOS-deficient mice by topical adenoviral-mediated gene transfer. J Clin.Invest.; 101: 967–971, 1998.

[73] *Diegelmann, R F, Rothkopf, L C and Cohen, I K:* Measurement of collagen biosynthesis during wound healing. J. Surg. Res. 19: 239–242, 1975.

[74] *Madden, J W and Peacock, E E:* Studies on the biology of collagen during wound healing I. Rate of collagen synthesis and deposition in cutaneous wounds of the rat. Surgery. 64: 288–294, 1969.

[75] *Kurkinen, M, Vaheri, A, Roberts, P J and Stenmam, S:* Sequential appearance of fibronectin and collagen in experimental granulation tissue. Lab. Invest. 60: 47–51, 1980.

[76] *Winter, G D:* Formation of the scab and role of epithelization in the skin of young domestic pigs. Nature 193: 293–294, 1962.

[77] *Stenn, K S and Depalma, L:* Re-epithelialization. In R. A. F. Clark and P. M. Hensen. (Eds): The molecular and cellular biology of wound repair., New York, Plenum, Pp. 321–335, 1988.

[78] *Johnson, F R and Mc Minn, R M H:* The cytology of wound healing of the body surface in mammals. Biol. Rev. 35: 364, 1960.

[79] *Woodley, D T, Bachman, P M and O"Keefe, E J:* The role of matrix components in human keratinocyte re-epithelialization. In A. Barbul, M. D. Caldwell, W. H. Eaglstein, T. K.

Hunt, D. Marshall, E. Pines and G. Skover. (Eds): Clinical and experimental approaches to dermal and epidermal repair. Normal and chronic wounds., New York, Wiley-Liss, Pp. 129–140, 1991.

[80] *Lynch, S E:* Interaction of growth factors in tissue repair. In A. Barbul, M. D. Caldwell, W. H. Eaglstein, T. K. Hunt, D. Marshall, E. Pines and G. Skover. (Eds): Clinical and experimental approaches to dermal and epidermal repair. Normal and chronic wounds., New York, Wiley-Liss, Pp. 341–357, 1991.

[81] *Mc Donald, J A, Quade, B J, Broekelmann, T J, LaChance, R, Forsman, K, Hasegawa, E and Akiyama, S:* Fibronectin's cell-adhesive domain and an amino terminal matrix assembly domain participate in its assembly into fibroblast pericellular matrix. J. Biol. Chem. 262: 2957–2967, 1987.

[82] *Levenson, S M, Geever, E F, Crowley, L V, Oates, J F, Bernard, C W and Rosen, H:* The healing of rat skin wounds. Ann. Surg. 161: 293–308, 1965.

[83] *Bailey, A J, Bazin, S, Simms, T J, LeLeus, M, Nicholetis, C and Delaunay, A:* Characterization of the collagen of hypertrophic and normal scars. Biochem. Biophys. Acta 405: 412–421, 1975.

[84] *Barnes, M J, Morton, L F, Bennet, R C and Bailey, A J:* Studies in collagen synthesis in the mature dermal scar in the guinea pig. Biochem. Soc. 3: 917–920, 1975.

[85] *Grillo, H C and Potsaid, M S:* Studies in wound healing: IV Retardation of contraction by local X-irradiation, and observations relating to the origin of fibroblasts in repair. Ann. Surg. 154: 741–750, 1961.

[86] *VanWinkle, W:* Wound contraction. Surg. Gyn. Obstet. 125: 131–139, 1967.

[87] *Ehrlich, H P:* The role of connective tissue matrix in wound healing. In A. Barbul, E. Pines, M. Caldwell and T. K. Hunt. (Eds): Growth Factors and Other Aspects of Wound Healing: Biological and Clinical Implications., Alan R. Liss, Inc, Pp. 243–258., 1988.

[88] *Gabbiani, G and Majno, G:* Presence of modified fibroblasts in granulation tissue and their possible role in wound contraction. Experimentia 27: 549–550, 1971.

[89] *Gabbiani, G, Hirschel, B J, Ryan, G B, Statkov, P R and Majno, G:* Granulation tissue as a contractile organ. J. Exp. Med. 135: 719–734, 1972.

[90] *Rudolph, R, Vande Berg, J and Pierce, G F:* Changing concepts in myofibroblast function and control. In H. Janssen, R. Rooman and J. I. S. Robertson. (Eds): Wound Healing, Petersfield, Wrightson UK, Pp. 103–119, 1991.

[91] *Bell, E, Ivarsson, B and Merrill, C:* Production of a tissue like structure by contraction of collagen lattices by human fibroblasts of different proliferative potential in vitro. Proc. Natl. Acad. Sci. (USA). 76: 1274–1278, 1979.

[92] *Grinnell, F and Lamke, C R:* Reorganization of hydrated collagen lattices by human skin fibroblasts. J. Cell Sci. 66: 51–63, 1984.

[93] *Wang, S Y, Merrill, C and Bell, E:* Effects of aging and long-term subcultivation on collagen lattice contraction and intra-lattice proliferation in three rat cell types. Mechanisms of Ageing and Development. 44: 127–141, 1988.

[94] *Barone E J, Yager D R, Pozez A L, et al.:* Interleukin-1alpha and collagenase activity are elevated in chronic wounds. Plast.Reconstr.Surg.; 102:1023–1027, 1998.

[95] *Yager D R, Zhang L Y, Liang H X, et al.:* Wound fluids from human pressure ulcers contain elevated matrix metalloproteinase levels and activity compared to surgical wound fluids. J.Invest.Dermatol.; 107:743–748, 1996.

[96] *Sefton M V, Woodhouse K A:* Tissue engineering. J Cutaneous Med Surg 3:S18–23, 1998.

[97] *Singer A J, Clark R A F:* Cutaneous wound healing. NEJM341:738–746, 1999.

[98] *Bello Y M, Phillips T J:* Recent advances in wound healing. JAMA 283:716–718, 2000.

[99] *Pham H T, Rosenblum B I, Lyons T E, et al.:* Evaluation of human skin equivalent for the treatment of diabetic foot ulcers in a prospective, randomized, clinical trial. Wounds 11:79–86, 1999.

Allografts and Burn Care

B. M. Achauer, V. M. VanderKam

Summary

The field of transplantation was given birth by skin allografting. The history of allografting, current techniques and areas for further research are outlined and discussed.

Introduction

Skin grafting has been used in medicine for about 2,500 years. Only in the last one hundred years have we understood the significance of allografts vs autografts. Initial problems were technical. Skin from amputated parts was used to cover the traumatic defect. In 1804, Baronio [1] documented skin grafting in sheep which led to the use in humans by pioneering surgeons in the first part of the 19th century. Initial grafts were of the pinch type, described by Reverdin. George David Pollock [2] (1818–1897) is said to be the first surgeon to use allografts for burn patients. Girdner [3] credits himself with being the first to use cadaver skin for burn coverage. He believed that these grafts from cadavers would be a permanent solution. During this same period of time, sheep and porcine skin were also used for the same purpose. These too were believed to represent a permanent cure.

Nobel Prize winning transplant surgeon Alexis Carrel [4], working in the early part of the 20th century, was not aware of the immune response. He felt the only barrier to organ transplantation was adequate surgical technique.

As so often occurs, war stimulates medical progress. There were many burn casualties in World War II. In clinical cases, Medawar and Gibson [5] were able to demonstrate the second set phenomenon, thus proving the "memory" of previous exposure. Thus began a period of experimentation during which the immune system was studied and defined. Skin grafting was a common model for this experimentation. At this time it was realized that allografts were only a temporary but still useful burn treatment. Medawar subsequently won the Nobel Prize for these contributions.

The temporary use of allograft skin has been an integral part of burn surgery for many years. Allografts have been successfully combined with autografts. Chinese surgeons have most dramatically demonstrated this technique. They used large sheets of allograft and then made small slits to insert postage stamp sized autografts. Using this technique, patients with massive injuries were salvaged. In the United States, widely meshed autografts (9:1 or 6:1) are placed first and then covered with less widely expanded allografts.

Modifying the Host

Interestingly, the field of transplantation grew out of skin transplants. It was not difficult to perform and the results could be observed directly. Transplantation Proceedings began as a supplement to Plastic and Reconstructive Surgery and its early contributors were plastic surgeons. In 1932, Padgett [6] used skin allografts from family and unrelated donors for patients with severe burns. The grafts from family members seemed to sur-

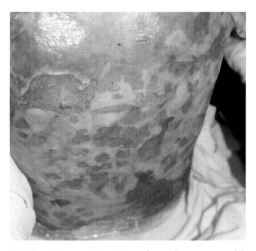 

Fig. 1a: Preoperative view of an eleven year old boy. At eighteen days post burn the back was excised and allografted with fresh skin from a kidney transplant donor.

Fig. 1b: Fifteen years later the back is well healed. There is a grafted appearance to the skin.

vive longer than those from unrelated donors, but it was hard to quantify. In 1937, James Barret Brown [7] of St. Louis performed skin grafts between monozygotic twins with permanent survival. It was out of frustration at the inability to create permanent take of skin grafts that scientists began to look at something less antigenic than skin. Joe Murray [8] used kidney transplants as a model for his research. This led to the first successful human transplant and resulted in a Nobel Prize for Joe Murray.

In the seventies, John Burke [9] used the then available immunosuppressive agents (azathioprine and anti-thymocyte globulin) to prolong the use of allografts in massively burned children. Patients were treated in a bacteriologically controlled nursing unit. Donors were living relatives who were tissue typed. White blood cell counts were followed and the medication withheld when it fell below 3500. He demonstrated improved survival compared to historical controls. Although successful, this regimen was felt to be too demanding and was eventually abandoned.

Our laboratory began experimentation with cyclosporine in the 1980s [10]. Cyclosporine is a more specific immunosup- pressive drug that does not interfere with host resistance to bacterial infections. Our hypothesis was that it would be less hazardous than previous immunosupressive regimens. A burned rat model was developed. We were able to demonstrate prolonged skin allograft survival with CyA. This eventually led to use in humans [11]. The massively burned patient is already immunocompromised. Blood transfusions commonly needed in severely burned patients also produce immune suppression. Thus, a relatively small dose, 8 mg/kg/day was used.

Several other clinical series involving extensive burn injuries and temporary immunosupression with cyclosporine followed [12–15].

Interestingly, in our single, reported case, [11], rejection never seemed to occur. CyA was started one day prior to allografting with cadaver skin. CyA was discontinued 120 days later. The patient was followed for two years. No obvious rejection occurred. Biopsies were taken. At no time did the allografts show classic histopathologic signs of rejection. After many years of being lost to follow up this patient was recently seen in our clinic. At this time he was fifteen

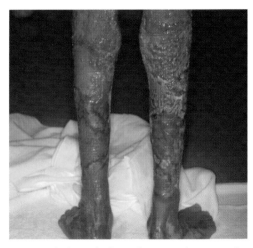

Fig. 2a: The lower limbs at three months post grafting. The grafts were from numerous donors, including a black skin donor. This gives a patchwork appearance to the legs.

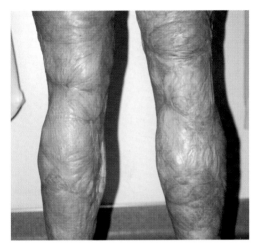

Fig. 2b: At fifteen years the legs are well healed and the appearance of skin grafts remains.

years status post allografting. His grafts were well healed. During the thirteen year hiatus he had no surgery, graft loss or complications. Biopsies taken on that day were HLA typed. There was no evidence of chimerism in either sample. A second DR allele was found. This could have been easily missed in previous typing. An intriguing question is thus raised. Has tolerance developed? If tolerance were routinely possible, allografting would have a much more important role to play in burn surgery. This could be a fruitful area for future research.

Modifying the Graft

In 1868, Paul Langerhans (a medical student) discovered dendritic cells of the epidermis. These cells, named after him, are one of the large families of cells expressing class II major histocompatibility complex antigens critical to antigen processing and presentation to specific T lymphocytes. Virtually all of the antigenic properties of the skin lie in the epidermis [17]. For years, scientists have hoped that autologous cultured epidermal cells could be combined with allograft dermis to produce a nonantigenic, permanent skin substitute. Keratinocytes are immunologically active and account for more than 90 % of epidermal cells.

An attractive option that has been used is to apply allografts and then later remove the epidermis and replace it with cultured autologous keratinocytes. Analogous options that have been used include using an artifical dermis such as Integra® followed by the application of sheets of autologous cultured cells once circulation has been established. AlloDerm® is a commercial product consisting of human dermis rendered antigen free (freeze-dried). This has been used to provide a dermal matrix over which a thin skin graft can be applied. This product is rapidly incorporated by the host. While autografts are most commonly used, cultured cells could be placed over the Alloderm at the time of initial excision and placement.

Topical Immunosupression

Skin grafts have been treated topically with cyclosporine in a rat model. CyA was combined with silver sulfadiazine and Pseudomonas was introduced. This drug combination significantly prolonged allograft survival and controlled infection [18]. FK506 has been used in a similar manner. Irradiation, ionizing and ultraviolet can be used to lower the antigenicity of skin grafts [19]. This is a field open to great advances in treatment of the extensively burned patient.

References

[1] Baronio G: Delgli Innesti Animali. Milan, Stamperia e Fonderia del Genio, 1804.

[2] Freshwater MF, Krizek TJ: George David Pollock and the development of skin grafting. Ann Plast Surg; 1:96–102, 1978.

[3] Girdner JH: Skin-grafting with grafts taken from the dead subject. Med Rec; 20:119–120, 1881.

[4] Carrel, A: Results of the transplantation of blood vessels, organs and limbs. J.A.M.A.; 51:1662–1667, 1907.

[5] Gibson T, Medawar PF: Fate of skin homografts in man. J. Anat; 77:299, 1943.

[6] Padgett EC: South Med J; 25:895, 1932.

[7] Brown JB: Surgery; 1:558, 1937.

[8] Murray JE, Merrill JP, Harrison JH, et al.: N Engl J Med; 268:1315, 1963.

[9] Burke JF, May JW, Albright N, et al.: Temporary skin transplantation and immunosupression for extensive burns. N Engl J Med; 290:269–271, 1974.

[10] Achauer BM, Hewitt CW, Black KS, et al.: CyA prolongs skin allografts in a rat burn model. Transpl Proc; 15:3073, 1983.

[11] Black KS, Hewitt CW, Achauer BM, et al.: Cyclosporine and skin allografts for the treatment of thermal injury: II. Development of an experimental massive third degree burn model demonstrating extensive graft survival. Transplantation; 45:13–16, 1988.

[12] Achauer BM, Hewitt CW, Black KS, et al.: Long-term skin allograft survival after short-term cyclosporine treatment in a patient with massive burns. Lancet; 1(4):13–15, 1986.

[13] Mindikoglu AN, Cerinkale O.: Prolonged allograft survival in a patient with extensive burns using cyclosproine. Burns; 19:70–72, 1993.

[14] Sakabu SA, Hansbrough JS, Cooper ML, et al.: Cyclosporine A for prolonging allograft survival in patients with massive burns. J Burn Care Rehab; 1:410–418, 1990.

[15] Frame JD, Sanders R, Goodacher TE, et al.: The fate of meshed allograft skin in burned patients using cyclosporine immunosupression. Br. J Plast Surg; 42:27–34, 1989.

[16] Eldad A, Benmeir P, Weinberg A, et al.: Cyclosporine A treatment failed to extend skin allograft survival in two burn patients. Burns; 20:262–264, 1994

[17] Salmon JK, Armstrong CA, Ansel JC: The sin as an immune organ. West J Med; 160:146–152, 1994.

[18] Lai CS, Miskell PH, Gonce SJ et al: Combined Use of Topical Cyclosporine A and Silver Sulfadiazine on Allografts Infected with Pseudomonas in Burned Rats. Burns 13: 181–184, 1987.

[19] Fujita T, Takahashi S, Yagihashi A, et al: Prolonged survival of rat skin allograft by treatment with FK506 ointment. Transplantation; 64:922–925, 1997.

Transfection of Human Keratinocytes in Vitro with the Particle Mediated Gene Transfer and the Liposome-Mediated Gene Transfer Method – Possible Future Trends to Optimize Cultured Skin Grafting

C. Andree, R. E. Horch, M. Voigt, D. Schaefer, K. Walgenbach, G. B. Stark, E. Eriksson

Summary

This chapter introduces the technique of gene transfer to optimize growth of cultured keratinocytes. The use of viral vectors is discussed; as is liposomal transfer *in vitro*. Direct injection of DNA into cell nuclei and particle-mediated gene transfer are also reviewed. Detailed reports are given from work carried out at our laboratory for particle-mediated gene transfer into human keratinocytes, and liposome-mediated transfer. In this rapidly dividing cell population, the results showed a transient declining concentration of DNA expression, and an approximately equal efficiency for the two techniques. These are promising techniques for modifying functtion in keratinocytes.

Introduction

Advances in recombinant DNA technology, beginning in the 1970's, brought the possibility of "gene therapy" closer to reality by enabling the isolation of purified genes on a preparative scale, their characterization at the nucleotide sequence level, and manipulation of their sequence. More recently, the development of gene transfer methods pro-vided an essential capability and led to the first publicly approved clinical applications of gene transfer to humans [1].

Gene transfer is a process in which DNA or RNA molecules are introduced into cells. Most frequently gene transfer is intended to result in the synthesis of the protein that the nucleic acid encodes, but the expression of RNA's that function directly without translation has also been demonstrated [2].

In considering gene transfer to humans it is important to distinguish between genetic modification of somatic cells which is not heritable, and modification of germ cells which would be passed on to subsequent generations. Gene transfer to germ cells has been used to alter the genotype of plants, laboratory animals and a few types of farm animals for both research and commercial purposes. Germ-line gene transfer is conceptually attractive for treatment of inherited diseases, at present, gene transfer is directed only toward somatic cells. It has been speculated that gene alteration in human germ cells will not occur for twenty years or more in the United States for a multitude of reasons including the scientific uncertainty and technical obstacles this approach faces at this time, as well as the philosophical, ethical, political and religious concerns that are raised. The relevant regulatory bodies in the US (the Recombinant DNA Advisory Committee of the National Institute of Health and the Food and Drug Administration) are not currently considering protocols involving gene transfer to human germ line cells, rather investigators are required to demonstrate that their protocols will not lead to unintended gene transfer to the germ line.

Transfer of a gene into a cell can lead to the addition of a function or inhibition of a pre-existing function. Both strategies could potentially be useful in the treatment of different cutaneous diseases, particularly in the epidermis and at the dermo-epidermal junction. The complementation of defective functions could be effective treatment for inherited skin diseases. Addition or augmentation of factors that promote repair might be useful in treating non-healing wounds. Alternatively, undesirable outcomes such as hypertrophic scaring or keloid formation might be lessened or avoided by inhibition of certain cell functions.

When DNA is transferred into a cell it may be stably incorporated into the chromosome of the host cell by chemical integration into the cellular DNA, or may exist as a separate molecule. Expression of the transferred gene may be transient or sustained. In cell culture where the cells are continually dividing, persistent presence of the transferred gene, a prerequisite for sustained expression, is typically associated with integration into the genome. Genes that are not integrated are lost over time. In intact animals, however, the correspondence between integration and persistence does not maintain. In some tissues, e.g. muscle, transferred DNA can be maintained and expressed for prolonged periods without integration into the genome [3], whereas in tissues that are continually renewing themselves, like skin, even stably integrated genes may be lost due to cell turnover [4].

One strategy for gene therapy involves isolation of cells from the patient, establishment of the cells in tissue culture, gene transfer to these cells, and subsequent reengraftment of the cells back into the patient. This strategy is termed *in vitro* gene transfer since the gene transfer is done in culture, outside of the patient. Frequently this approach is coupled with a selection and amplification step in tissue culture following gene transfer to enrich the cell population that is reintroduced to the patient. The selection/amplification step is accomplished by co-transfer of a selectable gene along with the therapeutic gene and subsequent growth in culture under conditions that favor cells possessing the selectable gene function. This strategy has been successful with cells that adapt well to culture and reengraftment, but has been somewhat unreliable with many primary human cell types. The *in vitro* approach is also labor intensive, and consequently costly.

An alternative strategy is to perform the gene transfer directly to cells in the patient. This strategy is termed *in vivo* gene transfer. The *in vivo* approach is clearly simpler than the *ex vivo* approach in a practical sense since it does not require tissue culture or engraftment of target cells, however, this approach is complicated by the requirement of effective gene transfer to the target cells, and ideally only to the target cells, in the intact organism.

In the context of both *in vitro* and in vivo gene transfer, epidermis appears to be an attractive target tissue since epidermal cells can be amenable to both brief culture period and autografting [5] as well as direct gene transfer [6].

The initial gene therapy protocols involved *in vitro* gene transfer, in part because this approach was amenable to the goals of the protocols, but also it was perceived as the more conservative, and thus potentially safer approach, in the face hypothetical but unknown risks. Results from these pioneering clinical trials provided better knowledge of the risk factors involved, and provided the necessary confidence to advance to *in vivo* gene therapy approaches, several of which are now in clinical trials [7].

Techniques For Gene Transfer

Viral Vectors

Viruses are obvious candidates as gene transfer vectors since their ability to efficiently transfer viral nucleic acid into host cell is an important part of their life cycles. Consequently, a number of viruses have been used for introduction of genes into cells. The most commonly used ones have been retrovirus, adenovirus (AV), Adeno-associated virus (AAV), vaccinia virus, and herpes virus (HSV) [7–10]. In general, the recombinant virus vectors are constructed by replacing one or more viral genes with the DNA of interest. Usually viral genes associated with pathology, replication and/or infectivity are deleted or disrupted, so the recombinant viral vectors are defective and avirulent.

Propagation of these recombinant viruses requires that the viral functions missing from the vectors be supplied. In some cases, (e.g. adeno-associated virus) this is accomplished by coinfection of the host cell with a helper virus. More commonly, specialized "producer" cell lines that contain and stably express integrated copies of viral genes are used to provide the necessary function. The former approach entails risk that the vector preparation will be contaminated with helper virus, thus the latter approach is generally preferred.

A major attraction of viral vectors is their efficiency, which can approach 100% in established cell lines. Retrovirally mediated gene transfer also leads to integration of the transferred genes into a host chromosome, making them a permanent part of the genome throughout the cell's lineage. A major disadvantage of viral gene transfer techniques is that they are laborious and require extensive safety measures. The preparation of high titer virus stocks is a significant undertaking, and not completely reliable at this time. Moreover, although the viral vectors are usually defective, there is concern that virulent viruses might be generated during propagation by recombination with genes of the producer cell lines [11], so thorough quality assurance is required. In some cases, for example herpes virus, viral toxicity occur even when the virus is replication deficient. The random integration of retroviral vectors is mutagenic and potentially carcinogenic. Viral vectors also frequently impose restrictions on the size and/or structure of the transferred DNA due to intrinsic requirements of their biology. The high efficiency observed with viral vectors in established cell lines and inbred laboratory animals is frequently lower and less reliable in primary cell cultures and natural populations.

Retroviral gene transfer techniques have been successfully applied to keratinocytes [12–14] and fibroblasts [15] in animal model systems using an *in vitro* strategy. The procedure involves establishment of primary cultures of the target keratinocytes, that are then grown to subconfluence and incubated with the retroviral vector, or vector producing cells. Subsequently, the transfected cells are amplified in tissue culture prior to autologous engraftment back onto the host. Commonly the retroviral vector includes a selectable marker like the neomycin resistance gene, so growth of the cells in media that contain gentamicin gives a competitive advantage to cells that contain and express the transferred genes, thereby providing a means to enrich these cells in the population during amplification in culture. Thus far, *in vivo* gene transfer to keratinocytes by retroviral vectors has not yet been reported. Adenoviral vectors have been shown to transfect mouse keratinocytes *in vivo*.

Preexisting immunity is a concern for *in vivo* gene transfer by viral vectors. Immunity to vaccinia is widespread (due to its use in smallpox vaccination programs) and poses a significant problem for subsequent use of this virus [16]. Immunity to AV is also likely to be widespread in humans, but the effect of such immunity on use of AV as a gene transfer vector is not yet clear.

It should also be noted that *in vitro* procedures are very tedious. Harvesting cells, establishing and growing them in culture, incubation of the cells with the virus, and subsequent amplification and preparation of the cells for autologous engraftment may take as long as 2–3 weeks. Establishment of primary cells in tissue culture in may be unreliable in some cases (e.g. human tumor cells), however, skin cells appear to be amenable to these procedures [17].

Chemically-Mediated Gene Transfer

A number of chemical compositions, most notably liposomes, calcium phosphate and DEAE-dextran have been used extensively for *in vitro* gene transfer to tissue culture cells [17–20]. Plasmid DNA forms complexes with these materials upon mixing and the complexes are transported into cells by endocytosis. These techniques are simple to perform and have great utility in *in vitro* gene transfer for research purposes. The efficiency of these methods is generally low, but sufficient to make them useful for gene transfer to established cell lines. The feasibility of liposome-mediated gene transfer *in vivo* is currently being investigated.

Electroporation

It has long been known that exposure of cells to electrical field pulses makes their membranes porous [21]. If the cells are made porous while bathed in medium that contains plasmid DNA, some of the DNA will enter the cell and be expressed. This technique is effective with cultured cells in suspension, but has not been applied widely to primary cell cultures or cells *in vivo*.

Injection of DNA

Direct injection of plasmid DNA into cell nuclei using microcapillaries, termed micro-injection, is a method of gene transfer commonly used to target cells in early stage embryos for the production of transgenic animals. The animals derived from treated embryos are usually chimeric, but some of these animals will pass the transgene through the germline to their progeny establishing a transgenic line. Gene expression has also been demonstrated following injection of DNA locally into muscle heart, liver, brain, skin and other organs using a standard hypodermic syringe. Among the tissues investigated, this method appears to be most effective for gene transfer to muscle. The level of gene expression obtained following intramuscular injection of DNA is relatively low, but can persist for a prolonged period. This feature appears to be characteristic of muscle rather than the gene transfer technique, since genes transferred to muscle by other methods (e.g. liposomes or particle-mediated gene transfer) also show prolonged expression. Intramuscular injection of genes encoding viral antigens has been shown to induce both cellular and humoral immunity directed toward the expressed antigens, suggesting it may be useful as a vaccine strategy [22].

Particle-Mediated Gene Transfer

Particle-mediated gene transfer was originally developed for gene transfer to plant cells [23], but more recently was shown to also be applicable to a wide variety of mammalian cells *in vitro* and *in vivo* [24]. The method is conceptually simple. DNA is coated onto microscopic gold particles (on the order of 1–5 μm in diameter). The DNA coated gold particles are then accelerated to high velocity by an electric arc discharge or a high pressure helium jet, and directed into the target cells. The DNA is usually a cloned recombinant plasmid, but can be in any form or size. Gold particles are used because they are dense, relatively inert, non-toxic and commercially available in appropriate particle sizes. The magnitude of the accelerating force, the number of particles per target area and the amount of DNA loaded onto each particle are all adjustable parameters in this system. Particle penetration in different tissues ranges from approximately 50–100 μm in skin up to 500 μm in liver. Using the optimal number of particles no measurable adverse effects result from penetration of particles into target tissue.

Particle-mediated gene transfer has been shown to be highly effective for gene transfer into skin and partial thickness wound beds *in vivo* [6]. Gene transfer by this method into intact skin has been shown to be an effective vaccine strategy leading to immune responses comparable to those obtained with antigen plus complete Freund's adjuvant, considered the "gold standard" in terms of eliciting the immune responses. Using this method it has been shown that transfer of a genetically engineered epidermal growth factor (EGF) gene to partial thickness wounds leads to production of relatively high levels of EGF over several days, and results in significantly accelerated (healing) re-epithelization of the wounds [6].

The general applicability of this method to a wide range of cell types and tissues is an attractive feature of this technique. The efficiency of gene transfer by this method can also be relatively high (ranging from 1–50% in different target systems), though optimization of the method for the cell or tissue type is important in maximizing gene transfer efficiency for different applications.

A potential complication associated with this method is that residual gold particles may be left in the patient. This concern is not an issue for applications that specifically target the epidermis (e.g. vaccination), since the cells that contain the gold particles and DNA eventually die and exfoliate from the body. Application of the technique to internal organs and wounds, however, does result in prolonged presence of gold particles in the tissue [25]. Prior use of elemental gold in dentistry and plastic surgery, as well as extensive experience with particle-mediated gene transfer in plant and animal systems indicate that acute toxicity is not likely to be a problem, but possible long-term complications, e.g. fibrosis, need further investigation.

Purpose of the Experiment

Skin is an attractive target for gene therapy. It is the largest organ of the body and has an excellent blood supply. It is easily accessible for different gene transfer techniques and for purposes of follow-up procedures. Epi-

dermal cells can be harvested and grown *in vitro*. The presence of keratinocyte stem cells in culture and a possibility of their stable transfection is likely to result in a prolonged transgene expression following keratinocyte transplantation back to the host though initial attempts at this strategy have yielded only transient expression.

Early reports employed retroviral and chemically-mediated gene transfer techniques to skin by using *in vitro* techniques. The skin cells were grown in *in vitro* primary culture. The cultured cells were then transfected by incubation with retrovirus RNA construct or with a plasmid in the case of chemically-mediated gene transfer. The transfected cells were then multiplied in culture with or without selected media and then transplanted back to the wound in an autologous fashion.

With the current particle mediated gene transfer device, epidermal layers in a wide range of mammalian species can be efficiently transfected. A broad range of cell cultures, adherent or in suspension, continous and established, can also be successfully transfected. The flexibility of the particle delivery system allows for fine-tuning of experimental parameters; however, it is necessary for each laboratory to determine the optimal parameters for their particular cell culture system. Any quantitative assay may be used to determine the optimum combination of critical parameters for the particular biological system under investigation.

A number of chemical compositions, most notably liposomes, have been used extensively for *in vitro* gene transfer to tissue culture cells. These techniques are simple to perform and have great utility in *in vitro* gene transfer for research purposes. The efficiency of these methods is generally low, but sufficient to make them useful for gene transfer to established cell lines.

In this investigating we tried to find optimal parameters, for both, the particle mediated gene transfer method and the liposome-mediated gene transfer method in an *in vitro* system.

Material and Methods

Tissue Culture Method

Split thickness human skin sections were harvested from skin discharged from plastic surgery operations under sterile conditons. The sections were first kept in Phosphate Buffered Saline (PBS) containing penicillin (100 units/ml), streptomycin (100 µg/ml) and amphotericin B (0.25 µg/ml) for two hours and then incubated with 0.25% Dispase at 37°C for two hours to separate the dermis from the epidermis. Fine sheets of epidermis were treated with a 0.1% trypsin/0.02% EDTA-solution at 37°C for 30 minutes to obtain single cell suspension. Keratinocyte clusters were dissociated with forceps and then neutralized with Keratinocyte SFM medium, containing 100 x MEM nonessential amino acids, L-arginine, Na-pyruvate, putrescine-HCl, insulin, hydrocortisone choleratoxin and penicillin (100 units/ml), streptomycin (100 µg/ml) and amphotericin B (0.25 µg/ml). The cells were then resuspended in a 25 ml pipette for 4 minutes to break the remaining cell to cell contacts, and filtered with a 100 µm mesh to separate any cell group. After 5 minutes centrifugation (1200 rpm, 5°C) the pellet was dissolved in 10 ml modified SFM medium. Keratinocyte viability was tested with trypan blue and cells were counted in a hemocytometer. Keratinocytes were transferred into 6-well tissue culture plates at a density of 2×10^5 cells per well and incubated at 37°C with 5% CO_2 until the cells reached 50–80% confluence.

Particle Mediated Gene Transfer Method

The particle delivery device employs a high velocity stream of helium to intracellularly deliver gold particles coated with the expression plasmid EGF. The discharge is initiated by triggering the solenoid. The pressure release causes a rapid acceleration of the helium down the bore of the device. The beads become entrained i the helium stream and begin to pick up speed. Immediately past the acceleration channel, the barrel begins to open as a cone. The slope of the cone causes the gas to be pulled outward, expanding the high pressure jet into a less destructive low velocity pulse, while the beads maintain a high velocity.

Prior to transfection, the plasmid DNA was attached to the gold particles. This was accomplished by precipitation of the DNA from solution in the presence of gold particles by the addition of the polycation spermidine and $CaCl_2$. The particles were then resuspended in ethanol and coated on to the inner wall of the tubing. The DNA/gold coated tubing was cut into 1.2 cm length cartridges which were inserted into the cylinder of the device. Discharging the device propelled the DNA/gold particles into the cultured cells.

The parameters were as follows:

gold particles:	1–3 µm
bead loading rate:	0.5 mg gold/cartridge
DNA loading rate:	2 µg DNA/mg gold
helium pressure:	5 bar; 10 bar; 15 bar; 20 bar; 25 bar.

In vitro **bombardment of tissue cultures**

In vitro tissue samples were placed into six well plates and grown to 60–80% subconfluence and bombarded at appropriate pressure settings as indicated. The medium was then sampled every day and assayed for EGF concentration using an ELISA method.

Liposomes Mediated Gene Transfer Method

The liposomes were obtained from LipofectAMINE. For this experiment, two groups of solutions were prepared for each transfection. 25 µg EGF expression plasmid and 50 µg of Liposomes with Opti-MEM were combined and mixed gently. The mixture was incubated at room temperature for 45 minutes. While the DNA-liposome complex is forming, the human keratinocytes were washed with phosphate buffered saline. Serum-free medium was then added to the tube containing the DNA-liposome complex. After mixing gently, the diluted complex solution was added to the cells. The cells were then incubated for five hours and the solution was exchanged with normal keratinocyte media. The medium was then exchanged as described above.

EGF-Plasmid

The expression plasmid used in this study was pWRG1630. The plasmid was propagated in *Escherichia coli* XL1-Blue MR and supercoiled DNA was prepared on Qiagen™ (Chatsworth, CA) chromatographic columns as recommended by the manufacturer. The plasmid was constructed from pAbP2, an expression/secretion vector (kindly provided by Michael D. Eisenbraun, Agracetus, Inc.) and a segment of the full-length human EGF cDNA clone, lambdaEGF116 (35, obtained from ATCC). A DNA segment containing the mature hEGF sequence (nucleotides 3347–3505 of Genbank accession no. X04571) was extracted from lambdaEGF116 by PCR.

The gene consists of the CMV immediate early transcriptional promoter (nucleotides 216 to 834 of Genbank accession no. K03104), followed by a portion of the human growth hormone (hGH) gene (nucleotides 275 to 686 of Genbank accession no. J00148 K00612), the mature hEGF coding region, and a segment containing the 3' untranslated sequence and polyadenylation signal of the bovine growth hormone gene (from pRc/CMV, Invitrogen, Inc.).

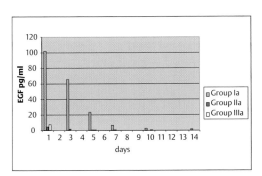

Fig. 1a: In vitro cultured human Keratinocytes.

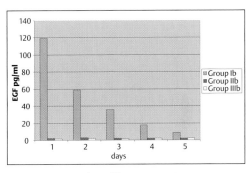

In vitro non-cultured human Keratinocytes.

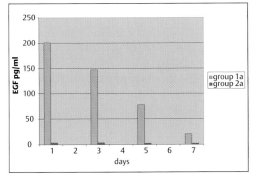

Fig. 1b: In vitro cultured human Keratinocytes.

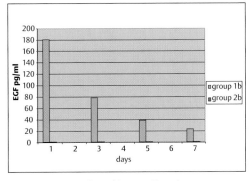

In vitro non-cultured human Keratinocytes.

Study Design

In the first set of the study, human keratinocytes, 60–80% confluent, were bombarded with the gold/DNA particles in concentrations as described above, with different pressure concentrations. As a control we used gold particles with no DNA. The medium was changed every day and an ELISA was performed to measure the EGF concentration.

In the second set of this experiment, keratinocytes were either transfected with lipofectamine, with lipofectamine and gold/DNA particles in the same concentration as above and 20 barr helium pressure and gold/DNA particles alone with 20 barr helium pressure. The medium was changed every day and an ELISA was performed to measure the EGF concentration.

Results

Viability of Cells After Transfection

Cells transfected with the particle bombardment showed less viability after transfection compared with the liposomall gene tranfer technique using the trypan blue exclusion.

EGF Transfection Efficiency Using the Particle Bombardment Method

We bombarded human keratinocytes grown to subconfluence with the expression plasmid EGF. The parameters used were gold particles 1–3 μm in size, the bead loading rate was 0.5 mg gold/cartridge, the DNA loading rate was 2 μg DNA/mg gold. We changed as one parameter the helium pressure with 5 bar; 10 bar; 15 bar; 20 bar; 25 bar. As controls we bombarde gold particles without DNA. Highest concentration of EGF was obtained at day 1 using the helium pressure of 20 bar. The expression was followed by a decline in EGF concentration after the next days. Lowest concentrations were observed using the helium pressures of 5–10 bar per discharge.

EGF Transfection Efficiency Using Liposomal Gene Transfer Method

Transfection using the liposomal gene transfer method showed comparable EGF concentrations on days 1–3. There were no significant differences between the two gene transfer techniques.

EGF Transfection Efficiency Using the Particle Bombardment Method and Liposomal Gene Transfer Together

After transfection of human keratinocytes first with the liposomes and then with the gold DNA particles showed no additive effect in EGF concentrations. Highest concentrations of EGF was obtained at day 1 using the helium pressure of 20 bar and the liposome gene transfer technique. The high expression was followed by a decline in EGF concentration over the next days.

Discussion

For nonviral gene transfer methods, little is known about the mechanism involved in transport of the DNA to the nucleus, the initiation of gene expression once it gets there; or the mechanism by which the DNA is eventually lost, maintained independently, or becomes integrated into the host genome. Meanwhile we studied the influence of biomatrices such as fibrin sealant to carry plasmids and to lead to an integration of such plasmids into cultured keratinocytes incubated in the fibrin matrix at the same time. This approach is currently under investigation and is subject to different publications. It is clear that the persistence of foreign plasmid DNA in cells is dependent on cell type. The presence and expression of the DNA in cultured cells which are continuously dividing is usually transient. A small fraction of the cells that take up the DNA, usually 0.1–1%, will integrate and stably express the foreign gene, but most of the cells will lose the gene, or extinguish its expression, over time. In cases where stably transformed cell lines are desired a strategy of selection is usually employed. As we have shown in this experiments a transient declining concentration was achieved using the particle bombardment and the liposomal gene transfer method.

The random pattern of integration into the genome shared by all current gene transfer methods can be mutagenic [26]. Consequently, there is concern that some of these insertions could result in oncogenic transformation of the target cells through activation of a proto-oncogene or insertional inactivation of a tumor suppressor gene. The level of this risk is unknown, but has been estimated to be low. Moolten and Cupples [27] have pointed out that quantitation of this risk will require much larger clinical trials than those in progress.

Site-specific integration either through reconstitution of the native AAV integration mechanism or through homologous recombination would be greatly reduce or eliminate potential complication due to random integration events, but neither are, at this time, technically practical for gene therapy applications. As noted previously, recombinant AAV vectors do not show site specific integration for reasons that are currently unknown. Homologous recombination of transferred DNA into the recipient genome has been repeatedly demonstrated, and has proven a powerful tool for creation of "knockout" mutations in transgenic mice to provide mouse models of human disease, but the efficiencies and requirements of the manipulations involved have not yet been reconciled with what is currently achievable in the clinic.

The frequency of homologous recombination is, in fact, surprisingly high relative to statistical expectations. Unfortunately, the number of nonhomologous recombination sites is also very high, so the overall efficiency of homologous recombination is relatively low compared to the background of random integration events. A major breakthrough enabling the production of "knockout" transgenic mice was development of continuously

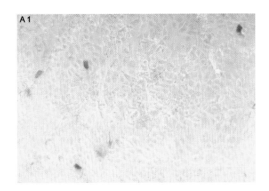

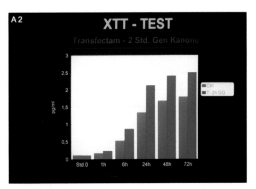

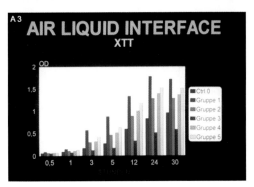

Fig. 2

cultured embryonic stem cells that can be incorporated into early stage mouse embryos and contribute transgenic cells to the mouse that develops. Elegant selection strategies can be applied to exclusively isolate homologous recombination events because the continuos cell lines allow the necessary manipulation in tissue culture. Gene transfer is not the limiting capability in this situation, and several of the gene transfer methods described above (with the exception of retroviral vectors which possess their own integration mechanisms independent of host recombination) have been successfully used to put DNA into cultured embryonic stem cells.

The basic strategy for genetic therapy when using keratinocytes as a target tissue has three principal approaches [27]. In the first one, the aim of the therapy would be to correct a gene whose malfunction affects the epidermis itself. In an *in vitro* experiment, the phenotype of cultured keratinocytes harvested from patients suffering from recessive X-linked ichthyosis was corrected following a gene transfer with a defective enzyme. A similar approach could be used in treatment of other dermatological diseases such as epidermolysis bullosa. The second approach is to engineer keratinocytes to release a peptide into the systemic circulation in case of enzyme or hormone deficiencies or to synthesize an antigen in case of vaccination [84], for example. In the third case, genetically modified keratinocytes might perform various metabolic functions or detoxify substances present in the systemic circulation. The accumulated expertise in culturing and autologously grafting skin cells is highly developed, comparable to that of bone marrow cells, suggesting that these cell types are good candidates for the extension of homologous recombination protocols to gene therapy objectives.

References

[1] *Rosenberg SA, Aebersold P, Cornetta K, et al.:* Gene transfer into humans – immunotherapy of patients with advanced melanoma, using tumor-infiltrating lymphocytes modified by retroviral gene transduction. N Engl J Med; 323:570–578, 1990

[2] *Izant JG, Weintraub H:* Inhibition of thymidine kinase gene expression by anti-sense RNA: a molecular approach to genetic analysis. Cell; 36:1007–1015, 1984

[3] *Wolff JA, Malone RW, Williams P, et al.:* Direct gene transfer into mouse muscle in vivo. Science; 247:1465–1468, 1990

[4] *Vogt PM, Thompson S, Andree C, et al.:* Genetically modified keratinocytes transplanted to wounds reconstitute the epidermis. Proc Natl Acad Sci USA; 91:9307–9311, 1994

[5] *Rheinwald JG, Green H:* Serial cultivation of strains of human epidermal keratinocytes; the formation of keratinizing colonies from single cells. Cell; 6:331–344, 1975

[6] *Andree C, Swain W, Page C, et al.:* In vivo transfer and expression of a human epidermal growth factor gene accelerates wound repair. Proc Natl Acad Sci, USA 1994;91:12188–12192

[7] Human gene marker/therapy clinical protocols. Hum Gene Ther; 5:1537–1551, 1994

[8] *Mc Lachlin JR, Cornetta K, Eglitis MA, et al.:* Retroviral-mediated gene transfer. Prog Nucleic Acid Res Mol Biol; 38:91–135, 1990

[9] *Brody SL, Crystal R:* Adenovirus-mediated in vivo gene transfer. Ann NY Acad Sci; 716:90–101, 1994

[10] *Piccini A, Paoletti E:* Vaccinia: virus, vector, vaccine. Adv Virus Res 1988;34:43–64

[11] *Kolberg R:* Gene-transfer virus contaminant linked to monkeys' cancer. J NIH Res; 4:43–44, 1992

[12] *Morgan J, Barrandon Y, Green H, et al.:* Expression of an exogenous growth hormone gene by transplantable human epidermal cells. Science; 237:1476–1479, 1987

[13] *Teumer J, Lindahl A, Green H:* Human growth hormone in the blood of athymic mice grafted with cultures of hormone-secreting human keratinocytes. FASEB J; 4:3245–3250, 1990

[14] *Flowers MED, Stockschlaeder MAR, Schuening FG et al.:* Long-term transplantation of canine keratinocytes made resistant to G418 through retrovirus-mediated gene transfer. Proc Natl Acad Sci USA; 87:2349–2353, 1990

[15] *Selden RF, Skoskiewicz MJ, Howie KB, et al.:* Implantation of genetically engineered fibroblasts into mice: implications for gene therapy. Science;236:714–718, 1987

[16] *Cooney EL, Collier AC, Greenberg PD, et al.:* Safety of and immunological response to a recombinant vaccinia virus vaccine expressing HIV envelope glycoprotein. Lancet; 337: 567–572, 1991

[17] *Jensen PKA, Bolund L:* Tissue culture of human epidermal keratinocytes: a differentiating model system for gene testing and somatic gene therapy. J Cell Sci; 100:255–259, 1991

[18] *Fraley R, Subramani S, Berg P, et al.:* Introduction of liposome-encapsulated SV40 DNA into cells. J Biol Chem; 255:10431–10435, 1980

[19] *Schaefer-Ridder M, Wang Y, Hofschneider PH:* Liposomes as gene carriers: efficient transformation of mouse L cells by thymidine kinase gene. Science (Wash.); 215:166–168, 1982

[20] *Wigler M, Silverstein S, Lee LS, et al.:* Transfer of purified herpes thymidine kinase gene to cultured mouse cells. Cell; 11:223–232, 1977

[21] *Neumann E, Rosenheck K:* Permeability changes induced by electric impulses in vesicular membranes. J Membrane Biol; 10:279–290, 1972

[22] *Cheng L, Ziegelhoffer PR, Yang NS:* In vivo promoter activity and transgene expression in mammalian somatic tissues evaluated by using particle bombardment. Proc Natl Acad Sci USA; 90:4455–4459, 1993

[23] *Christou P:* Application to plants. In Yang NS, Christou P (eds.). Particle bombardment technology for gene transfer. Oxford University Press, New York, 71–99, 1994

[24] *Williams RS, Johnston SA, Riedy M, et al.:* Introduction of foreign genes into tissues of living mice by DNA-coated microprojectiles. Proc Natl Acad Sci USA; 88:2726–2730, 1991

[25] *Yang NS, Swain WF:* Technology development in gene therapy, in particle bombardment technology for gene transfer. In Yang NS, Christou P (eds.). Particle bombardment technology for gene transfer. Oxford University Press, New York, 143–173, 1994

[26] *Jaenisch R:* Transgenic animals. Science; 240:1468–1474, 1988

[27] *Moolten FL, Cupples LA:* A model for predicting the risk of cancer consequent to retroviral gene therapy. Hum Gene Ther; 3:479–486, 1992

[28] *Carroll JM, Fenjves ES, Garlick JA, et al.:* Keratinocytes as a target for gene therapy. In Darmon M, Blumenberg M. Molecular Biology of the Skin. Academic Press, Inc., San Diego, 269–284, 1993

Keratinocyte Colony-Forming Cells as Determinants of the Transplantability of Human Squamous Epithelium Cultivated on a Fibrin Substrate

V. Ronfard, Y. Barrandon

Summary

Autologous cultured keratinocytes can be used to permanently cover third degree burn wounds. A variety of modifications to Green and colleagues' original technique have been suggested, including the use of a fibrin matrix. However, because changes in culture conditions may reduce keratinocyte lifespan and result in the loss of the transplanted epithelium, the properties of the cultured cells must be assessed using suitable criteria before a modified method of culture for therapeutic purposes is transferred to clinical use. Human keratinocytes grown on a fibrin matrix, were assayed for their colony-forming ability, their growth potential and their ability to generate an epidermis when grafted onto athymic mice. We found that human keratinocytes cultured on a fibrin matrix had the same growth capacity and transplantability as those cultured on plastic surfaces and that the presence of a fibrin matrix greatly facilitated the preparation, handling, and surgical transplantation of the grafts, which did not need to be detached enzymatically. The rate of take of grafts grown on fibrin matrices was high, and was similar to that of conventionally cultured grafts. The grafted autologous cells are capable of generating a normal epidermis for many years and favor the regeneration of a superficial dermis. In conclusion from our results it can be drawn that fibrin matrices have considerable advantages over plastic for the culture of skin cells for grafting and that the use of fibrin matrices significantly improves the transplantation of cultured epithelium grafts.

Keratinocyte Colony-Forming Cells

Human keratinocytes can initiate colonies in culture [1]. These keratinocyte colony-forming cells have different capacities for multiplication [2, 3]. The colony-forming ability and the growth capacity of cells contained in a culture can be evaluated by clonal analysis either of single cells or of a small number of cells. Clonal analysis of single cells evaluates the colony-forming ability and the growth capacity of individual cells. It necessitates the isolation of a number of single cells. Each cell is individually cultivated in a Petri dish containing a feeder layer of irradiated 3T3-J2 cells. After 7 days of cultivation, each dish is scanned under an inverted microscope for the presence of a clone. If a clone is found, it is passaged into 2 x 100 mm Petri dishes (indicator dishes) containing a feeder layer of freshly irradiated 3T3-J2 cells. The cells are then cultivated for 12 more days, before the dishes are fixed and stained. Two types of colonies are observed under a binocular microscope: growing colonies that contain small multiplying cells, and aborted colonies that contain only terminally differentiated squame-like cells.

The growth potential of the original keratinocyte is indicated by the frequency of aborted colonies that is formed by its progeny on the indicator dishes. Clonal analysis demonstrated that three types of colony-forming cells with different capacities for multiplication reside in the epidermis and in the hair follicles [2, 4]. These cells are the holoclone, the meroclone and the paraclone. The holoclone is a stem cell and has a lifespan up to 180 doublings [4, 5]. It gives rise to numerous progeny, of which holoclones, meroclones, and unfrequently paraclones (less than 5%). A holoclone can generate enough progeny to reconstitute the entire keratinocyte population contained in the epidermis of an adult human. The meroclone has a more restricted lifespan than the holoclone, and gives rise to meroclones and paraclones. The paraclone has a growth potential restricted to a maximum of 15 divisions and generates only paraclones. The conversion from holoclone to paraclone is an irreversible phenomenon that occurs both in the epidermis and in culture. This process which restricts a cell's lifespan is closely related to aging [2].

A colony-forming efficiency (CFE) evaluates the clone-forming ability and the growth capacity of a small number of cells. 100–1000 cells are plated onto a 100 mm Petri dish containing a feeder layer of freshly irradiated 3T3-J2 cells and cultivated for 12 days before the dishes are fixed and stained. The size and shape of the colonies are examined under a binocular microscope. In addition, the number of small multiplying cells or large terminally differentiated cells that are contained in each colony is evaluated. A colony can then be readily classified as growing, partially aborted or completely aborted. Growing colonies are initiated by holoclones and meroclones with significant growth potential, partially aborted colonies by meroclones with limited growth potential, and aborted colonies by paraclones. The growth capability of a keratinocyte culture is best evaluated by clonal analysis of single cell [2]. However, a colony-forming efficiency is usually informative and sensitive enough if one wants to assay the consequences on the cells of a modification of the cultivation technique.

Permanent coverage of third degree burn wounds can be obtained by transplantation of autologous human cultured epitheliums. The most commonly used method of transplanting cultivated human keratinocytes is that of Green and colleagues [6–9]. Human epidermal cells are isolated from a small skin biopsy and plated onto a feeder layer of lethally irradiated 3T3 cells, which support optimal keratinocyte growth [1]. Under these conditions, some keratinocytes (1–5%) initiate progressively growing colonies [1, 10]. This initial population of keratinocyte colony-forming cells (K-CFCs) is then amplified by one or two subcultivations depending on the size and growth rate of the initial inoculum. Cells aimed to be transplanted are grown to confluence to form an epithelium. Then each cultured epithelium needs to be detached as a coherent sheet from the culture vessel using an enzymatic treatment with Dispase [11] or thermolysin [12]. These epithelia are then able to engraft on a surgically prepared grafting bed [13] and provide permanent coverage of the excised third degree burn wound [14, 15]. The detachment of the cultured epitheliums as a coherent sheet requires close attention, is time consuming, fastidious and costly. One way around this difficulty is to grow the keratinocytes on a transplantable substrate that can be detached together with the epithelium and transferred to the wound bed [16]. Therefore, many modifications of the original technique have been proposed [17–21] including the use of single-cell suspensions of human keratinocytes in surgical glue [22, 23].

Cultivation of Human Keratinocytes on a Fibrin Substrate

Our human fibrin substrate is prepared from a commercially available surgical fibrin glue, virus inactivated by a solvent-detergent treat-

Table 1: Properties of the fibrin substrate.

Fibrin glue dilution	1	1/2	1/4
Protein concentration	116 g/l	59 g/l	32 g/l
Osmolarity	1486 mosm/l	640 mosm/l	325 mosm/l
Thrombin concentration	500 IU/ml	5 IU/ml	5 IU/ml
Clotting time	2 seconds	200 seconds	130 seconds
Breaking point	3400 N/m^2	> 6300 N/m^2	> 6300 N/m^2
Elasticity	+	+++	+++
Tensile strength	185 g/cm^2	124 g/cm^2	ND
Viscosity (20°C)	122 mPas	14 mPas	ND
Substrate appearance	opaque lines	transparent	opaque

ment [24, 25]. The detailed protein composi-tion of the fibrin glue Biocol™ is as described [25]. Briefly, it consists of fibrinogen 116g/l (+/– 2.49 g/l), clottable fibrinogen 98 g/l (+/– 4.08 g/l), fibronectin 5.9 g/l (+/– 0.51 g/l) and factor XIII 35 U/ml (+/– 2.88 U/ml). A 5 ml kit of Biocol™ is sufficient to prepare three cultured epithelium grafts of 144 cm^2 each. The fibrin substrate (50–100 µm thick) is transparent and suitable for microscopic examination of cultured cells when Biocol™ is diluted with twice the volume of aprotinin solution or sterile distilled water (Table 1). It is easily detached as a homogeneous sheet from the bottom of a bacteriological grade culture vessel and is then easily manipulated as it keeps its original size, strength and elasticity (Fig. 1).

Keratinocytes to be transplanted are plated onto a feeder layer of lethally irradiated 3T3 cells, previously seeded on the fibrin substrate and cultivated in a complete medium as described [4, 26]. The addition of an antiprotease (e. g. aprotinin) to the culture medium is however required to prevent fibrin degradation. Other brands of surgical glue are also efficacious. This once the conditions of use are adjusted to obtain a transparent matrix so that cell growth could be easily monitored microscopically [our unpublished results, 27].

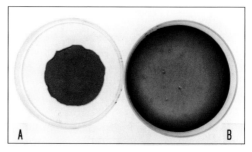

Fig. 1: Macroscopic aspect of transplantable cultured epithelium sheets. (A) Transplantable epithelium cultivated in absence of a fibrin substrate, and detached from the culture vessel by a conventional Dispase treatment. It has shrunk to one third of its original size. (B) Epithelium cultivated on a fibrin substrate and ready to be transplanted.

Evaluation of the Quality of the Graftable Epithelia

It is necessary to examine the properties of the cultured keratinocytes using suitable criteria before a modified method of cultivation of human keratinocytes for therapeutical purpose is transferred to clinical use. Altered conditions of cultivation can result in a dramatic diminution of the keratinocyte lifespan and loss of holoclones. Consequently, loss of the transplanted epithelium may occur

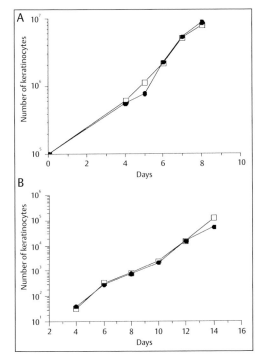

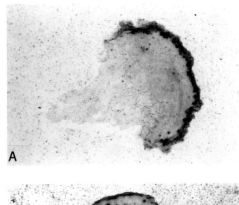

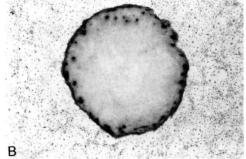

Fig. 2: Growth of human keratinocytes cultivated on a fibrin substrate. Human keratinocytes (strain YF29, culture V) were cultivated in absence (o) or in presence of a fibrin substrate (•). Panel A, high density inoculum (10^5 cells per 60 mm size Petri dishes); Panel B, clonal density inoculum (30 cells per 60 mm size Petri dishes). The number of cells was determined at regular intervals as described [25]. Keratinocyte growth was similar when the cells were cultivated in absence or in presence of a fibrin substrate.

Fig. 3: Appearance of keratinocyte colonies on a fibrin substrate. Human keratinocytes (strain YF 29) were grown in presence (A) or in absence (B) of a fibrin substrate. Colonies contain the same number of cells, even if they differ in size and shape. In presence of fibrin, the cells have a tendency to stratify and to form colonies of smaller size but the growth and the clonogenicity of the K-CFCs are not affected.

as permanent coverage necessitates the presence of keratinocyte stem cells (holoclones) in the graft [28]. Accordingly, we have evaluated the growth capacities of keratinocyte colony-forming cells (K-CFCs) [2] cultivated on a fibrin substrate, which greatly facilitates the transplantation of human cultured epithelium [16, 26, 27]. Human keratinocytes were inoculated at high density (5×10^3 cells/cm^2) and cultivated for 8 days, or were inoculated at clonal density (1.5 cells/cm^2) and cultivated for 12 days on a feeder layer of lethally irradiated 3T3 cells in presence or in absence of a fibrin substrate. The number of cells per culture plate (Fig. 2A),

the number of cells per colonies (Fig. 2B) and the number of colonies initiated were identical in both cases, thus indicating that K-CFCs adherence and growth were not affected by the presence of fibrin, even if the size and shape of the colonies are different from those grown in absence of fibrin (Fig. 3). CFE experiments, which results have been reported in detail elsewhere [26] further demonstrated that the presence of a fibrin matrix did not impair the number and the growth potential of K-CFCs.

A cultured human epithelium can form an epidermis when transplanted on athymic mice [29, 30]. Human keratinocytes were cultivated up to confluency in absence (control) or in presence of a fibrin substrate. Then, the control epithelium was detached from the culture vessel bottom with Dispase, and epithelium grown on fibrin was removed from the Petri dish without enzymatic treatment. Both Epithelium were grafted onto the back of athymic mice as previously described [30]. Special care being taken to maintain a proper orientation, i.e. the basal layer facing the grafting bed, and the fibrin substrate lying at the interface between the basal layer and the graft bed. The formation of a stratified epithelium resembling human epidermis was observed in all cases (41 mice grafted). The different epidermal layers were present, in particular a stratum granulosum and an orthokeratotic stratum corneum (Fig. 4 A, 4 B). Remnants of the fibrin substrate were still present under the epithelium after one week (Fig. 4 A), but it

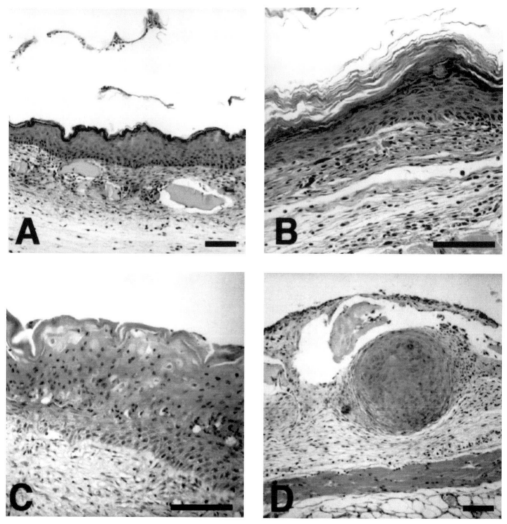

Fig. 4: Histological appearance of cultured epithelia transplanted onto athymic mice. Confluent cultured human epithelia were produced in presence (A) or in absence (B) of a fibrin substrate, and then transplanted onto athymic mice. Grafts were harvested 7 days after transplantation. 4 day-old keratinocyte colonies grown on fibrin substrate were transplanted onto athymic mice. Fibrin substrate applied directly to the graft site (C), or reversed (D). Grafts were harvested 10 days after transplantation. Bar: 100 μm.

was completely gone after 11 days (data not show). This data indicated that the presence of a fibrin substrate did not affect the transplantability of human cultured epithelium.

Human keratinocytes cultivated according to Green and colleagues can only be transplanted once they have form a coherent epithelial sheet. Indeed, it is impossible to transplant non confluent keratinocyte cultures because they form a lace-like epithelial sheet after Dispase treatment. However, keratinocytes could be transplanted earlier when they were cultivated on a fibrin matrix because they did not need to be detached from it. To test this hypothesis, human keratinocytes were cultivated for 4 days on a fibrin substrate. The fibrin substrate along with the growing keratinocyte colonies was then transplanted onto the back of athymic mice. After 10 days, a pluristratified epithelium had formed when the fibrin substrate was applied directly to the graft site (Fig. 4 C: normal orientation), the stratum corneum is parakeratotic as observed during the early phase of reepithelialization of a wound. On the other hand, epidermal cysts were formed when keratinocyte colonies were applied in direct contact to the graft bed (Fig. 4 D: reverse orientation). This suggests that human keratinocytes are polarized even after a few days in culture and that their polarity must be respected to form a coherent epidermis.

Conclusion

The presence of the fibrin substrate and of aprotinin in the culture medium does not affect the clonogenicity, the growth capacity of human keratinocyte colony-forming cells (K-CFCs), and their ability to generate human epidermis when grafted onto athymic mice. The quality of the graftable epithelia produced by this technique is thus equivalent to that of the graftable epithelia used by Gallico et al. [7]. This is confirmed by the results obtained in treating extensive burn wounds by transplantation of cultured epithelium autografts produced in absence or in presence of a fibrin substrate [26, 27]. It is now possible to generate enough cultured epitheliums from a 7 cm^2 size skin biopsy to transplant the entire body area (1.73 m^2) of an adult human in 16 days (Table 2). But it is possible only if human ke-

Table 2: Strategy of cultivation to generate 1.73 m2 of cultured epithelia in the shortest time.

Day 0	Biopsy (7 cm^2)	Yield – 40 x 10^6 cells Inoculation of primary culture 10 flasks (150 cm^2) at 4 x 10^6 cells	
Day 9	Harvest of culture I	Yield – 120 x 10^6 cells	
	Inoculation of culture II	On bare plastic 35 flasks at 1 x 10^6 cells	Final cultivation of epithelia on fibrin substrate 120 flasks at 1 x 10^6 cells
Day 14	Harvest of culture II	Yield – 350 x 10^6 keratinocytes	
		Final cultivation of conventional epithelia 346 flasks at 1 x 10^6 cells	
Day 16			Yield – 17300 cm^2 of transplantable epithelia on fibrin substrate (118 grafts of 144 cm^2)
Day 21		Yield – 17300 cm^2 of transplantable conventional Dispased epithelia (692 grafts of 25 cm^2)	

ratinocytes are cultivated according to Green and colleagues [1,4,7], if a fibrin substrate is used to grow human keratinocytes and if rigorous cultivation and transplantation techniques are used to preserve the greatest number of epidermal stem cells.

The calculation is based on the mean number of cells harvested per cm^2 of skin (5.7×10^6 /cm^2), and the size of the initial biopsy is 7 cm^2. The size of a conventional dispase epidermal sheet is 25 cm^2 [7] and of a fibrin substrate graft is 144 cm^2 [26].

References

[1] Rheinwald JG, Green H: Serial cultivation of strains of human epidermal keratinocytes: the formation of keratinizing colonies from single cells. Cell; 6: 331, 1975

[2] Barrandon Y, Green H: Three clonal types of keratinocyte with different capacities for multiplication. Proc. Natl. Acad. Sci. USA; 84: 2302, 1987

[3] Jones PH, Watt FM: Separation of human epidermal stem cells from transit amplifying cells on the basis of differences in integrin function and expression. Cell; 73: 713, 1993

[4] Rochat A, Kobayashi K, Barrandon Y: Location of stem cells of human hair follicles by clonal analysis. Cell; 76: 1063, 1994

[5] Mathor MB, Ferrari G, Dellambra E, Cilli M, Mavilio F, Cancedda R, De Luca M: Clonal analysis of stably transduced human epidermal stem cells in culture. Proc. Natl. Acad. Sci. USA; 93: 10371, 1996

[6] O'Connor NE, Mulliken JB, Banks-Schlegel S, Kehinde O, Green H: Grafting of burns with cultured epithelium prepared from autologous epidermal cells. The Lancet; i: 75, 1981

[7] Gallico GG III., O'Connor NE, Compton CC, Kehinde O, Green H.: Permanent coverage of large burn wounds with autologous cultured human epithelium. N. Engl. J. Med.; 311: 448, 1984

[8] Munster AM, Weiner SH, Spence RJ: Cultured epidermis for the coverage of massive burn wounds. A single center experience. Ann. Surg.; 211: 676, 1990

[9] Carsin H, Ainaud P, Le Bever H, Rives J, Lakhel A, Stephanazzi J, Lambert F, Perrot J: Culture epithelial autografts in extensive burns coverage of severely traumatized patients: a five years single- center experience with 30 patients. Burns; 26: 379, 2000

[10] Barrandon Y, Green H: Cell size as a determinant of the clone-forming ability of human keratinocytes. Proc. Natl. Acad. Sci. USA; 82: 5390, 1985

[11] Green H, Kehinde O, Thomas J: Growth of cultured human epidermal cells into multiple epithelia suitable for grafting. Proc. Natl. Acad. Sci. USA; 76: 5665, 1979

[12] Germain L, Rouabhia M, Guignard R, Carrier L, Bouvard V, Auger FA: Improvement of human keratinocyte isolation and culture using thermolysin. Burns; 19: 99, 1993

[13] Cuono C, Langdon R, McGuire J: Use of cultured epidermal autografts and dermal allografts as skin replacement after burn injury. Lancet; i: 1123, 1986

[14] Compton CC, Gill JM, Bradford DA, Regauer S, Gallico GG, O'Connor NE: Skin regenerated from cultured epithelial autografts on full-thickness burn wounds from 6 days to 5 years after grafting. Lab. Invest.; 60: 600, 1989

[15] Hickerson WL, Compton C, Fletchall S, Smith LR.: Cultured epidermal autografts and allodermis combination for permanent burn wound coverage. Burns; 20: s52, 1994

[16] Ronfard V, Broly H, Mitchell V, Galizia JP, Hochard D, Chambon F, Pellerin P, Huart JJ: Use of human keratinocytes cultured on fibrin glue in the treatment of burn wounds. Burns; 17: 181, 1991

[17] Raghunath M, Meuli M: Cultured epithelial autografts: diving from surgery into matrix biology. Pediatr. Surg. Int.; 12: 478, 1997

[18] Wright KA, Nadire KB, Busto P, Tubo R, Mc Pherson JM, Wentworth BM: Alternative delivery of keratinocytes using a polyurethane membrane and the implications for its use in the treatment of full-thickness burn injury. Burns; 24: 7, 1998

[19] Caruso DM, Schuh WH, Al-Kasspooles MF, Chen MC, Schiller WR: Cultured composite autografts as coverage for an extensive body surface area burn: case report and review of the technology. Burns; 25: 771, 1999

[20] Boyce ST, Kagan RJ, Meyer NA, Yakuboff KP, Warden GD: The 1999 clinical research award. Cultured skin substitutes combines with Integra Artificial Skin to replace native skin autograft and allograft for the closure of excised full-thickness burns. J. Burn Care Rehabil.; 20: 453, 1999

[21] Braye F, Oddou L, Bertin-Maghit M, Belgacem S, Damour O, Spitalier P, Guillot M, Bouchard C, Gueugniaud PY, Goudeau M, Petit P, Tissot E: Widely meshed autograft associated with cultured autologous epithelium for the treatment of major burns in children: report of 12 cases. Eur. J. Pediatr. Surg.; 10: 35, 2000

[22] Kaiser HW, Stark GB, Kopp J, Balcerkiewicz A, Spilker G, Kreysel HW: Cultured autologous keratinocytes in fibrin glue suspension, ex-

clusively and combined with STS-allograft (preliminary clinical and histological report of a new technique). Burns; 20: 23, 1994

[23] Horch RE, Bannasch H, Kopp J, Andree C, Stark GB: Single-cell suspensions of cultured human keratinocytes in fibrin-glue reconstitute the epidermis. Cell Transplantation; 3: 309, 1998

[24] Horowitz MS, Rooks C, Horowitz B, Hilgartner MW: Virus safety of solvent/detergent-treated antihaemophilic factor concentrate. The Lancet; ii: 186, 1988

[25] Burnouf-Radosevich M, Burnouf T, Huart JJ: Biochemical and physical properties of a solvent-detergent-treated fibrin glue. Vox Sang.; 58: 77, 1990

[26] Ronfard V, Rives JM, Neveux Y, Carsin H, Barrandon Y: Long term regeneration of human epidermis on third degree burns transplanted with autologous cultured epithelium grown on a fibrin matrix. Transplantation; 70: 1588, 2000

[27] Pellegrini G, Ranno R, Stracuzzi G, Bondanza S, Guerra L, Zambruno G, Micali G, De Luca M: The control of epidermal stem cells (holoclones) in the treatment of massive full-thickness burns with autologous keratinocytes cultured on fibrin. Transplantation; 68: 868, 1999

[28] Desai MH, Mlakar JM, McCauley RL, Abdullah KM, Rutan RL, Waymack JP, Robson MC, Herndon DN: Lack of long-term durability of cultured keratinocyte burn-wound coverage: a case report. J. Burn Care Rehabil.; 12: 540, 1991

[29] Banks-Schlegel S, Green H: Formation of epidermis by serially cultivated human epidermal cells transplanted as an epithelium to athymic mice. Transplantation; 29: 308, 1980

[30] Barrandon Y, Li V, Green H: New techniques for the grafting of cultured human epidermal cells onto athymic animals. J. Invest. Dermatol.; 91: 315, 1988

Genetic Modification of Cultured Skin Substitutes

D. M. Supp, S. T. Boyce

Summary

Cultured skin substitutes comprised of autologous cultured fibroblasts and keratinocytes attached to biopolymer substrates have been used as adjunctive therapies for the treatment of large burns and chronic wounds. Genetic modification of fibroblasts and keratinocytes offers the possibility to use cultured skin substitutes as vehicles for gene therapy. Preclinical studies utilizing fibroblasts or keratinocytes modified by replication-incompetent retroviral transduction have demonstrated the feasibility of gene therapy with cultured skin. Genetically modified cultured skin substitutes can prospectively be used to treat a wide range of cutaneous or systemic genetic disorders. In addition, genetic modification can be used to improve the composition or performance of skin analogues, making them more similar to native skin autograft and increasing their clinical efficacy.

Introduction

Morbidity and mortality from skin wounds remain important medical problems. Chronic wounds, such as decubitus, venous, and diabetic ulcers, are generally associated with impairments of one or more phases of wound healing [1, 2], and may be characterized by tissue hypoxia and/or failure of re-epithelialization [1]. Conventional management of relatively small non-healing wounds includes treatment with topical agents, use of occlusive dressings, and grafting of split-thickness or full-thickness skin [3]. Skin grafts provide timely wound coverage, but can lead to painful donor sites which are slow to heal and may be unsuccessful due to underlying deficiencies in wound healing. Patients with large acute wounds, such as burns, generally do not suffer from impaired wound healing, but permanent wound closure is limited by the lack of donor sites for autografting. Because most burn patients survive the resuscitation phase, even after very severe burns, wound management is critical for recovery. Delay in wound coverage increases the likelihood of infection, a major cause of burn mortality [4].

The need for wound closure in chronic and acute skin wounds has led to the development of a number of alternatives for wound treatment [4–7]. These include biologic skin replacements, such as cultured epithelial autograft and allograft [8–11], cryopreserved human skin allograft [12], decellularized dermal allograft [13], acellular collagen-based dermal substitutes [14, 15], keratinocyte-collagen membrane grafts [16], keratinocyte-fibrin-glue suspensions [17], and allogeneic or autologous composite cultured skin substitutes [18–23]. Skin replacements can be used as adjunctive therapies in patients who are also receiving conventional skin grafts to increase available material [18, 19, 21, 23, 24]. They are also used in combination with split-thickness autograft for improved outcome [15], or in place of autograft in patients where donor sites are unavailable or undesirable [2, 25, 26]. Performance of skin substitutes can be further enhanced by combining dermal replacements with epidermal sheet grafts [27,

28], epidermal suspensions [29–31], or composite cultured skin substitutes [24]. The most important function of skin substitutes is restoration of barrier function, to minimize protein and fluid loss and prevent infection [5]. Ideally, to be useful in a clinical setting, skin replacements for wound closure should: be ready to be used when needed; promote complete engraftment without contraction or the need for regrafting; allow rapid healing to form both dermal and epidermal layers; achieve favorable functional and cosmetic outcome; reduce requirement for surgical procedures and length of hospitalization; be free from risk of disease transmission; and have minimal immunological reaction [4].

There are currently no skin substitutes available which meet all of these requirements. However, cultured skin substitutes (CSS) comprised of cultured autologous keratinocytes and fibroblasts in a collagen-based matrix satisfy many of these criteria [19, 21, 24, 32, 33]. CSS have similar anatomy and physiology to split-thickness skin grafts and provide permanent replacement of both dermal and epidermal layers with good cosmetic outcome. For preparation of CSS, primary cultures of keratinocytes and fibroblasts are isolated using standard techniques [34–36] from small biopsies that are usually taken during a patient's first autografting procedure [19, 21, 32]. Primary cultures are harvested after 7–10 days and expanded prior to preparation of CSS. Because both fibroblasts and keratinocytes have an approximate doubling time of one day or less in vitro, large populations of cells can be generated within two to three weeks of receiving a patient biopsy. Fibroblasts and keratinocytes are inoculated serially at high density onto collagen-glycosaminoglycan substrates [18, 19, 37]. The grafts are submerged in culture medium for two days following keratinocyte inoculation; on day three, they are lifted on stainless steel mesh supports to the air-liquid interface. Culturing CSS in this manner promotes stratification and cornification of the epidermal layer, which is in contact with the air, while maintaining nutrient supply to the graft

through the dermal layer. Grafting to patients is generally performed within two weeks of inoculation of CSS, and cryopreservation of cells can be used to provide additional cells for subsequent graft preparations. After healing, grafted CSS have similar visco-elastic properties to healed split-thickness skin autograft [33].

However, because CSS contain only two cell types, they can provide barrier but cannot replace all of the functions of normal skin. Thus, despite clinical benefits from CSS, limitations in anatomy and physiology remain [19, 21]. For example, CSS lack a vascular plexus, leading to slower vascularization compared to native skin autograft. Split-thickness skin autografts have been shown to vascularize by a combination of processes, including inosculation and neovascularization [38]. Inosculation, the anastamosis of capillaries in the wound bed to the ends of severed vessels in the dermis, is the primary mechanism of early vascularization of split-thickness grafts. Neovascularization, the growth of new capillaries from the wound bed into the graft, occurs several days later [38]. Vascularization of CSS is slower than for split-thickness autografts because it occurs through the process of neovascularization alone. This contributes to cultured skin graft failure by increasing time for reperfusion, ischemia, and nutrient deprivation of grafted cells [6]. This limitation has been partially addressed by the application of topical antimicrobials [39] and nutrient solutions [40] to CSS for several days after grafting to improve the wound environment and nourish the cells until adequate vascularization is attained. Prospectively, improved engraftment and simplified post-operative wound care could be achieved by modifications of CSS that enhance vascularization after grafting.

Genetic engineering can hypothetically be used to overcome limitations inherent to cultured skin, or to augment their therapeutic value to patients. The tools of molecular biology can be used to modify the gene expression profiles of cells contained in CSS to enhance performance, resulting in skin substi-

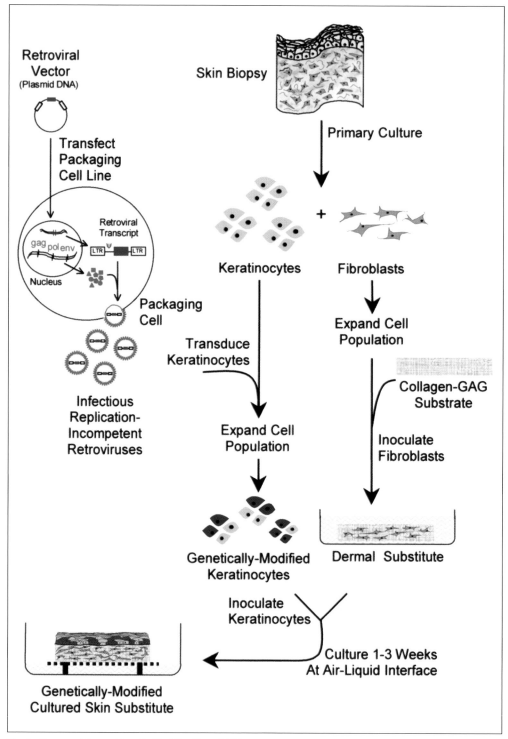

Fig. 1: Supp and Boyce. Genetic Modification of CSS.

tutes that function more like native human skin autograft. Cultured human keratinocytes and fibroblasts are both amenable to genetic modification by several methods, including calcium phosphate-mediated transfection, electroporation, adenoviral infection and retroviral transduction. For keratinocytes, which are sensitive to calcium levels and other treatments, retroviral transduction is perhaps the most efficient method for introduction of cloned genes.

Figure 1 outlines the steps involved in preparing genetically modified CSS using keratinocytes transduced with replication-incompetent retroviruses. The use of replication-incompetent vectors is a safety measure that theoretically eliminates the possibility of in-

Fig. 1: Preparation of genetically-modified cultured skin substitutes (CSS) by transduction of keratinocytes with a replication-incompetent retroviral vector. A replication-incompetent retroviral plasmid vector (top left) is constructed by cloning a gene of interest (illustrated in blue) between the retroviral long terminal repeat (LTR) sequences. The vector contains the sequence required for packaging viral particles (ψ), but not the viral structural proteins. This retroviral vector is transfected into a packaging cell line that has been independently transfected with the structural genes necessary for production of viral particles (gag, pol, and env). The retroviral vector DNA incorporates randomly into the genome of the packaging cell where it is transcribed into RNA, recognized by retroviral proteins (illustrated in red) and packaged into infectious retroviral particles. Human keratinocytes and fibroblasts are cultured from a small skin biopsy (top right). Keratinocytes are transduced either by co-culture with growth-inactivated packaging cells or by incubation with retrovirus-containing culture medium. Transduction efficiencies of approximately 50 % can be routinely achieved without applying selection to keratinocytes (modified keratinocytes are illustrated in blue). The dermal substitute consists of fibroblasts inoculated onto a collagen-GAG sponge. Keratinocytes are inoculated onto the dermal substitute one day after fibroblasts, and three days later the skin substitutes are lifted to the air-liquid interface on stainless steel mesh supports. The genetically modified cultured skin substitutes are incubated for an additional 1 to 3 weeks before grafting. Not illustrated here, fibroblasts can also be transduced by incubation with culture medium containing infectious retroviruses.

fectious retrovirus production by modified keratinocytes [41]. For replication-incompetent retroviral vectors used in molecular biology applications, the genes encoding viral capsid proteins are removed, but the sequence necessary for viral packaging (ψ) remains. The viral structural genes are replaced with the investigator's gene of interest, inserted between two retroviral long terminal repeat (LTR) sequences. The upstream (5') LTR acts as a promoter sequence and is the site of transcription initiation, and the downstream (3') LTR is the site of transcription termination. If desired, vectors can be engineered containing tissue-specific or inducible promoters for finely regulated expression, or drug-resistance genes for selection of modified cells [42]. The retroviral vector is produced from a bacterial plasmid (**Fig. 1**, upper left) that is transfected into a packaging cell line, where it randomly incorporates into the host genome. The packaging cell line, often derived from mouse fibroblast cells, has been independently transfected with the genes necessary for production of viral particles (gag, pol, and env). The retroviral genome is transcribed, the packaging sequence (ψ) is recognized by viral capsid proteins in the packaging cell, and RNA copies of the virus are packaged into infectious viral particles that bud from the cell [41]. These replication-incompetent retrovirus particles can be used to infect target cells, such as epidermal keratinocytes, which do not contain the viral genes needed for capsid formation. Thus, the viral vector incorporates into the keratinocyte genome and the retroviral RNA is transcribed, but it cannot be packaged into infectious particles. There are some drawbacks to the use of replication-incompetent retroviruses for gene modification [42]. These include the need for target cells to be dividing and expressing appropriate viral receptors, and the tendency for *in vivo* inactivation of the viral LTR promoter for reasons that are poorly understood. In addition, safety concerns include the possibility of insertional mutation at the site of vector integration and the slight risk of production

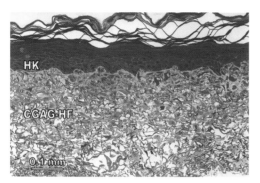

Fig. 2: Histology of cultured skin substitute genetically modified by retroviral transduction of keratinocytes. A control retroviral vector, without inserted gene sequences, was used to modify keratinocytes prior to preparation of the cultured skin substitute. A biopsy was taken at day 16 of *in vitro* incubation, embedded in plastic, and sections were stained with toluidine blue for light microscopy. Note the presence of a well-stratified epidermal layer: the basal, nucleated cells are attached to the collagen-glycosaminoglycan substrate, and well-keratinized layers analogous to stratum corneum are seen at the air-exposed surface. The dermal compartment is densely packed with fibroblasts. Abbreviations: HK, human keratinocytes; CGAG-HF, collagen-glycosaminoglycan substrate populated with human fibroblasts. Scale bar, 0.1 millimeter.

of infectious virus in target cells [42]. Nevertheless, transduction with replication- incompetent retroviruses is relatively safe and remains one of the most efficient means of genetically modifying human keratinocytes in culture.

Genetically modified keratinocytes can be readily incorporated into CSS (Fig. 1) without significantly increasing the time required for their preparation. The virus-packaging cell line is generally derived from NIH-3T3 cells; thus, these cells can be growth-inactivated by gamma irradiation or treatment with mitomycin C and used as a feeder cell layer for primary keratinocytes [43–45]. The cocultivation of keratinocytes with virus-producing cells leads to very efficient transduction, primarily due to the continuous production of recombinant retrovirus and the close contact between the keratinocytes and the packag-

ing cells. Keratinocytes can be selectively harvested from the coculture and expanded prior to preparation of CSS to eliminate carry-over of virus producing cells. The process of retroviral transduction does not affect the growth or differentiation of keratinocytes [46] and transduced keratinocytes can be used to populate the epidermal layer of CSS. Cultured skin grafts prepared with transduced keratinocytes (Fig. 2) are morphologically indistinguishable from controls; this depends, of course, on the choice of genes carried by the retroviral vector. Genes encoding factors that effect the growth characteristics of keratinocytes and/or fibroblasts may alter the morphogenesis of CSS, with either favorable or unfavorable results.

Genetic modification of keratinocytes has been evaluated in preclinical studies for its ability to improve the performance of epidermal sheet grafts. Cytokines that have been studied for this purpose include those that are expressed during the wound healing process or have been shown to improve healing upon topical application [47–49]. For example, platelet-derived growth factor (PDGF) is expressed in normal and wounded skin, and its expression is reduced in healing-impaired mice [50]. Both isoforms of PDGF, PDGF-A and PDGF-B, are expressed in the epidermis, and their receptors are expressed in the dermis [50, 51]. PDGF is mitogenic and chemotactic for cells of mesenchymal origin, and it has been shown to stimulate the healing of soft tissues [52], suggesting that it might be a good candidate for enhancing the functional performance of grafted keratinocytes. To investigate this possibility, Eming and colleagues used retroviral transduction to over-express the gene encoding PDGF-A in human keratinocytes [53]. PDGF-A-modified and control keratinocytes were grafted as epithelial sheets under full-thickness skin flaps of athymic mice, and the connective tissue subadjacent to the modified grafts was thicker, more cellular, and had more blood vessels at one week after grafting than control keratinocyte grafts [53]. In a subsequent study [54] PDGF-A-modified keratinocytes seeded on an acellular dermis were grafted to full thickness wounds on athymic mice. The performance of those grafts was improved by inclusion of the genetically modified cells: the PDGF-A-modified grafts exhibited increased dermal cellularity, vascularization and collagen deposition, and decreased wound contraction one week after grafting [54]. The results of that study suggested that elevated PDGF-A expression might have enhanced engraftment during the first week after grafting by accelerating the normal process by which host cells repopulated the dermis of the composite graft [54].

Interestingly, overexpression of PDGF-A in composite CSS containing both keratinocytes and fibroblasts had no measurable effect on morphogenesis or performance of CSS after grafting to athymic mice [55]. This apparent discrepancy in outcomes has been attributed to differences in the cultured skin models used. Because the models employed by Eming and colleagues contained only keratinocytes, fibroblasts present in the host wound bed were required to infiltrate the region beneath epidermal sheet grafts [53] or into acellular dermal substitutes to populate the dermis [54]. Both processes were enhanced by overexpression of PDGF-A in transplanted keratinocytes. Thus, genetic modification of keratinocytes with a PDGF-A retrovirus served to overcome the inherent dermal deficiencies of cultured skin models containing only keratinocytes. Composite cultured skin substitutes containing both keratinocytes and fibroblasts do not require additional PDGF-A because a dermal component is present prior to grafting [55]. However, there are other limitations of CSS that could theoretically be addressed by genetic modification of keratinocytes and/or fibroblasts.

For example, overexpression of an angiogenic cytokine could hypothetically be used to address one of the aforementioned limitations of CSS: the increased time to vascularization after grafting compared to native split-thickness skin autograft. To examine this hypothesis, keratinocytes were genetically modified using replication-incompetent retroviral transduction to overexpress vascular endothelial growth factor (VEGF), a potent and specific mitogen for microvascular endothelial cells [56]. CSS prepared with VEGF-modified keratinocytes and unmodified fibroblasts secreted significantly elevated levels of VEGF throughout a 3-week in vitro culture period. After grafting to full-thickness wounds on the flanks of athymic mice, high levels of human VEGF mRNA were detected in the genetically modified CSS, for up to two weeks after surgery [56]. Grafted CSS were excised for analysis at 3, 7, and 14 days after grafting. At all timepoints, the VEGF-modified CSS showed enhanced vascularization compared to control CSS (modified with a blank retroviral vector). At 3 days after grafting, no evidence of microvascular ingrowth was found in control CSS, but vessels were observed in the dermal compartments of VEGF-modified CSS, in the region adjacent to the wound bed. By 7 days after grafting, dermal vessels were observed in both VEGF-modified and control CSS, but the vessels were larger and more numerous in the VEGF-modified grafts, and more vessels were seen in proximity to the dermal-epidermal junction. Similar results were observed at 14 days after grafting [56]. Quantitative analysis demonstrated significantly more staining for the endothelial cell-specific marker CD31/PECAM-1 in the VEGF-modified grafts, compared to controls, at both 7 and 14 days after grafting. Interestingly, there was no statistically significant difference between dermal endothelial cell density in VEGF-modified CSS at 7 days after surgery and control CSS at 14 days after surgery. This suggested that overexpression of VEGF from the genetically modified keratinocytes reduced the time required for vascularization of grafted CSS [56]. Examples of healed grafted CSS are shown in Fig. 3.

This study demonstrated the feasibility of using genetically modified cells to enhance the biological activity of CSS containing both keratinocytes and fibroblasts. This improvement could be beneficial for coverage of large wounds, such as burns, and could theoretically provide an alternative means of treatment for chronic wounds resulting from tis-

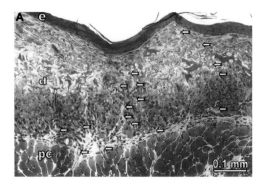

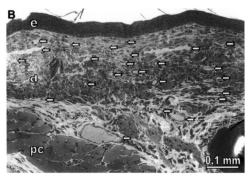

Fig. 3: Enhanced vascularization of VEGF-modified cultured skin substitutes (CSS) after grafting to athymic mice. Control (A) and VEGF-modified (B) CSS were grafted to full-thickness excisional wounds on the flanks of athymic mice. Biopsies shown were taken from grafted CSS two weeks after surgery. Specimens were embedded in plastic, sectioned, and stained with toluidine blue for light microscopy. Arrows point to examples of blood vessels in the dermal compartments of grafted CSS. Note that vessels are larger and more numerous in the VEGF-modified CSS (B) compared to control CSS (A). Abbreviations: e, epidermis; d, dermis; pc, panniculus carnosis (wound bed). Scale bars, 0.1 millimeter.

sue ischemia. Aberrant regulation of VEGF expression has been associated with defective wound repair, such as the abnormal wound healing seen in diabetic mice [57, 58]. In preclinical gene therapy studies, injection of an adenovirus vector encoding VEGF into ischemic tissues of diabetic mice restored vascularization to normal levels [58]. A small number of patients with chronic wounds have been treated with CSS containing allogeneic cells [2]. One patient with a diabetic

ulcer was treated and complete healing was achieved by three months after grafting, but two applications of CSS were required for complete wound closure. The use of allogeneic CSS genetically modified to overexpress VEGF could hypothetically improve vascularization of grafted tissue, thereby reducing the time required for healing of diabetic wounds and limiting the number of surgical procedures needed for wound closure. Because grafted allogeneic keratinocytes would be eventually replaced by recipient cells [11, 59, 60], genetically modified allogeneic CSS can prospectively be used to accelerate healing without persistence of the modified cells.

The enhanced vascularization of VEGF-modified CSS has implications not only for the improved performance of grafted CSS, but for its potential use in gene therapy applications as well. The findings indicated that VEGF produced by cells in the epidermis of modified cultured skin grafts could not only penetrate the dermal/epidermal basement membrane, but could penetrate the dermis to promote vascularization from mouse endothelial cells present in the wound bed. Thus, genetically modified CSS may act by paracrine mechanisms to stimulate host tissues. In theory, genetically modified cells in CSS might serve as gene delivery vehicles for gene therapy to treat disease [61–63]. Other investigators have explored the use of genetically modified keratinocytes for gene therapy purposes, with variable results. For example, human keratinocytes have been modified to express the human growth hormone (hGH) gene [46, 64]. Modified cells transplanted as epithelial sheets on athymic mice or in chamber-enclosed full-thickness wounds in pigs formed a differentiated epidermis; localized hGH expression was present after grafting, but in neither study were circulating levels detected [46, 64]. In another study, transgenic mice were generated using the keratinocyte-specific human keratin 14 (K14) promoter to drive expression of the hGH gene in the skin [65]. Expression of hGH in keratinocytes of transgenic mice resulted in high circulating levels of hGH protein [65]. Transgenic skin grafts from these mice continued to secrete hGH into the circulation after transplantation to non-transgenic recipients, at roughly 10% of physiological levels [65] Although this study was performed with whole skin grafts, not cultured keratinocytes, the results are significant because they suggest that keratinocyte-specific promoters might be beneficial for improving gene expression and protein secretion for keratinocyte gene therapy studies.

A similar series of experiments investigated the feasibility of keratinocyte gene therapy for treatment of hemophilia B, a bleeding disorder characterized by mutations in the clotting factor IX gene. Keratinocytes modified by retroviral transduction to express the human factor IX gene were transplanted under skin flaps in athymic mice, resulting in circulating factor IX for one week after grafting [66]. Increased duration of expression (4–5 weeks) was obtained by using a stronger promoter and a keratinocyte-specific enhancer to drive factor IX expression [67]. In other studies, factor IX-modified keratinocytes were grafted superficially to mice under a silicone transplantation chamber as part of a bilayered skin equivalent consisting of keratinocytes on a collagen matrix [68]. In that study, expression of factor IX was detected in mouse plasma for up to one year after grafting. The authors attributed the longer duration of expression to better design of the recombinant retroviral vector as well as an improved grafting procedure [68]. However, despite advances that lengthened the duration of circulating human factor IX, the levels achieved were not sufficient to provide a therapeutic benefit for treatment of hemophilia. The authors speculated [68] that a larger graft area might increase the plasma level to the required minimum for treatment to convert a patient from a severe to moderate phenotype.

In addition to the potential for systemic gene therapy, genetically modified CSS could hypothetically be used to treat genetic cutaneous defects. A promising candidate disease is lamellar ichthyosis, a disfiguring skin disease characterized by abnormal epidermal differentiation and defective barrier function [69]. The defect in keratinocytes is associated with loss of the enzyme transglutaminase 1. Primary keratinocytes isolated from lamellar ichthyosis patients were genetically modified by transduction with a retroviral vector encoding transglutaminase 1, resulting in restoration of enzyme expression [70]. Modified keratinocytes were seeded on acellular dermis and transplanted to athymic mice. The grafts containing modified patient cells showed normal transglutaminase 1 expression *in vivo*, and had normal epidermal architecture and barrier function. This indicated functional correction of the defect as a result of gene transfer [70]. Junctional epidermolysis bullosa (JEB) is another genetic skin disorder that could benefit from cutaneous gene therapy. JEB is a family of genetic blistering skin diseases resulting from a number of mutations in genes encoding structural proteins of the dermal-epidermal junction. For example, mutation in the beta 3 chain of laminin-5 (LAMB3) results in absence of hemidesmosomes and defective adhesion of epithelia [71]. Gene transfer of a LAMB3 transgene to primary keratinocytes isolated from a LAMB3-deficient JEB patient resulted in restoration of keratinocyte adhesion in cell and organotypic culture [71, 72], demonstrating the potential for cutaneous gene therapy to treat this disorder. Similarly, gene transfer of BP180, a type XVII collagen gene that is involved in another form of JEB, was used to correct the genetic deficiency in patient-derived keratinocytes [73]. Expression of the BP180 gene was restored in human skin substitutes generated with transduced cells after grafting to mice. These studies provide a foundation for future development of gene therapies to treat cutaneous diseases.

Cultured skin substitutes containing both keratinocytes and fibroblasts have several advantages for use in gene therapy studies compared to cultured epidermal autografts or allografts. Because they lack a dermal component, keratinocyte sheets are thin and fragile, and blistering can occur after grafting onto excised burn wounds [7]. These problems are overcome by combining epidermal keratinocytes with a dermal substitute prior to grafting [18, 74, 75]. Blistering, in particular, is decreased or eliminated in composite skin substitutes because the cell-substrate attachments are not enzymatically digested immediately before grafting, as with keratinocyte sheet grafts [75]. Additionally, the presence of fibroblasts seems to improve formation of basement membrane proteins that contribute to attachment of the epidermis [75]. It is likely that fibroblasts also act in a paracrine fashion to regulate epidermalization of the keratinocyte layer. Fibroblasts synthesize and remodel the extracellular matrix, and also secrete factors that stimulate and regulate epidermal growth [76, 77]. In addition to these benefits, the use of cultured skin substitutes composed of both fibroblasts and keratinocytes for gene therapy applications effectively doubles the number of cell types available for genetic manipulation. Like keratinocytes, genetically modified fibroblasts can be easily incorporated into CSS [55]; therefore, the opportunities for genetic modification and subsequent modulation of wound healing are greater than for cultured epidermal grafts.

Cultured skin substitutes will be a valuable vehicle for investigation of gene therapies for the treatment of many different skin disorders, including burns, chronic wounds, and genetic diseases. The human genome project will no doubt result in the identification of numerous candidate molecules for targeted therapies. Thus, the opportunities for intervention in wound healing using genetic engineering will continue to increase. This, combined with continued improvements in the tissue engineering of cultured skin, will lead to the fabrication of skin substitutes more homologous to native human skin and will enhance the efficacy and versatility of CSS for clinical use.

References

[1] *Falanga V:* Chronic wounds: pathophysiologic and experimental considerations. J Invest Dermatol; 100(5):721–725, 1993.

[2] *Boyce ST, Glatter R, Kitzmiller WJ:* Treatment of chronic wounds with cultured skin substitutes: a pilot study. Wounds; 7(1)23–29, 1995.

[3] *Phillips TJ, Gilchrest BA:* Cultured epidermal grafts in the treatment of leg ulcers. Adv Dermatol; 5:33–50, 1990.

[4] *Berthod F, Damour O:* In vitro reconstructed skin models for wound coverage in deep burns. Brit J Dermatol; 136:809–816, 1997.

[5] *Gallico GG:* Biologic skin substitutes. Clin Plast Surg; 17(3):519–526, 1990.

[6] Boyce ST: Cultured skin substitutes: a review. Tissue Engin; 2:255–266, 1996.

[7] *Phillips TJ:* New skin for old: developments in biological skin substitutes. Arch Dermatol; 134:344–349, 1998.

[8] *Barret JP, Wolf SE, Desai MH, Herndon DN:* Cost-efficacy of cultured epidermal autografts in massive pediatric burns. Ann Surg; 231(6): 869–876, 2000.

[9] *Carsin H, Ainaud P, Le Bever H, Rives J, Lakhel A, Stephanazzi J, Lambert F, Perrot J:* Cultured epithelial autografts in extensive burn coverage of severely traumatized patients: a five year single-center experience with 30 patients. Burns; 26(4):379–387, 2000.

[10] *Braye F, Pascal P, Bertin-Maghit M, Colpart JJ, Tissot E, Damour O:* Advantages of using a bank of allogeneic keratinocytes for the rapid coverage of extensive and deep second-degree burns. Med Biol Eng Comput; 38(2): 248–252, 2000.

[11] *Phillips TJ, Bhawan J, Leigh IM, Baum HJ, Gilchrest BA:* Cultured epidermal autografts and allografts: a study of differentiation and allograft survival. J Am Acad Dermatol; 23(2,1): 189–198, 1990.

[12] *Herndon DN:* Perspectives in the use of allograft. J Burn Care Rehabil; 18(1,2):S6, 1997.

[13] *Wainwright D, Madden M, Luterman A, Hunt J, Monafo W, Heimbach D, Kagan R, Sittig K, Dimick A, Herndon D:* Clinical evaluation of an acellular allograft dermal matrix in full-thickness burns. J Burn Care Rehabil; 17:124–136, 1996.

[14] *Stern R, McPherson M, Longaker MT:* Histologic study of artificial skin used in the treatment of full-thickness thermal injury. J Burn Care Rehabil; 11(1):7–13, 1990.

[15] *Soejima K, Nozaki M, Sasaki K, Takeuchi M, Negishi N:* Reconstruction of burn deformity using artificial dermis combined with thin split-skin grafting. Burns; 23(26):501–504, 1997.

[16] *Horch RE, Debus M, Wagner G, Stark GB:* Cultured human keratinocytes on type I collagen membranes to reconstitute the epidermis. Tiss Engin; 6(1):53–67, 2000.

[17] *Horch RE, Bannasch H, Kopp J, Andree C, Stark GB:* Single-cell suspensions of cultured human keratinocytes in fibrin-glue reconstitute the epidermis. Cell Transplantation; 7(3): 309–317, 1998.

[18] *Hansbrough JF, Boyce ST, Cooper ML, Foreman TJ:* Burn wound closure with cultured autologous keratinocytes and fibroblasts attached to a collagen-glycosaminoglycan substrate. JAMA; 262:2125–2130, 1989.

[19] *Boyce ST, Greenhalgh DG, Kagan RJ, Housinger T, Sorrell M, Childress CP, Rieman M, Warden GD:* Skin anatomy and antigen expression after burn wound closure with composite grafts of cultured skin cells and biopolymers. Plast Reconstr Surg; 91:632–641, 1993.

[20] *Kuroyanagi Y, Kenmochi M, Ishihara S, Takeda A, Shiraishi A, Ootake N, Uchinuma E, Torikai K, Shioya N:* A cultured skin substitute composed of fibroblasts and keratinocytes with a collagen matrix: preliminary results of clinical trials. Ann Plast Surg; 31:340–351, 1993.

[21] *Boyce ST, Goretsky MJ, Greenhalgh DG, Kagan RJ, Rieman MT, Warden GD:* Comparative assessment of cultured skin substitutes and native skin autograft for treatment of full-thickness burns. Ann Surgery; 222(6):743–752, 1995.

[22] *Zacchi V, Soranzo C, Cortivo R, Radice M, Brun P, Abatangelo G:* In vitro engineering of human skin-like tissue. J Biomed Mater Res; 40: 187–194, 1998.

[23] *Caruso DM, Schuh WH, Al-Kasspooles MF, Chen MC, Schiller WR:* Cultured composite autografts as coverage for an extensive body surface area burn: case report and review of the technology. Burns; 25(8):771–779, 1999.

[24] *Boyce ST, Kagan RJ, Meyer NA, Yakuboff K, Warden GD:* The 1999 Clinical Research Award: Cultured skin substitutes combined with Integra® to replace native skin autograft and allograft for closure of full-thickness burns. J Burn Care Rehab; 20:453–461, 1999.

[25] *Kumagai N, Oshima H, Tanabe M, Ishida H:* Treatment of giant congenital nevi with cryopreserved allogeneic skin and fresh autologous cultured epithelium. Ann Plast Surg; 39(5):483–488, 1997.

[26] *Simman R, Priebe CJ Jr, Simon M:* Reconstruction of aplasia cutis congenita of the trunk in a newborn infant using acellular allogenic dermal graft and cultured epithelial autografts. Ann Plast Surg; 44(4)451–454, 2000.

[27] *Orgill DP, Butler C, Regan JF, Barlow MS, Yannas IV, Compton CC:* Vascularized collagen-glycosaminoglycan matrix provides a dermal substrate and improves take of cultured epithelial autografts. Plast Reconstr Surg; 102(2): 423–429, 1998.

[28] *Pandya AN, Woodward B, Parkhouse N:* The use of cultured autologous keratinocytes with Integra in the resurfacing of acute burns. Plast Reconstr Surg; 102(3):825–828, 1998.

[29] *Medalie DA, Eming SA, Tompkins RG, Yarmush ML, Krueger GG, Morgan JR:* Evaluation of human skin reconstituted from composite grafts of cultured keratinocytes and human acellular dermis transplanted to athymic mice. J Invest Dermatol; 107:121–127, 1996.

[30] *Compton CC, Butler CE, Yannas IV, Warland G, Orgill DP:* Organized skin structure is regenerated in vivo from collagen-GAG matrices seeded with autologous keratinocytes. J Invest Dermatol; 110:908–916, 1998.

[31] *Horch RE, Bannasch H, Stark GB:* Cultured human keratinocytes as a single cell suspension in fibrin glue combined with preserved dermal grafts enhance skin reconstitution in athymic mice full-thickness wounds. Eur J Plast Surg; 22:237–243, 1999.

[32] *Harriger MD, Warden GD, Greenhalgh DG, Kagan RJ, Boyce ST:* Pigmentation and microanatomy of skin regenerated from composite grafts of cultured cells and biopolymers applied to full-thickness burn wounds. Transplantation; 59:702–707, 1995.

[33] *Boyce ST, Supp AP, Wickett RR, Hoath SB, Warden GD:* Assessment with the dermal torque meter of skin pliability after treatment of burns with cultured skin substitutes. J Burn Care Rehabil; 21:55–63, 2000.

[34] *Boyce, ST, Ham RG:* Calcium-regulated differentiation of normal human epidermal keratinocytes in chemically defined clonal culture and serum-free serial culture. J Invest Dermatol; 81(suppl):33–40, 1983.

[35] *Boyce ST, Ham RG:* Cultivation, frozen storage, and clonal growth of normal human epidermal keratinocytes in serum-free media. J Tissue Cult Meth;9:83–93, 1985.

[36] *Boyce ST:* Methods for the serum-free culture of keratinocytes and transplantation of collagen-GAG-based skin substitutes. In: Morgan JR, Yarmush, ML, eds: Methods in Molecular Medicine: Tissue Engineering Methods and Protocols. Totowa, NJ: Humana Press, Inc; 365–389, 1998.

[37] *Boyce ST, Hansbrough JF:* Biologic attachment, growth, and differentiation of cultured human epidermal keratinocytes on a graftable collagen chondroitin-6-sulfate substrate. Surgery; 103(4):421–431, 1988.

[38] *Young DM, Greulich KM, Weier HG:* Species-specific in situ hybridization with fluorochrome-labeled DNA probes to study vascularization of human skin grafts on athymic mice. J Burn Care Rehabil; 17:305–310, 1996.

[39] *Boyce ST, Harriger MD, Supp AP, Warden GD, Holder IA:* Effective management of microbial contamination in cultured skin substitutes after grafting to athymic mice. Wound Rep Regen; 5:191–197, 1997.

[40] *Boyce ST, Supp AP, Harriger MD, Greenhalgh DG, Warden GD:* Topical nutrients promote

engraftment and inhibit wound contraction of cultured skin substitutes in athymic mice. J Invest Dermatol; 104:345–349, 1995.

[41] *Danos O, Mulligan RC:* Safe and efficient generation of recombinant retroviruses with amphotropic and ecotropic host ranges. Proc Natl Acad Sci USA; 85(17):6460–6464, 1988.

[42] *Rivière I, Sadelain M:* Methods for the construction of retroviral vectors and the generation of high-titer producers. In Robbins PD, ed.: Gene Therapy Protocols. Totowa, NJ: Humana Press, Inc.; 59–78, 1997.

[43] *Rheinwald JG, Green H:* Formation of a keratinizing epithelium in culture by a cloned cell line derived from a teratoma. Cell; 6(3):317–330, 1975.

[44] *Rheinwald JG, Green H:* Serial cultivation of strains of human epidermal keratinocytes: the formation of keratinizing colonies from single cells. Cell; 6(3):331–343, 1975.

[45] *Eming SA, Morgan JR:* Methods for the use of genetically modified keratinocytes in gene therapy. In Robbins PD, ed: Gene Therapy Protocols. Totowa, NJ: Humana Press, Inc; 265–280, 1997.

[46] *Vogt PM, Thompson S, Andree C, Liu P, Breuing K, Hatzis D, Brown H, Mulligan RC, Eriksson E:* Genetically modified keratinocytes transplanted to wounds reconstitute the epidermis. Proc Natl Acad Sci USA; 91:9307–9311, 1994.

[47] *Lynch SE, Colvin RB, Antoniades HN:* Growth factors in wound healing: single and synergistic effects on partial thickness porcine skin wounds. J Clin Invest;84:640–46, 1989.

[48] *Bennett NT, Schultz GS:* Growth factors and wound healing: Part II. Role in normal and chronic wound healing. Am J Surgery;166: 74–81, 1993.

[49] *Brown RL, Breeden MP, Greenhalgh DG:* PDGF and TGF-a act synergistically to improve wound healing in the genetically diabetic mouse. J Surg Res;56:562–70, 1994.

[50] *Beer H-D, Longaker MT, and Werner S:* Reduced expression of PDGF and PDGF receptors during impaired wound healing. J Invest Dermatol;109:132–38, 1997.

[51] *Ansel JC, Tiesman JP, Olerud JE, Krueger JG, Krane JF, Tara DC, Shipley GD, Gilbertson D, Usui ML, Hart CE:* Human keratinocytes are a major source of cutaneous platelet-derived growth factor. J Clin Invest;92:671–78, 1993.

[52] *Heldin C-H, Westermark B:* Role of platelet-derived growth factor in vivo. In Clark RAF ed: The Molecular and Cellular Biology of Wound Repair. New York, NY: Plemum Press; 249–73, 1996.

[53] *Eming SA, Lee J, Snow RG, Tompkins RG, Yarmush ML, Morgan JR:* Genetically modified human epidermis overexpressing PDGF-A directs the development of a cellular and vascular connective tissue stroma when transplanted to athymic mice – implications for the use of genetically modified keratinocytes to modulate dermal regeneration. J Invest Dermatol; 105:756–763, 1995.

[54] *Eming SA, Medalie DA, Tompkins RG, Yarmush ML, Morgan JR:* Genetically modified human keratinocytes overexpressing PDGF-A enhance the performance of a composite skin graft. Hum Gene Ther; 9:529–539, 1998.

[55] *Supp DM, Bell SM, Morgan JM, and Boyce ST:* Genetic modification of cultured skin substitutes by transduction of keratinocytes and fibroblasts with platelet derived growth factor A. Wound Repair Regen; 8:26–35, 2000.

[56] *Supp DM, Supp AP, Bell SM, and Boyce ST:* Enhanced vascularization of cultured skin substitutes genetically modified to overexpress vascular endothelial growth factor. J Invest Dermatol; 114:5–13, 2000.

[57] *Frank S, Hübner G, Breier G, Longaker MT, Greenhalgh DG, Werner S:* Regulation of vascular endothelial growth factor expression in cultured keratinocytes: implications for normal and impaired wound healing. J Biol Chem; 270:12607–12613, 1995.

[58] *Rivard A, Silver M, Chen D, Kearney M, Magner M, Annex B, Peters K, Isner JM:* Rescue of diabetes-related impairment of angiogenesis by intramuscular gene therapy with adeno-VEGF. Am J Pathol; 154:355–363, 1999.

[59] *Gielen V, Faure M, Mauduit G, Thivolet J:* Progressive replacement of human cultured epithelial allografts by recipient cells as evidenced by HLA class I antigens expression. Dermatologica; 175(4):166–170, 1987.

[60] *Brain A, Purkis P, Coates P, Hackett M, Navsaria H, Leigh I:* Survival of cultured allogeneic keratinocytes transplanted to deep dermal bed assessed with probe specific for Y chromosome. BMJ; 298:917–919, 1989.

[61] *Boyce ST:* Epidermis as a secretory tissue. J Invest Dermatol; 102(1): 8–10, 1994.

[62] *Krueger GG, Morgan JR, Jorgensen CM, Schmidt L, Li HL, Kwan MK, Boyce ST, Wiley HS, Kaplan J, Petersen MJ:* Genetically modified skin to treat disease: potential and limitations. J Invest Dermatol; 103:76S–84S, 1994.

[63] *Greenhalgh DA, Rothnagel JA, Roop DR:* Epidermis: an attractive target tissue for gene therapy. J Invest Dermatol; 103:63S–69S, 1994.

[64] *Morgan JR, Barrandon Y, Green H, Mulligan RC:* Expression of an exogenous growth hormone gene by transplantable human epidermal cells. Science; 237:1476–1479, 1987.

[65] *Wang X, Zinkel S, Polonsky K, Fuchs E:* Transgenic studies with a keratin promoter-driven growth hormone transgene: prospects for

gene therapy. Proc Natl Acad Sci USA; 94: 219–226, 1997.

[66] *Gerrard AJ, Hudson DL, Brownlee GG, Watt FM:* Towards gene therapy for haemophilia B using primary human keratinocytes. Nature Gen; 3:180–183, 1993.

[67] *Page SM, Brownlee GG:* An ex vivo keratinocyte model for gene therapy of hemophilia B. J Invest Dermatol; 108:139–145, 1997.

[68] *White SJ, Page SM, Margaritis P, Brownlee GG:* Long-term expression of human clotting factor IX from retrovirally transduced primary human keratinocytes in vivo. Hum Gene Ther; 9:1187–1195, 1998.

[69] *Bale SJ, Doyle SZ:* The genetics of ichthyosis: a primer for epidemiologists. J Invest Dermatol; 102:49S–50S, 1994.

[70] *Choate KA, Medalie DA, Morgan JR, Khavari PA:* Corrective gene transfer in the human skin disorder lamellar ichthyosis. Nature Med; 2(11):1263–1267, 1996.

[71] *Dellambra E, Vailly J, Pellegrini G, Bondanza S, Golisano O, Macchia C, Zambruno G, Meneguzzi G, De Luca M:* Corrective transduction of human epidermal stem cells in laminin-5-dependent junctional epidermolysis bullosa. Hum Gene Ther; 9(9):1359–1370, 1998.

[72] *Vailly J, Gagnoux-Palacios L, Dell'Ambra E, Romero C, Pinola M, Zambruno G, De Luca M, Ortonne JP, Meneguzzi G:* Corrective gene transfer of keratinocytes from patients with junctional epidermolysis bullosa restores assembly of hemidesmosomes in reconstructed epithelia. Gene Ther; 5(10):1322–1332, 1998.

[73] *Seitz CS, Giudice GJ, Balding SD, Marinkovich MP, Khavari PA:* BP180 gene delivery in junctional epidermolysis bullosa. Gene Ther; 6(1): 42–47, 1999.

[74] *Boyce WT, Foreman TJ, English KB, Stayner N, Cooper ML, Sakabu S, Hansbrough JF:* Skin wound closure in athymic mice with cultured human cells, biopolymers, and growth factors. Surgery; 110:866–876, 1991.

[75] *Cooper ML, Andree C, Hansbrough JF, Zapata-Sirvent RL, Spielvogel RL:* Direct comparison of a cultured composite skin substitute containing keratinocytes and fibroblasts to an epidermal sheet graft containing human keratinocytes on athymic mice. J Invest Dermatol; 101:811–819, 1993.

[76] *Coulomb B, Lebreton C, Louis Dubertret L:* Influence of human dermal fibroblasts on epidermalization. J Invest Dermatol; 92:122–125, 1989.

[77] *Smola H, Thiekotter G, Fusenig NE:* Mutual induction of growth factor gene expression by epidermal-dermal cell interaction. J Cell Biol; 122:417–429, 1993.

Keratinocyte-Mediated Cell and Gene Therapy

M. De Luca, L. Guerra, E. Dellambra, G. Pellegrini

Summary

Although some markers for the epidermal stem cell compartment have been proposed, their role in specifically identifying keratinocyte stem cells is still controversial. Therefore, the identification of surface epithelial stem cells relies on either the evaluation of their proliferative capacity or on the identification of slow-cycling, [3H]TdR- and BrdU-retaining cells, the latter being feasible only on laboratory animals. The proliferative capacity of human lining epithelial stem cells can be evaluated *in vitro* by means of clonal analysis. Indeed, three types of keratinocytes with different capacities for multiplication have been identified and isolated in human epidermis, hair follicle, limbal-corneal and conjunctival epithelia, i.e. holoclones, meroclones and paraclones. The authors have recently demonstrated that cultured autografts bearing holoclones can indeed rapidly and permanently cover a large body surface. Preparation of the wound bed and maintenance of epidermal stem cells in culture are found to be crucial to the clinical success of the technology. The implications and clincial results of permanent coverage of massive full-thickness burns, treatment of "stable" vitiligo with cultured epidermal autografts and permanent coverage of damaged ocular surfaces after complete loss of the corneal-limbal epithelium as well as ex vivo gene therapy of junctional epidermiolysis bullosa are reported in this study and literature review. Basic "quality controls" of the culture system may eliminate one important hitherto uncontrolled variable in the evaluation of cultured autograft clinical performance and should represent a starting point for improving epithelial cultivation, in order to achieve satisfactory and reproducible clinical result.

Introduction

Epithelial Stem Cells

Surface epithelia are renewed constantly during the lifetime of an organism. For instance, human epidermis is replaced approximately every month [1], while corneal epithelium is renewed in 9–12 months [2]. To accomplish their self-renewal process, these epithelia (as well as other self-renewing tissues) rely on the presence of stem and transient amplifying cells, which are the only proliferative cells in a normal tissue [3–5]. Stem cells can be defined as cells endowed with a very high (virtually unlimited) self-renewal capacity and the ability to generate differentiated progeny [3–8]. The extensive proliferative capacity, maintained through the lifetime of an organism, is considered the basic and essential characteristic of a stem cell [5]. Transient amplifying cells, which arise from stem cells, have a low proliferative capacity and represent the largest group of dividing cells [3, 4, 6].

Although some markers for the epidermal stem cell compartment have been proposed [9–12], their role in specifically identifying keratinocyte stem cells is still controversial. Therefore, the identification of surface epithelial stem cells relies on either the evaluation of their proliferative capacity [13–18] or on the identification of slow-cycling, [3H]TdR- and BrdU-retaining cells [4, 19–23], the latter being feasible only on laboratory animals. The proliferative capacity of human lining epithelial stem cells can be evaluated *in vitro* by means of clonal analysis [13, 24]. Indeed, three types of keratinocytes with different capacities for multiplication have been identified and isolated in human epidermis, hair follicle [13, 14], limbal-corneal and conjunctival epithelia [18], i.e. holoclones, meroclones and paraclones.

The holoclone has the highest proliferative capacity (being able to undergo up to 200 cell divisions before senescence), and is considered the epidermal stem cell [3, 13, 15–18]. The paraclone is a transient amplifying cell which is committed to a maximum of 15 cell divisions and generates aborted colonies containing only terminally differentiated cells [13]. The meroclone is an intermediate type of cell and is a reservoir of transient amplifying cells [3, 10, 13]. The transition from holoclone to meroclone to paraclone is a unidirectional process which occurs during natural aging as well as during repeated keratinocyte sub-cultivation [3].

One might argue that, since holoclones have been taken from their natural "niche" [4, 14, 19, 25] and forced to undergo rapid proliferation *in vitro*, they have irreversibly lost their "stem-ness", hence they should not be considered as representative of the stem cell compartment. However, permanent epithelial regeneration obtained with cultured keratinocytes in massive full-thickness burns [17, 26–29, see below] and in severe defects of the corneal epithelium [30, see below) gives compelling evidence that stem cells are indeed preserved in culture. Hence, since holoclones are endowed with the highest proliferative potential *in vitro* [13, 17, 18], account for the entire proliferative capacity of the original mass culture destined to transplantation [13, 17, 18], are able to generate a fully differentiated epidermis [15] and can be rescued after grafting (unpublished data), we feel quite confident in considering them as *bona fide* keratinocyte stem cells. The notion of holoclones arising from stem cells has been recently confirmed by the observation that unlimited proliferation can be obtained by forcing keratinocytes into the holoclone compartment [31].

In human skin, holoclones are uniformly distributed in the basal layer of interfollicular epidermis [13], whereas, in the human hair follicle, they are segregated in a specific region of the outer root sheath below the midpoint of the follicle, and also in the matrix [14]. Recently, we identified holoclones in cultured limbal, forniceal and bulbar human ocular epithelia [18]. Interestingly, ocular holoclones have a lower proliferative potential (80–100 doublings) [18] than epidermal holoclones (120–180 doublings) [3, 13–15]. This might reflect the fact that human epidermis is renewed monthly, while the ocular epithelium is renewed every year, and suggests that holoclones can adjust their proliferative potential according to the needs of the tissue of origin. The discrete location of corneal stem cells in the limbus and the absence of cells with proliferative capacity in the central cornea, suggests that corneal epithelium is formed mostly by transient amplifying cells. This gradient of distribution of cells with different capacity for multiplication fits well with the hypothesis of a continuous centripetal migration of limbal stem cell-derived transient amplifying cells, which is governed by a circadian rhythm [32] and is strongly increased in wound healing [21]. Conjunctival keratinocytes give also rise to the the mucin-producing goblet cells, suggesting that both cell types are derived from a common bipotent progenitor [18, 33]. Committment to differentiate into goblet cells occurs relatively late, so that goblet cells are preferentially generated by transient amplifying cells, and the decision of a conjunctival stem cell to generate a goblet cell appears to be dependent upon an intrinsic "cell doubling clock" [18].

Cell Therapy Using Cultured Epithelial Stem Cells

Cell therapy is an emerging therapeutical strategy aimed at replacing or repairing severely damaged tissues with cultured cells [34]. The choice of cells to be propagated in culture strictly depends on the function that is required of the cell after transplantation, in order to assure the persistence and function of the regenerated tissue through the life-span of the patient.

Permanent Coverage of Massive Full-Thickness Burns

Autologous cultured keratinocytes (cultured autografts) have been widely used for the permanent coverage of massive full-thickness burns [17, 26–29, 35 and refs herein], and epidermal regeneration obtained with cultured autografts can be life-saving [17, 26–29, 36–38]. Permanent "take" of cultured autografts has been formally proven by re-expression of site-specific differentiation markers in vivo [39]. By the early 1990s, the initial optimism for this technique declined, mainly because of the poor clinical results that have been consistently reported by different Burn Units [see 40–42 and references herein]. We have recently demonstrated, however, that cultured autografts bearing holoclones can indeed rapidly and permanently cover a large body surface [17]. To our opinion, preparation of the wound bed and maintenance of epidermal stem cells in culture are crucial to the clinical success of the technology.

Control of infection and proper preparation of the wound bed with allogeneic human dermis, a natural substrate for keratinocyte adhesion, growth and proper differentiation, allow a good "take down" of cultured autografts, that is "take" of the cultures at the first clinical evaluation (7–10 days after grafting) [38, 40, 43–47]. The importance of allogeneic dermis in determining the "take" of cultured autografts has been previously highlighted [38, 40, 43–45], and has been recently confirmed [17]. Histology and electron-microscopy indicate that, when keratinocytes are applied onto allogeneic dermis, both rete ridges development and regeneration of anchoring fibrils are accelerated when compared to wound beds devoid of homograft dermis [29, 47], conferring a faster stability to the epithelium. Donor dermis decreases retraction problems and scarring usually observed when keratinocytes are applied directly on the muscular fascia or on granulating tissue [17]. Electron microscopy data also suggest that allodermis is completely remodelled by the host in approximately one year [17]. However, the key aim of the clinical response to the treatment of full-thickness burns with cultured autografts is the ensuing permanent epidermal regeneration ("final take"). Since human epidermis is replaced monthly, the long-term persistence of the regenerated epidermis requires stem cell transplantation, hence a careful control of holoclone maintenance in the cultured autografts. Indeed, it has been recently reported that when cultured autografts bearing holoclones are applied on massive full-thickness burns, the "final take" of keratinocytes can be high (90–100%), reproducible and permanent [17].

Therefore, it is conceivable to speculate that poor clinical performance of cultured autografts might arise from unproperly prepared wound bed and/or from depletion of stem cells in culture. Likewise, an unexplained loss of the cultured autografts after an initial "take down" on a properly prepared wound bed, might arise from depletion of stem cells during cultivation. Loss of epidermal holoclones can be due to:

1. incorrect culture conditions (our unpublished data),
2. environmental damage of the exposed basal layer of cultured grafts,
3. use of new substrates or culture technologies not pre-tested for stem cell preservation.

The latter is of particular importance since several laboratories new culture technologies envisaging cultivation of epidermal cells onto different carriers [for review see 35, 48 and references herein]. Maintenance of stem cells, however, has never been demonstrated in these new culture systems, sharpening the lack of trust to the technology. It should be considered that irreversible holoclone, meroclone, paraclone conversion occurs slowly during natural ageing *in vivo* [3, 13] as well as during serial keratinocyte cultivation *in vitro* [13, 15, 16, 31]. Incorrect culture conditions can irreversibly accelerate clonal evolution, hence can cause a rapid disappearance of stem cells (our unpublished data), rendering the cultured autograft transplantation useless.

Permanent Coverage of Damaged Ocular Surfaces

Complete loss of the corneal-limbal epithelium, as with chemical or thermal injuries, leads to re-epithelialisation by bulbar conjunctival cells [49, 50]. Since conjunctival and corneal-limbus cells are phenotypically distinct [50–52], corneal repair by the conjunctival epithelium is followed by neo-vascularisation, chronic inflammation, recurrent epithelial defects and stromal scarring, hence causing severe discomfort and decrease of the visual acuity [49, 50]. As with allogenic epidermal cells, allogenic limbal epithelium stimulate the host immune response [53]. Therefore, even though penetrating keratoplasty is crucial for the reconstruction of damaged corneal stroma, it promotes authentic corneal re-epithelialisation only if residual autologous limbal epithelial stem cells are present in the injured eye [51, 54]. In the absence of naturally occurring limbal cells, penetrating keratoplasty is therefore destined to failure and corneal re-epithelialisation occurs through the migration of neighbouring conjunctival cells [54].

Unilateral defects of the corneal-limbus epithelium can be restored by the transplantation of limbal grafts taken from the uninjured eye [55]. This procedure, however, requires a large limbal withdrawal from the healthy eye, and it is not possible for severe bilateral lesions. We have recently shown that

1. cultured limbal stem cells generate cohesive sheets of authentic corneal epithelium,
2. autologous cultured corneal epithelium can permanently restore the corneal surface of patients with complete destruction of the limbus,
3. patients can recover their visual acuity as a result of combined penetrating keratoplasty and autologous corneal epithelium transplantation [30].

Conceptually, the use of combined keratoplasty/cultured corneal-limbus cells for the reconstruction of the anterior ocular surface parallels the use of combined allodermis/cultured autografts for the reconstruction of skin in full-thickness burns.

The conjunctival epithelium is populated by goblet cells [56], which are unicellular mucin-secreting glands representing the primary source of the mucin of the tear film [57, 58]. Goblet cells are essential in maintaining the integrity of the ocular surface, since goblet cell-dependent mucin-deficiency has been implicated in various disorders, including ocular cicatricial pemphigoid, Stevens-Johnson syndrome, xerophthalmia and certain sicca syndromes as a result of chronic keratoconjuntivitis [59]. Conjunctival epithelium bearing goblet cells can be reconstituted *in vitro* from stem cells isolated from a tiny biopsy which can be taken not only from the fornix, but from any spared area of the conjunctival surface [18]. The engraftment of cultured sheets of conjunctival epithelium bearing goblet cells may accomplish for the above diseases what has already been accomplished for corneal epithelium by the engraftment of limbal cultures.

Treatment of "Stable" Vitiligo with Cultured Epidermal Autografts

Melanocytes are neural crest-derived cells located mainly in the basal layer of the epidermis and in the matrix of hair follicles [60];

melanocytes synthesize the melanin pigment, transfer mature melanosomes to basal keratinocytes and are therefore responsible for skin color and protection against photocarcinogenesis [60].

Vitiligo is a common idiopathic skin disease [61–66] which affects 1–2% of the world's population, causes selective destruction of melanocytes and leads to the development of achromic lesions [66–70]. The cosmetic disfigurement caused by vitiligo has profound psychological effects on patients and gives rise to serious emotional stress in approximately two thirds of them [71].

Vitiligo is usually "active", i.e. is characterized by progression of old lesions, development of new lesions and appearance of white macules after traumas (Koebner phenomenon) [72]. In patients affected by segmental vitiligo the causative factor(s) usually disappears, thereby leaving well defined achromic lesions [62]. Similarly, generalized vitiligo can enter long phases of clinical quiescence [61–70, 72] in which the size and number of lesions are stationary for several years and the Koebner phenomenon is absent [72]. This stage of the disease is therefore referred to as "stable" vitiligo. Several findings strongly support the view that melanocytes are eventually destroyed in "stable" vitiligo [62].

Distinction between "active" and "stable" phases of the disease is important for selecting the more appropriate therapy. "Active" vitiligo usually requires medical therapy [73, 74]; surgical therapy entails melanocyte transplantation, is demanded when medical therapy fails, and could actually be considered as the first therapeutical choice for the treatment of "stable" vitiligo.

Several methods of autologous melanocyte transplantation have been developed, including suction blister grafts, thin split-thickness skin grafts and minigrafting [see 75, 76 for review]. Complications of these commonly adopted surgical methods can lead to cobblestoned surface, spotty pigmentation or lack of pigmentation of the treated areas as well as to scarring of the donor sites [75]. Transplants of cultured melanocytes

have been proposed as a possible, although still experimental, alternative to conventional surgical methods [75, 76]. Melanocytes can be isolated from a small biopsy, taken from an unaffected area, and cultured *in vitro* [77–79, 80]. Cultured melanocytes can be inoculated as pure cell suspension or in co-culture with keratinocytes, as with cultured epidermal sheets [80, see 75, 76 for review]. However, the amount of data available on the use of cultured melanocytes is still very limited [76], banishing this technology at a developmental stage quite far from routine daily practice.

Recently, we demonstrated that cultured epidermal grafts bearing melanocytes can indeed be considered as a real therapeutical alternative for patients affected by "stable" vitiligo [80]. Our data showed that the success rate of cultured epidermal autografts can be comparable to the highest success rate usually achieved by split-thickness skin grafts or epidermal blister grafts [76], and that repigmentation can be obtained by means of true "take" of cultured melanocytes, as opposed to migration (potentially induced by surgical maneuvers) of resident melanocytes from surrounding skin or from hair follicles [80]. Several considerations convinced us that the use of cultured epidermal sheets is more appropriate than that of pure melanocyte cultures. Indeed,

1. keratinocytes regulate melanocyte growth and differentiation, as well as the proper M/K ratio [77, 78];

2. melanocytes organize themselves into the basal layer of the cultured epidermis, develop dendritic arborization with melanosome-containing processes and transfer melanosomes into basal keratinocytes [77–79], hence melanocytes maintain their physiological characteristics when co-cultured with keratinocytes;

3. keratinocyte cultivation allows the easy production of large quantities of cultured autografts (up to 2 m²) [17, 26–29, 80] in a shorter time than that required for pure melanocyte cultivation;

4. lastly, but most importantly, cultured epidermal grafts have been widely used worldwide since 20 years for the treatment of thousands of patients suffering from large skin and mucosal defects [17, 18, 26–30, 80, 81–83], and it has never been reported an increased risk of either carcinoma or melanoma.

This last consideration is of particular relevance, since the though remote possibility of undesired tumorigenic risks due to cultivation has so far limited the use of pure melanocyte cultures [75, 76].

Large areas of the body can be de-epithelialized by TIMEDsurgery, which allows selective removal of the epidermis from the underlying dermis while maintaining the integrity of dermal papillae [80]. The procedure is carried out in local anesthesia, without bleeding or significant inflammation. When cultured epidermal autografts containing a physiological number of melanocytes are applied onto vitiligo lesions prepared by TIMEDsurgery, complete re-pigmentation can be obtained without any cicatricial outcome [80]. In this case, the maintenance of the proper melanocyte concentration within the epidermal grafts is the most important quality control. Therefore, evaluation of the M/K ratio in culture should be performed routinely before grafting.

Ex Vivo Gene Therapy of Junctional Epidermolysis Bullosa

Basal keratinocytes firmly adhere to the epidermal basement membrane by means of hemidesmosomes, multiprotein complexes linking the epithelial intermediate filament network to the dermal anchoring fibrils [for review see 84, 85]. Hemidesmosome-mediated adhesion relies on the binding of the $\alpha6\beta4$ integrin to laminin-5, a major basal lamina component formed by three distinct polypeptides, $\alpha3$, $\beta3$ and $\gamma2$, encoded by the LAMA3, LAMB3 and LAMC2 genes, respectively [84]. Laminin-5 binds to the basal keratinocyte cell surface through the $\alpha6\beta4$ integrin and tightens the dermal-epidermal junction by binding also to the aminoterminal NC-1 domain of type VII collagen [86]. The crucial importance of laminin-5 and of its receptor in maintaining the integrity of the integument in humans has been confirmed by the identification of gene mutations in patients suffering from junctional epidermolysis bullosa (JEB), a devastating skin blistering disorder. In most cases, JEB is due to mutations in LAMA3, LAMB3 and LAMC2 genes [87–90] and in ITGA6 and ITGB4 genes, which encode alpha and beta integrin subunits, respectively [91, 92]. Mutations in ITGA6 and ITGB4 are usually associated to pyloric atresia (PA-JEB) [91, 92].

Since basal keratinocytes are responsible for the synthesis of all the proteins involved in the dermal-epidermal junction, any attempt at gene therapy of JEB would require the genetic modification of these cells. However, a number of issues need to be addressed before considering gene therapy by genetically-modified keratinocytes. These are:

1. transduction efficiency of the appropriate target cell,
2. long-term expression of the transgene,
3. immunogenicity of the transgene product, and
4. for an ex vivo approach, implantation of a transduced cell graft.

It has been shown that epidermal stem cells can be stably transduced with retroviral constructs expressing different cDNAs, and that the transgene is expressed at constant levels during the entire life-span (more than 150 cell generations) of the stem cell culture [15, 16]. Moreover, optimized retroviral infection ex vivo and appropriate grafting procedures onto athymic animals allow long-term expression of the transgene also in vivo, provided that stem cells are effectively transduced [93–97].

In order to assess whether retroviral-mediated gene transfer could correct laminin-5-dependent JEB, we have recently isolated epidermal keratinocytes from a patient affected by a lethal form of JEB characterized by a homozygous deletion of the LAMB3 gene. *In vitro*, β3-null keratinocytes were unable to synthesize laminin-5 and to assemble hemidesmosomes, maintained the impairment of their adhesive properties, and displayed a decreased colony-forming ability [16]. A retroviral vector expressing a human β3 cDNA was then used to transduce primary β3-null keratinocytes. Clonogenic β3-null cells were transduced with virtually 100% efficiency. Transduced keratinocytes were able to synthesize and secrete mature heterotrimeric laminin-5. Gene correction fully restored the keratinocyte adhesion machinery, including the capacity of proper hemidesmosomal assembly, and prevented the loss of the colony-forming ability, suggesting a direct link between adhesion to laminin-5 and keratinocyte proliferative capacity [10, 98]. Finally, clonal analysis demonstrated that holoclones expressed the transgene permanently, suggesting stable correction of epidermal stem cells [16].

Once the "molecular" feasibility of keratinocyte-mediated gene therapy has been demonstrated, the overall "clinical" feasibility of the ex vivo approach, that is, the surgical procedure to adopt in order to graft transduced keratinocytes back onto patients, becomes a very relevant issue. The skin is the largest organ of the body, and an adult human being is covered by approximately 1.8 m² of epidermis. Based on data generated in the last 15 years [35], it would be certainly possible to cover an entire human being by cultured epidermis. Currently, the composite allodermis/cultured epidermal autograft technique allows the permanent coverage of massive full-thickess skin lesions in approximately two weeks [17]. However, for gene therapy purposes, an invasive surgical procedure invariably destined to leave unacceptable scars on the patient's body cannot be proposed. This umpteenth obstacle has been recently overcome by the development of new, non invasive surgical maneuvers using TIMEDsurgery followed by transplantation of autologous cultured epidermal grafts [80]. This technique allows replacement of natural epidermis

without generating scars, and has been recently adopted for the treatment of vitiligo [80, see above]. Thus, TIMEDsurgery appears to be ideally suited for replacement of JEB epidermis by autologous grafts of genetically-corrected keratinocytes. Moreover, since JEB keratinocytes have severe adhesive defects and impaired proliferative capacity [16], corrected epidermal stem cells could have a selective advantage over resident, defective cells, and eventually replace a fraction of the skin even larger than the actual graft.

Obviously, the next step will be to perform clinical trials in order to validate the *ex vivo* genetic modification of epidermal stem cells in a clinical setting, to prove its overall safety, and to analyze critical issues such as long-term survival of the genetically-modified implant, immune response against the product of the transgene, persistence of transgene expression at therapeutic levels, and possible mobilization of genetically modified stem cells outside the area of the implant.

Conclusions

1. The possibility of cultivating lining epithelia,
2. the availability of surgical protocols that allow to use cultured epithelia to permanently restore massive skin defects or severely damaged ocular surfaces, and to graft large skin areas with non invasive procedure (as in vitiligo patients),
3. the demonstration of sustained transgene expression *in vitro* and in vivo and of stable gene correction of epidermal stem cells, demonstrate that cell therapy is currently feasible, and that *ex vivo* gene therapy might be feasible in the near future.

However, the key issue for the successful clinical outcome of cell (and gene) therapy deals with the "quality control" of the culture system. Unsatisfactory epithelial regeneration from cultured autografts might arise from the depletion of epithelial stem cells in culture. Similarly, failure to achieve long-term gene expression in transduced keratin-ocytes can be attributed to a failure to target epithelial stem cells, while unsatisfactory re-pigmentation of achromic lesions treated with cultured autografts might arise from the absence of the proper melanocyte con-centration within epidermal grafts.

In our opinion, basic "quality controls" of the culture system eliminate one important hitherto uncontrolled variable in the evalua-tion of cultured autograft clinical perform-ance and should represent a starting point for improving epithelial cultivation, in order to achieve satisfactory and reproducible clin-ical results.

References

[1] *Green H:* The keratinocyte as differentiated cell type. Harvey Lect. 74: 101–139, 1980

[2] *Wagoner M D:* Chemical injuries of the eye: current concepts in pathophysiology and therapy. Surv. Ophthalmol. 41: 275–313, 1997

[3] *Barrandon Y:* The epidermal stem cell: an overview. Develop. Biol. 4:209–215, 1993

[4] *Lavker R M, Miller S, Wilson C, Cotsarelis G, Wei Z-G, Yang J-S, and Sun T-T:* Hair follicle stem cells: their location, role in hair cycle, and in-volvment in skin tumor formation. J. Invest. Dermatol. (Suppl.). 101:16S–26S, 1993

[5] *Morrison S J, Shah N M, and Anderson D J:* Reg-ulatory mechanisms in stem cell biology. Cell. 88: 287–298, 1997

[6] *Lajtha L G:* Stem cell concepts. Differentia-tion. 14:23–34, 1979

[7] *Watt F M and Hogan B L M:* Out of eden: stem cells and their niches. Science. 287:1427–1430, 2000

[8] *Fuchs E and Segre J A:* Stem cells: a new lease on life. Cell. 100: 143–155, 2000

[9] *Zieske J D, Bukusogiu G, and Yankauckas M A:* Alpha-enolase is restricted to basal cells of stratified squamous epithelium. Dev. Biol. 151:18–26,1992

[10] *Jones P H, and Watt F M:* Separation of hu-man epidermal stem cells from transient amplifying cells on the basis of differences in integrin function and expression. Cell. 73:713–724, 1993

[11] *Li A, Simmons P J, and Kaur P:* Identifica-tion and isolation of candidate human keratino-cyte stem cells based on cell surface pheno-type. Proc. Natl. Acad. Sci. USA. 95:3902–3907, 1998

[12] *Zhu A J and Watt F M:* Beta catenin signalling modulates proliferative potential of human epidermal keratinocytes independently of intercellular adhesion. Development. 127: 2285–2298, 1999

[13] *Barrandon Y, and Green H:* Three clonal types of keratinocytes with different capacities for multiplication. Proc. Natl. Acad. Sci. USA. 84:2302–2306, 1987

[14] *Rochat A, Kobayashi K, and Barrandon Y:* Lo-cation of stem cells of human hair follicles by clonal analysis. Cell. 76: 1063–1073, 1994

[15] *Mathor M B, Ferrari G, Dellambra E, Cilli M, Mavilio F, Cancedda R, and De Luca M:* Clonal analysis of stably transduced human epider-mal stem cells in culture. Proc. Natl. Acad. Sci. USA. 93:10371–10376, 1996

[16] *Dellambra E, Vailly J, Pellegrini G, Bondanza S, Golisano O, Macchia C, Zambruno G, Meneguzzi G, and De Luca M:* Corrective transduction of human epidermal stem cells in laminin-5-dependent junctional epider-molysis bullosa. Hum. Gene Ther. 9:1359–1370, 1998

[17] *Pellegrini G, Ranno R, Stracuzzi G, Bondanza S, Guerra L, Zambruno G, Micali G, and De Luca M:* The control of epidermal stem cells (holoclones) in the treatment of massive full-thickness burns with autologous kera-tinocytes cultured on fibrin. Transplanta-tion. 68: 868–879, 1999

[18] *Pellegrini G, Golisano O, Paterna P, Lambiase A, Bonini S, Rama P and De Luca M:* Location and clonal analysis of stem cells and their dif-ferentiated progeny in the human ocular sur-face. J. Cell Biol. 145:769–782, 1999

[19] *Cotsarelis G, Cheng S-Z, Dong G, Sun T-T, and Lavker R M:* Existence of slow-cycling lim-bal epithelial basal cells that can be prefer-entially stimulated to proliferate: implica-tions on epithelial stem cells. Cell. 57:201–209, 1989

[20] *Cotsarelis G, Sun T-T, and Lavker R M:* Label-retaining cells reside in the bulge area of pi-losebaceous unit: implications for follicular stem cells, hair cycle, and skin carcinogene-sis. Cell. 61:1329–1337, 1990

[21] *Lehrer M S, Sun T-T, and Lavker R M:* Strategies of epithelial repair: modulation of stem cell and transient amplyfing cell proliferation. J. Cell Sci. 111:2867–2875, 1998

[22] *Schermer A, Galvin S, and Sun T-T:* Differenti-ation-related expression of a major corneal keratin in vivo and in culture suggests limbal location of corneal epithelial stem cells. J. Cell Biol. 103:49–62, 1986

[23] *Wei Z-G, Cotsarelis G, Sun T-T, and Lavker R M:* Label-retaining cells are preferentially located in the forniceal epithelium: implications on

conjunctival epithelial homeostasis. Invest. Ophthalmol. Vis. Sci. 36: 236–246, 1995

[24] *Rheinwald J G, and Green H:* Serial cultivation of strains of human epidermal keratinocytes: the formation of keratinizing colonies from single cells. Cell. 6:331–344, 1975

[25] *Potten C S, and Loeffler M:* Stem cells: attributes, cycles, spirals, pitfalls and uncertainties. Lessons for and from the crypt. Development. 110:1001–1020, 1990

[26] *O'Connor N E, Mulliken J B, Banks-Schlegel S, Kehinde O, and Green H:* Grafting of burns with cultured epithelium prepared from autologous epidermal cells. Lancet. i:75–78, 1981

[27] *Gallico G G, O'Connor N E, Compton C C, Kehinde O, and Green H:* Permanent coverage of large burn wounds with autologous cultured human epithelium. N. Engl. J. Med. 311: 448–451, 1984

[28] *De Luca M, Albanese E, Bondanza S, Megna M, Ugozzoli I, Molina F, Cancedda R, Santi P L, Bormioli M, Stella M, and Magliacani G:* Multicentre experience in the treatment of burns with autologous and allogenic cultured epithelium, fresh or preserved in a frozen state. Burns. 15: 303–309, 1989

[29] *Compton C C, Gill J M, Bradford D A, Regauer S, Gallico G G, and O'Connor N E:* Skin regenerated from cultured epithelial autografts on full-thickness burn wounds from 6 days to 5 years after grafting. A light, electron microscopic and immunohistochemical study. Lab. Invest. 60:600–612, 1989

[30] *Pellegrini G, Traverso C E, Franzi A T, Zingirian M, Cancedda R, and De Luca M:* Long-term restoration of damaged corneal surfaces with autologous cultivated corneal epithelium. Lancet. 349:990–993, 1997

[31] *Dellambra E, Golisano O, Bondanza S, Siviero E, Lacal P, Molinari M, D'Atri S, and De Luca M:* Downregulation of 14-3-3s prevents clo-nal evolution and leads to immortalization of primary human keratinocytes. J Cell Biol. 149:1117–1129, 2000

[32] *Lavker R M, Dong G, Cheng S Z, Kudoh K, Cotsarelis G, and Sun T-T:* Relative proliferative rates of limbal and corneal epithelia. Implications of corneal epithelial migration, circadian rhythm, and suprabasally located DNA-synthesizing keratinocytes. Invest. Ophthalmol. Vis. Sci. 32:1864–1875, 1991

[33] *Wei Z-G, Lin T, Sun T-T, and Lavker R M:* Clonal analysis of the in vivo differentiation potential of keratinocytes. Invest. Ophthalmol. Vis. Sci. 38: 753–761, 1997

[34] *Gage FH:* Cell therapy. Nature; 392 (supp): 18–24, 1998

[35] *Pellegrini G, Bondanza S, Guerra L, and De Luca M:* Cultivation of human keratinocyte stem cells: current and future clinical application. Cell. Eng. 36:1–13, 1998

[36] *Odessey R:* Addendum: multicenter experience with cultured epidermal autograft for treatment of burns. J Burn Care Rehabil. 13:174–180, 1992

[37] *Still J M, Orlet H K, Law E J:* Use of cultured epidermal autografts in the treatment of large burns. Burns. 20:539–541, 1994

[38] *Munster A M:* Cultured skin for massive burns. A prospective, controlled trial. Ann Surg. 224:372–377, 1996

[39] *Compton C C, Nadire K B, Regauer S, Simon M, Warland G, O'Connor N E, Gallico G G, and Landry D B:* Cultured human sole-derived keratinocyte grafts re-express site-specific differentiation after transplantation. Differentiation. 64:45–53, 1998

[40] *Nguyen T T, Gilpin D A, Meyer N A, Herndon D N:* Current treatment of severely burned patients. Ann Surg. 223:14–25, 1996

[41] *Munster A M:* Wither skin replacement? Burns. 23:1, 1997

[42] *Choucair M M, Phillips T J:* What is new in clinical research in wound healing. Dermatol Clin. 15:45–58, 1997

[43] *Cuono C, Langdon R, and McGuir J:* Use of cultured epidermal autografts and dermal allografts as skin replacement after burn injury. Lancet. i: 1123–1124, 1986

[44] *Cuono C B, Langdon R, Birchall N, Barttelbort S and McGuire J:* Composite autologous-allogenic skin replacement: development and clinical application. Plast Reconstr Surg. 80: 626–635, 1987

[45] *Hickerson W L, Compton C C, Fletchall S, and Smith L R:* Cultured epidermal autografts and allodermis combination for permanent burn wound coverage. Burns. 20:S52–S56, 1994

[46] Nave M. 1992. Wound bed preparation: approaches to replacement of dermis. J Burn Care Rehabil. 13: 147–153.

[47] *Compton C C, Hickerson W, Nadire K, and Press W:* Acceleration of skin regeneration from cultured epithelial autografts by transplantation to homograft dermis. J Burn Care Rehabil. 14:653–662, 1993

[48] *Phillips T J:* New skin for old: developments in biological skin substitutes. Arch Dermatol. 134:344–349, 1998

[49] *Dua H, and Forrester J V:* The corneoscleral limbus in human corneal epithelial wound healing. Am. J. Ophthalmol. 110:646–656, 1990

[50] *Tsai R J-F, Sun T-T, Tseng S C G:* Comparison of limbal and conjunctival autograft transplantation in corneal surface reconstruction in rabbits. Ophthalmology. 97:446–455, 1990

[51] *Wei Z-G, Wu R L, Lavker R M, and Sun T-T: In vitro* growth and differentiation of rabbit bul-

bar, fornix, and palpebral conjunctival epithelia: implications on conjunctival epithelia transdifferentiation and stem cells. Invest. Ophthalmol. Vis. Sci. 34:1814–1828, 1993

[52] Wei Z-G, Sun T-T, and Lavker R M: Rabbit conjunctival and corneal epithelial cells belong to two separate lineages: further evidence against the "transdifferentiation" theory. Invest. Ophthalmol. Vis. Sci. 37:523–533, 1996

[53] Tsai R J F, Tseng S C G: Human allograft limbal transplantation for corneal surface reconstruction. Cornea. 13:389–400, 1994

[54] Kruse F E, Cheng J J Y, Tsai R J F, Tseng S C G: Conjunctival transdifferentiation is due to incomplete removal of limbal basal epithelium. Invest Ophthalmol Vis Sci. 31:1903–1913, 1990

[55] Kenyon K R, Tseng S C G: Limbal autograft transplantation for ocular surface disorders. Ophthalmology. 96:709–723, 1989

[56] Friend J, and Kenyon K R: Physiology of the conjunctiva: metabolism and biochemistry. In Smolin, G., Thoft, R.A., eds. The cornea. Scientific Foundation and clonical practice. Boston: Little, Brown. 16–38, 1987

[57] Dilly P N: Structure and function of the tear film. In Sullivan, D.A., ed. Lacrimal gland, tear film, and dry eye syndromes. New York: Plenum Press. 239–247, 1994

[58] Tiffany J M: Composition and biophysical properties of the tear film: knowledge and uncertainty. In Sullivan, D.A., ed. Lacrimal gland, tear film, and dry eye syndromes. New York: Plenum Press. 231–238, 1994

[59] Tseng S C G, Hirst L W, Maumenee A D, Kenyon K R, Sun T-T, and Green W R: Possible mechanism for the loss of goblet cells in mucin-dedicient disorders. Ophthalmology. 91:545–552, 1984

[60] Quevedo Jr W C, Fitzpatrick T B, Szabò G and Jimbow K: Biology of melanocytes. In: Fitzpatrick T.B., Eisen A.Z., Wolff K., Freedberg I.M., Austen K.F. (eds): Dermatology in General Medicine'. McGraw-Hill Inc, New York, 3rd ed. 224–251, 1987

[61] Ortonne J-P and Bose S K: Vitiligo: where do we stand? Piment Cell Res. 6:61–72, 1993

[62] Norris D A, Horikawa T, and Morelli J G: Melanocyte destruction and repopulation in vitiligo. Pigment Cell Res. 7:193–203, 1994

[63] Castanet J and Ortonne J-P: Pathophysiology of vitiligo. Clin Dermatol. 15:845–851, 1997

[64] Le Poole I C and Das P K: Microscopic changes in vitiligo. Clin Dermatol. 15:863–873, 1997

[65] Nordlund J J and Majumder P P: Recent investigations on vitiligo vulgaris. Dermatol Clin. 15: 69–78, 1997

[66] Kovacs S O: Vitiligo. J Am Acad Dermatol. 38: 647–666, 1998

[67] Grimes P E: Vitiligo. An overview of therapeutic approaches. Dermatol Clin. 11: 325–338, 1993

[68] Nordlund J J, Halder R M and Grimes P: Management of vitiligo. Dermatol Clin. 11: 27–33, 1993

[69] Le Poole C and Boissy R E: Vitiligo. Semin Cut Med Surg. 16:3–14, 1997

[70] Jimbow K: Vitiligo. Therapeutic advances. Dermatol Clin. 16:399–407, 1998

[71] Hautmann G and Panconesi E: Vitiligo: a psychologically influenced and influencing disease. Clin Dermatol. 15:879–890, 1997

[72] Njoo M D, Das P K, Bos J D, and Westerhof W: Association of the Kobner phenomenon with disease activity and therapeutic reponsiveness in vitiligo vulgaris. Arch Dermatol. 135: 407–413, 1999

[73] Drake L A, Dinehart S M, Farmer E R, Goltz R W, Graham G F, Hordinsky M K, Lewis C W, Pariser D M, Skouge J W, Chanco Turner M L, Webster S B, Whitaker D C, and Lowery B J: Guidelines of care for vitiligo. J Am Acad Dermatol. 35:620–626, 1996

[74] Njoo M D, Spuls P I, Bos J D, Westerhof W, and Bossuyt P M M: Nonsurgical repigmentation therapies in vitiligo. Meta-analysis of the literature. Arch Dermatol. 134: 1532–1540.

[75] Falabella R: Surgical therapies for vitiligo. Clin Dermatol. 15:927–939, 1998, 1997

[76] Njoo M D, Westerhof W, Bos J D, and Bossuyt P M M: A systematic review of autologous transplantation methods in vitiligo. Arch Dermatol. 134:1543–1549, 1998

[77] De Luca M, Franzi A T, D'Anna F, Zicca A, Albanese E, Bondanza S, Cancedda R: Coculture of human keratinocytes and melanocytes: differentiated melanocytes are physiologically organized in the basal layer of the cultured epithelium. Eur J Cell Biol. 46:176–180, 1988

[78] De Luca M, D'Anna F, Bondanza S, Franzi A T and Cancedda R: Human epithelial cells induce human melanocyte growth in vitro but only skin keratinocytes regulate its proper differentiation in the absence of dermis. J Cell Biol. 107:1919–1926, 1988

[79] De Luca M, Bondanza S, Di Marco E, Marchisio P C, D'Anna F, Franzi A T and Cancedda R: Keratinocyte-melanocyte interactions in in vitro reconstituted normal human epidermis. In: Leigh I., Lane B. and Watt F. (Eds): 'The Keratinocyte Handbook', (Cambridge Univerity Press, Cambridge, UK). 95–108, 1994

[80] Guerra L, Capurro S, Melchi M, Primavera G, Bondanza S, Cancedda R, Luci A, De Luca M, and Pellegrini G: Treatment of "stable" vitiligo by Timedsurgery and transplantation of cultured epidermal autografts. Arch. Dermatol 136: 1380–1389, 2000

[81] *De Luca M, Albanese E, Megna M, Cancedda R, Mangiante P E, Cadoni A, and Franzi A T:* Evidence that human oral epithelium reconstituted *in vitro* and transplanted onto patients with defects in the oral mucosa retains properties of the original donor site. Transplantation. 50:454–459, 1990

[82] *Romagnoli G, De Luca M, Faranda F, Brandelloni R, Franzi A T, Cataliotti F, Cancedda R:* Treatment of posterior hypospadias by the autologous graft of cultured urethral epithelium. New Engl J Med. 323:527–530, 1990

[83] *Romagnoli G, De Luca M, Faranda F, Franzi A T and Cancedda R:* One-step treatment of proximal hypospadias by the autologous graft of cultured urethral epithelium. J Urol. 150: 1204–1207, 1993

[84] *Christiano A M and Uitto J:* Molecular complexity of the cutaneous basement membrane zone. Exp. Dermatol. 5:1–11, 1996

[85] *Borradori L and Sonnenberg A:* Structure and function of hemidesmosomes: more than simple adhesion complexes. J. Invest. Dermatol. 112:411–418, 1999

[86] *Rousselle P, Keene D R, Ruggiero F, Champliaud M F, Van Der Rest M and Burgeson R E:* Laminin-5 binds the NC-1 domain of type VII collagen. J. Cell Biol. 138:719–728, 1997

[87] *Aberdam D, Galliano M F, Vailly J, Pulkkinen L, Bonifas J, Christiano A M, Tryggvason K, Uitto J, Epstein E H, Ortonne J P and Mene-guzzi G:* Herlitz's junctional epidermolysis bullosa is linked to mutations in the gene (LAMC2) for the g2 subunit of nicein/kalinin (LAMININ-5). Nat. Genet. 6: 299–304, 1994

[88] *Pulkkinen L, Christiano A M, Gerecke D, Wagman D W, Burgeson R E, Pittelkow M R and Uitto J:* A homozygous nonsense mutation in the b3 chain gene of laminin-5 (LAMB 3) in Herlitz junctional epidermolysis bullosa. Genomics 24:357–360, 1994

[89] *Vidal F, Baudoin C, Miquel C, Galliano M-F, Christiano A M, Uitto J, Ortonne J-P and Meneguzzi G:* Cloning of the laminin _3 chain and identification of a homozygous deletion in a patient with Herlitz junctional epidermolysis bullosa. Genomics. 30:273–280, 1995

[90] *Vailly J, Pulkkinen L, Miquel C, Christiano A M, Gerecke D, Burgeson R E, Uitto J, Ortonne J P, Meneguzzi G:* Identification of a homozygous one base-pair deletion in exon 14 of the LAMB3 gene in a patient with Herlitz junctional epidermolysis bullosa and prenatal diagnosis in a family at risk for recurrence. J. Invest. Dermatol. 104:462–466, 1995

[91] *Vidal F, Aberdam D, Miquel C, Christiano A M, Pulkkinen L, Uitto J, Ortonne J-P and Meneguzzi G:* Integrin b4 mutations associated with junctional epidermolysis bullosa with pyloric atresia. Nat. Genet. 10:229–234, 1995

[92] *Ruzzi L, Gagnoux-Palacios L, Pinola M, Belli S, Meneguzzi G, D'Alessio M and Zambruno G:* A homozygous mutation in the integrin a6 gene in junctional epidermolysis bullosa with pyloric atresia. J. Clin. Invest. 99:2826–2831, 1997

[93] *Deng H, Lin Q and Khavari P A:* Sustainable cutaneous gene delivery. Nat. Biotech. 15:1388–1391, 1997

[94] *Ng R L H, Woodward B, Bevan S, Green C and Martin R:* Retroviral marking identifies grafted autologous keratinocytes in porcine. J. Invest. Dermatol. 108:457–462, 1997

[95] *Levy L, Broad S, Zhu A J, Carrol J M, Khazaal I, Peault B and Watt, F M:* Optimised retroviral infection of human epidermal keratinocytes: long-term expression of transduced integrin gene following grafting on to SCID mice. Gene Ther. 5:913–922, 1998

[96] *Kolodka T M, Garlick J A and Taichman L B:* Evidence for keratinocyte stem cells *in vitro*: long term engraftment and persistence of transgene expression from retrovirus-transduced keratinocytes. Proc. Natl. Acad. Sci. USA. 95:4356–4361, 1998

[97] *White S J, Page S M, Margaritis P and Brownlee G G:* Long-term expression of human clotting factor IX from retrovirally transduced primary human keratinocytes in vivo. Hum. Gene Ther. 9:1187–1195, 1998

[98] *Watt F M:* Epidermal stem cells: markers, patterning and the control of cell fate. Phil. Trans. R. Soc. Lond. B. 353:831–837, 1998

Possible Influence Upon Granulation Tissue Maturation by Vanadate and Implication on Grafted Cultured Skin Substitution

H. P. Ehrlich

Summary

The composition of the graft bed for the placement of keratinocyte grafts is important for the success of those grafts. The modulation of the graft bed (healing full excision wounds in rats) was investigated. Rats ingesting drinking water spiked with vanadate, an inhibitor of tyrosine-phosphate phosphatases, were compared to rats ingesting saline. Closure of open wounds by wound contraction, differences in quality of deposited granulation tissue and gains in wound breaking strength were measured.

The rate of closure of open wounds and amount of granulation tissue deposited in treated and control rats were identical. Histologically, polarized light microscopy and electron microscopy showed that vanadate ingestion induced the deposition of highly ordered collagen fiber bundle arrays. Associated with the ingestion of vanadate and the deposition of more uniformly organized collagen fiber was a doubling of wound breaking strength at 7 days. Myofibroblasts, specialized fibroblasts of granulation tissue, are identified by α smooth muscle (SM) actin positive stress fibers. By immunohistology vanadate treated rat granulation tissue was devoid of myofibroblasts expressing α SM actin while controls had myofibroblasts, α SM actin expressing fibroblasts. These findings were confirmed by Western-blot analysis.

By electron microscopy, control wounds contained myofibroblasts associated with collagen fiber bundles organized in random arrays. Wounds of vanadate treated rats had unencumbered fibroblasts associated with neatly ordered, parallel collagen fiber bundle arrays. The conclusions are 1) myofibroblasts are not required for wound contraction; 2) in the absence of myofibroblasts, collagen fiber bundles are packed in more ordered arrays; 3) the differentiation of fibroblasts into myofibroblasts is dependent upon the dephosphorylation of select tyrosine phosphate residues.

Introduction

The goals of the keratinocyte graft are to rapidly close an open wound and prevent abnormal scarring. The graft bed, where transplanted keratinocytes are placed contains an underlying connective tissue matrix. That underlying connective tissue matrix is a product of the repair process. A high cell density, a high concentration of capillaries and randomly organized fine collagen fiber bundles, characterizes granulation tissue of open wound repair. A modest number of cells, nominal vascular density and randomly arranged parallel arrays of collagen fiber bundles of variable diameters characterize the underlying matrix of a grafted open wound. In contrast, normal dermis has a modest cell density, moderate vasculature and thick collagen fiber bundle arrays of equal diameters organized in a basket-weave pattern. With few exceptions, dermal loss results in its replacement with poorly organized scar. The placement of a keratinocyte graft will not induce the regeneration of a new dermis. The assumption is made that the more dermal-like the underlying matrix the more skin-like the tissue-engineered skin replacement. Here the effect of vanadate on the character of granulation tissue is presented.

In vivo the quantity of scar deposited in full excisional wounds in rats is limited because of wound contraction, where normal skin is pulled into the defect. Normal skin fills the contracted healed skin wound. The pulling of skin into the defect is through forces created by the continuing reorganization of the collagen fibers by granulation tissue [1]. The role of a specialized fibroblast, the myofibroblast, generating the forces required for organizing granulation tissue collagen is questioned. It is proposed that the contraction of myofibroblasts neither produce the forces responsible for wound contraction nor are responsible for the maturation of granulation tissue into scar. The organization of collagen is though the translocation of collagen fibers by tractional forces generated by fibroblasts [1].

Cell crawling is required for the migration of fibroblasts into the wound site during the early proliferative phase of repair. One cytoskeletal feature of cell crawling requires the polymerization of a portion of cell's actin into a network of filaments at the leading edge of the cell. Another portion of actin filaments is located within the cytoplasm of the cell. That actin is arranged in microfilaments of an ambulatory fibroblast [2]. In sedentary fibroblasts the microfilaments are arranged in stress fibers. Actin bundles of stress fibers demonstrate minimal branching and terminate in the focal adhesion plaque structures at the cell's plasma membrane. Focal adhesion plaques contain a number of proteins that are involved in cell signaling [3]. Tyrosine phosphorylation and dephosphorylation of proteins within focal adhesions play a role in the organization of the cytoskeleton as well as transferring information between the cell and the extracellular matrix [4]. When a cell is anchored to a rigid substratum, the cell maintains tension on that substrate by developing a cytoskeleton composed of prominent focal adhesion plaques linked to cytoplasmic stress fibers [5].

The appearance of myofibroblasts in established granulation tissue may represent a change in the phosphorylation state of select tyrosine residues of key proteins. The presence or level of tyrosine-phosphorylated proteins may influence the generation of stress fibers and/or expression of α SM actin. Vanadate is a potent inhibitor of a group of phosphatases that specifically dephosphorylate tyrosine-phosphate residues. It is proposed that in the presence of vanadate the turnover of tyrosine phosphate residues will be altered. The possibility of modulating the wound healing process through the ingestion of vanadate is examined. Possibilities addressed include:

1. is tyrosine phosphate turnover involved in the appearance of myofibroblasts;
2. are myofibroblasts critical for wound contraction;
3. are there differences between fibroblasts and myofibroblasts at organizing collagen and
4. does the organization of collagen fiber bundles affect the gain in wound breaking strength?

Methods

Adult male Sprague Dawley rats (375 to 400 g) were weighed then placed in one of two treatment groups. Vanadate treated rats received sodium vanadate in their drinking water at 0.2 mg/ml in physiological saline. Control rats received physiological saline in place of drinking water. Vanadate or saline drinking water regiments were continued for 1 week with incisional wounds and for 2 weeks with implants and wound contraction studies. The salted water was necessary to make the vanadate palatable. Unlike other animals, rats tolerate the chronic ingestion of saline in place of water.

The set of rats having sponge implants and open wounds were anesthetized. On the dorsum of each rat, 4 square, full thickness, excisional wounds (15 mm on each side) were made, their edges tattooed and photographed with a ruler in place. A single incision was made on the abdomen, subcutaneous pockets were produced on each side of the midline, and PVA sponge disks (3 mm thick by 12 mm diameter) were placed in the subcutaneous pockets. The incisional wound was closed with staples and each rat returned to his cage, where he continued on the drinking water regimen for 2 additional weeks.

Another set of rats was anesthetized and two 6 cm incisions made 1 cm from and parallel to the spine. The wounds were closed with a continuous stitch using 3-0 stainless steel suture and the incisions were left undressed. Each rat was returned to his cage and remained on the drinking water regimen for 7 more days.

At the end of the post operative healing period, the rats were killed, their weights recorded, and the open wounds photographed with a ruler in place. The incisional wound sutures were carefully removed, and the entire incisional wound was excised with the inclusion of a margin of 1.5 cm of surrounding skin. The excised wound strip was cut into 0.5 cm by 3 cm segments. Cut segments were immediately tested in a Rheometer tensiometer (Diastron, Ltd., UK) to determine wound breaking strength. The open wounds and sponge implants were harvested. One half of the implants were processed for biochemical analysis and the other half processed for histological analysis.

The samples selected for histological analysis were either fixed for paraffin sectioning, light microscopy; frozen for cryosectioning, immunohistology; or fixed for transmission electron microscopy (TEM) [6, 7]. Paraffin sections were processed for hematoxylin and eosin (H&E) staining and Sirius red [6]

staining. Cryosections 4 μ to 6 μ thick were incubated with mouse monoclonal anti-α SM actin primary antibody, followed by fluorescein-conjugated anti-mouse IgG secondary antibody. The same sections were incubated with rhodamine conjugated phalloidin (rh-phalloidin) to demonstrate filamentous actin. The tissues processed for TEM analysis were fixed, stained with 1% aqueous uranium acetate, embedded in Spurs resin, sectioned and viewed on a Phillips 400 Electron Microscope.

Tissue samples for biochemical analyses were homogenized in SDS lysis buffer. Equal aliquots of soluble protein were separated by SDS polyacrylamide gel electrophoresis. The proteins were transferred to a PVDF membrane and sequentially immuno-blotted with antibodies directed to α SM actin, vinculin or β actin.

Results

Control rats gained 21 ± 5 g of body weight and the vanadate treated group gained 15 ± 3 g after 3 weeks on their drinking water regiments. Based upon the Student t test, there were no statistical weight gain differences between the 2 groups. During the 2 week healing period, wound contraction was responsible for a 75 % decrease in area of full excisional wounds in both treatment groups. Systemic vanadate had no effect upon wound contraction. Fig. 1 shows representative wounds made on the backs of rats from the two experimental groups, at 0 time and 2 weeks post wounding.

The 2 week old PVA sponge implants net weight gains were 63 ± 36 mg for controls and 77 ± 40 mg for vanadate treated rats. There was no statistical difference between sponge implant wet weights harvested from control or treated rats. The ingestion of vanadate did not alter the whole body weight gain, the rate of wound contraction nor the amount of granulation tissue deposited in PVA sponge implants.

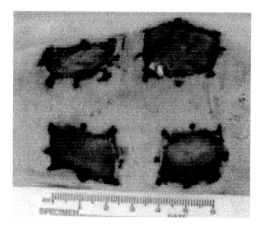

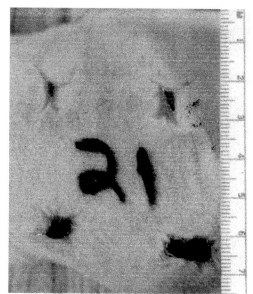

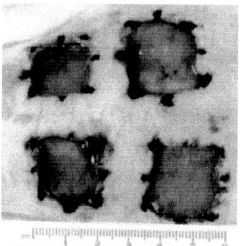

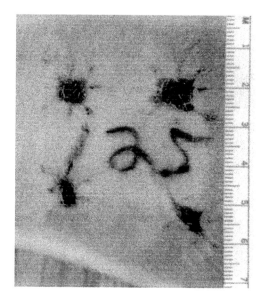

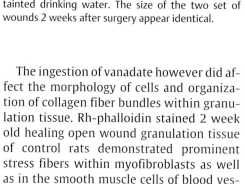

Fig. 1: Wound contraction at 2 weeks. The left column of the figure shows open wounds that were tattooed immediately after wounding. The right column shows those same wounds 2 weeks later. The top row shows rat #21 maintained on saline (controls) and the bottom row shows rat #125 maintained on vanadate tainted drinking water. The size of the two set of wounds 2 weeks after surgery appear identical.

The ingestion of vanadate however did affect the morphology of cells and organization of collagen fiber bundles within granulation tissue. Rh-phalloidin stained 2 week old healing open wound granulation tissue of control rats demonstrated prominent stress fibers within myofibroblasts as well as in the smooth muscle cells of blood vessels. In contrast, the rh-phalloidin stained healing open wound granulation tissue at the same time point from vanadate treated rats were void of cells with prominent stress fibers, myofibroblasts. However, rh-phalloidin stained stress fibers were present in smooth muscle cells of blood vessels in the same histological sections. Vanadate blocked

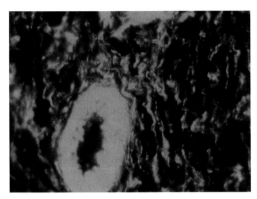 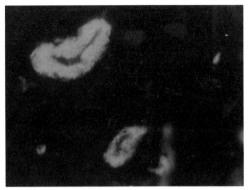

Fig. 2: Frozen sections of healing open wounds stained for α SM actin. The histology of the wound on the left is from a control showing α SM actin stained stress fibers in myofibroblasts and in smooth muscle cells within blood vessels (magnification 200 times)

The histology on the right is from a wound of a vanadate treated rat showing α SM actin staining limited to blood vessel smooth muscle cells (magnification 100 times). Fibroblasts in the granulation tissue of vanadate treated rats do not become myofibroblasts.

the development of stress fibers forming in myofibroblasts but not in the smooth muscle cells of blood vessels.

Myofibroblasts, specialized fibroblasts initially described in contracting rat wounds, have been characterized by prominent cytoplasmic stress fibers containing α SM actin [8, 9]. Stress fibers with α SM actin were readily identified in granulation tissue from control rats, where both myofibroblasts and smooth muscle cells were stained, see Fig. 2A. Granulation tissue from vanadate treated rats had α SM actin stained stress fibers limited to smooth muscle cells of blood vessels, see Fig. 2B. There were no fibroblasts positive for α SM actin, myofibroblasts, in granulation tissue of vanadate treated rats. Though the degree of wound contraction was identical in open wounds from treated and control rats; there were major morphological differences in the expression of α SM actin and/or the presence of cytoplasmic stress fibers. Similar findings were found with rh-phalloidin and α SM actin immuno-staining of the granulation tissue contained in PVA sponge implants. Like vanadate-treated open wounds, the granulation tissue of PVA sponge implants was devoid of myofibroblasts, while smooth muscle cells of blood vessels were positive for α SM actin. Western blot analysis

supported the morphological findings. The expression of vinculin, representative of focal adhesion plaques; α SM actin, the actin isoform of myofibroblast stress fibers and smooth muscle cells; and β actin of microfilaments were examined in homogenates of PVA sponge implants. The expression of vinculin and β actin was not affected by the ingestion of vanadate, see Fig. 3. However, the ingestion of vanadate reduced the levels of α SM actin as compared to controls (Fig. 3). The α SM actin expressed in vanadate treated rat granulation tissue was from smooth muscle cells of blood vessels.

By TEM the granulation tissue from contracting open wounds of control rats had high density of myofibroblasts. Aggregates of microfilaments were located at the periphery of the myofibroblast populations found throughout the granulation tissue of controls. The collagen fiber bundles contained in the extracellular matrix were in randomly organized arrays, see Fig. 4. Granulation tissue of vanadate treated rats contained independent cell populations lacking microfilament aggregates at the periphery of the cell. The arrangement of collagen fiber bundles was striking in the granulation tissue of vanadate treated rats, see Fig. 4. The collagen fiber bundles all had equivalent diameters,

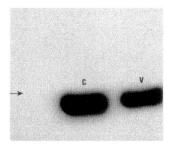
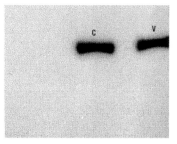
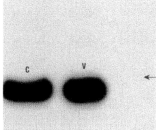

Fig. 3: Western blots of α SM actin, vinculin and β actin of sponge implants. Left panel shows the reduced levels of α SM actin in lane v (vanadate-treatment) compared to lane c (control). Middle panel shows that there are equivalent levels of vinculin, a focal adhesion protein between the two treatment groups. Right panel shows equivalent densities of β actin in both c and v lanes. The arrows on the left and right sides of the figure indicate the location of the 66,000 molecular weight marker.

were equally spaced and arranged in orderly parallel arrays. The systemic ingestion of vanadate prevented the appearance of myofibroblasts and promoted the arrangement of collagen fibers in distinct, highly ordered, parallel arrays.

The degree of granulation tissue ingrowth into PVA sponge implants from both treatment groups was similar. The density of cell populations, number of blood vessels and concentration of connective tissue matrix appeared similar between groups. However, by Sirius red/polarized light microscopy, differences in the organization of collagen fiber bundles were apparent between treatment groups. The collagen fiber bundles of granulation tissue from a control PVA sponge implant showed modest birefringence intensity. Those collagen fiber bundles were organized in fine arrays, see fig. 5

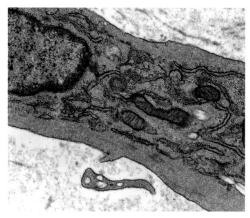
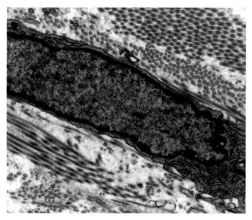

Fig. 4: TEM micrographs from 2 week old contracting open wounds. Panel on left shows a myofibroblast from a control wound at 7600 magnification, where the collagen fiber bundles are arranged in a random fashion. There are areas at the periphery of the myofibroblast, just beneath the plasma membrane, enriched with microfilaments. The panel on the right is a fibroblast from a vanadate treated rat wound at 6000 magnification. Numerous subcellular organelles are located just beneath the cell's plasma membrane. There are no microfilament structures at the plasma cell surface. The collagen fiber bundles are prominent, equal in diameter, equally spaced and arranged in parallel ordered arrays.

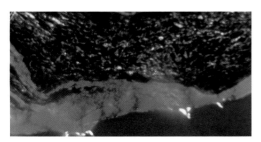 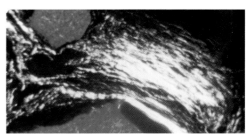

Fig. 5: Formalin fixed sections from 2 week old PVA sponge implants were stained with Sirius red and viewed with polarized light optics. The panel on the left shows the modest birefringence pattern from a control rat. The panel on the right shows the birefringence pattern, which is more intense because of thicker, more parallel, collagen fiber bundles associated with vanadate ingestion.

on left. On the other hand, granulation tissue of vanadate treated rats demonstrated more intense birefringence, that is there was more uniform collagen fiber bundles organized in ordered parallel arrays, see fig. 5 on right. The differences in birefringence patterns were consistent with the TEM findings, where more ordered collagen fiber bundles were evident in the vanadate treatment group.

Significant differences in wound breaking strength at 7 days were found between groups. Incisional wounds from controls developed 165 ± 58 g of breaking strength at 7 days, while the vanadate treated incisions had developed 332 ± 37 g of breaking strength. The gain in wound breaking strength of the vanadate treated rats was twice that of the controls and that difference was highly significant with a $p \geq 0.0003$, using the two-tailed Student "t" test. The physical increase in wound breaking strength is consistent with the morphological differences between groups. A better organized collagen matrix would be expected to generate a stronger incisional wound.

Discussion

The ingestion of vanadate in drinking water for 3 weeks is not toxic to adult rats, as noted by similar weight gains in controls and treated rats. Likewise the ingestion of vanadate

has no effects upon the rate of wound contraction or the amount of granulation tissue deposited within PVA sponge implants. However, the chronic ingestion of vanadate doubles the gain in wound breaking strength, which appears associated with the deposition of better organized collagen fiber bundles.

Myofibroblasts are specialized fibroblasts containing α SM actin that are proposed to be responsible for wound contraction [8]. However that role in wound repair is in question because here the ingestion of vanadate eliminated the appearance of myofibroblasts yet those wounds contract equally to controls. These findings support the hypothesis that fibroblasts not myofibroblasts are responsible for generating the forces for wound contraction [1]. The ingestion of vanadate inhibits the formation of stress fibers in fibroblasts but does not prevent stress fibers from developing within the smooth muscle cells of blood vessels. This implies that the control of the formation of stress fibers in fibroblasts is different from that of smooth muscle cells. Vanadate is an inhibitor of tyrosine-phosphatases, which play a role in cell signaling. As an example, *in vitro* vanadate down regulates P^{125} focal adhesion kinase, which is associated with the absence of both stress fibers and focal adhesions [10]. There are numerous reports of tyrosine phosphorylation of focal adhesion proteins controlling cell shape, microfilament organization and cell locomotion [4, 11, 12].

It is proposed that cell "tractional forces" generate the forces that organize collagen fiber bundles required for the contraction of open wounds and the evolution of scar integrity [1, 13, 14]. The fine microfilaments of fibroblasts are responsible for the tractional forces involved in the translocation of collagen fibrils. Myofibroblasts with prominent stress fibers are ill equipped at translocating collagen fibrils [14]. The ingestion of vanadate *in vivo* prevents the formation of stress fibers and the expression of α SM actin. More importantly the ingestion of vanadate is associated with the deposition of more orderly packed collagen fibers. As demonstrated by both TEM and polarized light optics, granulation tissue collagen fiber bundles are more organized. Vanadate therapy neither changes the amount of granulation tissue deposited nor the cell density of granulation tissue. By immuno-histology vanadate ingestion blocks the maturation of fibroblasts into myofibroblasts. When tyrosine phosphate turnover is blocked, there is a change in the interaction of cells with collagen. This change may produce a better graft bed for the transfer and placement of keratinocyte grafts.

References

[1] *Ehrlich, H P:* Granulation tissue maturation and wound contraction. J Surg Pathol 2:243–249, 1997.
[2] *Stossel, T P:* On the crawling of animal cells. Science 260:1086–1094, 1993.
[3] *Sexton, B M, Hunter, T, Ball, EH, Singer, S J:* Vinculin: a cytoskeletal target of transformation protein of Rous sarcoma virus. Cell 24: 165–174, 1981.
[4] *Romer, L H, McLean, N, Turner, C E, Burridge, K:* Tyrosine kinase activity, cytoskeletal organization and motility in human vascular endothelial cells. Molec Biol Cell 5: 349–361, 1994.
[5] *Kornberg L, Earp H S, Parsons J T, Schaller M, Juliano R L:* Cell adhesion or integrin clustering increases phosphorylation of a focal adhesion-associated tyrosine kinase. J Biol Chem 267:2343–23442, 1992.
[6] *Ehrlich, H P, Desmouliere, A, Diegelmann, R F, Cohen, I K, Compton, C C, Garner, W L, Kapanci, Y, Gabbiani, G:* Morphological and immunochemical differences between keloids and hypertrophic scar. Am J Pathol 145:105–113, 1994
[7] *Ehrlich, H P, Keefer, K A, Myers, R I, Passaniti, A:* Wound contraction, vanadate and myofibroblasts. Arch Surg 134:494, 1999.
[8] *Darby, I, Gabbiani, G:* α smooth muscle actin is transiently expressed by myofibroblasts during experimental wound healing. Lab Invest 65:21–29, 1990.
[9] *Majno, G, Gabbiani, G, Hirschel, B J, Ryan, G B, Statkov, P R:* Contraction of granulation tissue in vitro: Similarity to smooth muscle. Science 173:548–550, 1971.
[10] *Retta S F, Barry S T, Critchley D R, Defilippi P, Silengo L, Tarone G:* Focal adhesion and stress fiber formation is regulated by tyrosine phosphatase activity. Exp Cell Res 229: 307–317, 1996.
[11] *DeClue, J E, Martin, G S:* Phosphorylations of talin at tyrosine in Rous sarcoma virus – transformed cells. Mole Cell Biol 7:371–378, 1987.
[12] *Enomoto, T, Okamoto, T, Soto, J D:* Vascular endothelial growth factor induces the disorganization of actin stress fibers accompanied by protein tyrosine phosphorylation and morphological change in BALB/C3T3 cells. Biochem Biophys Res Comm 202:1716–1723, 1994.
[13] *Harris, A K, Wild, P, Stopak, D:* A new wrinkle in the study of cell locomotion. Science 280: 177–179, 1980.
[14] *Ehrlich, H P, Rajaratnam, J B M:* Cell locomotion forces versus cell contraction forces for collagen lattice contraction: an in vitro model of wound contraction. Tiss Cell 22:407–417, 1990.

Multiple Applications of Tissue-Engineered Human Skin

L. Germain, V. Moulin, F. Berthod, A. Carlos, C. A. López Valle, F. Goulet and F. A. Auger

Summary

The progress in tissue engineering has lead to the development of tri-dimensional tissues that can be used in vitro for various applications. Different methods have been designed to produce reconstructed dermis or skin *in vitro*. This chapter describes the human skin models and substitutes with respect to the evolution of their complexity as well as some of their potential applications. Dermal fibroblasts or myofibroblasts included in floating collagen gels produce useful wound healing models. Bilayered human skin constructs comprising both the dermis and the epidermis could serve for fundamental (e.g. cell-matrix interactions) or applied (e.g. dermatoabsorption) studies. Another skin substitute is produced by seeding keratinocytes on fibroblasts cultured in a collagen-chondroitin 4–6-sulfates and chitosan sponge. The addition of endothelial cells to this model lead to the formation of capillary-like structure in the dermis. Finally, a method of human reconstructed skin production by the "auto-assembly" approach is presented. This model is developed from cells that produce their own extracellular matrix. No synthetic material or exogenous matrix proteins is added. Thus it could be completely autologous.

Tissue engineered skin is an attractive tissue for gene therapy. Cells could be transplanted safely in vitro, evaluated for gene expression before their incorporation in reconstructed tissue and grafting in vivo. Of particular importance will be skin stem cells that have a long term regeneration potential and that can be cultured in vitro. The progress accomplished in tissue engineering of skin is now applied to the reconstruction of other tissues and more complex organs such as ligaments, bronchi, bladder, cornea and blood vessels. These tissues could provide therapeutic alternatives in organ transplantation as well as models for various in vitro applications.

Introduction

At present time, a wide number of research teams are progressing at very high speed to discover the complex mechanisms which control cell growth, differentiation and functional activities, with respect to their respective tissular origins. The latest advances in tissue engineering are closely associated with the discoveries accomplished at the molecular levels of gene and protein expressions. Skin was one of the first tissues, if not the first, to be reconstructed in culture. Indeed, several types of human skin substitutes have been developed through tissue engineering in the world, including those produced in our laboratory. Why skin? Likely because of its important and unique roles in protecting the body, being at the same time the first accessible target of traumatic injuries. Cultured skin substitutes have been created to serve as models for in vitro studies but primarily to be transplanted on patients, notably the victims of deep and extensive burns [1]. To reach these goals, several parameters are critical to monitor during the production of tissue-engineered skins. For instance, the quality of cell organization and the maintenance of important functional activities have a great impact on the features of the skin grown in culture. For the same reasons, the living cells included in each reconstructed skin substitute must retain their morphology, proliferative capacities and expression of tissue-specific functions. Thus, the culture conditions including the media, additives, matrix and three-dimensional environment have to be properly assessed and selected.

Tissue-engineered skin substitutes frequently contain two cell types; epithelial cells or keratinocytes and dermal fibroblasts. Bilayered skin constructs [2–5] have been developed by adding a dermal component to the simplest but the first type of human cutaneous substitute, the epithelial cell sheet, produced by Rheinwald and Green in 1975 [6–8]. A third generation of skin constructs was recently created with the evolution of tissue engineering: the endothelialized human skin substitutes [9]. This chapter describes the human skin

models and substitutes with respect to the evolution of their complexity as well as some of their potential applications.

Culture of Human Skin Cells

From serial culture of human epidermal cells to skin bioengineering, several observations have been reported about the functional properties of epidermal skin cells. For instance, the expression of keratins as differentiation markers [10] and involucrin [11] have helped to characterize the various epidermal layers of skin. Similarly, the lipid composition of reconstructed epidermis have been used as functional indicators of the integrity of the cells upon culture time [12]. The development of dermal constructs, initially introduced as collagen lattices [13–15] have also been useful to study mesenchymal cell properties.

Dermal Fibroblasts and Myofibroblasts Seeded in Floating Collagen Lattices

Floating (non anchored) collagen lattices seeded with fibroblasts (Fig. 1) remain useful bioengineered constructs to study the contractile

Fig. 1: Floating (non anchored) collagen lattices seeded with 1×10^5 human skin fibroblasts (A) and myofibroblasts isolated from wounds (B) to compare their contractile properties. These pictures were taken 24 hrs after seeding the cells in the gels and each cell population contracted the matrix at different rates according to their respective phenotypes.

properties of dermal cells in culture [16], including the phenotypic behavior of myofibroblasts [17–19], described in wounds by Gabbiani, Ryan and Majno in 1971 [20]. Floating dermal constructs have also been used to study the effects of various factors on collagen synthesis and contraction by dermal fibroblasts [21]. Dermo-epidermal cellular cooperation has been observed in vitro, the dermal fibroblasts promoting epidermal cell growth and organization in indirect coculture [22] and in vivo, notably during collagen remodelling by metalloproteinases [23]. The epithelialized floating collagen lattice was the first bilayered skin construct developed in vitro [24–25]. Its considerable contraction upon culture time remained its main weakness, notably as potential skin graft.

Bilayered Human Skin Constructs Using Hydrated Collagen Gels

When the concept of anchoring methods for tissue constructs was introduced [26], three-dimensional bioengineered skin substitutes started developing. The basement membrane components secreted by cutaneous cells in vivo are considered as essential markers to monitor the evolution of skin constructs in vit-

ro [27]. The method combining the use of thermolysin and irradiated 3T3 feeder layers to isolate pure populations of epidermal and dermal cells from the same human skin biopsy has contributed to promote the development of bilayered skin substitutes [28]. Skin constructs using fibroblast-populated collagen gels as dermal counterparts have opened new research paths, enhancing the development of industrial applications such as percutaneous absorption studies [29]. Comparisons between human bioengineered skins produced with type I collagens of human and bovine sources (Fig. 2) have shown different characteristics in vitro, showing the important role of cell-matrix interactions [30]. The same skin models have also been useful to develop serum-free culture conditions which modulate metalloproteinases expression in culture and allow longer culture periods [4]. In absence of serum, this type of skin constructs could be useful to see the effects of exogenous growth factors on the expression of metalloproteinases and collagen remodeling in vitro.

The collagen gel seeded with dermal fibroblasts could also be enriched with additional extracellular matrix constituents which effects are interesting to assess. When grafted in vivo, the addition of a dermal layer to the epidermal sheet led to successful graft take, enhanced healing and provided mechanical re-

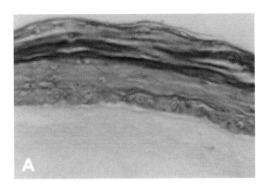 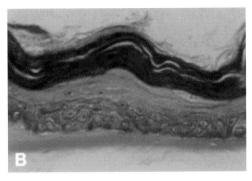

Fig. 2: Histological sections of anchored bilayered human skin constructs using hydrated type I bovine (A) and human (B) collagens, after 10 days of culture at the air-liquid interface. Note the thicker stratum corneum of the skin substitute produced with human collagen and the good statification of its epidermal layers. The authors thank Rina Guignard and Nathalie Tremblay for this figure.

sistance to the grafts posttransplantation [31]. Skin models made with human type I collagen contracted significantly less than the other group post-grafting [31]. *In situ* analysis of the grafts over 90 days showed a good ultrastructural organization, including the deposition of a continuous basement membrane as soon as a week following surgery [31]. With time, other bioengineered skin substitutes have been produced using human cells. Various technologies were developed to create new dermal constructs such as collagen sponges.

Tissue-Engineered Skin Made of a Collagen Sponge Biomaterial:

A collagen sponge biomaterial based upon the work of Yannas and Burke [32–33] and Boyce [34] has been developed by Collombel and Damour [35, 36] to produce a new reconstructed skin model. This sponge biomaterial is obtained by freeze-drying a mixture of type I bovine collagen, chondroitin 4-6-sulfates and chitosan. The strength of the collagen sponge is achieved by the ionic bonds created between chitosan and collagen [36].

This sponge acts as a scaffold of highly modular shape in which fibroblasts migrate and synthesize high amounts of a well-organized human extracellular matrix [37–40]. Thus, the dermal component of this reconstructed skin model can be prepared in the form of a thick tissue (5 mm thick or more) of variable size, following a process easy to use and industrialize. Autologous keratinocytes are then seeded on the top of the fibroblasts-populated sponge to prepare the reconstructed skin [41]. This sponge has been transplanted on mice with very encouraging results [42].The main limitation of grafting a thicker reconstructed skin on wounds could be a delay in revascularization, leading to necrosis of the epidermis [43]. Indeed, the rapid nutrition of the epidermis after conventional grafting of split-thickness skin autografts has been shown to proceed by a process called "inosculation" in which the vascular network of the graft connects with the

host's blood vessels [44]. Therefore, we developed an endothelialized reconstructed skin to take advantage of this inosculation process in order to speed up the revascularization of the reconstructed skin. However, human endothelial cells are known to require extraphysiological amounts of growth factors or culture substrates (such as PMA, a tumor promotor, or Matrigel™, an extracellular matrix produced by tumor cells) to be cultured in vitro, in contrast with animal endothelial cells. Meanwhile, we demonstrated that human umbilical vein endothelial cells spontaneously formed capillary-like structures when cultured in our reconstructed skin model, in a standard culture medium containing only 10 % fetal calf serum [9]. The spontaneous reconstruction of a capillary-like network in vitro with human endothelial cells is a breakthrough in the field of angiogenesis (Fig. 3). This result has been achieved because our reconstructed skin reproduces an ideal balance between cell-cell interactions and cell-matrix interactions in an in vitro environment that closely mimics the in vivo situation. This reconstructed skin model opens the way for an alternative to split-thickness autografts in the treatment of deep and extensive burns, as well as exciting applications as the first human in vitro angiogenesis model for the development of new angiogenesis inhibitors to treat solid tumors.

Tissue-Engineered Skin Produced From Cells: the Self-Assembly Method

Another method of production of reconstructed human skin in vitro was adapted from the tissue-engineered blood vessel in which the production of the media and the adventitia was based on a new method called self-assembly approach [45]. Briefly, when cultured in the presence of serum and ascorbic acid, fibroblasts produce and organize their own extracellular matrix comprising collagen and glycosaminoglycans and could be detached together with this dense matrix as a sheet to produce the dermis, 3 sheets are superposed. Then, the reconstructed skin is obtained by seeding keratinocytes on the top and culturing at the air-liquid interface [46] to induce differentiation and stratum corneum formation (Fig. 4).

The advantages of this reconstructed skin for eventual use in vivo for transplantation are related to the absence of synthetic material and/or exogenous proteins, it is a completely biologic tissue. The collagen is synthetized by the cells, which are the only starting material with medium. This would minimize the infectious risks related to the addition of exogenous material.

This reconstructed skin has also in vitro applications. For example, this tissue engineered model allowed to better understand percutaneous absorption pathways because it was possible to produce reconstructed skin with or without hairs. Then, the transfollicular pathway was shown to be faster than the transepidermal pathway indicating its potential importance in percutaneous absorption [46]

Conclusion

Tissue engineered skin is an attractive tissue for gene therapy. Cells could be transfected safely in vitro, evaluated for gene expression before their incorporation in reconstructed tissue and grafting in vivo. Of particular importance will be skin stem cells that have a long term regeneration potential and that can be cultured in vitro [47, 48].

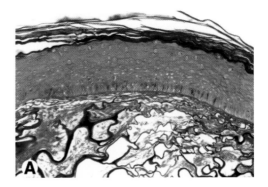

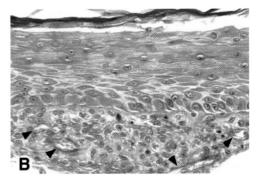

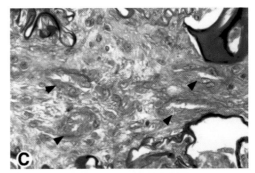

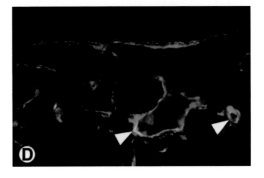

Fig. 3: Histological aspect of the reconstructed skin cultured 15 days at the air-liquid interface (A), and the endothelialized reconstructed skin cultured 14 days at the air-liquid interface (B) (arrow heads show capillary-like tubules), enlargement of capillary-like tubules in the ERS (C), immunohistochemical staining of the ERS cultured 14 days at the air-liquid interface (D). Capillary-like tubules (arrow heads) are stain by an antibody specific to laminin, a major component of basement membranes, and by an antibody specific to platelet endothelial cell adhesion molecule, a marker of endothelial cells.

The progress accomplished in tissue engineering of skin is now applied to the reconstruction of other tissues and more complex organs such as ligaments, bronchi, bladder, cornea and blood vessels [45–47, 49–53]. These tissues could provide therapeutic alternatives in organ transplantation as well as models for various in vitro applications.

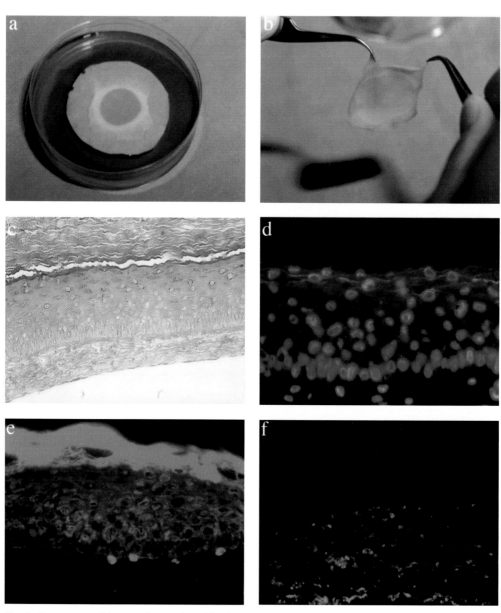

Fig. 4: Reconstructed human skin produced by the auto-assembly approach. Macroscopic view of the tissue after culture at the ait-liquid interface (a, b). Histological staining with Masson's Trichrome (c), Hoechst nuclei staining (d), Keratin (e) and Vimentin (f) labeling of the human reconstructed skin. The authors thank Annie Beauparlant and Hubert Robitaille for this figure.

References

[1] *Auger FA:* The role of cultured autologous human epithelium in large burn wound treatment. Transplantation/Implantation today 5: 21–24, 1988

[2] *Boyce ST, Christianson DJ, Hansborough JF:* Structure of a collagen-GAG dermal skin substitute optimized for cultured epidermal keratinocytes. J Biomed Mater Res 22:939–957, 1988

[3] *Bouvard V, Germain L, Rompré P, Roy B, Auger F A:* Influence of dermal equivalent maturation on a skin equivalent development. Biochem Cell Biol 70:34–42, 1992

[4] *Auger FA, Pouliot R, Tremblay N, Guignard R, Noël P, Juhasz J, Germain L, Goulet F:* Multistep production of bioengineered skin substitutes: sequential modulation of culture conditions. In Vitro Cell Dev Biol 36(2): 96–103, 2000

[5] *Berthod F, Auger FA:* In vitro applications of skin substitutes for dermatological purposes, in Rouabhia, M. (Ed.): Skin substitute production by tissue engineering: clinical and fundamental applications (Austin, Landes Bioscience), pp. 211–237, 1997

[6] *Rheinwald JG, Green H:* Serial cultivation of strains of human epidermal keratinocytes: the formation of keratinizing colonies from single cells. Cell 6:331–344, 1975

[7] *Rheinwald JG, Green H:* Epidermal growth factor and the multiplication of cultured human epidermal keratinocytes', Nature 265: 421–424, 1977

[8] *Green H, Kehinde O, Thomas J:* Growth of cultured human epidermal cells into multiple epithelia suitable for grafting. Proc Natl Acad Sci (USA) 76:5665–5668, 1979

[9] *Black A, Berthod F, L'Heureux N, Germain L, Auger FA:* In vitro reconstruction of a human capillary-like network in a tissue-engineered skin equivalent. FASEB J 12:1331–1340, 1998

[10] *Moll R, Franke WW, Schiller DL:* The catalog of human cytokeratins: Patterns of expression in normal epithelia, tumors and cultured cells. Cell 31:11–24, 1982

[11] *Simon M, Green H:* Enzymatic cross-linking of involucrin and other proteins by keratinocyte particulates in vitro. Cell 40:677–683, 1985

[12] *Ponec M:* Reconstruction of human epidermis on de-epidermized dermis: Expression of differentiation-specific protein markers and lipid composition. Toxic In Vitro 5:597–606, 1991

[13] *Bell E, Ivarsson B, Merrill C:* Production of a tissue-like structure by contraction of collagen lattices by human fibroblasts of different proliferative potential in vitro. Proc Natl Acad Sci (U.S.A) 76:1274–1278, 1979

[14] *Coulomb B, Dubertret L, Merrill C, Touraine R, Bell E:* The collagen lattice: a model for studying the physiology, biosynthetic function and pharmacology of the skin. Br J Dermatol 111:83–87, 1984

[15] *Grinnell F, Lamke CR:* Reorganization of hydrated collagen lattices by human skin fibroblasts. J Cell Sci 66:51–63, 1984

[16] *Moulin V, Auger FA, O'Connor-McCourt M, Germain L:* Fetal and postnatal sera differentially modulate human dermal fibroblast phenotypic and functional features in vitro. J Cell Physiol 171:1–10, 1997

[17] *Germain L, Jean A, Auger FA, Garrel D R:* Human wound healing fibroblasts have greater contractile properties than dermal fibroblasts. J Surg Res 57:268–273, 1994

[18] *Moulin V, Castilloux G, Jean A, Garrel DR, Auger F A, Germain L:* In vitro models to study wound healing fibroblasts. Burns 22:359–362, 1996

[19] *Moulin V, Castilloux G, Auger FA, Garrel D, O'Connor-McCourt M, Germain L:* Comparison of human wound healing myofibroblasts with dermal fibroblasts in vitro. Exp Cell Res 238:283–293, 1997

[20] *Gabbiani G, Ryan GB, Majno G:* Presence of modified fibroblasts in granulation tissue and their possible role in wound contraction. Experientia 27:549–550, 1971

[21] *Geesin JC, Brown LJ, Gordon JS, Berg RA:* Regulation of collagen synthesis in human dermal fibroblasts in contracted gels by ascorbic acid, growth factors, and inhibitors of lipids peroxidation. Exp Cell Res 206: 283–290, 1993

[22] *Goulet F, Poitras A, Rouabhia M, Cusson D, Germain L, Auger FA:* Stimulation of human keratinocyte proliferation through growth factor exchanges with dermal fibroblasts in vitro. Burns 22:107–112, 1996

[23] *Oikarinen A, Kylmäniemi M, Autio-Harmainen H, Autio P, Salo T:* Demonstration of 72-kDa and 92-kDa forms of type IV collagenase in human skin: variable expression in various blistering diseases, induction during re-epithelialization, and decrease by topical glucocorticoïds. J Invest Dermatol 101:205–210, 1993

[24] *Bell E, Ehrlich HP, Buttle DJ, Nakatsuji T:* Living tissue formed in vitro and accepted as skin-equivalent tissue of full thickness. Science 211:1052–1054, 1981

[25] *Coulomb B, Lebreton C, Dubertret L:* Influence of human dermal fibroblasts on epidermalization. J Invest Dermatol 92:122–125, 1989

[26] *López Valle CA, Auger FA, Rompré P, Bouvard V, Germain L:* Peripheral anchorage of dermal equivalents. Br J Dermatol 127:365–371, 1992

[27] *Woodley DT, Peterson HD, Herzog SR:* Burn wounds resurfaced by cultured epidermal autografts show abnormal reconstitution of anchoring fibrils. JAMA 259:2566–2571, 1988

[28] Germain L, Rouabhia M, Guignard R, Carrier L, Bouvard V, Auger FA: Improvement of human keratinocyte isolation and culture using thermolysin. Burns 19:99–104, 1993

[29] Michel M, Auger FA, Germain L: Anchored skin equivalent cultured in vitro: A new tool for percutaneous absorption studies. In vitro Cell Dev Biol 29A:834–837, 1993

[30] Auger FA, López Valle CA, Guignard R, Tremblay N, Noël B, Goulet F, Germain L: Skin equivalents produced using human collagens. In Vitro Cell Dev Biol 31:432–439, 1995

[31] López Valle CA, Germain L, Rouabhia M, Xu W, Guignard R, Goulet F, Auger FA: Grafting on nude mice of living skin equivalents produced using human collagens. Transplantation 62:317–323, 1996.

[32] Yannas IV, Lee E, Orgill D P, Skrabut EM, Murphy GF: Synthesis and characterization of a model extracellular matrix that induces partial regeneration of adult mammalian skin. Proc Natl Acad Sci U S A 86:933–937, 1989

[33] Yannas I V, Burke J F: Design of an artificial skin: Basic design principles. J Biomed Mater Res 14:65–81, 1980

[34] Boyce ST, Christianson DJ, Hansborough JF: Structure of a collagen-GAG dermal skin substitute optimized for cultured epidermal keratinocytes. J Biomed Mater Res 22:939–957, 1988

[35] Collombel C, Damour O, Gagnieu C, Marichy J, Poinsignon F: Biomaterials with a base of mixtures of collagen, chitosan and glycosaminoglycans, process for preparing them and their application in human medecine. Int Patent PCT/FR/8800303:15 june 1989,

[36] Berthod F, Saintigny G, Chretien F, Hayek D, Collombel C, Damour O: Optimization of thickness, pore size and mechanical properties of a biomaterial designed for deep burn coverage. Clin Mater 15:259–265, 1994

[37] Duplan-Perrat F, Damour O, Montrocher C, Peyrol S, Grenier G, Jacob M, Braye F: Keratinocytes influence the maturation and organization of the elastin network in a skin equivalent. J Invest Dermatol 114:365–370, 2000

[38] Berthod F, Sahuc F, Hayek D, Damour O, Collombel C: Deposition of collagen fibril bundles by long-term culture of fibroblasts in a collagen sponge. J Biomed Mater Res 32: 87–94, 1996

[39] Berthod F, Germain L, Guignard R, Lethias C, Garrone R, Damour O, van der Rest M, Auger F A: Differential expression of collagen XII and XIV in human skin and in reconstructed skin. J Invest Dermatol 108:737–742, 1997

[40] Berthod F, Hayek D, Damour O, Collombel C: Collagen synthesis by fibroblasts cultured within a collagen sponge. Biomaterials 14:749–754, 1993

[41] Sahuc F, Nakazawa K, Berthod F, Damour O, Collombel C: Mesenchymal-epithelial interactions regulate gene expression of type VII collagen and kalinin in keratinocytes and dermal-epidermal junction formation in a skin equivalent model. Wound Rep Reg 4:93–102, 1996

[42] Li H, Berthod F, Xu W, Germain L, Auger FA: Use of in vitro reconstructed skin to cover skin flap donor site. J Surg Res 73:143–148, 1998

[43] Boyce ST, Supp AP, Harriger DM, Greenhalgh D G, Warden G D: Topical nutrients promote engrafment and inhibit wound contraction of cultured skin substitutes in athymic mice. J Invest Dermatol 104:345–349, 1995

[44] Young DM, Greulich KM, Weier HG: Species-specific in situ hybridization with fluorochrome-labeled DNA probes to study vascularization of human skin grafts on   athymic mice. J Burn Care Rehabil 17:305–310, 1996

[45] L'Heureux N, Pâquet S, Labbé R, Germain L, Auger FA: A completely biological tissue-engineered human blood vessel. FASEB J 12: 47–56, 1998

[46] Michel M, L'Heureux N, Pouliot R, Xu W, Auger FA, Germain L: Characterization of a new tissue-engineered human skin equivalent with hair. In vitro Cellular and Developmental Biology 35:318–326, 1999

[47] Michel M, Török N, Godbout M-J, Lussier M, Gaudreau P, Royal A, Germain L: Keratin 19 as a biochemical marker of skin stem cells in vivo and in vitro: keratin 19 expressing cells are differentially localized in function of anatomic sites, and their number varies with donor age and culture stage. J Cell Sci 109: 1017–1028, 1996

[48] Jones PH, Watt FM: Separation of human epidermal stem cells from transit amplifying cells on the basis of differences in integrin function and expression. Cell 73:713–724, 1993

[49] Oberpenning F, Meng J, Yoo JJ, Atala A: De novo reconstitution of a functional mammalian urinary bladder by tissue engineering. Nat Biotechnol 17:149–155, 1999

[50] Goulet F, Germain L, Rancourt D, Caron C, Normand A, Auger FA: Tendons and ligaments. In Principles of tissue engineering. R. Lanza, R. Langer, and W.L. Chick, editors. Academic Press, San Diego. 633–644, 1997

[51] Germain L, Auger FA, Grandbois E, Guignard R, Giasson M, Boisjoly H, Guérin SL: Reconstructed human cornea produced in vitro by tissue engineering. Pathobiology 67:140–147, 1999

[52] Paquette J-S, Goulet F, Boulet L-P, Laviolette M, Tremblay N, Chakir J, Germain L, Auger FA: Three-dimensional production of bronchi in vitro. Can Respir J 5:43, 1998

[53] L'Heureux N, Germain L, Labbé R, Auger FA: In vitro construction of a human blood vessel from cultured vascular cells: a morphologic study. J Vasc Surg 17:499–509, 1993

Fibrin Microbeads (FMB) for Wound Healing and Tissue Engineering of Skin

R. Gorodetsky, A. Vexler, G. Marx

Summary

Current dermal substitutes are not ideal, because they don't provide the ideal environment for vascularization which would support transplanted keratinocytes. For this to occur, it is necessary to supply the dermal bed with viable cells capable of producing factors which promote vascularization. Fibrin microbeads are completely biodegradable, and a large variety of cultured cells grow well on these beads as their bed. Work in our laboratory shows excellent regeneration of skin wounds, but poor growth on keratinocytes in the presence of fibrin microbeads. The current strategy will be directed at providing a "cellular slurry" to the wound bed, and then layer keratinocytes on top of this system.

Background

Fibrin clots in normal circumstances are formed from blood plasma fibrinogen (2–5 mg/mL). The fibrin as well as fibrin(ogen) degradation products are present in every wound (1–4). Fibrin glues at much higher concentrations of fibrinogen (40–80 mg/mL) and thrombin have been recently developed for wound sealing [5–8]. Extensive research work elucidated fibrinogen's structure and the biochemical mechanisms of clot formation. However, the activity of fibrin(ogen) is not limited to its role as a "first aid" hemostatic agent, it also serves as an interim matrix to recruit cells needed to form granulation tissue [3]. The chemotactic and haptotactic properties of fibrin can modulate the migration of cells from structures buried within the skin and the tissues surrounding wound [9–12]. The cells also participate in the degradation of the fibrin by virtue of plasmin activators that they present on their membranes, as they meander along the fibrin web [13]. The cells induce clot retraction and secrete new collagen and other extracellular matrix (ECM) molecules [14]. Platelet derived and vascular endothelial growth factors (PDGF and VEGF respectively), are two factors that attract endothelial cells into the granulation tissue and induce them to construct neo-vasculature. Keratinocytes migrating to the wound-bed seem to have weak adherence to fibrin [15], though they may help in degrading it away [16].

Due to the complex structure of skin, the practice of skin tissue engineering is not straightforward. Most currently employed techniques are based on building in-vitro sheets of skin-like tissue replacement using a biodegradable natural or synthetic polymer scaffold seeded with parenchymal cell types to simulate the organization of normal skin, possibly with the addition of cocktails of growth factors. After an appropriate incubation time in vitro, the cells are expected to multiply and fill the three-dimensional scaffold. The general approach with such "engineered skin" produced by different commercial entities [reviewed in 17–27] is based on the use a matrix sheet of collagen, as practiced by Ortec, ATS, Integra, Fibrogen and Organogenesis, or hyaluronic acid derivatives (Fidia) or the combination of such materials with cells generally derived from foreskin (Ortec, ATS, Fidia and Organogenesis). Unlike human skin, the above engineered skin substitutes do not contain Langerhan's cells, hair follicles, sweat glands, melanocytes, or any connection to blood supply. Another approach is to use autografts from patient donor sites (Integra). The transplanted "engineered skin" is expected to induce blood vessels growth from the wound bed. Unfortunately, even if the grafted material contains all the components and cell types with appropriate extracellular matrix (i.e. an area of skin harvested from the same individual), there are difficulties in the "take" of such full depth skin transplants. Even when fully functional skin is grafted onto the same individual, unless vascularization is maintained, as by using flap techniques that allow minimal blood perfusion into the area (as commonly practiced in plastic surgery), the transplanted tissue will lack immediate oxygen and nutrient supplies, resulting in the death of most cells and ultimately a poor Atake of the transplant.

The lack of initial vascularization, which would not allow the cells to survive, proliferate and regenerate the damaged tissue, is the critical issue for all tissue transplantation techniques. In the case of engineered artificial skins, extremely elaborate techniques are used to ensure that the artificial matrix will be "cell friendly", non-immunogenic and biodegradable. Notwithstanding, where foreign allogeneic cells are used, they are prone to be ultimately rejected due to immunologic rejection. Moreover, without vascularization, the chances that transplanted cells in engineered skin will survive are low. Thus, one could characterize engineered skin replacement grafts as a sophisticated bandage.

One approach to avoid the above difficulties is to supply the wound bed with an adequate number of viable cells under conditions that would allow them to regenerate the missing tissue. Such an approach has already been attempted for cartilage repair, where allogeneic or syngeneic chondrocytes were iso-

lated and injected into the cartilage lesions [29–42]. The limitation of such a direct cell transfer technique is that only a few of the chondrocytes injected in suspension survive.

In order to deliver appropriate cells in conditions where they would remain viable and survive the transplantation procedure, biocompatible cell carriers are needed. A carrier loaded with high titer of cells in vitro could deliver cells to the target site, where they could download and degrade the carrier while re-building the damaged tissue.

Tissue Engineering with Cell-Loaded Fibrin-Microbeads (FMB)

The biodegradable, non-toxic and non-immunogenic properties of fibrin glue suggest it as an ideal material for producing bio-engineering matrices. In vitro responses of cultured cells to fibrin and its components

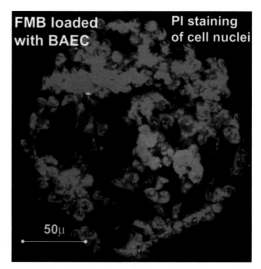

Fig. 1: Confocal microscopy of a single FMB loaded with high density of normal bovine aortic endothelial cells. The nuclei of the cells loaded on the FMB were stained red by propidium iodide (PI). The sections through the bead were superimposed to demonstrate the total number of cells loaded per one bead. The faint autofluorescence of the FMB is shown in green.

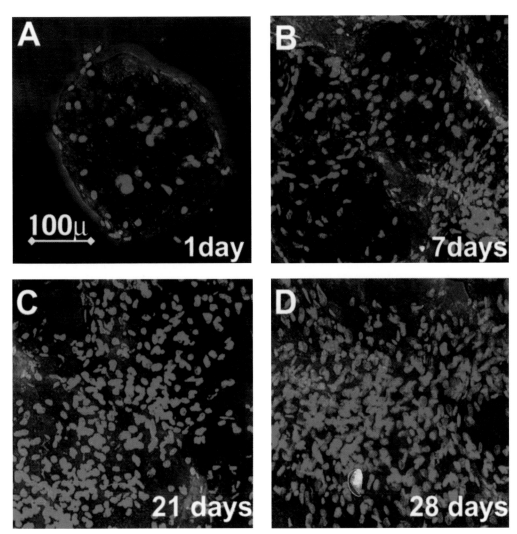

Fig. 2: Confocal microscopy of human fibroblasts attached and grown on FMB. The cells' nuclei were stained red by PI and the fluorescence of nuclei as well as the Nomarsky's reconstructed images were superimposed to show all cell nuclei as well as the structures of the FMB and the extracellular matrix. The cells are shown 1,7,21 and 28 days after their loading on FMB. It is obvious that cell number increased on the FMB while degrading them and excreting the new extracellular matrix. The FMB outline is lost while a tissue-like extracellular structures are being formed.

were evaluated. For example, a fibrin clot recruited cultured human fibroblasts (HF) and endothelial cells from the surrounding area. Fibrinogen only slightly increased fibroblast proliferation while thrombin enhanced their proliferation by a factor of 1.5–1.8 [3]. A cell attachment assay showed the haptotactic response of normal and transformed cells for fibrin(ogen) and thrombin. Based on these findings, microbeads based on fibrin as a matrix were fabricated for cell culturing purposes. Such fibrin microbeads (FMB) (50–200 micron in diameter) were manufactured from viral inactivated blood fibrinogen by a

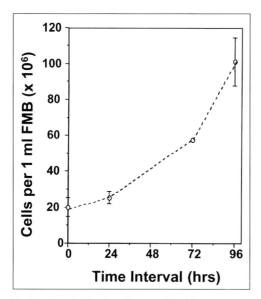

Fig. 3: Growth kinetics of human fibroblasts on FMB evaluated by the MTS assay. Cells were loaded on FMB by mixing in rotation in a CO_2 incubator. The number of cells on FMB were recorded by a modified MTS colorimetric method that measures the density of cell number by their dehydrogenase activity. The assay was modified for cells loaded on FMB with adequate calibration for measurement of number of cells per ml of FMB. The fast rate of proliferation of cells on FMB to high cell density is clearly manifested.

unique technology [4]. FMB comprise the essential normal coagulation proteins, namely of fibrin(ogen), activated by thrombin and cross-linked by endogenous factor XIII and partially heat denatured. Just like human fibrin(ogen), FMB are non-toxic, entirely biodegradable and not immunogenic.

FMB have been studied in various tissue culture and animal models. They appear to possess unique and powerful bio-properties that can be exploited for a wide variety of applications that require manipulation of cells. In particular, cells-on-FMB can be transferred without trypsinization. FMB can act as a substrate for the growth of cells in vitro and can act as biologically active and totally degradable carrier for cultured cells (Fig. 1). A large variety of cells, mostly from mesenchymal origin adhere to FMB and proliferate thereon

to very high densities (Figs. 2–3). These include fibroblasts, osteoblasts, chon-drocytes, endothelial, smooth muscle cells and mesenchymal stem cells.

By contrast, cultured keratinocytes did not show haptotactic activity with fibrin(ogen) and they attached poorly to FMB. While some groups employ suspensions of fibrin with keratinocytes to coat wounds with cells, keratinocytes do not seem to be attracted by fibrin [15, 16]. Rather, they could be physically entrapped in the fibrin from which they migrated out. Actually, this is consistent with their physiologic behavior during the healing of normal skin wounds, where keratinocytes migrate under the fibrin clot to reform the epidermal layer, while helping to digest the fibrin and eject the remaining clot.

Use of Cells on FMB for Wound Healing and Contribution to Vascularization

Just as it is a main requirement for normal tissue or tumor viability [9, 28], the availability and the development of a an adequate blood supply is the critical parameter for successful "tissue engineering". Endothelial cells have been found to respond to fibrinogen in terms of attachment, migration and formation of capillary structures [11–14]. Moreover, when the cells loaded in high density on FMB are introduced onto the wound-bed, they may secrete factors such as VEGF that could further contribute to the induction of growth of capillaries to the implanted area, to support the formation of the new tissue.

In a pig skin wound healing model, the advantage of the FMB as cell carriers in enhancing wound healing was clearly demonstrated (Fig. 4). The FMB (density of 1.3) loaded with cells were able to settle directly onto the bed of full thickness wounds where the cells downloaded.. Three days after wounding and implantation (a time point when normally granulation tissue does not yet occur), the

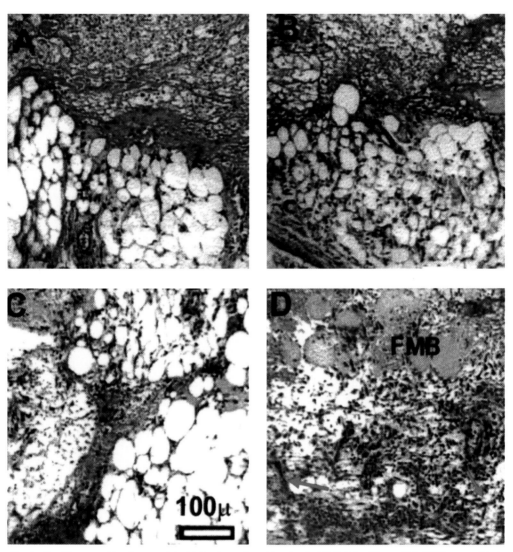

Fig. 4: Pig skin wound healing model with implant of fibroblasts on FMB. Histology of full depth punch wounds (1 cm in diameter) in pig skin. A selection of sections taken from the different treatments, with 3 mg/mL of fibrin is presented: A. Control: no addition other than human fibrin. This shows no evidence of granulation tissue. B. Exogenous addition of PDGF-BB showed increased fibroblast number beneath the wound, with no granulation tissue. C. When trypsinized fibroblasts suspended in fibrin were added, individual fibroblasts in the fibrin clot are observed, but with no apparent granulation tissue. D. When fibro- blast loaded FMB (10 million cells/g FMB) were added, FMB were seen along the base of the wound. A large number of fibroblasts were observed between the FMB and the underlying subcutaneous tissue. Note the development of numerous blood capillaries to the granulation tissue (arrows). Note the degrading FMB at the periphery and base of the wound bed. In all combinations tested, FMB + cells appeared to download fibroblasts into the wound-bed with significant granulation tissue formation. Moreover, 3 days after implant, the FMB loaded with cells were significantly smaller in size, due to biodegradation.

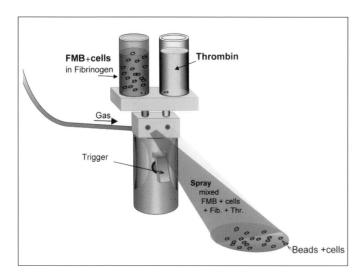

Fig. 5: Proposed spray application of fibroblasts-on-FMB for tissue engineering. An approach to spraying cells on FMB in fibrin. This technique may allow the gradual buildup of missing tissue by exogenous cells introduced while allowing them to recruit endogenous vascularization from the wound bed.

wounds treated with cells on FMB exhibited granulation tissue with neovascularization (Fig. 4D). Probably, the wound bed where FMB settled became enriched in fibrin degradation fragments that helped enlist endothelial cells from the surrounding tissue. Our positive results with the skin wound system indicate that implanted FMB with cells have great advantage over current approaches for enhancing the healing of skin wounds. We project that FMB with cells may be used to regenerate skin in situ. Rather than transplant a fixed sheet of matrix substrate embedded with 1 or more cell types, our approach is to suspend a slurry of FMB loaded with cells (fibroblasts and possibly also endothelial cells) in a fibrinogen solution, then co-spray it with thrombin, directly onto the site of the lesion. This would lay down the 1st layer of fibroblasts in proximity to the vasculature of the wound-bed. The FMB-cell layer would become fixed quickly in place by the coagulation of the fibrin. In order to regenerate the full skin thickness, other layers of fibroblasts on FMB would be sprayed on subsequently. Finally, a layer of keratinocytes could be sprayed on to generate the epidermal layer. The delivery of the cells-on-FMB suspended in fibrinogen could be carried out with gas-driven fibrin spray applicators [43, 44] adapted to this purpose (Fig. 5).

Conclusion

We propose using cells-on-FMB applied in a fibrinogen suspension as a scaffold-less technique to transplant cells onto tissue. We propose that for skin regeneration, dermal cells such as fibroblasts-on-FMB could be sprayed directly onto the wound bed possibly followed by a sprayed layer of keratinocytes in fibrin sealant with a specially designed fibrin glue applicator. Current work is aimed at expanding our experience of cells-on-FMB in animal models for regenerating skin.

Acknowledgment

We wish to thank our current and former coworkers (Drs. Xioude Mou, Jianqian An, Lila Levdansky) who contributed much to the successful execution of many of the experiments described above. We appreciate Dr. Richard Clark's (SUNY Stony Brook) participation in carrying out the pig skin transplantation experiments. We also acknowledge

Dr. Mark Tarshish (Interdepartment Unit, Hadassah Medical School, Jerusalem) for his help with the confocal microscopy.

This work is supported by HAPTO Biotech. Ltd. and by research grants from the Israel Academy of Sciences, Basic Research Foundation 697/00 to RG.

References

[1] *Mosesson MW and Doolittle R:* The Molecular Biology of Fibrinogen and Fibrin. Ann. N.Y. Acad. Sci. USA v. 408, (1983).

[2] *Sanders RP, Goodman N C, Amiss L R, Pierce R A, Moore M, Marx G, Morgan RF, Spotnitz W:* Effect of fibrinogen and thrombin concentrations on mastectomy seroma prevention. J. Surg. Res. 61: 65–70 (1996).

[3] *Gorodetsky R, Vexler A, An J, Mou X, Marx G:* Haptotactic and growth stimulatory effects of fibrin(ogen) and thrombin on cultured fibroblasts. J. Lab. Clin. Med. 131: 269–280 (1998).

[4] *Gorodetsky R., Vexler A., Shamir M, An J, Levdansky L, Marx G:* Fibrin microbeads (FMB) as biodegradable carriers for culturing cells and for accelerating wound healing. J. Invest. Dermatol. 112, 866–872 (1999).

[5] *Radosevich M, Goubran HA, Burnouf T:* Fibrin sealant: Scientific rationale, production methods, properties and current clinical use. Vox Sang. 72: 133–143 (1997).

[6] *Alving BM, Weinstein MJ, Finlayson JS, Menitove JE, Fratantoni JC:* Fibrin Sealant: Summary of a conference on characteristics and clinical uses. Transfusion 35: 783–790 (1995).

[7] *Marx G:* Kinetic and mechanical parameters of fibrin glue. Symposium on Surgical Tissue Adhesives: Atlanta GA In: Current Trends in Surgical Tissue Adhesives. Sierra D. & Saltz R. (Eds) (1996).

[8] *Marx G, Mou X, Freed R, Ben-Hur E, Yang C, Horowitz B:* Protecting fibrinogen with rutin during UVC irradiation for viral inactivation. Photochem. Photobiol. 63: 541–546 (1996).

[9] *Browder T, Folkman J, Pirie-Shepherd S:* The hemostatic system as a regulator of angiogensesis. J. Biol. Chem. 275: 1521–1524 (2000).

[10] *Suehiro K, Gailit J, Plow EF:* Fibrinogen is a ligand for integrin $\alpha5\beta1$ on endothelial cells. J. Biol. Chem. 272: 5360–5366 (1997)

[11] *Dejana, E, Languino, LR, Polentarutti, N, Balconi, G, Ryckewaert, JJ, Larieu, MJ Donati, MB, Mantovani, A, Marguerie, G:* Interaction between fibrinogen and cultured endothelial cells: Induction of migration and specific binding. J. Clin. Invest. 75, 11–18 (1985).

[12] *Chalupowicz DG, Chowdhury IA, Bach TL, Barsigian C, Martinez J:* Fibrin II induces endothelial cell capillary tube formation. J. Cell Biol. 130: 207–215 (1995).

[13] *Ge M, Tang G, Ryan T J, Mali A B:* Fibrinogen degradation product fragment D induces endothelial cell detachment by activation of cell-mediated fibrinolysis. J. Clin. Invest. 90, 2508–2516 (1992).

[14] *Smith, R, Mosesson, M, Rooney, M, Lord, S, Daniels, A, Gartner T:* The role of putative fibrinogen Aa, Bb and gA-chain integrin binding sites in endothelial cell-mediated clot retraction. J. Biol. Chem. 272, 220–228 (1997).

[15] *Weiss E, Yamaguchi Y, Falabella A, Crane S, Tokuda Y, Falanga V:* Uncross-linked fibrin substrates inhibit keratinocyte spreading and replication. J. Cell Physiol. 174: 58–65 (1998).

[16] *Donaldson DJ, Mahan JT, Amrani DL, Farrel DH, Sobel JH:* Further studies on the interaction of migrating keratinocytes with fibrinogen. Cell Adhes. Commun. 2: 299–308 (1994).

[17] *Bonassar LJ, Vacanti CA:* Tissue engineering: The first decade and beyond. J Cell Biochem Suppl 30–31 297–303 (1998).

[18] *Zdrahala RJ, Zdrahala IJ:* In vivo tissue engineering: Part I. Concept genesis and guidelines for its realization. J Biomater Appl 14: 192–209 (1999).

[19] *Kim BS, Mooney DJ:* Development of biocompatible synthetic extracellular matrices for tissue engineering.Trends in Biotech. 16:5: 224–230 (1998).

[20] *Minuth WW, Sittinger M, Kloth S:* Tissue engineering: generation of differentiated artificial tissues for biomedical applications. Cell Tissue Res 291: 1–11 (1998)

[21] *Sittinger M, Bujia J, Rotter N, Reitzel D, Minuth WW, Burmester GR:* Tissue engineering and autologous transplant formation: practical approaches with resorbable biomaterials and new cell culture techniques. Biomaterials 17: 237–42 (1996)

[22] *Knedlitschek G, Schneider F, Gottwald E, Schaller T, Eschbach E, Weibezahn KF:* A tissue-like culture system using microstructures: Influence of extracellular matrix material on cell adhesion and aggregation. J Biomech Eng 121: 35–9 (1999).

[23] *Marler JJ, Guha A, Rowley J, Koka R, Mooney D, Upton J, Vacanti JP:* Soft-tissue augmentation with injectable alginate and syngeneic fibroblasts. Plast Reconstr Surg 105: 2049–58 (2000)

[24] *Zdrahala RJ, Zdrahala IJ:* In vivo tissue engineering: Part I. Concept genesis and guidelines for its realization. J Biomater Appl 14: 192–209 (1999).

[25] *Teumer, J, Hardin-Young, J, Parenteau, NL:* Tissue Engineered Skin. In: Patrick, Charles W,

Jr., Mikos, Antonios G. and McIntire, Larry V, Eds. Frontiers in Tissue Engineering. Elsevier Science Ltd., 1998.

[26] *Young J, Teumer J, Kemp P, Parenteau N:* Approaches to Transplanting Engineered Cells and Tissues. In: Lanza, R, Langer, R, Chick, W, (Eds). Principles of Tissue Engineering. R.G. Landes Company, pp. 297–307, (1997).

[27] *Michaeli D, McPherson M:* Immunlogic study of artificial skin used in the treatment of thermal injuries. J Burn Care Rehabil. 11:21–26, (1990).

[28] *Folkman J:* Angiogenesis: initiation and control. Ann. N Y Acad. Sci. 401:212–27 (1982).

[29] *Saadeh PB, Brent B, Mehrara BJ, Steinbrech DS, Ting V, Gittes GK, Longaker MT:* Human cartilage engineering: Chondrocyte extraction, proliferation, and characterization for construct development. Ann Plast Surg 42: 509–13 (1999).

[30] *Tubo RA, Barone LM, Wrenn CA:* Methods and compositions for the repair of articular cartilage defects in mammals US Patent 5,786,217 (Genzyme), (1998).

[31] *Caplan A, Syftestad GT:* Process of and material for stimulating growth of cartilage and bony tissue at anatomical sites US patent 4,609,551 (Osiris), (1986).

[32] *Purchio AF, Naughton BA:* Production of cartilage tissue using cells isolated from Wharton's jelly. US Patent 5,919,702 (ATS), (1999).

[33] *Vacanti JP, Vacanti CA, Langer RS:* Neo-morphogenesis of cartilage in vivo from cell culture US Patent 5,041,138(MIT), (1989) .

[34] *Vacanti JP, Langer RS:* Preparation of three-dimensional fibrous scaffold for attaching cells to produce vascularized tissue in vivo US Patent 5,770,193 (MIT), 1998.

[35] *Vacanti JP, Vacanti CA, Langer RS:* Biodegradable synthetic polymeric fibrous matrix containing chondrocyte for in vivo production of a cartilaginous structure US Patent 5,736,372 (MIT), (1998).

[36] *Vacanti JP, Vacanti CA, Langer RS:* Neomorphogenesis of cartilage in vivo from cell culture. US Patent 5,041,138 (MIT), (1991).

[37] *Griffith-Cima L, Atala A, Vacanti CA, Paige KT:* Tissue formation by injecting a cell-polymeric solution that gels in vivo. US Patent 5,709,854, (MIT), 1998.

[38] *Hunziker EB, Riedholz A:* Methods and compositions for the treatment and repair of defects or lesions in cartilage or bone US Patent 5,368,858 (Shaw), (1994).

[39] *Tubo RA, Barone LM, Wrenn CA:* Methods and compositions for the repair of articular cartilage defects in mammals. US Patent 5,786, 217 (Genzyme), (1991).

[40] *Schreiber RE, Dunkelman NS, Naughton G, Ratcliffe A:* A method for tissue engineering of cartilage by cell seeding on bioresorbable scaffolds. Ann N Y Acad Sci. 18;875:398–404, (1999).

[41] *Mueller W, Thaler T:* Process for regenerating bone and cartilage. US Patent 5,837, 235 (Sulzer), (1998)

[42] *Brekke JH:* Device and methods for in vivo culturing of diverse tissue cells. US Patent 5, 981, 825 (1999). (THM)

[43] *Marx G:* Fibrin glue gun. US Patent 5, 759, 169 (1998).

[44] *Marx G:* Fibrin sealant glue-gun with insertable compressed gas cartridge and Luer-type reservoir. US Patent 6, 059, 749 (2000).

Cultured Keratinocytes: Experimental and Clinical Directions in the Quest for Tissue Engineering New Skin

R. Martin, S. Bevan, J. Boorman, I. Grant, S. E. James, I. Jones, N. Parkhouse, R. Ng, P. Rubin, B. Woodward

Summary

Autologous and allogeneic cultured keratinocytes have been applied for a number of years to wounds in a variety of clinical situations. This chapter describes how a porcine model has been developed through the use of different dermal materials and by the addition gene marking techniques to investigate the fate of cultured keratinocytes when delivered to cutaneous wounds. A particular focus has been to improve the clinical use of cultured autologous keratinocytes in combination with the commercially available skin substitute Integra™. This study shows among other new approaches to keratinocyte transplantation the use of artificial skin (Integra™) sheets that had cultured MFGlacZnls labeled porcine keratinocytes simply applied to the lower surface of the matrix. The cells are adsorbed into the lower surface and in the pig at least, are able to grow upwards through the matrix after the seeded Integra™ was grafted in the normal fashion. It remains to be seen whether the success in the pig model is repeated for patients.

Introduction

Cultured autologous keratinocyte therapies for full thickness wounds have been available for more than 20 years [1, 2]. Sufficient evidence has accumulated to show that the de-livery of autologous keratinocyte sheets can prove both lifesaving and give improved cosmetic appearance [3–8]. However, this success is dependent on meticulous and co-ordinated attention to detail in the tissue culture laboratory, the operating theatre and during post-operative care. Consequently, very few centres have experienced continued good outcomes with a full restoration of a long-lived stable epidermis on unequivocal full thickness wounds. The therapeutic benefits of autologous Rheinwald & Green technology also come at a relatively high cost. Each patient's skin sample is handled as an individual batch since full automation has not yet replaced skilled technical personnel in the establishment, maintenance and provision of cultured autologous keratinocyte sheets.

The treatment of partial thickness and chronic wounds is less exacting. Here it seems likely that the provision of cytokine and growth factor signals from applied cultured epidermal and or dermal cells can be sufficient to stimulate the healing response and close the wound. In this context, allogeneic cells are likely to be as successful as autologous cultured grafts [9, 10]. Indeed, it has been established that allogeneic cell therapies can achieve closure through the encouragement of intrinsic tissues, rather than from a long term contribution, by looking for markers on the donor cells [11, 12]. Most donor cells do not survive for more than a few weeks, although sporadically some cells can survive for an appreciable time [13]. This realisation has not inhibited the development of allogeneic keratinocyte or fibroblast based therapies, either alone or as part of a composite tissue [14, 15]. Although the use of allogeneic tissue brings with it the need to screen for the transmission of disease, this is offset by the ability to manufacture large uniform batches and to carry out the production and testing at relative leisure. This is an ideal scenario for an industrial approach. The greater number of patients who might benefit from allogeneic-based therapies for chronic or partial-thickness wounds than for full-thickness autologous reconstruction, has further economic attractions for the manufacturer of skin cell products.

Notwithstanding the benefit that may be generated through allogeneic therapies, the use of autologous keratinocytes during reconstructive surgery or in the treatment of acute injury remains, in many minds, a more fascinating and exciting challenge, since one is truly undertaking tissue engineering for skin regeneration from it's constituent cell components. This chapter will review the different approaches that have been used in our group over the past 5 years. The aim has been to address the problems of skin replacement using cultured autologous cells in clinical situations and to understand the processes taking place on treated wounds through the testing of different keratinocyte technologies in a porcine model. A key to our work has been to employ retroviral gene transfer so that we can track the fate of autologous cells once they have been delivered to a wound.

The Clinical Questions

Figure 1 shows a series of pictures illustrating one clinical use of cultured keratinocytes prepared using Rheinwald & Green technology to culture epidermal cell sheets on irradiated 3T3 mouse fibroblast feeder cells [1, 2]. Fig. 1 illustrates a before, during and after sequence in which a pigmented burn scar was excised and covered with a large sheet of cultured autologous keratinocytes. The procedure was performed following local experience that indicated a good cosmetic appearance and a reduction in wound pain could be achieved fol-

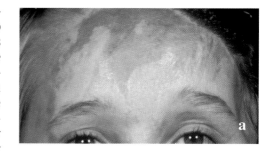
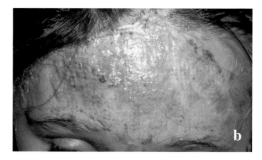
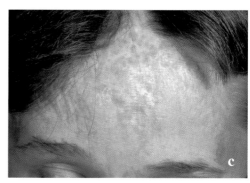

Fig. 1: Clinical applications of cultured keratinocytes as an accessory to wound healing. (a) A pigmented scar on a teenage girl who received a severe burn as a young child. The next day a biopsy of normal skin was taken from the forehead and used for keratinocyte culture. Twenty seven days later a single sheet of autologous cultured keratinocytes was applied to the scar area following dermabrasion. (b) The appearance of the wound site 7 days after keratinocyte sheet application. (c) Appearance of wound site 6 months following dermabrasion and keratinocyte application.

lowing the cell sheet application. However, it is very difficult to answer the question: how much do the autologous cells survive and contribute to the healed wound? Figure 2 shows the application of cultured autologous keratinocyte sheets to a full thickness burn wound grafted with Integra™ artificial skin [16]. The expectation that Integra™ (if applied to a cleanly and early excised full-thickness burn wound) can remain in place with a protective silicone upper layer for several weeks, in theory makes Integra™ an ideal partner for cultured autologous keratinocyte technology that takes two to three weeks to come on-stream. In the clinical case in Fig. 2 epidermis was regenerated on Integra™ neo-dermis using cultured cell sheets, yet the sheets did not take in every place they were applied [17]. What factors govern the adhesion and acceptance of cultured autologous sheets by the neo dermal Integra™ wound bed? We have attempted to recreate each of the clinical situations represented by Fig. 1 & 2 in a porcine wound chamber model in order to address these and other questions concerning the delivery of cultured autologous keratinocytes.

Testing Applications in a Porcine Skin Tissue Engineering Model

The wound-healing model we have employed was developed by Kangesu and colleagues [18, 19]. In order to prevent interference of the cells and materials within the test wound, a rigid 4 cm diameter PTFE chamber is inserted into a full thickness excision to muscle fascia. Three chambers per flank in a Large White pig of 20 kg and upwards are permitted under the current UK Home Office Licensing regulations. Fig. 3 shows an operative photograph with three chambers *in situ*. The particular experiment illustrated was to test the bio-integration of an acellular processed dermis that is visible within the chambers. The wounds will be covered with a non-adhesive dressing, packed with moistened gauze and enclosed in a protective jacket. The chambers can remain in place for approximately 5–6 weeks during which time the internal wound area is isolated from the surrounding tissue. After this time the chambers begin to extrude and the animals are sacrificed.

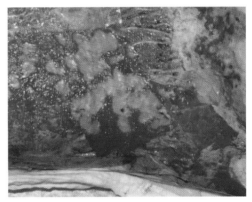

Fig. 2: Clinical applications of cultured keratinocytes to reconstruct full thickness skin injury. Following a significant full thickness burn injury (60 % TBSA) to a teenage boy, early excision and grafting with Integra™ was carried out. A biopsy of normal skin was taken for keratinocyte culture. (a) At 21 days after Integra™ application sheets of autologous cultured keratinocytes were applied on Vaseline gauze backing dressings to one complete side of the upper torso after removal of the silicone upper layer. (b) The same area viewed in (a) after 16 days. There are areas of epidermis that expanded in subsequent weeks, although take was not uniform.

If autologous skin is harvested from the dorsal area of the animal and subjected to Dispase incubation, the epidermal layer can be removed. The subsequent autologous De-Epidermalised Dermis (DED) can be grafted into the chamber. This technique has been employed to provide a fresh dermal substrate for keratinocyte grafts where the in-

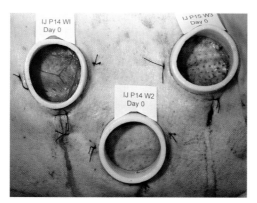

Fig. 3: Porcine chamber model. The porcine chamber originally developed by Kangesu et al [19]. One flank of the Large White pig showing 3 chambers in place. The PTFE chambers are rigid but some distortion can result through repeated use and sterilisation.

vestigators have sought to eliminate any allogeneic response to the dermis [18, 20]. However, there are risks to this approach. Fig. 4 (a) shows the relationship between the thickness of the DED and the subsequent emergence of epidermal tissue after two weeks. When the DED is below 200 µm there is virtually no regeneration and cultured keratinocyte grafts give rise to a statistically significant increase in epidermal area. As thicker DED is harvested, epidermal regeneration from remnants within the dermis escape removal by Dispase and survive to resurface the wound. Fig. 4 (a) shows that regeneration is proportional to DED thickness. Thus above a certain threshold, grafts of autologous DED can be represented as a

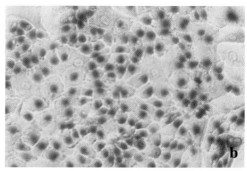

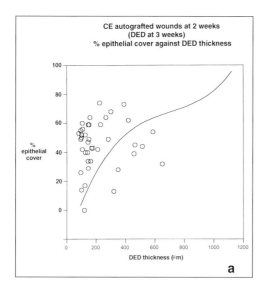

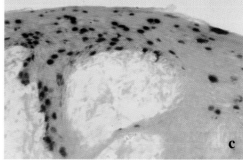

Fig. 4 Delivery of cultured autologous keratinocytes to fresh de-epidermalised dermis (DED) in porcine wound chambers. (a) The relationship between DED thickness and the resultant re-epithelialisation from dermal epidermal remnants (solid line n=33 polynomial regression $r^2 = 0.75$). The open circles show the epidermal area on a particular thickness DED following application of cultured autologous keratinocyte sheets, n= 40. (b) Porcine keratinocytes growing as a monolayer transduced with *MFGlacZnls* retrovirus and stained with the substrate X-gal. (c) Cryosection through a DED wound (approx. 400 µm thickness) grafted with a sheet of *MFGlacZnls* marked keratinocytes (approximately 15 % marked) 2 weeks earlier and stained with X-gal and eosin.

type of partial thickness wound healing model. If cultured autologous keratinocytes are applied to DED wounds with a partial regenerative capacity, how can one distinguish between the stimulation of the epidermal remnants by the cultured cell sheet from the establishment of replacement epidermis from the cells that were in culture? This situation is analogous to the question posed by the clinical photographs in Figure 1. In the Large White pig we have addressed this issue by using retroviral gene transfer to mark cultured cells whilst they are in culture [21, 22]. The cultured cells and their descendants can then be tracked in the regenerating wound.

Tracking the Fate of Cultured Keratinocytes Using Retroviral Marking

Retroviral mediated gene transfer (transduction) is the ideal means for marking autologous cells that need to be followed over many cell divisions. The viral vector integrates at random into the target cell genome and is replicated and expressed over many cell divisions [23]. Other methods such as membrane dye marking or DNA labeling with BrdU or Hoechst 33342 may be harmful to the cells, the label may leak into unlabelled cells and in any case, the marker intensity halves every time the cell divides [24]. Adenoviral gene transfer, although more efficient than retrovirus, is transient and the adenoviral genes can give rise to an immune response against the transduced cells [25]. Markers can become permanently integrated following chemical or physical methods of DNA transfection, but the efficiency of this is very low and a period of selection needs to be applied to expand a population of cells marked by the transfected gene [26]. Consequently it is less likely that primary cells will survive with enough population doublings following transfection and selection to enjoy sufficient remaining growth potential when they are returned to the host. Furthermore, in experiments with autologous animal cells, the donor animal would need to be kept and maintained for what might be a significant period whilst the transfection-selection process is carried out.

In our laboratory we have used the widely available murine moloney leukemia based *MFGlacZnls* vector [27]. This introduces the *E. coli lacZ* gene encoding the enzyme β-galactosidase to which a nuclear localising sequence has been inserted. The "nls" triggers the transport of all the β-galactosidase molecules into the nucleus. This has the effect of concentrating the enzyme into a smaller volume and increasing the chance of histochemical detection. It also enables the distinction between genuine *MFGlacZnls* cell transductants from other cells that might be expressing endogenous mammalian β-galactosidase. Endogenous β-galactosidase is always in the cytoplasm. Retroviral gene transfer requires a cell line that produces the viral gene products *gag, pol* and *env*. The cell line will use these to package any retroviral vector RNA sequence that is expressed in the cell. Typically such cell lines have been derived from murine 3T3 fibroblasts. An efficient means of transducing cultured keratinocytes is therefore to γ-irradiate the retroviral producer cell line and use this as a fibroblast feeder in the normal way. We have used a culture method for porcine keratinocytes that requires collagen-I coated tissue culture plastic and irradiated fibroblast feeders. Under these conditions primary porcine keratinocytes can be expanded for many passages from relatively low seeding densities in conditions of 1% foetal calf serum and 0.5 mM Calcium [22]. Fig. 4 (b) shows a monolayer of porcine keratinocytes in culture transduced with *MFGlacZnls*. The cells never reach more than about 2–3 cell layers thick in the media as described, but they will form sheets sufficient to be graftable. Fig. 4 (c) shows a DED wound with some regenerative capability removed from the pig 2 weeks after grafting with a retroviral labeled sheets of autologous cultured keratinocytes. Clearly the epidermis is a combination of the cells from culture, not all of which were marked, and the endogenous epithelium from the wound bed. Thus when reflecting on the clinical situation in Fig. 1, one can feel justified on the evidence of the marking experiments that cultured keratinocytes and endogenous epidermis can form an intermingled tissue, at least for a significant period. How long the cultured cells remain components of the new tissue will depend on the number of renewable "stem cells" that are part of the cultured cell population. Retroviral labeling has been used as an informative way of assess-

ing the proliferative unit in skin in a number of animal models [22, 26, 28, 29].

Application of Cultured Keratinocytes to Integra Artificial Skin

Given the unpredictable efficiency of the application of cultured keratinocytes to biointegrated Integra™ artificial skin in patients (see Fig. 2), we have sought to test the application

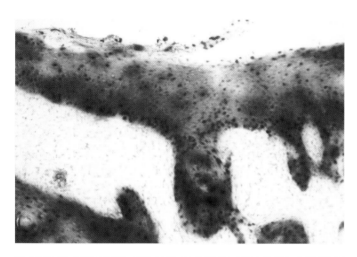

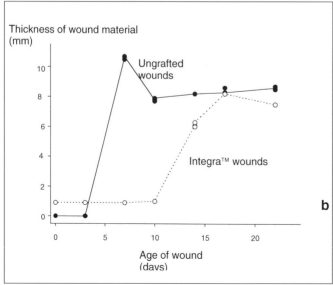

Fig. 5: Integra™ artificial skin as a wound bed for cultured keratinocytes in porcine wound chambers. (a) Cryosection through a wound grafted with Integra™ artificial skin to which a sheet of *MFGlacZnls* cultured autologous keratinocytes was applied after 10 days. The marking frequency was approximately 90% in this case. (b) A comparison of the thickness of tissue accumulating in the porcine wound chamber in ungrafted and Integra grafted wounds. The data were obtained by excising individual wound chambers at the indicated times and measuring the depth of the unfixed fresh tissue accumulating above the original muscle fascia.

of cultured cells to Integra™ in pigs. With a few modifications to the grafting protocol the take of Integra™ can reach close to 100% in the chambered pig model [30]. Figure 5 (a) shows an image of a wound in the pig that was grafted with Integra and after 10 days was grafted with a thin sheet of cultured autologous keratinocytes that had been labeled to high efficiency with the *MFGlacZnls* retrovirus. The *lacZ* labeled epidermis proves that bio-integrated Integra can support cultured epidermal sheets, a finding that has also been demonstrated by other groups working with the pig but without the added confidence of using labeled cells [31]. It is interesting and important however to consider, on what tissue the cultured cells are found. Fig. 5 (b) shows the result of an experiment in the porcine chamber model in which the thickness of new granulation tissue deposited on an open wound surface was compared to that of a wound grafted with Integra™. Whilst the silicone membrane is intact there is no change in the depth of tissue deposited in the wound. In the non-Integra™ wound covered with a non-adherent dressing and saline-soaked gauze, about 8mm of scar tissue has formed after 8 days. The Integra™ matrix fills with cells, but there is no increase in tissue depth for 10 days. In contrast, when the silicone sloughs off the bio-integrated Integra™ matrix (which occurs in the pig after 10 days), there is then a steady accumulation of granulation tissue/scar tissue that matches the ungrafted wound within 7 days. Consequently when thin cultured epidermal sheets that provide a minimal epidermal barrier function are grafted onto bio integrated Integra™, the result is an epidermis situated on a layer of granulation/scar tissue, not epidermis on an Integra™ neo-dermal matrix.

New Techniques to Deliver Cultured Keratinocytes

The recognition that the clinical efficiency of cultured epidermal cell sheets applied to Integra™ artificial skin is less than satisfactory and that the granulation tissue response is not

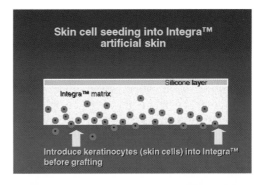

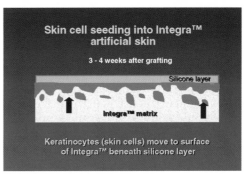

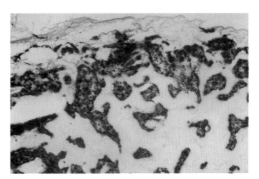

Fig. 6: Skin cell seeding into Integra™ artificial skin. (a) Diagrammatic representation of the introduction of skin cells into the collagen-gag matrix layer of Integra™ artificial skin by centrifugation. (b) Diagrammatic representation of the anticipated outcome following skin cell seeding into Integra™. (c) Cryosection of Integra™ artificial skin removed from a porcine wound chamber and stained with X-gal substrate where a suspension of *MFGlacZnls* labeled autologous porcine keratinocytes was applied to the lower surface of the Integra™ matrix without centrifugation 7 days earlier. The cells are able to proliferate and move upwards through the matrix.

dampened by a thin sheet of cultured cells, has prompted other avenues of exploration. One approach is to apply a more fully formed *in vitro* cultivated epidermal-dermal composite so that the problems of barrier function and adhesion of the epidermis to the Integra™ matrix are overcome [32]. An alternative approach that avoids a complex tissue engineering process is to centrifuge isolated but non-cultured skin cells into the Integra™ matrix so that they come to rest beneath the silicone layer (see Fig. 6 a & b). When grafted on to guinea pig wounds an epidermis was regenerated [33]. Although this has been described several years ago for a forerunner to Integra™ it has not yet emerged in clinical practice. The potential advantage is that an epidermal barrier is regenerated beneath the protection of the silicone cover. Subsequently the same centrifuge approach has been applied with cultured as well as uncultured cells in pigs [34–36]. Recently we have asked whether the cumbersome centrifugation step is in fact necessary. Fig. 6 (c) shows an image of an Integra™ sheet that had cultured *MFGlacZnls* labeled porcine keratinocytes simply applied to the lower surface of the matrix. The cells are adsorbed into the lower surface and in the pig at least, are able to grow upwards through the matrix after the seeded Integra™ was grafted in the normal fashion [37]. This represents a simpler and more amenable procedure than centrifugation. It remains to be seen whether the success in the pig model is repeated for patients. This work is currently in progress.

Acknowledgements

This work has been funded by the East Grinstead Medical Research Trust (Reg. UK charity 258154) through grants from among others the Royal College of Surgeons of England, The Band Trust, & Smiths Charities. We are grateful to Integra Life Sciences Inc. for the provision of Integra™ Artificial skin. We are also indebted to Prof. Colin Green for his support during his time as Director at the Blond McIndoe Centre. (The order of the co-authors following the first author was determined alphabetically).

References

[1] *Rheinwald JG, Green H:* Serial cultivation of strains of human epidermal keratinocytes: the formation of keratinising colonies from single cells. Cell 6:331–344 (1975)
[2] *Green H, Kehinde O, Thomas J:* Growth of cultured human epidermal cells into multiple epithelia suitable for grafting. Proc.Natl.Acad. Sci.U.S.A. 76:5665–5668 (1979)
[3] *Gallico GG, O'Connor NE, Compton CC, Kehinde O, Green H:* Permanent coverage of large burn wounds with autologous cultured human epithelium. New Eng J Med 311:448–451 (1984)
[4] *Hickerson WL, Compton C, Fletchall S, Smith LR:* Cultured epidermal autografts and allodermis combination for permanent burn wound coverage. Burns. 20 Suppl 1:S52–S55 (1994)
[5] *Langdon RC, Cuono CB, Birchall N, Madri JA, Kuklinska E, McGuire J:* Reconstitution of structure and cell function in human skin grafts derived from cryopreserved allogeneic dermis and autologous cultured keratinocytes. Journal of Investigative Dermatology 91:478–485 (1988)
[6] *De Luca M, Albanese E, Bondanza S, Megna M, Ugozzoli L, Molina F, Cancedda R, Santi PL, Bormioli M, Stella M:* Multicentre experience in the treatment of burns with autologous and allogenic cultured epithelium, fresh or preserved in a frozen state. Burns. 15:303–309 (1989)
[7] *Munster AM:* Cultured skin for massive burns. A prospective, controlled trial. Annals of Surgery 224:372–377 (1996)
[8] *Pellegrini G, Ranno R, Stracuzzi G, Bondanza S, Guerra L, Zambruno G, Micali G, De Luca M:* The control of epidermal stem cells (holoclones) in the treatment of massive full-thickness burns with autologous keratinocytes cultured on fibrin. Transplantation 68:868–879 (1999)
[9] *Fratianne R, Papay F, Housini I, Lang C, Schafer IA:* Keratinocyte allografts accelerate healing of split-thickness donor sites: applications for improved treatment of burns. Journal of Burn Care & Rehabilitation 14:148–154 (1993)
[10] *Oliver AM, Kaawach W, Mithoff EW, Watt A, Abramovich DR, Rayner CR:* The differentiation and proliferation of newly formed epidermis on wounds treated with cultured epithelial allografts. British Journal of Dermatology 125:147–154 (1991)

[11] *Burt AM, Pallett CD, Sloane JPO, Hare MJ, Schafler KF, Yardeni P, Eldad A, Clarke JA, Gusterson BA:* Survival of cultured allografts in patients with burns assessed with probe specific for Y chromosome. BMJ. 298:915–917 (1989)

[12] *Brain A, Purkis P, Coates P, Hackett M, Navsaria H, Leigh I:* Survival of cultured allogeneic keratinocytes transplanted to deep dermal bed assessed with probe specific for Y chromosome. BMJ 298:917–919 (1989)

[13] *Otto WR, Nanchahal J, Lu QL, Boddy N, Dover R:* Survival of allogeneic cells in cultured organotypic skin grafts. Plast.Reconstr.Surg. 96:166–176 (1995)

[14] *Hansbrough JF, Morgan J, Greenleaf G, Underwood J:* Development of a temporary living skin replacement composed of human neo natal fibroblasts cultured in Biobrane, a synthetic dressing material. Surgery 115:633–644 (1994)

[15] *Falanga V, Sabolinski M:* A bilayered living skin construct (APLIGRAF) accelerates complete closure of hard-to-heal venous ulcers. Wound.Repair Regen. 7:201–207 (1999)

[16] *Heimbach D, Luterman A, Burke J, Cram A, Herndon D, Hunt J, Jordan M, McManus W, Solem L, Warden G:* Artificial dermis for major burns. A multi-center randomized clinical trial. Ann.Surg. 208:313–320 (1988)

[17] *Pandya AN, Woodward B, Parkhouse N:* The use of cultured autologous keratinocytes with Integra in the resurfacing of acute burns. Plast.Reconstr.Surg. 102:825–825 (1998)

[18] *Kangesu T, Navsaria HA, Manek S, Fryer PR, Leigh IM, Green C:* Kerato-dermal grafts: the importance of dermis for the in vivo growth of cultured keratinocytes. British Journal of Plastic Surgery 46:401–409 (1993)

[19] *Kangesu T, Navsaria HA, Manek S, Shurey CB, Jones CR, Fryer PR, Leigh IM, Green CJ:* A porcine model using skin graft chambers for studies on cultured keratinocytes. British Journal of Plastic Surgery 46:393–400 (1993)

[20] *Myers SR, Grady J, Soranzo C, Saunders R, Green C, Leigh IM, Navsaria H A:* A hyaluronic acid membrane delivery system for cultured keratinocytes: clinical "take" rates in the porcine kerato-dermal model. Journal of Burn Care & Rehabilitation 18:214–222 (1997)

[21] *Bevan S, Woodward B, Ng RLH, Green C, Martin R:* Retroviral gene transfer into porcine keratinocytes following improved methods of cultivation. Burns 23:525–532 (1997)

[22] *Ng RLH, Woodward B, Bevan S, Green C, Martin R:* Retroviral marking identifies grafted autologous keratinocytes in porcine wounds receiving cultured epithelium. J.Invest.Dermatol 108:457–462 (1997)

[23] *Fenjves ES:* Approaches to gene transfer in keratinocytes. J.Invest.Derm. 103 (Suppl): 70S–75S (1994)

[24] *Mosahebi A, Woodward B, Green C, Martin R, Terenghi G:* Long-term effect of vital labelling on mixed Schwann cell cultures. The Histochemical Journal 32:337–343 (2000)

[25] *Setoguchi Y, Jaffe HA, Danel C, Crystal RG:* Ex vivo and in vivo gene transfer to the skin using replication-deficient recombinant adenovirus vectors. J.Invest.Dermatol. 102:415–421 (1994)

[26] *Bevan S, Martin R, McKay IA:* The production and application of genetically modified skin cells. In: Biotechnology and Genetic Engineering Reviews. SE Harding, ed. Intercept Ltd, Andover, UK. Volume 16, chapter 9. 231–256pp (1999)

[27] *Ferry N, Duplessis O, Houssin D, Danos O, Heard JM:* Retroviral-mediated gene transfer into hepatocytes in vivo. Proc.Natl.Acad.Sci.U.S.A. 88:8377–8381 (1991)

[28] *Ng RLH, Woodward B, Bevan S, Martin R:* Another support for the location of epidermal stem cells residing adjacent to the tips of dermal papillae in the interfollicular epidermis. J.Invest.Dermatol 109:697 (1997)

[29] *Kolodka TM, Garlick JA, Taichman BL:* Evidence for keratinocyte stem cells in vitro: long term engraftment and persistence of transgene expression from retrovirus-transduced keratinocytes. Proc Natl Acad Sci USA 95:4356–4361 (1998)

[30] *Grant, I., Green, C., and Martin, R.:* Strategies to improve the take of a commercially available collagen/glycosaminoglycan wound repair material investigated in an animal model. Burns (2001). In Press.

[31] *Orgill DP, Butler CE, Regan JF, Barlow MS, Yannas IV, Compton CC:* Vascularized collagen-glycosaminoglycan matrix provides a dermal substrate and improves take of cultured epithelial autografts. Plast.Reconstr.Surg. 102: 423–429 (1998)

[32] *Boyce ST, Kagan RJ, Meyer NA, Yakuboff KP, Warden GD:* The 1999 clinical research award. Cultured skin substitutes combined with Integra Artificial Skin to replace native skin autograft and allograft for the closure of excised full-thickness burns. J Burn Care Rehabil 20:453–461 (1999)

[33] *Yannas IV, Lee E, Orgill DP, Skrabut EM, Murphy GF:* Synthesis and characterization of a model extracellular matrix that induces partial regeneration of adult mammalian skin. Proc Natl Acad Sci U.S.A. 86:933–937 (1989)

[34] *Butler CE, Orgill DP, Yannas IV, Compton CC:* Effect of keratinocyte seeding of collagen-glycosaminoglycan membranes on the re-

generation of skin in a porcine model. Plast.Reconstr.Surg. 101:1572–1579 (1998)

[35] *Butler CE, Yannas IV, Compton CC, Correia CA, Orgill DP:* Comparison of cultured and uncultured keratinocytes seeded into a collagen-GAG matrix for skin replacements. Br.J.Plast.Surg. 52:127–132 (1999)

[36] *Compton CC, Butler CE, Yannas IV, Warland G, Orgill DP:* Organized skin structure is regenerated in vivo from collagen-GAG matrices seeded with autologous keratinocytes. J.Invest.Dermatol. 110:908–916 (1998)

[37] *Jones, I, James, L, Rubin, P, Green, C, Martin, R:* Confluent epidermal regeneration following application of disaggregated cultured autologous keratinocytes beneath Integra artificial skin (Abstract). Cells Tissues Organs 166, 39 (2000)

The Role and Requirements of Dermis in Keratinocyte Grafting

R. D. Price, I. M. Leigh, H. A. Navsaria

Summary

This is a review of dermal substitutes in keratinocyte grafting. Our porcine chamber model is described, in which a chamber is inserted into a full-thickness wound created on the back of pigs. When a dermal component is added, epidermal regeneration improves; when epidermal cover is provided, angiogenesis and collagen reorganization improve. The use of hyaluronic acid and collagen as dermal matrices are described. Hyaluronic acid, formed by fibroblasts, is upregulated during wound healing. Chemical modification of hyaluronic acid leads to forms which can be handled and moulded. Both porcine chamber experiments and clinical trials with this material (Laserskin®) have been promising.

The material produced by the Rheinwald & Green system was, typically, only a few cells thick and very fragile to handle (Fig. 1). It was released from the flask by the application of dispase and contraction of the graft was a dominant feature, even when backing systems to ease surgical grafting were used. These difficulties were compounded by early observations that the grafts took poorly on deep wounds, especially full thickness injuries excised to subcutis, and were fragile for a period of weeks. The long-term outcome was also marred by a propensity to blister and shear spontaneously. Both of the latter features have been attributed to the abnormal dermo-epidermal junction formed after grafting onto fascia or deep dermis, in particular the lack of rête ridges formed during wound healing.

Despite these problems, early results using this technology were very promising. Early work by Leigh et al [2] showed that al-

Introduction

It is over twenty-five years since Rheinwald and Green [1] published their method of human keratinocyte culture in the laboratory and the initial euphoria surrounding the discovery led to the belief that provision of skin cover in injuries as diverse as burns, chronic ulcers, scar revision surgery and vitiligo could now be addressed. The issue itself might be addressed in several ways; both autologous and allogenic keratinocyte grafting would be possible, possibly with the addition of xeno-grafting.

Fig. 1: Keratinocyte sheet held by surgeon. The material is so thin as to appear transparent and its appearance demonstrates the ease which it may be damaged.

logenic cells accelerated the healing of chronic venous ulcers and that autologous cells could be used to re-epithelialise the oral cavity [3]. Other workers showed that this technology could accelerate the healing of both acute [4] and chronic wounds [2] but whether allogenic cells were truly repopulating the neo-epidermis or simply accelerating healing remained in doubt until 1989 when Brain et al [5] used a human model to graft allogenic cells. Having taken biopsies they performed in-situ hybridisation for the Y chromosome and demonstrated that no cells persisted, work that was mirrored in the burn wound by Burt et al [6]. Frustratingly, formal rejection has been difficult to elicit [7] and studies showing second-set accelerated rejection [8] have failed to show the florid reaction one would expect of cells expressing the Major Histocompatability Antigen (MHC) class II molecules *in vivo*.

Evidence for rejection of allogenic keratinocytes came in 1991 when Carver et al [9] used the open porcine wound model to demonstrate clinical and histological rejection after grafting. They demonstrated a lymphohistiocytic infiltrate under the allogenic material and foci of necrotic keratinocytes, features that were maximal at day 13. Persistence of these cells was only seen when immunosuppression was used, for example when animals were treated with cyclosporin [10] in the same model. In this instance, no clinical or histological evidence for rejection was seen up to 17 days after grafting.

The Porcine Wound Chamber Model

A number of animal models are used for the investigation of wound healing. Small animal work centres around the mouse, either athymic or immunocompetent, and occasionally the rat. The latter is particularly used where chambers are to be inserted as it is larger and more manageable than the mouse. Both rodent models suffer, however, because of the amount of skin that is avail-

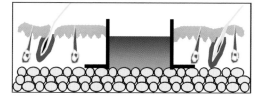

Fig. 2: Porcine chamber model.

able to scientists. Although relatively cheap and therefore useful for experiments involving large numbers, each animal may only host a maximum of two experiments. Equally, the micro-anatomy of the skin is dissimilar to that of human; there is only minimal dermis and the nature of furry skin prevents direct comparison with human. For these reasons, the pig model has been adopted. The original model involved the excision of defined areas on the flanks of the animal, allowing up to eight wounds of 16 cm^2 on each animal. However wound contraction made this a scientifically poor model since it was difficult, after the initial weeks of study, to differentiate between host and donor epidermis and, by extension, the relative contributions of each to the healed wound.

In order to circumvent these problems, our centre developed the pig chamber model [11, 12]. In this method, a full-thickness wound is created on the flank of the animal by the excision of skin and subcutaneous tissue. Initial excision was to the level of the underlying panniculosis carnosis muscle, but with confirmation in 1998 by Miller et al [13] that deeply-placed sweat glands could re-epithelialise such wounds, most workers now excise to the layer of investing fascia. After creation of the wound, the edges are undermined for a distance of approximately 1 cm before a chamber made of polytetrafluoroethylene is inserted. The chamber has a flange, which is sited subcutaneously and after being sutured in place isolates the wound bed (Fig.2). The penalty for the flange is a fall in the number of wounds available to three per flank (Fig. 3).

Fig. 3: Flank of pig showing three chambers in situ. The subcutaneous flanges prevent greater numbers from being applied.

The model described at the Centre for Cutaneous Research is useful for the scientific study of wound healing as it provides a well-defined and delineated wound of known depth and size. Any regeneration of skin and, particularly, epidermis must be due to scientific intervention and assessments such as biopsies and estimates of epithelial cover are simple and accurate. However the model differs from clinical practice in a number of respects; it is an acute wound and therefore not necessarily indicative of wounds found in the hospital setting. The chamber prevents epithelial migration or dermal contraction, both of which are to be expected in clinical practice. However, experience over time has shown it to be a suitable model for investigating wound healing, particularly within the field of tissue engineering, and it is now one of the commonest models used.

Development of Dermal Equivalents

Elucidating the cause of poor take in keratinocyte technology proved challenging and it was not until the end of the 1970's that the requirement for a dermal component began to be appreciated. In 1979 Prunièras [14] de-

scribed a method of removing the epidermal component of whole skin, leaving de-epidermalised dermis (DED), one of several methods now recognised for production of the material. The method of removal and subsequent preservation affects the nature of the basement membrane components that remain and are therefore available for keratinocyte attachment.

The appreciation that a dermis was required led, in the mid-1980's, to the emergence of cadaver grafting as an alternative, but using a modified method in order to preserve a degree of temporary barrier function. Cuono first described his method of allogenic/autologous grafting in 1986 [15] based upon the acute grafting of allogenic whole skin, followed after two weeks by mechanical removal of the (allogenic) epidermal component and engraftment of cultured ep-

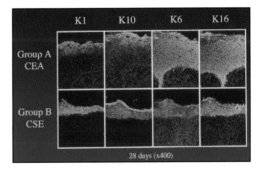

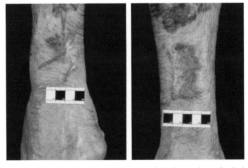

Fig. 4: (a) Keratin expression with cultured epithelial autograft (CEA) placed directly onto wound bed, compared to cultured skin equivalent (CSE), (b) Clinical photographs showing differences between (i) keratinocyte sheet grafting and (ii) composite grafting.

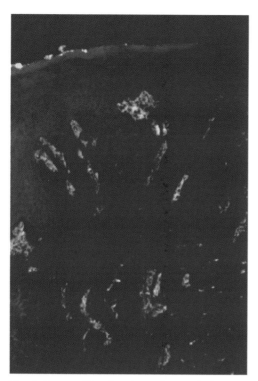

Fig. 5: Immunohistochemistry of wound showing angiogenesis; monoclonal antibody directed against von Willebrand factor, x 10.

idermal autograft (CEA) sheets. The method proved successful but, importantly, it was based on the belief that allogenic epidermis would not survive grafting, a concept that would take several years to be generally accepted. Clear evidence for this concept was provided by the first study to use the porcine chamber model; in 1993 Kangesu et al [16] demonstrated markedly improved results with two-stage grafting compared against keratinocyte sheets. In this study, dermal grafts were produced in vitro before being grafted onto acute full-thickness wounds within the chambers, followed by keratinocyte sheets. The control group consisted of keratinocyte sheets grafted onto a fascial bed and the results showed that not only was a greater take rate to be expected, but the epidermal differentiation was grossly improved (Fig. 4a).

Our centre [17] went on to investigate the regeneration to be expected when a dermal component was used in 1998. The study demonstrated superior nerve and blood vessel ingrowth and organisation when a dermal component was added to the system (Fig. 5). Other findings were, particularly, that (a) neoangiogenesis and innervation were prominent only where epidermal cover was provided, (b) that collagen re-organisation was superior under the same circumstances, and (c) that conversely, good epidermal regeneration only occurred in the prescence of a dermal component. These, along with work by investigators such as Bell et al [18, 19], Cuono et al [15, 20] and Yannas et al [21–23] confirmed the belief that a dermal component was necessary. It was because of these and other works that biopolymers were developed; dermal templates that could be mass produced and which would enhance wound healing.

The first bio-engineered dermal equivalent was that described by Bell et al as early as 1979 [24], based upon a simple collagen lattice which was contracted *in vitro* by fibroblasts. Two years later Burke et al [21] demonstrated clinically the possibility of providing superior skin cover using a modification of this material, with added chondroitin-6-sulphate, a modification that slowed collagen degradation [25] within the system. The material integrated and provided a supporting substrate upon which a split-thickness autograft could be used and which, over a period of months, regenerated into a structure not dissimilar to native dermis. It was these discoveries that began the search for an optimal dermal replacement strategy, a challenge that has persisted for over twenty years.

Amongst the newer biotechnologies are several materials that provide the same basic function, with some variations between them. Their common aim is to provide a scaffold for the host tissue to re-organise and regenerate into dermis. For this reason they are all formed of endogenous components of the extracellular matrix (ECM), although each technology addresses one component preferentially. The commonest materials in use are those based upon collagen or hyaluronic acid. The former is generally presented in the form of xenogenic material which acts as a gel or scaffold for the controlled in-growth of granulation tissue, by which it is degraded. Hyaluronic acid is an exception to this as it has been shown to actively enhance wound healing, and will be discussed further remove below.

Hyaluronic Acid

Hyaluronic acid (also known as hyaluronan) is a large-chain polysaccharide endogenous to normal skin. Formed, it is thought uniquely, at the cell surface of fibroblasts by extrusion into the ECM, it is up-regulated during normal wound healing [26] where it may act via its hydrostatic properties [27]. The molecule as a whole also has properties that include free-radical scavenging [28, 29], and modulation of granulation tissue formation [30, 31], and has been implicated in scarless fetal healing [32–34].

Fibroblasts appear to carry at least three receptors allowing specific attachment to hyaluronic acid; RHAMM (the Receptor for Hyaluronic Acid Mediated Motility), ICAM-1 (InterCellular Adhesion Molecule) and CD44, allowing attachment and migration along such molecules (and, by extension, matrices made of the material). Furthermore, fibroblasts also elaborate hyaluronidase, the enzyme responsible for degradation of the large polymer and are able to internalise both the original molecule and, particularly, its breakdown products [35]. Such degradation relies upon the cleaving of short-chain polymers of between 2 and 12 units in length, each of which appears to carry specific properties affecting wound healing. The longer chains specifically enhance, amongst others, the angiogenic [36, 37] and neurogenic responses during healing, whilst the medium length chains appear to modulate the deposition of collagen [38, 39] and decrease fibrinolytic activity [40], encouraging the formation of a more functional scar. There is dispute over the function of the

shorter chains with some authors showing increased epidermal proliferation [41] and some decreased.

The macrommolecule therefore gives rise to large numbers of smaller, active substances as it is degraded, and can therefore be considered as more than a simple scaffold. It is an active biological determinant of wound healing and is relatively unique in this regard.

Naturally-occurring hyaluronic acid is, however, soluble in water and forms a liquid gel which is degraded within 24 hours. However by chemically modifying the molecule, specifically by alcohol esterification, the tensile and degradation properties of the material can be altered. This allows the formation of a material which is much stronger and as such may be woven or moulded into a number of forms, at the same time preventing rapid degradation and therefore allowing prolonged delivery of the breakdown products to the wound bed. The matrices thus formed therefore not only provide a dermal template but also a degree of active modulation of wound healing, properties which are unique within this field. The three-dimensional nature of some of the materials formed further lends itself to the field of tissue engineering; in this respect it has applications outside of skin that include cartilage and bone engineering.

Studies undertaken at our centre have demonstrated clinical benefits associated with the use of hyaluronic acid. In the pig chamber model, it has been used for wound bed preparation prior to second-stage grafting with autologous keratinocytes. The resultant neo-dermis formed was superior to that associated with direct grafting and the take rates of the epithelium were superior (Fig. 6). More recently, Myers et al [42] have trialled a membrane delivery system (Laserskin®, Fidia Advanced Biopolymers, Italy) for keratinocytes based upon a thin sheet of fully-esterified hyaluronic acid. This allowed grafting of keratinocytes at early confluence and showed equal or greater take rates compared to sheet grafting. Most recently this method has been further refined

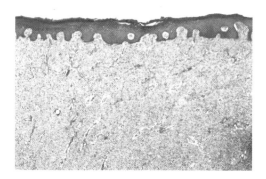

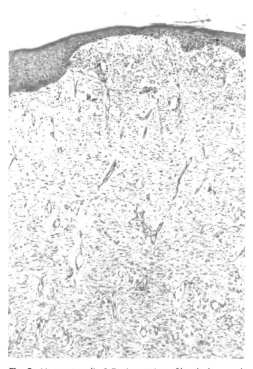

Fig. 6: Haematoxylin & Eosin section of healed wound (a) with and (b) without dermal pre-treatment.

In Vitro Culture Prior to Grafting

In recent years the possibility of allowing in vitro modification of dermal analogues prior to engraftment has been investigated. Many authors have shown that the product obtained in the laboratory following a period of culture with fibroblasts is more complex than the initial material onto which those cells were seeded. For example, Landeen [47] has shown that after a short lag phase there is a linear rise in concentration of certain ECM components, associated with increasing fibroblast number. After a period, some levels appear to stabilise and this would be in keeping with an attempt by the cell to modulate its local environment to mimic more closely that found *in vivo*. Using this principle, culturing these dermal analogues for a period prior to grafting would be expected to produce a matrix which more closely resembles native dermis.

There is a substantial body of evidence to suggest that this technique might confer benefits in terms of improved wound healing. Benefits shown include improved collagen deposition and remodelling [48, 49], increased survival of keratinocytes [50–52], improved Dermo-Epidermal Junction formation [53] with both autologous and allogenic fibroblast seeding, increased growth factor production, whilst several authors have shown less myofibroblast formation and an associated decrease in wound contraction.

The fundamental question of function of grafted fibroblasts on the wound bed and, in particular their longevity, has troubled workers in the field. Given the gross influx of host cells in relation to those grafted, some doubt as to the *in vivo* efficacy of the technique must be raised. Cell senescence has been demonstrated in chronic wounds [54–57], possibly because of altered cytokine profiles or responsiveness [58–61], and abnormal responses shown in hypertrophic or keloid wounds [62–64], but little effort has been given to cell dynamics in the normal (acute) healing wound. The only area to be extensively assessed is that pertaining to the removal of the large influx of host inflammatory cells

by Harris et al [43] to allow grafting at a pre-confluent stage, which allows either earlier preparation of cells or greater numbers of sheets. The development of pre-confluent delivery systems has invlolved other groups developing fibrin glue delivery systems, first as a net [44] and more recently as a spray-on aerosol [45, 46].

as the wound closes. In this regard much of the evidence points to apoptosis [65–68] as the mechanism for reducing cell numbers; levels are high in wounds that heal successfully, and surgically providing full thickness wound cover provokes a significant increase as compared to granulating wounds [69]. It is not unreasonable to conclude that when partial thickness wound cover is provided a similar method of removal might be observed.

In terms of allogenic cell transfer the earliest published work and, to date, the gold standard in the field, is from Sher et al [70] who transplanted allogenic cells in a rat model, performed explant cultures and karyotyped proliferating cells. Using these methods, they showed that female cells survived in a male host as late as 210 days. More recently, Hultman et al [71] have shown that allogenic cells cannot be detected by MHC Class II-specific staining after eight days, although it is unclear whether fibroblasts would express this molecule *in vivo*; results might have been due to either down-regulation of the molecule or to cell clearance. There is therefore some polarity regarding this question; older methods have been superseded by newer technologies and the persistent uncertainty regarding *in vivo* expression of cell surface markers prevents the formation of accurate conclusions. We therefore set out to assess how long allogenic cells survived after grafting and, if cleared, how that might take place.

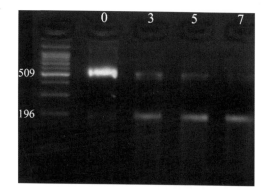

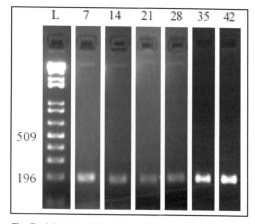

Fig. 7: (a) PCR gel showing mal DNA (size 509 bp) at days 3,5 and 7. PCR for chromosome 3 is 196 bp in length and confirms the presence of female DNA. (b) PCR gel showing no evidence of male-specific DNA at any further time-point.

Allogenic Fibroblast Survival

Hyaluronic acid matrices were seeded with male porcine fibroblasts *in vitro* and cultured for one week before being grafted onto the porcine chamber model; onto an equal number of wounds were grafted acellular matrices as controls. Biopsies were taken at 3,5 and 7 days before the epithelial component was added. Repeat biopsies were then taken at weekly intervals for 5 weeks. Genomic DNA was extracted from each biopsy and assayed for male DNA. Positive results were found at days 3 and 5, but none thereafter (Fig. 7). We therefore concluded that allogenic fibroblasts did not survive transplantation and were cleared within one week. Analysis of apoptosis and by inflammatory markers failed to identify a method for cell removal (Price et al, unpublished).

Human Models for Tissue Engineering

All animal models are, by definition, imperfect and there has therefore been a drive to find a human model for the tissue engineering of skin. In the United Kingdom, cosmetic surgery is not provided by the National Health Service and nor, equally, is the removal of unwanted tattoos. Within East London there exists a demand for tattoo removal and this provides an opportunity to investigate wound healing in humans. By excising the tattoo, an acute wound bed is formed upon which the investigator may work. The wound is an open model and therefore not dissimilar to clinical practice; it will contract appropriately and re-epithelialise from the edges. However the ethical removal of the tattoo prevents the surgeon from creating a full-thickness wound and so epithelial regeneration from skin appendages cannot be excluded. Clinically, however, the wounds behave as full-thickness injuries and epithelial regeneration is rare within the time course of an acute study.

Using this model we have been able to pursue a number of lines of study. The first study, by Myers et al [72], assessed the keratin profiles of healing wounds. The second, by Harris et al and as yet unpublished, compared single-stage composite grafting based on DED to pre-confluent Laserskin® delivery on a deep dermal wound bed. Those authors demonstrated the superior results obtained with composite grafting using de-epidermalised dermis. The benefits were evident in both histological and clinical terms (Fig. 4b). Most recently, we have used the model to compare the efficacy of two similar dermal analogues, based upon hyaluronic acid, with differing pharmacodynamic properties. This has allowed us to determine which method gives the greater epithelial cover and superior histology.

The Treatment of Burn Victims

It is with the treatment of major burn injuries in mind that the majority of work in this field has been undertaken. Trials in such patients are fraught with complications as diverse as concurrent illness, nature of burn and adjunctive treatment modalities. The success or failure of a skin replacement strategy is difficult to assess in these circumstances as failure may be as much a consequence of superficial

infection as of the technology itself. Despite these reservations, the various technologies are now being applied clinically to burn victims and early studies are entering the medical literature. One example is a case with which we were closely involved, that of a man sustaining 50% full-thickness and 30% partial-thickness burns [73]. After tangential excision the wound was treated with either allograft of Hyaluronic Acid matrix with pre-cultured allogenic fibroblasts before the application of Laserskin® to all areas. After 24 days there was an 80% epithelial take and histology of the HYAFF areas showed the successful formation of neodermis. Both the donor- and HYAFF-based areas demonstrated acanthotic, continuous epidermis with the formation of dermo-epidermal interdigitations. The case history demonstrates one example of how these technologies may be used and the quality of regenerated skin obtained.

The introduction of biotechnologies has undoubtedly revolutionised the field of tissue engineering. Their introduction has allowed quantum leaps in the search for the ultimate off-the-shelf skin replacement and opened areas for research that were previously inaccessible. Unfortunately the technology carries a premium and, with it, the potential for great financial reward. This has meant that manufacturers have been very protective over their materials and are reticent about the prospect of unfavourable comparison. For this reason the technologies developed have never been compared against each other in the form of a prospective, randomised trial; manufacturers have failed to support such a project and those workers funded by them have been reluctant to pursue the issue. We would like to see more open, formal scientific evaluation of these technologies in controlled studies so that the materials can be genuinely assessed.

Finally, the advent and discovery of the putative keratinocyte stem cell promises to revolutionise the field of tissue engineering. If such a cell can be truly isolated and cultured, it may be possible to pursue a number of approaches within the field; these include the massive proliferative potential that such a cell might have, the possibility of genetically modifying it to prevent allo-antibody reactions, or even the possibility of providing gene therapy by the transplantation of such cells. However the pursuit of academic excellence must be tinged with the realisation that only by performing controlled, randomised trials will the true benefits of such a technology be realised.

If such an objective assessment can be made it will advance the field enormously. The potential contained within the field is enormous and we feel that it is only a matter of when, not if, the Holy Grail of an off-the shelf-skin substitute is achieved.

Acknowledgements

The authors would like to acknowledge the contributions made by the following surgical research fellows: Nigel Carver, Loshan Kangesu, Simon Myers and Paul Harris.

References

[1] Rheinwald JG, Green H: Serial Cultivation of Strains of Human Epidermal Keratinocytes: the Formulation of Keratinising Colonies from Single Cells. Cell; 6:331–344, 1975

[2] Leigh IM, Purkis PE, Navsaria HA, Phillips TJ: Treatment of chronic venous ulcers with sheets of cultured allogenic keratinocytes. British Journal Of Dermatology; 117(5):591–7, 1987

[3] Langdon JD, Leigh IM, Navsaria HA, Williams DM: Autologous oral keratinocyte grafts in the mouth [letter; comment]. Lancet; 335(8703): 1472–3, 1990

[4] Gallico GGd, O'Connor NE, Compton CC, Remensnyder JP, Kehinde O, Green H: Cultured epithelial autografts for giant congenital nevi [see comments]. Plastic And Reconstructive Surgery; 84(1):1–9, 1989

[5] Brain A, Purkis P, Coates P, Hackett M, Navsaria H, Leigh I: Survival of cultured allogeneic keratinocytes transplanted to deep dermal bed assessed with probe specific for Y chromosome. British Medical Journal; 298:917–9, 1989

[6] Burt AM, Pallett CD, Sloane JP, et al.: Survival of cultured allografts in patients with burns assessed with probe specific for Y chromosome. British Medical Journal; 298:915–7, 1989

[7] Bagot M, Bertaux B, Heslan M, Coulomb B, Dubertret L: Reconstructed human epidermis: absence of Langerhans cells and failure to stimulate allogenic lymphocytes in vitro. Clinics in Experimental Immunology; 71: 138–143, 1988

[8] Auböck J, Irschick E, Romani N, et al.: Rejection, after a slightly prolonged survival time, of Langerhans cell-free allogeneic cultured epidermis used for wound coverage in humans. Transplantation; 45(4):730–7, 1988

[9] Carver N, Navsaria HA, Green CJ, Leigh IM: Acute rejection of cultured keratinocyte allografts in nonimmunosuppressed pigs. Transplantation; 52(5):918–21, 1991

[10] Carver N: Keratinocyte grafting as a means of skin replacement. MS: London, 1992

[11] Kangesu T, Navsaria HA, Manek S, et al.: A porcine model using skin graft chambers for studies on cultured keratinocytes. British Journal Of Plastic Surgery; 46(5):393–400, 1993

[12] Navsaria HA, Kangesu T, Manek S, Green CJ, Leigh IM: An animal model to study the significance of dermis for grafting cultured keratinocytes on full thickness wounds. Burns; 20 Suppl 1:S57–60, 1994

[13] Miller SJ, Burke EM, Rader MD, Coulombe PA, Lavker RM: Re-epithelialization of porcine skin by the sweat apparatus. journal of investigative dermatology; 110(1):13–9, 1998

[14] Prunieras M, Regnier M, Schlotterer M: Nouveau procede de culture des cellules epidermiques humaines sur derme homologue ou heterologue: Preparation de greffons recombines. Annn Chir Plast; 24:357–362, 1979

[15] Cuono C, Langdon R, McGuire J: Use of cultured epidermal autografts and dermal allografts as skin replacement after burn injury. The Lancet: 1123–1124, 1986(May 17)

[16] Kangesu T, Navsaria HA, Manek S, Fryer PR, Leigh IM, Green C J: Kerato-dermal grafts: the importance of dermis for the in vivo growth of cultured keratinocytes. British Journal Of Plastic Surgery; 46(5):401–9, 1993

[17] Kangesu T, Manek S, Terenghi G, et al.: Nerve and blood vessel growth in response to grafted dermis and cultured keratinocytes. Plastic And Reconstructive Surgery; 101(4):1029–38, 1998

[18] Dubertret L, Coulomb B, Saiag P, et al.: Reconstruction in vitro of a human living skin equivalent. Life Support Systems; 3 Suppl 1:380–7, 1985

[19] Bell E, Rosenberg M, Kemp P, et al.: Recipes for reconstituting skin. Journal Of Biomechanical Engineering; 113(2):113–9, 1991

[20] Langdon RC, Cuono CB, Birchall N, et al.: Reconstitution of structure and cell function in human skin grafts derived from cryopre-

served allogenic dermis and autologous cultured keratinocytes. Journal of Investigative Dermatology; 91(5):478–485, 1988

[21] *Burke JF, Yannas IV, Quinby WCJ, Bondoc CC, Jung WK:* Successful use of a physiologically acceptable artificial skin in the treatment of extensive burn injury. Annals Of Surgery; 194(4):413–28, 1981

[22] *Murphy GF, Orgill DP, Yannas IV:* Partial dermal regeneration is induced by biodegradable collagen-glycosaminoglycan grafts. Laboratory Investigation; 62(3):305–13, 1990

[23] *Yannas IV:* Studies on the biological activity of the dermal regeneration template. Wound Repair Regen; 6(6):518–23, 1998

[24] *Bell E, Ivarsson B, Merrill C:* Production of a tissue-like structure by contraction of collagen lattices by human fibroblasts of different proliferative potential in vitro. Proceedings Of The National Academy Of Sciences Of The United States Of America; 76(3): 1274–8, 1979

[25] *Woodley DT, Kalebec T, Banes AJ, Link W, Prunieras M, Liotta L:* Adult human keratinocytes migrating over nonviable dermal collagen produce collagenolytic enzymes that degrade type I and type IV collagen. Journal Of Investigative Dermatology; 86(4):418–23, 1986

[26] *Oksala O, Salo T, Tammi R, et al.:* Expression of proteoglycans and hyaluronan during wound healing. The Journal of Histochemistry and Cytochemistry; 43(2):125–135, 1995

[27] *King SR, Hickerson WL, Proctor KG:* Beneficial actions of exogenous hyaluronic acid on wound healing. Surgery; 109:76–84, 1991

[28] *Foschi D, Castoldi L, Radaelli E, et al.:* Hyaluronic acid prevents oxygen free-radical damage to granulation tissue: a study in rats. International Journal of Tissue Reaction; 12(6):333–339, 1990

[29] *Tokita Y, Sakashita H, Okamoto A, Kubota K:* Kinetic study of a radical scavenging effect of hyaluronic acid. Polymer International; 38: 161–164, 1995

[30] *Rydell N:* Decreased granulation tissue reaction after installment of hyaluronic acid. Acta Orthopaedica Scandinavica; 41(3):307–11, 1970

[31] *Murashita Y, Nakayama Y, Hirano T, Ohashi S:* Acceleration of granulation tissue ingrowth by hyaluronic acid in artificial skin. British Journal of Plastic Surgery; 49:58–63, 1996

[32] *Krummel T M, Mast B A, Haynes JH, Diegelmann R F, Cohen I K:* Characteristics of fetal repair. Progress In Clinical And Biological Research; 365:167–76, 1991

[33] *Mast BA, Haynes JH, Krummel TM, Diegelmann RF, Cohen IK:* In vivo degradation of fetal wound hyaluronic acid results in increased fibroplasia, collagen deposition, and neovas-

cularization. Plastic And Reconstructive Surgery; 89(3):503–9, 1992

[34] *Longaker MT, Adzick NS:* The biology and therapeutic implications of fetal wound healing. Clinical Materials; 8:223–227, 1991

[35] *Bertolami CN, Berg S, Messadi DV:* Binding and internalisation of hyaluronate by human cutaneous fibroblasts. Matrix; 11: 11–21, 1992

[36] *West DC, Hampson IN, Arnold F, Kumar S:* Angiogenesis induced by degradation products of hyaluronic acid. Science; 228: 1324–6, 1991

[37] *Sattar A, Rooney P, Kumar S, et al.:* Application of angiogenic oligosaccharides of hyaluronan increases blood vessel numbers in rat skin. The Journal of Investigative Dermatology; 103:576–579, 1994

[38] *Kielty CM, Whittaker SP, Grant ME, Shuttleworth CA:* Type IV collagen microfibrils: evidence for a structural association with hyaluronan. The Journal of Cell Biology; 118(4):979–990, 1992

[39] *Rooney P, Kumar S:* Inverse relationship between hyaluronan and collagens in development and angiogenesis. Differentiation; 54:1–9, 1993

[40] *Scully MF, Kakkar VJ, Goodwin CA, O'Regan M:* Inhibition of fibrinolytic activity by hyaluronan and its alcohol ester derivatives. Thrombosis Research; 78(3):255–258, 1995

[41] *Tammi R, Tammi M:* Correlations between hyaluronan and epidermal proliferation as studied by3H-glucosamine and 3H-thymidine incorporations and staining of hyaluronan on mitotic keratinocytes. Experimental Cell Research; 195:524–527, 1991

[42] *Myers SR, Grady J, Soranzo C, et al.:* A hyaluronic acid membrane delivery system for cultured keratinocytes: clinical take rates in the porcine kerato-dermal model. Journal Of Burn Care And Rehabilitation; 18(3):214–22, 1997

[43] *Harris PA, Leigh IM, Navsaria H A:* Preconfluent keratinocyte grafting: the future for cultured skin replacements? [editorial]. Burns; 24(7):591–3, 1998

[44] *Hunyadi J, Farkas B, Bertényi C, Oláh J, Dobozy A:* Keratinocyte grafting: covering of skin defects by separated autologous keratinocytes in a fibrin net [letter]. Journal Of Investigative Dermatology; 89(1):119–20, 1987

[45] *Kaiser HW, Stark GB, Kopp J, Balcerkiewicz A, Spilker G, Kreysel HW:* Cultured autologous keratinocytes in fibrin glue suspension, exclusively and combined with STS-allograft (preliminary clinical and histological report of a new technique). Burns; 20(1):23–9, 1994

[46] *Horch RE, Bannasch H, Kopp J, Andree C, Stark GB:* Single-cell suspensions of cultured hu-

man keratinocytes in fibrin-glue reconstitute the epidermis. Cell Transplantation; 7(3): 309–17, 1998

[47] Landeen LK, Zeigler FC, Halberstadt C, Cohen R, Slivka SR: Characterisation of a human dermal replacement. Proceedings of the Symposium on Advanced Wound Care and The Medical Research Forum on Wound Repair; 4(5):167–75, 1992

[48] Lamme EN, van Leeuwen RTJ, Jonker A, van Marle J, Middlekoop E: Living Skin Substitutes: Survival and Function of Fibroblasts Seeded in a Dermal Substitute in Experimental Wounds. Journal of Investigative Dermatology; 111(6):989–995, 1998

[49] De Vries HJ, Zeegelaar JE, Middelkoop E, et al.: Reduced wound contraction and scar formation in punch biopsy wounds. Native collagen dermal substitutes. A clinical study. British Journal Of Dermatology; 132(5):690–7, 1995

[50] Krejci NC, Cuono CB, Langdon RC, McGuire J: In vitro reconstitution of skin: fibroblasts facilitate keratinocyte growth and differentiation on acellular reticular dermis. Journal of Investigative Dermatology; 97(5):843–848, 1991

[51] Maraguchi T, Maraguchi Y, Suzuki S, Matsuda K, Toda K-I, Isshiki N: A new skin equivalent: keratinocytes proliferated and differentiated on collagen sponge containing fibroblasts. Plastic & Resconstitutive Surgery; 93 (3): 537–44, 1993

[52] Tseng SC, Kruse FE, Merritt J, Li DQ: Comparison between serum-free and fibroblast-cocultured single-cell clonal culture systems: evidence showing that epithelial anti-apoptotic activity is present in 3T3 fibroblast-conditioned media. Current Eye Research; 15(9): 973–84, 1996

[53] Coulomb B, Friteau L, Baruch J, et al.: Advantage of the presence of living dermal fibroblasts within in vitro reconstructed skin for grafting in humans. Plastic And Reconstructive Surgery; 101(7):1891–903, 1998

[54] van de Berg JS, Rudolph R, Hollan C, Haywood-Reid PL: Fibroblast senescence in pressure ulcers. Wound Repair & Regeneration; 6(1):38–49, 1998

[55] Bruce SA, Deamond SF: Longitudinal study of in vivo wound repair and in vitro cellular senescence of dermal fibroblasts. Experimental Gerontology; 26(1):17–27, 1991

[56] Hehenberger K, Heilborn JD, Brismar K, Hansson A: Inhibited proliferation of fibroblasts derived from chronic diabetic wounds and normal dermal fibroblasts treated with high glucose is associated with increased formation of l-lactate. Wound Repair Regen; 6(2): 135–41, 1998

[57] Regan MC, Kirk SJ, Wasserkrug HL, Barbul A: The wound environment as a regulator of fibroblast phenotype. Journal Of Surgical Research; 50(5):442–8, 1991

[58] He C, Hughes MA, Cherry GW, Arnold F: Effects of chronic wound fluid on the bioactivity of platelet-derived growth factor in serum-free medium and its direct effect on fibroblast growth. Wound Repair Regen; 7(2): 97–105, 1999

[59] Hasan A, Murata H, Falabella A, et al.: Dermal fibroblasts from venous ulcers are unresponsive to the action of transforming growth factor-beta 1. Journal Of Dermatological Science; 16(1):59–66, 1997

[60] Stanley AC, Park HY, Phillips TJ, Russakovsky V, Menzoian JO: Reduced growth of dermal fibroblasts from chronic venous ulcers can be stimulated with growth factors. Journal Of Vascular Surgery; 26(6):994–9; discussion 999–1001, 1997

[61] Unemori EN, Ehsani N, Wang M, Lee S, McGuire J, Amento EP: Interleukin-1 and transforming growth factor-alpha: synergistic stimulation of metalloproteinases, PGE2, and proliferation in human fibroblasts. Experimental Cell Research; 210(2): 166–71, 1994

[62] Cracco C, Stella M, Teich Alasia S, Filogamo G: Comparative study of Langerhans cells in normal and pathological human scars. II. Hypertrophic scars. European Journal Of Histochemistry; 36(1):53–65, 1992

[63] Ehrlich HP, Kelley SF: Hypertrophic scar: an interruption in the remodeling of repair – a laser Doppler blood flow study. Plastic And Reconstructive Surgery; 90(6):993–8, 1992

[64] Yang CC, Lin SD, Yu HS: Effect of growth factors on dermal fibroblast contraction in normal skin and hypertrophic scar. Journal Of Dermatological Science; 14(2):162–9, 1997

[65] Brown DL, Kao WW, Greenhalgh DG: Apoptosis down-regulates inflammation under the advancing epithelial wound edge: delayed patterns in diabetes and improvement with topical growth factors. Surgery; 121(4): 372–80, 1997

[66] Desmoulière A, Redard M, Darby I, Gabbiani G: Apoptosis mediates the decrease in cellularity during the transition between granulation tissue and scar. American Journal Of Pathology; 146(1):56–66, 1995

[67] Desmoulière A, Badid C, Bochaton-Piallat ML, Gabbiani G: Apoptosis during wound healing, fibrocontractive diseases and vascular wall injury. International Journal Of Biochemistry And Cell Biology; 29(1):19–30, 1997

[68] Greenhalgh DG: The role of apoptosis in wound healing. International Journal Of

Biochemistry And Cell Biology; 30(9):1019–30, 1998

[69] *Garbin S, Pittet B, Montandon D, Gabbiani G, Desmouliere A:* Covering by a flap induces apoptosis of granulation tissue myofibroblasts and vascular cells. Wound Repair & Regeneration; 4(2):244–251, 1996

[70] *Sher SE, Hull BE, Rosen S, Church D, Friedman L, Bell E:* Acceptance of allogeneic fibroblasts in skin equivalent transplants. Transplantation; 36(5):552–7, 1983

[71] *Hultman CS, Brinson GM, Siltharm S, et al.:* Allogeneic fibroblasts used to grow cultured epithelial autografts persist in vivo and sensitise the graft recipient for accelerated second-set rejection. Journal ofTrauma; 41(1): 51–60, 1996

[72] *Myers SR, Navsaria HA, Brain AN, Purkis PE, Leigh IM:* Epidermal differentiation and dermal changes in healing following treatment of surgical wounds with sheets of cultured allogeneic keratinocytes. Journal Of Clinical Pathology; 48(12):1087–92, 1995

[73] *Harris PA, di Francesco F, Barisoni D, Leigh IM, Navsaria, HA:* Use of hyaluronic acid and cultured autologous keratinocytes and fibroblasts in extensive burns. Lancet; 353 (9146):35–6, 1999

Keratinocyte Growth Factor (KGF): Its Possible Use in Tissue Engineering

E. E. Putnins

Introduction

In the last decade, Keratinocyte Growth Factors (KGF-1 and KGF-2) have been shown to be potent regulators of epithelial cell behavior. Readers are directed to two reviews which provide an excellent overview [1, 2]. This chapter focuses its discussion on the role that KGFs play in regulating epidermal homeostasis and wound healing.

Keratinocyte Growth Factors

Two of the 23 member fibroblast growth factor (FGF) family that have been described to date now carry the common designation, Keratinocyte Growth Factors (**Table 1**). Collectively members of the FGF family have been shown to stimulate cells of ectodermal and mesodermal origin [19, 20]. However, KGF-1 (FGF-7) and KGF-2 (FGF-10) are different from other FGF's in that they are specific paracrine mediators for epithelial cell growth. KGF-1 was initially purified from the conditioned media of human embryonic fibroblasts and identified as a specific stimulator of epithelial cell proliferation [9]. Since the initial discovery of KGF-1, FGF-10 was isolated from rat embryos by a homology-based polymerase chain reaction [12]. The structure and biological activity of human FGF-10 is similar to FGF-7 (KGF-1). FGF-10 shares approximately 60% amino acid sequence identity with FGF-7 and it also specifically stimulates epithelial but not fibroblast cell proliferation [21]. Based on its sequence identity and similar stimulatory effects on epithelial cells, FGF-10 has been described as KGF-2 [22–24].

Information on the role of KGF-2 in regulating epidermal homeostasis and wound healing is more limited. Therefore, KGF-1 will be the focus of the discussion.

Table 1: The FGF Family.

FGF Designation	Common Name	Reference
FGF-1	acidic FGF (aFGF)	[3]
FGF-2	basic FGF (bFGF)	[4]
FGF-3	int-2	[5]
FGF-4	Kaposi FGF (K-FGF); hst-1	[6]
FGF-5	–	[7]
FGF-6	hst-2	[8]
FGF-7	Keratinocyte Growth Factor-1 (KGF-1)	[9]
FGF-8	Androgen Induced Growth Factor (AIGF)	[10]
FGF-9	Glial Activate Factor (GAF)	[11]
FGF-10	Keratinocyte Growth Factor-2 (KGF-2)	[12]
FGF-11	FGF Homologous Factor (FHF-1)	[13]
FGF-12	FHF-2	[13]
FGF-13	FHF-3	[13]
FGF-14	FHF-4	[13]
FGF-15	–	[14]
FGF-16	–	[15]
FGF-17	–	[16]
FGF-18	–	[17]
FGF-19	–	[18]

At press time FGF-20, -21 and -23 have now been described.

Expression of KGF and its Receptor in Epidermal Tissues

KGF-1 mRNA transcripts are expressed in the dermis of embryonic and adult skin [25–27]. Specifically, stromal fibroblasts derived from epithelial tissues, microvascular endothelial cells, smooth muscle cells and activated $\gamma\delta T$ cells from skin and intestine all express KGF-1 [25, 28–30]. Epithelial cells do not express KGF-1 but express a KGF-specific receptor. This receptor is a splice variant of the fibroblast growth factor receptor FGFR2 (FGFR2-II-Ib) family and is designated as the keratinocyte growth factor receptor (KGFR). The KGFR avidly binds KGF-1, KGF-2 and acidic FGF [31–33]. KGF-specific binding to the KGFR is due to the expression of an alternate exon coding for a 49-amino acid sequence in the carboxyl half of the third immunoglobulin loop of the KGFR [34, 35]. In skin, this receptor is only expressed in the epidermis [36, 37].

KGF-1 is required for maintenance of epidermal homeostasis. When expressed as a constitutively active autocrine mediator in transgenic mice, significant epidermal changes were found. In particular, increased basal cell keratinocyte proliferation and epidermal hypertrophy was observed in these KGF-1 overexpressing mice [38]. In contrast, blocking KGFR function by the expression of a dominant-negative KGF receptor mutant resulted in a disorganized atrophic epidermis and reduced keratinocyte steady-state proliferation [39]. Therefore, KGF-1 is specifically secreted by dermal cells and is a paracrine mediator of epidermal cells. The specific stimulation of epidermal cells is due to their specific expression of the KGFR. KGF-1 regulates normal epidermal homeostasis but it is also significantly upregulated during wound healing.

KGF Upregulation in Wound Healing Sites

After wounding, a myriad of cytokines (Il-1-α, Il-1β and TNF-α) and growth factors (FGF-7, EGF, TGF-α, HB-EGF and TGF-β1) are ex-pressed by dermal fibroblasts, keratinocytes, macrophages, platelets and recruited inflammatory cells [40]. The expression of pro-inflammatory cytokines IL-1β, IL-α, IL-6 and TNF-α likely initiates the rapid and early upregulation of KGF-1 [41–43]. In mice, KGF-1 expression was upregulated: 9-fold at 12 hours, 160-fold at 24 hours and 100-fold on day 7 [44]. Increased expression was localized with *in situ* hybridization to dermal cells below the wound and at the wound edge [44]. In agreement with mouse wound healing studies re-epithelialization of human skin wounds is also associated with KGF-1 transcript and protein level increases of 8 to 10-fold and 2 to 3-fold, respectively [45]. In contrast, experimental wounds that heal more slowly because of metabolic disease (diabetes) or drugs (glucocorticoids) were associated with delayed and reduced KGF-1 expression levels [46, 47]. In KGF-1 knock-out mice somewhat surprising results were found. In particular, no abnormalities in epidermal growth or wound healing were found [48]. This may be explained by the expression of an alternate KGFR ligand like KGF-2 that could compensate for missing KGF-1 expression. This is supported by a study in which KGFR function was blocked by the expression of a dominant negative KGFR mutant. In this study a reduced re-epithelialization rate during wound healing was observed [39]. The involvement of KGF-2 in wound healing has not been as extensively examined. FGF-10 upregulation one day after wounding was shown in one study but was not confirmed by another [49, 50]. However, topical application of KGF-2 (FGF-10) to wounds enhanced wound tensile and breaking strength, accelerated re-epithelialization and increased epidermal thickness [22, 24].

KGF-1 Enhancement of Keratinocyte Adhesion and Migration

A rapid induction of KGF-1 expression after wounding (9-fold increase at 12 hours) and the KGF-1 expression in focal dermal cells below the wound and particularly at the

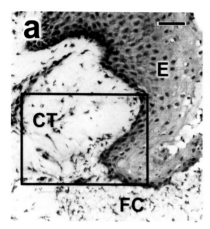
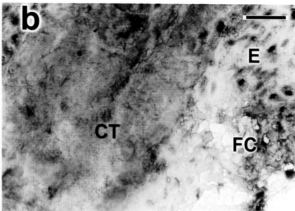

Fig. 1: KGF-1 Protein is Expressed at Margin of Human Palatal Mucosal Wounds. A 3 day palatal mucosal biopsy was collected from an experimental excisional wound and frozen sections stained with hematoxylin. (a) The wound margin with proliferating and migrating epithelium (E) into fibrin clot area (FC) with surrounding connective tissue (CT) is shown. (b) A parallel section that was stained using a polyclonal anti KGF-1 antibody shows KGF-1 protein expression (purple staining) localized to the wound margin connective tissue. Bar=200µm.

wound edge has previously been shown [44]. This early upregulation and localization to the wound edge suggests KGF-1 regulates aspects of early wound re-epithelialization. This increase in KGF-1 protein expression at the wound edge is also found in human mucosal wounds (**Fig. 1**). In the microenvironment of the wound edge, two major cellular processes associated with re-epithelialization occur. These are keratinocyte migration on a wound provisional matrix and proliferation of keratinocytes that seed cells into the wound [51]. KGF-1 has clearly been shown to induce keratinocyte proliferation in cell culture [9, 52–55]. In addition, targeting KGF-1 expression to basal cells of transgenic mice approximately doubles basal epidermal cell proliferation [38]. The provisional wound matrix is rich in fibronectin and fibrin, but also contains type I collagen, vitronectin and, in older wounds, tenascin [56–59]. Keratinocyte adhesion to these provisional matrix proteins is crucial for wound healing. Interestingly, KGF-1 seems to be involved in regulating this process by stimulating keratinocyte cell attachment and migration on provisional matrix proteins [60]. This KGF-1 stimulation

of keratinocyte attachment to type I collagen and fibronectin is integrin dependent but no change in the surface expression of the collagen ($\alpha2\beta1$) nor the fibronectin integrin receptor subunits ($\alpha5\beta1$ and αv) was found [60]. No change in $\beta1$ subunit integrin affinity (activity) was found in KGF-treated keratinocytes, but confocal microscopy localized significant $\beta1$ clustering and well-organized actin filaments to focal complexes at the basal surface of keratinocytes (**Fig. 2**) [60]. These data suggest KGF-stimulated attachment was regulated through a process of inside-out signaling to induce integrin avidity [61–63]. Therefore, early upregulation of KGF expression in the dermis at the wound edge likely contributes not only to induction of keratinocyte proliferation but also to the activation of keratinocyte movement towards provisional matrix proteins.

KGF-1 induction of keratinocyte migration is supported by *in vivo* studies that found topical application of KGF-1 to porcine and rabbit wounds enhanced partial- and full-thickness wound re-epithelialization rates and epidermal thickness [64, 65]. *In vitro* cell culture studies support this find-

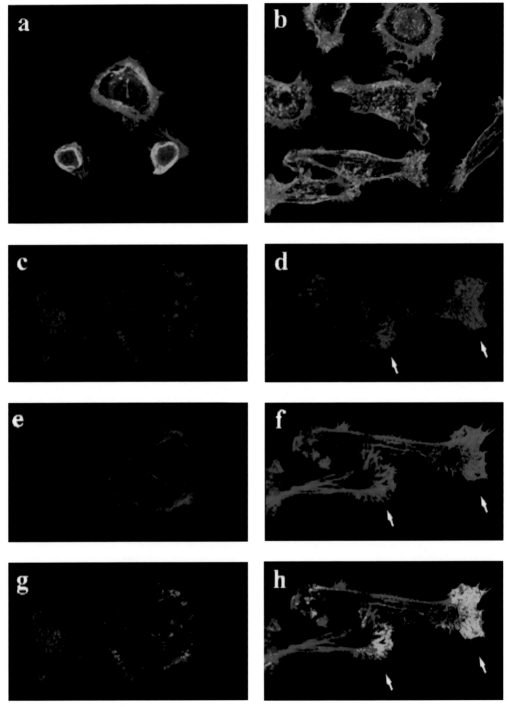

Fig. 2: KGF-treated Keratinocytes Show Increased Focal Staining for β1 and Actin Filament Organization at the Basal Cell Surface. Equal numbers of control (a,c,e,g) and KGF-treated cells (b,d,f,h) were plated on glass coverslips precoated with 10 μg/ml of Type I collagen. At 3 h unattached cells were washed away,

Fig. 3: KGF Induction of Keratinocyte Migration is Extracellular Matrix Dependent. a) Tissue culture wells were coated with 10 μg/ml of Type I Collagen (Col I), Fibronectin (Fn), Vitronectin (Vn), Tenascin (Tn), Type IV Collagen (Col IV) and Laminin-1 (Ln). A stainless steel flat bottom cylinder with a 2.8 mm central opening was placed into the well and approximately 10,000 cells added and allowed to attach for 24 h. The cylinders were removed and the cells stimulated with 20 ng/ml of KGF. Keratinocytes were allowed to migrate for 96 h, fixed, stained and destained. Using an optical linear scale incorporated into the eyepiece of a Leica dissecting microscope KGF induction of keratinocyte radial migration compared to controls (CTL) was quantitated. For each well three measurements were made and averaged. All values are presented as mean ± SD, n=3 replicates. (b) Representative example of nonmigrating (control) migrating (KGF-treated) keratinocytes that was plated onto fibronectin. Arrows mark original edge from which keratinocytes migrated. Adapted with permission [60].

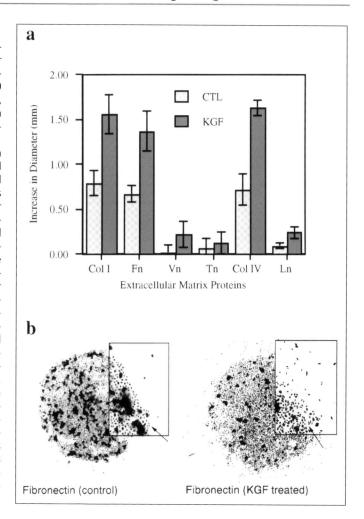

Fig. 2 continued

attached cells were fixed, permeabilized, reacted with β1 specific monoclonal antibody followed with an rhodamine conjugated secondary antibody and Bodipy FL phallacidin. All samples were analyzed with a confocal laser microscope and optical z-axis sections were recorded. Images were merged into a single RGB file for the total z-axis (a,b). Total merged β1 (red) and actin filament (green) protein localization image for control (a) and KGF-treated cells (b) is presented. The z-sections corresponding to the basal cell layers were identified (c–h). The localization of β1 (c,d), actin filaments (e, f) and the merged RGB file (g,h) are shown. Intense colocalization (yellow) of β1 integrins and actin filaments at the basal surface of the leading edges of KGF-treated cells are marked with arrows (d, f, h). Reprinted with permission [60].

ing that KGF-1 induces keratinocyte migration [54, 55, 60]. Since keratinocytes are exposed to different ECM proteins in the provisional matrix, a subsequent study examined the role that fibronectin and type I collagen may have on KGF-1 induction of migration. Based on the current understanding that high concentrations of ECM proteins induce cell adhesion and decrease migration [66], these migration studies were done in the presence of low ECM protein concentrations. Under these conditions KGF-1 specifically induced keratinocyte migration when these cells were plated on fibronectin, and type I and IV collagen (**Fig. 3**). For cell migration to occur across the wound provisional matrix, localized degradation of ECM proteins is required [67]. Matrix metalloproteinases (MMP) are a large family of enzymes that collectively degrade all ECM proteins. Matrix metalloproteinases-9, -1, and -10 are three MMPs that are upregulated during wound healing and all three are induced by KGF-1 in cell culture [67–71]. Activation of latent MMPs often occurs by a plasmin-dependent step. With respect to this, KGF-1 stimulates expression of urokinase-type plasminogen activator (uPA), an activator of plasminogen to plasmin [55, 69]. Plasmin activation is crucial for keratinocyte movement through the clot. KGF-1 regulation of both plasmin and MMPs adds another important function to its wound healing repertoire. In summary, KGF-1 is the only epithelial specific growth factor/cytokine found to be able to regulate all three crucial events in wound healing, namely keratinocyte proliferation, migration and localized proteolysis.

What KGF-1 does not appear to affect is epithelial stratification and differentiation. In KGF-treated wounds, immunostaining for cytokeratins showed normal keratinocyte differentiation had occurred [64]. Similar results were found in cell culture. Expression of early and late differentiation markers, keratin-1 and filaggrin, were found in KGF-treated cultures that were induced to differentiate with high calcium

(1.0 mM) [53]. When keratinocytes were treated with EGF or TGF-α, calcium induced differentiation did not occur. This finding about KGF-1 may prove to be very significant. Future attempts at KGF-1 gene transfer may result in increased keratinocyte proliferation and migration but no inhibition of normal keratinocyte differentiation. All of these aspects are highly desirable.

Future Considerations

Wound healing research is currently examining methods to improve or accelerate wound re-epithelialization. Transient transfection with growth factor cDNA is showing promising results. *In vivo* transfection of wound site fibroblasts with epidermal growth factor (EGF) and acidic fibroblast growth factor cDNA showed high growth factor expression and improved wound healing [72–74]. Similar experiments with KGF may prove equally effective in stimulating wound re-epithelialization. In addition, grafting success of single epithelial cells or epithelial sheet grafts to wound site dermis is often limited by poor graft adherence. At present, techniques are being developed to improve keratinocyte graft adherence and survivability [75]. Induction of KGF-1 in the dermis may prove to be an effective means to improve the initial adhesion and stimulate proliferation of keratinocytes. Future studies should focus on finding safe and effective ways to deliver the KGF gene into non-healing wounds or burn victims in order to prove the potential therapeutic use of KGF in the promotion of wound healing.

Acknowledgements

I would like to thank Dr. Hannu Larjava for his review and helpful suggestions on this manuscript. In addition I am grateful to Dr. Lari Häkkinen and Mr. Ali-Reza Sanaie for their preparation and anti-KGF-1 staining of the human palatal wound tissue samples.

References

[1] *Werner, S:* Keratinocyte Growth Fcator: A unique player in epithelial repair proces-ses. Cytokine Growth Factor Rev, 9:153–165, (1998)

[2] *Rubin, JS, Bottaro, DP, Chedid, M, Miki, T, Ron D, Cheon, H-G, Taylor, WG, Fortney, E, Sakata, H., Finch, PW, LaRochelle, W J:* Keratinocyte Growth Factor. Cell Biol Int, 19: 399–411, (1995)

[3] *Gimenez-Gallego, G, Rodkey, R, Bennett, C, Rios-Candelore, M, Disalvo, J, Thomas, KA:* Brain-derived acidic fibroblast growth factor: complete amino acid sequence and homologies. Science, 230:1385–1388, (1985)

[4] *Abraham, JA, Whang, JL, Tumolo, A, Mergia, A, Fiddes, JC:* Human basic fibroblast growth factor: nucleotide sequence, genomic organization, and expression in mammalian cells Cold Spring Harb Symp Quant Biol, 51 Pt 1:657–668, (1986)

[5] *Moore, R, Casey, G, Brookes, S, Dixon, M, Peters, G, Dickson, C:* Sequence, topography and protein coding potential of mouse int-2: a putative oncogene activated by mouse mammary tumor virus EMBO J, 5(5):919–924, (1986)

[6] *Taira, M, Yoshida, T, Miyagawa, K, Sakamoto, H, Terada, M, Sugimura, T:* cDNA sequence of human transforming gene hst and identification of the coding sequence required for transforming activity. Proc Natl Acad Sci USA, 84(9):2980–2984, (1987)

[7] *Zhan, X, Bates, S, Hu, Z, Goldfarb, M:* Human FGF-5 gene encodes a novel protein related to fibroblast growth factors. Mol Cell Biol, 8: 3487–3495, (1988)

[8] *Marics, I, Adelaide, J, Raybound, F, Mattei, MG, Coulier, F, Planche, J, de Lapeyriere, O, Birnbaum, D:* Characterization of HST related FGF-6 gene, a new member of the fibroblast growth factor family. Oncogene, 4:335–340, (1989)

[9] *Rubin, JS, Osada, H, Finch, PW, Taylor, WG, Rudikoff, S, Aaronson, SA:* Purification and characterization of a newly identified growth factor specific for epithelial cells. Proc Natl Acad Sci USA, 86:802–806, (1989)

[10] *Tanaka, A, Miyamoto, K, Minamino, N, Takeda, M, Sato, B, Matsuo, H, Matsumoto, K:* Cloning and characterization of an androgen induced growth factor essential for the androgen dependent growth of mouse mammary carcinoma cells. Proc Natl Acad Sci USA, 89:8928–8932, (1992)

[11] *Miyamoto, M, Naruo, K, Seko, C, Matsumoto, S, Kondo, T, Kurokawa, T:* Molecular cloning of a novel cytokine cDNA encoding the 9th member of the fibroblast growth factor family which has a unique secretion property. Mol Cell Biol, 13: 4251–4259, (1993)

[12] *Yamasaki, M, Miyake, A, Tagashira, S, Itoh, N:* Structure and expression of the rat mRNA encoding a novel member of the fibroblast growth factor family. J Biol Chem, 271(27): 15918–15921, (1996)

[13] *Smallwood, PM, Munoz-Sanjuan, I, Tong, P, Macke, JP, Hendry, SH, Gilbert, DJ, Copeland, NG, Jenkins, NA, Nathans, J:* Fibroblast growth factor (FGF) homologous factors: new members of the FGF family implicated in nervous system development. Proc Natl Acad Sci USA, 93(18):9850–9857, (1996)

[14] *McWhirter, JR, Goulding, M, Weiner, JA, Chun, J, Murre, C:* A novel fibroblast growth factor gene expressed in the developing nervous system is a downstream target of the chimeric homeodomain oncoprotein E2A-Pbx1. Development, 124(17):3221–3232, (1997)

[15] *Miyake, A, Konishi, M, Maritin, FH, Hernday, N, Ozaki, K, Yamamoto, S, Mikami, T, Arakawa, T, Itoh, N:* Structure and expression of a novel member, FGF-16 of the fibroblast growth factor family. Biochem Biophys Res Commun, 243:148–152, (1998)

[16] *Hoshikawa, M, Ohbayahi, N, Yonamine, A, Konishi, M, Ozaki, K, Fukui, S, Itoh, N:* Structure and expression of a novel fibroblast growth factor, FGF-17 preferentially expressed in the embryonic brain. Biochem Biophys Res Commun, 244:187–191, (1998)

[17] *Ohbayashi, N, Hoshikawa, M, Kimura, S, Yamasaki, M, Fukui, S, Itoh, N:* Structure and expression of the mRNA encoding a novel fibroblast growth factor, FGF-18. J Biol Chem, 273(29): 18161–18164, (1998)

[18] *Nishimura, T, Utsunomiya, Y, Hoshikawa, M, Ohuchi, H, Itoh, N:* Structure and expression of a novel human FGF, FGF-19, expressed in the fetal brain. Biochem Biophys Acta, 1444(1):148–151, (1999)

[19] *Szebenyi, G Fallon, JF:* Fibroblast growth factors as multifunctional signaling factors. Int Rev Cytol, 185:45–106, (1999)

[20] *Slavin, J:* Fibroblast Growth Factors: At the heart of angiogenesis. Cell Biol Int 19:431–444, (1995)

[21] *Emoto, H, Tagashira, S, Mattei, M-G, Yamasaki, M, Hashimoto, G, Katsumata, T, Negoro, T, Nakatsuka, M, Birnbaum, D, Coulier, F, Itoh, N:* Structure and expression of human fibroblast growth factor-10. J Biol Chem, 272:23191–23194, (1997)

[22] *Jimenez, PA, Rampy, MA:* Keratinocyte growth factor-2 accelerates wound healing in incisional wounds. J Surg Res, 81:238–242, (1999)

[23] *Miceli, R, Hubert, M, Santiago, G, Yao, D-L, Coleman, TA, Hyddleston, KA, Connolly, K:* J Pharmacol Exp Ther 290:464–471, (1999)

[24] *Soler, PM, Wright, TE, Smith, PD, Maggi, SP, Hill, DP, Ko, F, Jimenez, PA, Robson, MC:* In vivo characterization of keratinocyte growth factor-2 as a potential wound healing agent. Wound Rep Reg 7:172–178, (1999)

[25] *Finch, PW, Rubin, JS, Miki, T, Ron, D, Aaronson, SA:* Human KGF is FGF-related with properties of a paracrine effector of epithelial cell growth. Science, 245:752–755, (1989)

[26] *Mason, YJ, Fuller-Pace, F, Smith, R, Dickson, C:* FGF-7 (Keratinocyte growth factor) expression during mouse development suggests roles in myogenesis, forebrain regionalization and epithelial-mesenchymal interactions. Mech Dev, 45:15–30, (1994)

[27] *Finch, PW, Cunha, GR, Rubin, JS, Wong, J, Ron, D:* Pattern of keratinocyte growth factor receptor expression during mouse fetal development suggests a role in mediating morphogenetic mesenchymal epithelial interactions. Dev Dyn, 203:223–240, (1995)

[28] *Winkles, JA, Alberts, GF, Chedid, M, Taylor, W G Demartino, S, Rubin, J S:* Differential expression of the keratinocyte growth factor (KGF) and KGF receptor genes in human vascular smooth muscle cells and arteries. J Cell Physiol, 173:380–386, (1997)

[29] *Boismenu, R, Havran, WL:* Modulation of epithelial cell growth by intraepithelial γδT cells. Science, 266:1253–1255, (1994)

[30] *Smola H, Thiekötter, G, Fusenig, NE:* Mutual induction of growth factor gene expression by epidermal-dermal cell interaction. J Cell Biol, 122:417–429, (1993)

[31] *Igarashi, M, Finch, PW, Aaronson, SA:* Characterization of recombinant human fibroblast growth factor (FGF)-10 reveals functional similarities with keratinocyte growth factor (FGF-7). J Biol Chem, 273:13230–13235, (1998)

[32] *Miki, T, Fleming, TP, Botarro, DP Rubin, D, Aaronson, SA:* Expression cDNA cloning of the KGF receptor by creation of a transforming autocrine loop. Science, 251:72–75, (1991)

[33] *Bottaro, DP, Rubin, JS, Ron, D, Finch, PW, Florio, C, Aaronson, SA:* Characterization of the receptor for keratinocyte growth factor. J Biol Chem, 265:12767–12770, (1990)

[34] *Miki, T, Bottaro, D, Fleming, TP, Smith, CL, Burgess, WH, Chan, AM, Aaronson, SA:* Determination of ligand-binding specificity by alternate splicing: two distinct growth factor receptors encoded by a single gene. Proc Natl Acad Sci USA, 89:246–250, (1992)

[35] *Yayon, A, Zimmer, Y, Shen, GH, Avivi, A, Yarden, Y, Givol, D:* A confined variable region confers ligand specificity on fibroblast growth factor receptors: implication for the origin of the immunoglobulin fold. EMBO J, 11:1885–1890, (1992)

[36] *Orr-Urtreger, A, Bedford, MT, Burakova, T, Arman, E, Zimmer, Y, Yayon, A, Givol, D, Lonai, P:* Developmental localization of the splicing alternatives of fibroblast growth factor receptor-2 (FGFR2). Dev Biol, 158:475–486, (1993)

[37] *Werner, S, Weinberg, W, Liao, X, Peters, KG, Blessing, M, Yuspa, SH, Weiner, RL, Williams, L T:* Targeted expression of a dominant-negative FGF receptor mutant in the epidermis of transgenic mice reveals a role of FGF in keratinocyte organization and differentiation. EMBO J, 12:2635–2643, (1993)

[38] *Guo, L, Yu, Q-C, Fuchs, E:* Targeting expression of keratinocyte growth factor to keratinocytes elicits striking changes in epithelial differentiation in transgenic mice. EMBO J, 12:973–986, (1993)

[39] *Werner, S, Smola, H, Liao, X, Longaker, MT, Krieg, T, Hofschneider, PH, Williams, LT:* The function of KGF in morphogenesis of epithelium and reepithelialization of wounds. Science, 266:819–822, (1994)

[40] *Martin, P:* Wound healing – Aiming for perfect skin regeneration. Science, 276:75–81, (1997)

[41] *Tang, A, Gilchrest, BA:* Regulation of keratinocyte growth factor gene expression in human skin fibroblasts. J Dermatol Sci, 11:41–50, (1996)

[42] *Brauchle, M, Angermeyer, K, Hübner, G, Werner, S:* Large induction of keratinocyte growth factor expression by serum growth factors and pro-inflammatory cytokines in cultured fibroblasts. Oncogene, 9:3199–3204, (1994)

[43] *Chedid, M, Rubin, JS, Csaky, KG, Aaronson, SA:* Regulation of keratinocyte growth factor gene expression by interleukin-1. J Biol Chem, 269:10753–10757, (1994)

[44] *Werner, S, Peters, KG, Longaker, MT, Fuller-Pace, F, Banda, MJ, Williams, LT:* Large induction of keratinocyte growth factor expression in the dermis during wound healing. Proc Natl Acad Sci USA, 89:6896–6900, (1992)

[45] *Marchese, C, Chedid, M, Dirsch, OR, Csaky, KG, Santanelli, F, Latini, C, LaRochelle, WJ, Torrisi, MR, Aaronson, SA:* Modulation of keratinocyte growth factor and its receptor in re-epithelializing human skin. J Exp Med, 182:1369–1376, (1995)

[46] *Brauchle, M, Fässler, R, Werner, S:* Suppression of keratinocyte growth factor expression by glucocorticoids in vitro and during wound healing. J Invest Dermatol, 105:579–584, (1995)

[47] *Werner, S, Breeden, M, Hübner, G, Greenhalgh, DG, Longaker, MT:* Induction of keratinocyte growth factor expression is reduced and delayed during wound healing in the genetically diabetic mouse. J Invest Dermatol, 103:469–473, (1994)

[48] Guo, L, Degenstein, L, Fuchs, E: Keratinocyte growth factor is required for hair development but not for wound healing. Genes Dev, 10:165–175, (1996)

[49] Tagashira, S, Harada, H, Katsumata, T, Itoh, N, Nobuyuki, I: Cloning of mouse FGF10 and up-regulation of its gene expression during wound healing. Gene, 197:399–404, (1997)

[50] Beer, H-D, Florence, C, Dammeier, J, McGuire, L, Werner, S, Duan, DR: Mouse fibroblast growth factor 10: cDNA cloning, protein characterization, and regulation of mRNA expression. Oncogene, 15:2211–2218, (1997)

[51] Woodley, DT: Reepithelialization: In. The Molecular and Cellular Biology of Wound Repair (second edition). ed. Clark, R.A.F., Plenun Press, New York, pp339–347, (1996)

[52] Danilenko, DM, Ring, BD, Yanagihara, D, Benson, W, Wiemann, B, Starnes, CO, Pierce, GF: Keratinocyte growth factor is an important endogenous mediator of hair follicle growth, development, and differentiation. Am J Pathol, 147:145–154, (1995)

[53] Marchese, C, Rubin, J, Ron, D, Faggioni, A, Torrisi, M R, Messina, A, Frati, L Aaronson, SA: Human keratinocyte growth factor activity on proliferation and differentiation of human keratinocytes: differentiation response distinguish KGF from EGF family. J Cell Physiol, 144:326–332, (1990)

[54] Sato, C, Tsuboi, R, Shi, C-M, Rubin, JS, Ogawa, H: Comparative study of hepatocyte growth factor/scatter factor and keratinocyte growth factor effects on human keratinocytes. J Invest Dermatol, 104:958–963, (1995)

[55] Tsuboi, R, Sato, C, Kurita, Y, Ron, D, Rubin, JS, Ogawa, H: Keratinocyte growth factor (FGF-7) stimulates migration and plasminogen activator activity of normal human keratinocytes. J Invest Dermatol, 101:49–53, (1993)

[56] Cavanni, A, Zambruno, G, Marconi, A, Manca, V, Marchetti, M, Giannetti, A: Distinctive integrin expression in the newly forming epidermis during wound healing in humans. J Invest Dermatol, 10:600–604, (1993)

[57] Juhasz I, Murphy GF, Yan H-C, Herlyn M, Albelda, SM: Regulation of extracellular matrix proteins and integrin cell substratum adhesion receptors on epithelium during cutaneous human wound healing in vivo. Am J Pathol, 143:1458–1469, (1993)

[58] Larjava, H, Salo, T, Haapasalmi, K, Kramer, RH, Heino, J: Expression of integrins and basement membrane components by wound keratinocytes. J Clin Invest 92:1425–1435, (1993)

[59] Clark RAF, Lanigan JM, DellaPella P, Manseau E, Dvorak HF, Colvin RB: Fibronectin and fibrin provide a provisional matrix for epidermal cell migration during wound reepithelialization. J Invest Dermatol, 79: 262–269, (1982)

[60] Putnins, E E, Firth, J D, Lohachitranont, A, Uitto, V-J, Larjava, H: Keratinocyte growth factor (KGF) promotes keratinocyte cell attachment and migration on collagen and fibronectin. Cell Adhes Commun, 7:211–221, (1999)

[61] Takada, Y, Kamata, T, Irie, A, Puzon-Mclaughlin, W, Zhang, X-P: Structural-basis of integrin-mediated signal transduction. Matrix Biol, 16:143–151 (1997)

[62] Yamada, K M: Integrin signaling. Matrix Biol, 16:137–141, (1997)

[63] Stewart, M, Hogg, N: Regulation of leukocyte integrin function: affinity vs. avidity. J Cell Biochem, 61:554–561, (1996)

[64] Pierce, G F, Yanagihara, D, Klopchin, K, Danilenko, D M, Hsu, D M, Kenney, W C, Morris, C F: Stimulation of all epithelial elements during skin regeneration by keratinocyte growth factor. J Exp Med, 179:831–840, (1994)

[65] Staiano-Coico, L, Krueger, J G, Rubin, J S, D'limi, S, Vallat, V P, Valentino, L, Fahay III, T, Hawes, A, Kingston, G, Madden, M R, Mathwich, M, Gottlieb, A B, Aaronson, S A: Human keratinocyte growth factor effects in a porcine model of epidermal wound healing. J Exp Med, 178:865–878, (1993)

[66] Palacek, S P, Loftus, J C, Ginsberg, M H, Lauffenburger, D A, Horwitz, A F: Integrin-ligand binding properties govern cell migration speed through cell-substratum adhesiveness. Nature, 385:537–540, (1997)

[67] Parks, W C: Matrix Metalloproteinases in repair. Wound Rep Reg, 7:423–432, (1999)

[68] Putnins, E E, Firth, J D, Uitto, V-J: Stimulation of collagenase (Matrix metalloproteinase-1) synthesis in histiotypic epithelial cell culture by heparin is enhanced by keratinocyte growth factor. Matrix Biol, 15:21–29, (1996)

[69] Putnins, E E, Firth, J D, Uitto, V-J: Keratinocyte growth factor stimulation of gelatinase (MMP-9) and plasminogen activator (uPA) in histiotypic cell culture. J Invest Dermatol, 104:989–994, (1995)

[70] Madlener, M, Mauch, C, Conca, W, Brauchle, M, Parks, W, Werner, S: Regulation of the expression of stromelysin-2 by growth factors in keratinocytes: implication for normal and impaired wound healing. Biochem J, 320:659–664, (1996)

[71] Salo, T, Mäkelä, M, Kylmäniemi, M, Autio-Harmainen, H, Larjava, H: Expression of matrix metalloproteinases-2 and -9 during early human wound healing. Lab Invest, 70: 176–182, (1994)

[72] Sun, L, Xu, L, Chang, H, Henry, FA, Miller, RM, Harmon, JM, Nielson, TB: Transfection with

aFGF cDNA improves wound healing. J Invest Dermatol, 108:313–318, (1997)

[73] Rosenthal, FM, Cao, L, Tanczos, E, Kopp, J, Andree, C, Stark, GB, Mertelsmann, R, Kulmburg, P:Paracrine stimulation of keratinocytes in vitro and continuous delivery of epidermal growth factor to wounds in vivo by genetically modified fibroblasts transfected with a novel chimeric construct. in vivo, 11:201–208, (1997)

[74] Andree, C, Swain, WF, Page, CP, Macklin, MD, Slama, J, Hatzis, D, Eriksson, E: In vivo transfer and expression of a human epidermal growth factor gene accelerates wound repair. Proc Natl Acad Sci USA , 91:12188–12192, (1994)

[75] Horch, RE, Bannasch, H, Kopp, J, Andree, C, Stark, GB: Single-cell suspension of cultured human keratinocytes in fibrin-glue reconstitute the epidermis. Cell Transpl, 7:309–317, (1998)

Current Status of Cultured Epidermal Skin Substitutes

H. O. Rennekampff, J. F. Hansbrough

Summary

This is a review of recent work on both temporal and permanent cultured epidermal substitutes. It has been found that the differentiation of keratinocytes in culture resembles that of senescent cells, with subsequent less than optimal "take" of grafts. When keratinocytes are cultured on a number of novel polymeric films, growth and experimental "take" rates can be improved. Combinations of keratinocytes with hyaluronic acid, fibrin glue, collagen GAG, and other materials is discussed.

General Considerations

In the case of large deep dermal and full thickness wounds skin loss is often marked by short and long term complications. Acute complications include serious and life threatening wound infection and loss of body fluids. In the long term the most important complications are scar formation with hypertrophy, contracture, and scar instability.

Although conventional split thickness skin grafts can provide wound closure even for large wounds, delays in wound closure can contribute substantially to local and systemic complications [43]. In addition harvesting of split thickness skin grafts impose additional risks on the patient e.g. bleeding and scarring.

To facilitate early coverage of wounds of different origin allogeneic skin has been used as a temporal biological dressing. While increased rate of survival was reported for burn victims with large excisional wounds and faster healing was seen in partial thickness wounds covered with allogeneic skin severe problems e.g. viral infection were linked to the use of allogenic skin [32].

To improve the availability of autologous skin, *in vitro* culture techniques to grow autologous epidermis have been utilized [13, 14]. Since the breakthroughs of Rheinwald and Green [37] in the culture and serial subculture of human keratinocytes, this technology is now commercially available. Yet time requirements are high, as cultured epithelial sheet grafts are usually not available until at least three weeks after harvesting of the skin and initiation of cultures. Furthermore, cultured epithelial grafts are very expensive and difficult to handle. Take rates of the grafts and the necessity to regraft have been variable [9, 39]. Non-adherence and the long-term tendency to form blisters following mechanical stress may be caused by disturbed adhesion properties of the keratinocytes and abnormal structure of anchoring fibrils [44].

Extracellular matrices of the wound were reported to have a major effect on the healing process and additional extracellular matrix components were documented to enhance wound healing [19]. The use of dermal substitutes simultaneously applied with cultured epithelial grafts and cultured single cell suspensions also highlight matrix requirements for epithelial regulation and subsequent regeneration.

In this report we summarize the current concepts for temporal and permanent cultured epidermal replacement.

Cultured, non Viable Epidermal Substitute

The need for a temporal skin substitute excluding the risk of viral transmission led to a bilaminate product which is commercialy available as Transcyte™. This material consists of a human matrix containing collagen and a variety of of other important dermal molecules produced by human fibroblasts

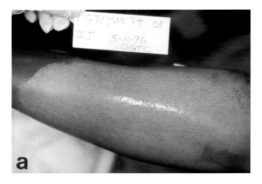

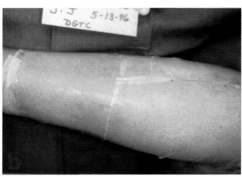

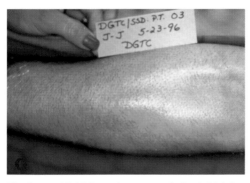

Fig. 1: Partial thickness burn wound after initial debridement (a) , application of Transcyte (b) and subsequent healing (c).

cultured on a nylon mesh [18]. A meticulous screened fibroblast population and a freeze-thaw cycle lead to a nonviable product with highest viral safety.

Transcyte has been used for the temporal coverage of full thickness excised wounds as well as for the temporal coverage of partial thickness wounds. For excised wounds Transcyte performed similar or better than allogeneic cadaver skin [33]. Most striking is the effect of this product in the treatment of partial thickness wounds (Fig. 1). In comparison to standard treatment a more rapid healing was noticed [30]. It is speculated that this epidermal substitute stimulates the remaining keratinocytes and protects them during outgrowth. By increasing the rate of reepithelialization the quality of healing is improved and scar formation reduced [8]. Consequently by the use of Transcyte a reduced scarring was noticed in the treatment of mid partial thickness wounds [30].

Keratinocyte Sheet Grafts

The Rheinwald and Green method for *in vitro* passaging of single cell suspensions of keratinocytes on an irradiated mouse fibroblast line coupled with mitogens to form multilayered epithelial sheets is well described [14, 37] and remains a standard for permanent epidermal replacement. Confluent and stratified sheets (4 to 6 cell layers thick) are transferred to a backing material prior to grafting. Starting with a biopsy size of 1 to 5 cm², about 3 weeks are required to culture a sufficient number of autologous epithelial sheets (Epicel^{SM}) to cover an adult (17,000 cm²) with a 70 % TBSA burn.

Numerous reports on the clinical use of cultured epidermal sheets have appeared with variable results. Early and late graft losses and friability of healed skin are reported. Early take rates of cultured epithelium are reported from as low as 40 % to 80 % depending on the individual technique (Freising/Horch, pp. 220–226 in this book).

Basic science demonstrates that keratinocytes in differentiated cultured epithelial autografts resemble more a senescent cell than an activated phenotype [34]. Integrin expression on basal keratinocyte of differentiated sheet grafts is more akin to that of normal unwounded skin, i.e. faint or absent integrin α5 reactivity. This may at least in part explain a certain lack of adhesiveness on a fibronectin-rich wound bed, while "take" rates on a dermal bed are reported to be significantly higher. In addition exposure of cultured epithelial sheet grafts to Dispase leads to integrin α6β4 internalization which may also affect keratinocyte survival [31]. In a recent paper engraftment of epithelial sheet grafts could be enhanced by the application of the matrix ligand for the integrin α6β4, laminin 5 [40].

Despite many drawbacks of cultured epithelial sheets, cultured grafts are utilized in the treatment of extensive skin loss in the absence of sufficient autologous donor skin. Further advances in generation and release of cultured epithelial sheets could significantly enhance the use of this product.

The use of cultured epithelial sheet grafts was also reported for the temporal treatment of superficial partial thickness wounds of the face. Rapid healing with reduced scarring was noticed in these patients [22].

Keratinocytes Cultured on Membranes

Serious limitations of the application of autolougous epithelial sheets include the requirement for enzymatic removal of the epithelial sheet from the flask, culture on a fibroblast feeder layer and shrinkage of released sheets following exposure to Dispase or Thermolysin. These limitations led to the consideration of different methods for the application of cultured keratinocytes.

Novel synthetic polymer films which are non-cytotoxic support the growth of human keratinocytes as well as, or better than, standard tissue culture plastic. Some of these membranes were tested in our laboratory for their ability to transfer actively growing keratinocytes to wounds [35]. Keratinocytes were grown on a synthetic hydrophilic polyurethane membrane dressing, Hydroderm®. This specialized polyurethane membrane has the unique characteristic of markedly increasing its water-vapor permeability when becoming wet. Hydrophilic films can potentially solve the accumulation of exudates. This variability in water vapor permeability can be useful in maintaining an optimum healing environment since the dressing can respond to changing conditions of exudate. For the past several years Hydroderm was successfully utilized as a dressing for donor site wounds [21].

Human keratinocytes seeded at a density of 5×10^4 cells/cm^2 of Hydroderm are cultured with the membranes submerged in serum-free medium. After 2 days of culture the Hydroderm membrane showed confluent coverage of keratinocytes. Data drawn from culturing multiple donors of different ages and with various morbidities showed that 0.5 square meter of membrane containing cells can be made readily available in 17 days. These cultured grafts can then be inversely applied to the wound without the necessity of enzymatically detaching the cells. In addition this method allows precise timing of the transplantation, as the culture process on the membrane is only started 2 days before transplantation.

In a variety of experiments on full-thickness wounds in animals, with and without the utilization of a dermal replacement, we have shown that application of a single layer of cultured keratinocytes attached to polyurethane membranes can result in a multilayered epithelium on the wound [35, 36]. In a pilot experiment in humans full thickness wounds simultanously covered with a single layer of cultered keratinocytes on Hydroderm overlayed on a dermal substitute resulted in a normal epidermal architecture (Fig. 2).

A recently commercially available hyaluronic acid membrane (Laserskin™) can also function as a carrier system for cultured keratinocytes (Vivoderm™). Hyaluronic acid is an important natural, water-retaining polysaccharide in the soft tissue. Furthermore hyaluronic acid influences cell behavior including motility, adhesion

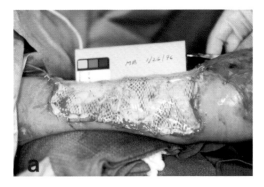

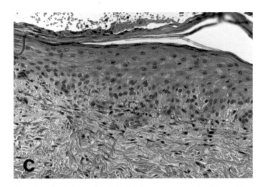

Fig. 2: Grafting of a full thickness wound with a single layer of cultured autologous keratinocytes on Hydroderm overlaid on AlloDerm dermal matrix (a). Three weeks after grafting wound closure is achieved (b). Histology demonstrates a multilayed stratified epithelium and a vascularized dermis (c).

and detachment [41]. The receptors for hyaluronic acid belong to a family of proteins called CD 44, which are involved in adhesion in connective tissue and epithelial cells [42]. The properties of hyaluronic acid include biocompatibility and low antigenicity [5]. Therefore hyaluronic acid derivatives have been proposed for use in a variety of clinical treatments, including the promotion of wound healing [7]. Partial to complete esterification of hyaluronic acid with ethyl or benzyl linkages produces materials of high biocompatibility and intermediate to long half-lives. Laserskin has microholes which allows vapor permeation and also migration of cells. Autologous keratinocytes separated from a patient biopsy are expanded in number using a conventional method and seeded on the membrane [29] coated with a radiated murine 3T3 feeder layer. After keratinocytes had formed a multilayer, stratified epithelium, the membrane was transplanted to wounds. *In vivo* reports of this technique have included full-thickness wounds in porcine models and partial thickness wounds in humans, with excellent take rates reported [1, 10]. Compared to cultured keratinocyte sheets without a substrate, more rapid reepithelialization on the wound was noted. However it seems that the advantages of this approach are not fully explored with the recommended technique. Avoiding the lengthy culture periods which are required until a differentiated, stratified epithelium is achieved on Laserskin could enhance the product's use. Furthermore it is not nesessary to utilize a radiated murine feeder layer, which may eventually co-transplant onto the patient. It is reported that transplanted mouse 3T3 fibroblasts may induce a rejection response which can contribute to late graft loss [4]. Taking these considerations into account a single layer of keratinocytes cultured as a mono-layer on the hyaluronic acid membrane without the murine feeder layer should result in an improved technique. In any case clinical performance must be demonstrated with this technique.

Keratinocytes Suspended in Fibrin Glue

As reepithelialization is dependent on the non-differentiated, migratory phenotype of the keratinocytes, it was hypothetized that single cells on a wound bed would be sufficient for subsequent reepithelialization. Fibrin glue was used as a vehicle for the delivery of such a single cell suspension of keratinocytes to wounds. Fibrin glue has widespread real and potential applications in various surgical fields [11, 25, 45]. It was shown to be effective for the fixation of autologous meshed split thickness skin grafts and subsequent healing of these grafts. The application of non-cultured keratinocytes in a fibrin glue suspension was first reported by Hunyadi [24]. Now various clinical reports including the editor's document the success of cultured keratinocyte suspensions in fibrin glue for reepithelialization of deep partial- and full-thickness wounds [2, 15, 23, 27]. Most clinical reports lack information on seeding densities per treated area and on quality of subsequent epithelial coverage. Therefore it remains to be seen how keratinocytes in fibrin glue suspension will perform in comparison to cultured epithelial sheets and other described methods, in terms of time, costs and quality of wound coverage. One of the advantages is that the fibrin glue suspension method is technically easy to perform, particularly because fibrin glue is commercially available in most European countries. Similar to cultured epithelial sheet grafts a complete commercial product of autologous keratinocytes derived from a patient biopsy is now available in Germany (bioseed™).

Dermal Substrates for Keratinocyte Growth and Delivery

Clinical results in transplanted epithelium have led to a consensus among most clinicians that a dermal substitute is needed to enhance the function of epithelial grafts. Therefore efforts were taken to combine dermal substitutes and cultured keratinocytes *in vitro* prior to grafting. Handling properties of the "composite" grafts improved dramatically, and in addition the use of enzymes to remove the sheets from the culture vessel surface are not necessary. The delivery of either a single layer of keratinocytes or a differentiated epithelium on a dermal substrate, as a composite graft, has been subject to extensive work and is still ongoing. It seems obvious that applying a functional skin replacement rather than a pure epidermal replacement most closely resembles the eventual need for tissue. Several variants on this technique have been described. In general these include dermis-derived lattices, collagen derived matrices and cultured substrates [16].

In vitro experiments demonstrated the importance of an intact basement membrane, dermal structure and viable keratinocytes for optimal cell growth [28]. These conclusions were included in the development of a dermal lattice composed of collagen and glycosaminglycans (collagen-GAG). Inoculation of the matrix with fibroblasts resulted in an acceptable matrix for keratinocytes [3, 17] Collagen-GAG based autologous composite grafts are currently used for burn patients with good results at the Shriners Burn Hospital, Cincinnati.

A similar poduct based on collagen and glycosaminglycans utilizes allogeneic keratinocytes and fibroblasts (Apligraf™). While this product was used in the treatment of small chronic wounds, no reports are available on extensive full thickness wounds. In addition one has to be concerned about the immunogenic potential of the cells especially keratinocytes in this product. Therefore stimulation of wound repair seems possible, while permanent engraftment in large wounds has to be demonstrated.

A major problem with dermal substrates for the delivery of keratinocytes as a composite graft is the availability for grafting of extensive wounds. It is optimal if dermal matrices are readily available from the shelf to fit the need of the burn centers. In an effort to meet this goal a dermal replacement composed of fibroblasts cultured on a biodegradable polyglactin mesh was developed [6]. This cultured dermal replacement (Dermagraft™) supported autologous keratinocyte attachment and proliferation *in vitro* [12]. Further experiments showed that this cultured composite graft can be transplanted to animal wounds, resulting in skin regeneration [20]. Currently this complete epidermal-dermal product is not commercially available.

Future Perspectives

Coverage of extensive wounds with viable autologous keratinocytes remains a treatment option if autologous donor skin is not available. Cultured epithelial autografts are the standard in cultured epidermal replacements. However there is evidence that proliferating keratinocytes as suspended cells or as a single layer are sufficient for re-epithelialization of a wound surface. There is obvious need for controlled animal and human studies for determining seeding densities and time requirements in the culture process and evaluation of wound healing compared to standard grafting techniques.

A small number of relatively undifferentiated keratinocytes, which may include keratinocyte stem cells, may be sufficient for achieving subsequent epidermal outgrowth. Implications from the keratinocyte stem cell models indeed suggest that these cells can give rise to a complete epidermis [26, 38].

Understanding keratinocyte-matrix interactions will not only allow us to influence keratinocyte outgrowth, adhesion and migration, but may also lead to modalities of additional matrix molecule treatment for enhancing keratinocyte or epithelial take.

Further strategies may include the generation of genetically manipulated non immunogenic keratinocytes which allow the utilization of an off-the-shelf epidermal replacement. Biotechnoloy has to focus on dressings to protect the regenerating epidermis until permanent wound closure is achieved.

References

[1] Andreassi L, Casini L, Trabucchi E, Diamantini S, Rastrelli, A Donati L, Tenchini ML, Malcovati M: Human keratinocytes cultured on membranes composed of benzyl ester of hyaluronic acid, suitable for grafting. Wounds 3:116, 1991.

[2] Brody M, Kaiser HW, Bertlich R, Fratila A, Beichelt D, Kreysel HW: Kombinierte tangentiale Exzision und Keratinozytentransplantation zur Entfernung von Tätowierungen. Z Hautkr 67:347, 1992.

[3] Boyce S, Christianson D, Hansbrough JF: Structure of a collagen-GAG skin substitute optimized for cultured human epidermal keratinocytes. J Biomed Mater Res 22:939, 1988.

[4] Cairns BA, deSerres BA, Brady LA, Hultman CS, Meyer AA: Viable, immunologically active, mouse 3T3 fibroblasts persist in human cultured epidermal autografts used in burn wound coverage. Abstract, Am Assoc Surg Trauma, San Diego CA, Sept-Oct 1994.

[5] Cortivo E, Brun P, Rastrelli A, Abatangelo G: In vitro studie on the biocompatinbility of hyaloronic acis esters. Biomaterials 12:727, 1991.

[6] Cooper ML, Hansbrough JF, Spielvogel RL, Cohen R, Bartel R, Naughton G: In vivo optimization of a living dermal substitute employing cultured human fibroblasts on a biodegradable polyglycolic acid or polyglactin mesh. Biomaterials 12:243, 1991.

[7] Davidson JM, Nanney LB, Broadley KN, Whitsett JS, Aquino AM, Beccaro M, Rastrelli A: Hyaluronic derivates and their application to wound healing. Clin Mater 8:171, 1991.

[8] Deitch EA, Wheelahan TM, Rose MP, Clothier J, Cotter J: Hypertrophic burn scars: analysis of variables. J Trauma 23:895, 1983.

[9] Desai MH, Mlakar JM, McCauley RL, Abdullah KM, Ruran RL, Waymack JP, Robson MC, Herndon D N: Lack of long-term durability of cultured keratinocyte burn-wound coverage: A case report. J Burn Care Rehab 12:540, 1991.

[10] Donati L, Marazzi M, Veronesi AM, Ordanini MN, Falcone L, Ferrone M, Mauri S: Treatment of cutaneous wounds with cultured human keratinocytes on hyaluronic acid membrane. Wound Rep Reg 3:363,1995.

[11] Eckert P, Häring R, Satter P, Zwank L: Fibrinklebung, Indikation und Anwendung. München: Urban & Schwarzenberg, 1986.

[12] Fleischmajer R, MacDonald ED, Contard P, Perlish JS: Immunochemistry of a keratinocyte-fibroblast co-culture model for reconstruction of human skin. J Histochem Cytochem 41:1359, 1993.

[13] Gallico GG, O'Connor NE, Compton CC, Kehinde O, Green H: Permanent coverage of large

burn wounds with autologous cultured human epithelium. N Engl J Med 311:448,1984.

[14] *Green H, Kehinde O and Thomas J:* Growth of cultured human epidermal cells into multiple epithelia suitable for grafting. Proc Natl Acad Sci USA 76:5665, 1979.

[15] *Hafemann B, Hettich R, Ensslen S, Kowol B, Zuhlke A, Ebert R, Konigs M, Kirkpatrick CJ:* Treatment of skin defects using suspensions of in vitro cultured keratinocytes. Burns 20: 168, 1994.

[16] *Hansbrough JF:* Wound Coverage with Biologic Dressings and Cultured Skin Substitutes. Austin: RG Landes Inc, Pp. 93–114, 1992.

[17] *Hansbrough JF, Boyce ST, Cooper ML, Foreman TJ:* Burn wound closure with cultured autologous keratinocytes and fibroblasts attached to a collagen-glycosaminoglycan substrate. J Am Med Assoc 262:2125, 1989.

[18] *Hansbrough WB, Hansbrough JF, Doré C:* Successful coverage of donor site wounds with an adhesive polyurethane membrane with high water-vapor permeability. Abstract, 9th Congress, Internat Soc Burn Injuries, Paris, June 1994 b.

[19] *Hansbrough JF, Herndon D, Heimbach DM, Solem LD, Gamelli RL, Tompkins R:* Accelerated healing and reduced need for grafting in pediatric patients with burns treated with Arginine-Glycine-Aspartic acid peptide matrix. J Burn Care Rehabil 16:377, 1995.

[20] *Hansbrough JF, Morgan JL, Greenleaf GE, Bartel R:* Composite grafts of human keratinocytes grown on a polyglactin mesh-cultured fibroblast dermal substitute function as a bilayer skin replacement in full-thickness wounds on athymic mice. J Burn Care Rehabil 14:485, 1993.

[21] *Hansbrough JF, Morgan JL, Greenleaf GE, Underwood J:* Development of a temporary living skin replacement composed of human fibroblasts cultured in Biobrane, a synthetic dressing material. Surgery 115:663, 1994 a

[22] *Henckel von Donnersmark G, Mühlbauer W, Höfter E, Hartinger A:* Die Verwendung von Keratinozytenkulturen in der Schwerbrandverletztenbehandlung – bisherige Erfahrungen, Ausblicke zur weiteren Entwicklung. Unfallchirurg 98:229, 1995

[23] *Horch R, Bannasch H, Kopp J, Andree C, Stark GB:* Single-cell suspensions of cultured human keratinocytes in fibrin-glue reconstitute the epidermis. Cell Transplant 7:309, 1995

[24] *Hundyadi J, Farkas B, Bertenyi C, Olah J, Dobozy A:* Keratinocyte grafting: a new means of transplantation for full-thickness wounds. J Dermatol Surg Oncol 14:75, 1988.

[25] *Jabs AD, Todd MW, De Bellis J, Hugo NE:* The effect of fibrin glue on skin grafts in infected sites. Plast Reconstr Surg 89:268,1992.

[26] *Jones PH, Harper S, Watt FM:* Stem cell patterning and fate in human epidermis. Cell 80:83, 1995.

[27] *Kaiser HW, Stark GB, Kopp J, Balcerkiewicz A, Spilker G, Kreysel HW:* Cultured autologous keratinocytes in fibrin glue suspension, exclusively and combined with STS-allograft (preliminary clinical and histological report of a new technique). Burns 20:23, 1994.

[28] *Krejci NC, Cuono CB, Langdon RC, McGuire J:* In vitro reconstitution of skin: fibroblasts facilitate keratinocyte growth and differentiation on acellular reticular dermis. J Invest Dermatol 97:843, 1991.

[29] *Myers SR, Navsaria HA, Grady J, Sanders R, Green C, Leigh IM:* A hyaluronic acid membrane delivery system for cultured keratinocyte autografts: Clinical "take" rates in a porcine kerato-dermal model. Wound Rep Reg 3:390, 1995.

[30] *Nordenboos J, Dore C, Hansbrough JF:* Safety and efficacy of Transcyte for the treatment of partial–thickness burns. J Burn Care Rehabil 20:275, 1999.

[31] *Poumay Y, Leclercq-Smekens M, Grailly S, Degen A, Leloup R:* Specific internalization of basal membrane domains containing the integrin _6_4 in Dispase-detached cultured human keratinocytes.Eur J Cell Biology 60: 12, 1993.

[32] *Pruitt Jr BA:* The evolutionaty development of biologic dressings and skin substitutes. J Burn Care Rehabil 18:S2, 1997

[33] *Purdue GF, Hunt JL, Still JrJM, Law EJ, Herndon DN, Goldfarb IW, Schiller WR, Hansbrough JF, Hickerson WL, Himel HN, Kealey GP, Twomey J, Missavage AE, Solem LD, Davis M, Totoritis M, Gentzkow GD:* A multicenter clinical trial of a biosynthetic skin replacemnt, Dermagraft-TC , compared with cryopreserved human cadaver skin for temporary coverage of excised burn wounds. J Burn Care Rehabil 18:52, 1997.

[34] *Rennekampff HO, Hansbrough JF, Woods VJr, Kiessig V:* Integrin and matrix molecule expression in cultured skin replacements. J Burn Care Rehabil, 17:213, 1996 a

[35] *Rennekampff HO, Hansbrough JF, Kiessig V, Tenenhaus M, Abiezzi S, Woods VJr:* Wound closure with human keratinocytes cultured on a polyurethane dressing overlaid on a cultured human dermal replacement. Surgery 120:1996 b

[36] *Rennekampff HO, Kiessig V, Griffey S, Greenleaf G, Hansbrough JF:* Acellular human dermis promotes cultured keratinocyte engraftment. J Burn Care Rehabil 18:535, 1997

[37] *Rheinwald JG, Green H:* Serial cultivation of strains of human keratinocytes-the forma-

tion of keratinizing colonies from single cells. Cell 6:331, 1975.

[38] *Rochat A, Kobayashi K, Barrandon Y:* Localisation of stem cells of human hair follicles by clonal analysis. Cell 76:1063, 1994.

[39] *Rue LWIII, Cioffi W G, McManus WF, Pruitt BAJr:* Wound closure and outcome in extensively burned patients treated with cultured autologous keratinocytes. J Trauma 34:662, 1993.

[40] *Takeda A, Kadoya K, Shioya N, Uchinumura E, Tsunenaga M, Amano S, Nishiyama T, Burgeson R E:* Pretreatment of human keratinocyte sheets with laminin 5 improves their grafting efficiency. J Invest Dermatol 113:38, 1999

[41] *Turley EA, Bowman P, Kytyrik MA:* Effects of hyaluronate and hyaluronate-binding pro-

teins on cell motile and contact behaviour. J Cell Sci 78:133, 1985.

[42] *Underhill CCD44:* The hyaluronan receptor. J Cell Sci 103:293, 1992.

[43] *Wolfe RA, Roi LD, Flora JD, Feller I, Cornell RG:* Mortality differences and speed of wound closure among specialized burn care facilities. J Am Med Assoc 250:763, 1983.

[44] *Woodley DT, Peterson HD, Herzog SR, Stricklin GP, Burgeson RE, Briggaman RA, Cronce DJ, O'Keefe EJ:* Burn wounds resurfaced by cultured epidermal autografts healing in humans. J Invest Dermatol 101:600, 1993.

[45] *Zellner PR:* Fibrinklebung in der Verbrennungschirurgie-Plastische Chirugie. Berlin: Springer Verlag, 1988.

An Overview of Epidermal Stem Cells: Biological Characterization and Future Therapeutic Directions

N. Wasif, S. Schwartz, L. Staiano-Coico

Summary

The human skin presents a dynamic interface with the environment. Multilayered and multifunctional, it is regulated by complex relationships we are just beginning to appreciate. Orchestrating these interactions is the epidermal stem cell- responsible for the precise balance between regeneration and loss. The investigative work leading to the characterization of stem cells and their *in vitro* and *in vivo* behavior is briefly chronicled. The hunt for cellular and molecular stem cell markers ignited by flow cytometric technology, the implications of stem cell research and the exciting prospects of keratinocyte gene therapy are presented.

Stem Cell Concepts

Epithelial surfaces subject to physiological shedding due to everyday wear and tear need a pool of regenerative cells to maintain status quo. These proliferating cells, or stem cells, were recognized at the turn of the century as 'a cell that remains in the tissue of origin and retains the ability to proliferate throughout life' [1].

The advent of tissue culture allowed investigators to study *in vitro* behavior of the putative stem cells and differentiate them from their less replication proficient counterparts. In vivo stem cells were initially identified with the help of thymidine labelling kinetic studies and later marked at the cellular and molecular level by using flow cytometric technology. Kinetic studies enabled investigators not only to localize stem cells *in vivo* but also to track their replication status. Consequently, the original definition has now been expanded to include the histologic and kinetic aspects of stem cell behavior.

Ultrastructurally, stem cells have an undifferentiated morphology with few organelles and a large nuclear to cytoplasm ratio. They are slow cycling *in vivo* but have a proliferative reserve that exceeds the lifetime of the individual. Comprising a small percentage of the total cell population, these cells can be pluripotent (hematopoietic) or unipotent (epidermal). Stem cells occupy specific locations in the tissue of origin leading to the concept of a stem cell 'niche'. Finally, the origin of cancer in stem cells or early progenitor cells has been established and yields a potential target for curative therapy [16, 54, 44, 70, 111].

Initially stem cells divide to give rise to daughter cells, some of which reconstitute the stem cell population whereas others represent 'transient amplifying' or TA cells. These cells form an intermediate, rapidly proliferating population that expands clonally for a variable number of generations. Ultimately the progeny of TA cells undergo terminal differentiation to constitute a third cell population: the post-mitotic cells. Regenerating tissues thus have three functional classes of cells: the stem cells→transient amplifying cells→ post-mitotic cells. Each subpopulation of cells has a characteristic morphology and kinetic behavior *in vitro* as well as *in vivo* [95].

Epidermal Stem Cells

Human epidermis is the prototype of self-regenerating tissue, comprised of layers of keratinocytes in various stages of differentiation and proliferation. The outermost layer of cells in the entire epidermis is shed and replaced every day [102]. The basal layers show the highest proliferative activity and the cell population with the least differentiated morphology [88]. As the cells commit to differentiate they move up to the suprabasal layers. The further up the epidermis the cells migrate the more differentiated they become, culminating in the acellular protein-filled keratinocytes of the stratum corneum, the cornified envelopes, quite distinct from their primitive forefathers in the basal layers [36, 55, 121].

Kinetic Studies

Cell kinetic studies provided the first direct evidence for stem cells and transient amplifying (TA) cells. The low rate of stem cell proliferation exactly compensates for cells lost from the stratum corneum. The shed cells constitute the post-mitotic non-dividing cell population. Consequently, in normal skin, the main population of proliferating cells, will be the TA cells. If skin in the steady state is pulse labelled with radioactive thymidine, the metabolicaly active TA cells wil be labeled, whereas the slow cycling stem cells show minimal uptake because they are less likely to be in the S phase. With time, the rapidly dividing TA cells will dilute the label to undetectable levels, whereas the stem cells retain what they initially picked up because of infrequent division. Single pulse labeling will thus mark the proliferating TA cells, whereas with longer exposure the stem cells are marked. This simple yet elegant concept forms the basis of kinetic studies to investigate stem cell behavior [55].

Regular columns of suprabasal cells were shown to be present in mouse epidermal skin. More frequent mitosis were noted in the peripheral basal layer of these columns as compared to the central region. They suggested a higher rate of cycling for these peripheral cells as compared to the central cells [61]. This observation was duplicated by Potten and others later on, leading to the speculation that stem cells were present in the center of the columns and TA cells at the periphery [15, 76, 91].

Studies on monkey palm skin pulse labeled with radioactive thymidine showed a lack of uptake in the rete ridges (the deepest projection of the epidermis into the dermis)-pointing to a stem cell reservoir at that location. The greatest uptake was in the suprabasal cells, suggesting a high proliferative capacity and a possible location for transient amplifying cells [51].

Patterning of Epidermal Stem Cells

Stem cells are not arranged randomly in skin but show a spatial organization that has both structural and functional implications. At present, there are two theories for stem cell patterning in the epidermis.

Epidermal proliferation Unit (EPU)

Coined by Potten [91], this model proposes a microscopic organization of epidermal cells in discrete vertical hexagonal units. Each of these columns constitutes an epidermal proliferation unit (EPU). In the center of the base of each EPU is a single stem cell. Around the stem cell, and in the immediate suprabasal layers are 8–10 transient amplifying cells. At the most superficial level reside multiple post-mitotic, committed cells. This model arose from studies on murine and hamster trunk skin [20, 60, 61, 64, 91].

Support for the EPU model has come from a number of sources. The first studies to demonstrate kinetic heterogeneity in the epidermal cells displayed patterning consistent with EPUs. Injection of fluorescein dye into epidermal cells leads to a pattern of vertical columns in the skin [42]. More conclusively, it was shown that the label retaining, slow cycling cells in the skin are present in the center and not at the periphery of columns of proliferative units [76]. Using a replication deficient retroviral vector carrying the B-galactosidase marker gene, Mackenzie transduced murine keratincoytes *in vitro*. After transplantation back to the in vivo environment, the marker was detected in columns of cells, with the highest concentration in the center of each column [62].

However, not all studies have yielded the vertical column patterning that the EPU model proposes. These units have not been found in human volar skin nor in mouse trunk epidermis [20, 64, 106].

The Rete Ridge Model

Lavker and Sun studied monkey palm epithelium to show a distribution of stem cells in an alternating 'deep' and 'shallow' rete ridge pattern. Kinetic studies by the same investigators had either revealed cells located in the deep rete ridges which do not pick up label when pulse labeled withradioactive thymidine. These cells were morphologically primitive, non-serrated and slow cycling properties characteristic of stem cells. Cells immediately above the basal layer were labeled and showed greater proliferative activity, identifying them as the transient amplifying cells or TA cells. In the shallow rete ridges, the basal cell show a more differentiated morphology, including a serrated cell appearance. The investigators suggested that the basal cells of the shallow rete ridges were TA cells from the suprabasal layers of the deep rete ridges that migrated up to serve an anchorage function. They concluded that stem cells were localized to the basal layer of the deep rete ridges [50, 51].

This organization of serrated (TA) and non-serrated (stem) cells in shallow and deep rete ridges has been observed in human epidermal skin from the arm, leg, back, abdomen and face [51]. Supportive evidence for this model comes from the identification

of epidermal growth factor (EGF) receptors in the base of the deep rete ridges [71].

A unifying model of these two concepts remains elusive. It is possible that the differences observed may indicate an innate difference between glabrous (hairless) or volar epithelium. Alternatively, mouse skin studies may not represent the true pattern in human skin.

In Vitro Behavior

Tissue culture techniques allowed investigators to study epidermal stem cell behavior in detail and delineate morphological as well as kinetic characteristics. The technique involves growing cells on a feeder layer of 3T3 cells using medium supplemented with a range of additives to promote growth *in vitro* [99, 100].

In vitro keratinocytes have been shown to form three distinct types of colonies. The first is characterized by undifferentiated cells with a high proliferative capacity. These cells have been dubbed holoclones. A second, paraclone cells, has cells that undergo a limited number of mitotic cycles and then differentiate. Meroclones are intermediate between the two and may represent cells in transition from one stage to another [11]. Kinetically, this can be correlated to the behavior of epidermal cells in vivo by considering the holoclones to represent stem cells and the paraclones to be transient amplifying cells.

Many investigators have independently observed the *in vitro* epidermal population to have cells with different cycling times. The slowest cycling, and thus label retaining cells are also morphologically the most primitive, ie. small size, undifferentiated phenotype, long generation time, low RNA content and increae in density [9, 37, 78, 112].

All label-retaining cells from intact epidermis when recovered and cultured from colonies of homogeneously small keratinocytesa morphology characteristic of undifferentiated stem cells [86]. Others have correlated an increase in keratinocyte size with a decreased proliferative capacity and a commitment to differentiate [10, 115].

Differences are also revealed on treating with agents 12-O-tetradecanoylphorbol-13-acetate (TPA) and phorbol, 12-myristate, 13-acetate (PMA). While most of the cells assume a differentiated morphology after exposure to these agents, a subpopulation does not and repsonds by proliferating [25, 128]. These proliferating cells are localized to the central basal cells of the EPU (Morris 1985). Morris extended this work by directly demonstrating that label retaining cells in the epidermis are the ones showing this paradoxical proliferative response to differentiating agents [78]. Finally, it was demonstrated that cells adhering most rapidly to type IV collagen, fibronectin or keratinocyte extracellular matrix in culture had the longest generation times [38].

Stem Cell Fraction

The fraction of epidermal cells that constitute the stem cell population is in the range of 1–10 % as detrmined by different investigators using a variety of techniques. Studies in which irradiated mice were allowed to reform the epidermal layer yielded a number in the vicinity of 10 % [90, 125]. Using labeling techniques, [76] noted that 1 % of the basal cell population retain the label. Gravity centrifugation techniques were used by Pavlovitch [86] to separate an actively proliferating basal cell population and isolate 1% of these cells as representing a possible stem cell population. Of the remaining cell population, those basal cells that are still capable of dividing (50%) constitute the TA cells. The non-dividing cells (40%) left in the basal layer presumably represent the post-mitotic cell population [95].

Stem Cell Niche

The precise location of stem cells in epidermal skin has led many investigators in the past to speculate about a possible role for the microenvironment in providing a favorable stem cell 'niche' for the cells. This concept is derived from earlier work on hematopoietic stem cells [107]. A specialized locale may function to protect the cells physically, help to maintain an undifferentiated morphology, and play a role in signaling.

The basal location of the cells and the fact that they have a 'cap' consisting of melanosomes protects from the deleterious effects of ultraviolet light. The underlying dermis has a high density of blood vessels ensuring a good, uninterrupted blood supply [50, 51].

The undifferentiated cells in the lower epidermal layers have also been shown to have many gap junctions between them. As markers of differentiation appear, these junctions gradually disappear. Cell to cell communication is facilitated by these junctions in the basal layers and may play a role in the regulation of epidermal stem cell differententiation [42].

Merkel cells appear to be concentrated in the vicinity of the deep rete ridges, suggesting neural mediation in stem cell regulation [74]. More recently an alternate theory has been cited which is, that stem cell patterning is an intrinsic property of keratinocytes, established by interactions set up between keratinocytes themselves, and therefore must be autoregulated. This has been demonstrated through use of Beta-1 integrin expression to determine the location of stem cells and TA cells *in vivo*, to isolate each subpopulation directly from human epidermis, and to follow their fate in culture. The cells with high Beta-1 levels are found in clusters localized at the tips of dermal papillae in most body sites, but at the tips of the rete ridges in epidermis of the palm and the sole [39, 40]. The actively cycling cells are concentrated in the areas of low Beta-1 integrin expression. Patches of integrin-bright and integrin-dull cells similar in size to those noted in epidermis in vivo, can be recreated in vitro, in the absence of dermis. Thus, pattern formation does not appear to be contingent on the presence of dermis, but rather dependent on keratinocyte-keratinocyte interactions [39, 40]. There is evidence for signaling between both stem and TA compartments. Notch, a transmembrane receptor that binds its ligands, Delta and Serrate (also transmembrane proteins) on an adjacent cell, is thought to be involved. Notch signaling is an evolutionary mechanism that controls cell fate through local intercellular interactions in adult and embryonic tissues (Artavanis-Tsakonas, 1999). It is expressed in all postnatal human epidermal layers, whereas Delta-1 is confined to the basal layer, and is most abundant in cell clusters expressing hight levels of Beta-1 integrins (Lowell, 2000). There is evidence that high Delta-1 expression by epidermal stem cells has three effects: a protective effect on stem cells via blocking Notch signaling; enhanced cohesiveness of stem cell clusters which may interface with intermingling among neighboring cells; and signaling to cells at the periphery of clusters to become TA cells (Lowell, 2000).

Hair Follicle Stem Cells

These cells constitute a distinct population of cells separate from the interfollicular epidermal stem cells discussed earlier. Evidence for the existence of hair follicle stem cells came from follicular cell preparation in response to epidermal injury or loss [7, 8]. Both clinical and lab experience had also suggested that in excised wounds after split-skin surgical removal of epidermis, repair occurs from skin appendages such as hair follicles [35]. As investigators attempted to localize these cells, more was learnt about their properties and the way hair follicle stem cells differ from interfollicular stem cells.

Location of Follicular Stem Cells

The exact location of stem cells in the hair follicles has been debated among researchers with evidence to suggest that they are located either on the outer root sheath near an area known as the 'bulge' or in the base of the hair matrix that remains after a hair has been plucked. The weight of the availa-

ble evidence leans more towards the bulge theory at this time.

Initially, researchers placed hair follicular stem cells in the germinative matrix of the hair bulb. Even when a hair is plucked clean and most of the lower matrix removed, a small band of putative stem cells remains attached to the dermal-epidermal junction [59]. Observations that suggest this location for regenerative cells include the differentiation of matrix cells into the medulla, hair cortex and inner root sheath cells, a high proliferative rate during the anagen phase of the hair growth cycle, and interactions between the matrix and dermal papilla [75, 89, 97, 98, 119]. Reynolds [97, 98] also showed an ultrastructurally undifferentiated appearance for these cells and *in vitro* growth potential.

Despite this evidence for the location of follicular stem cells in the hair matrix, many researchers are of the view that the actual location may be the upper portion of the outer root sheath, near the insertion of the arrector pili muscles- an area known as the bulge. Early experiments involved the direct removal of the lower hair follicle, including the matrix, and then growing the entire hair follicle from the remnant [83, 84]. Plucking a hair follicle does not remove the outer root, which may explain the regeneration seen [12, 21]. More directly, cells recovered from the bulge region of rat vibrissa grown *in vitro* gave rise to colonies of keratinocyte forming cells [41].

Micro-dissection experiments in which the hair folicle is dissected on a scale of micrometers and each section grown *in vitro* have also supported the bulge region of the outer hair sheath as the location of a stem cell population. The greatest proliferative potential in these experiments was obtained from mid-dermal explants containing the follicular infundibula [96]. Yang [127] repeated these observations with upper follicular keratinocytes, discovering them to have the highest proliferative potential. In the same experiment, the matrix cells had poor *in vitro* growth. Many investigators have carried this a step further and shown outer root sheath cells to reconstitute normal interfollicular epidermis *in vitro*. This suggest that, unlike interfollicular stem cells, follicular stem cells are pluripotential [56, 57].

Perhaps the most conclusive evidence comes from kinetic studies. Following epidermal damage, labeling of several cells in the region of the upper follicle was noted by Al Bawari [8]. This region corresponds to the region of the bulge or site of attachment of the arrector pili muscle to the outer root sheath of the hair follicle. Potten postulated these cells to represent a reserve population of stem cells which are activated in damage states to augment the response of interfollicular stem cells (1981). Labeling with single pulse 3H-TdR by Lavker [53] revealed uptake above the level of the bulge, suggesting a population of actively dividing TA. In further studies, no label retaining cells were found in the bulb region of pelage, eyelash or vibrissa follicles of mice. The only label retaining cells identified in these studies were present in the upper outer root sheath. Single-pulse labeling, which identifies the TA cells, revealed prominent labeling in the hair matrix, again arguing against a stem cell reservoir at this location [21, 52].

Repeated micro-dissection experiments have failed to replicate previous results and suggest that human hair follicles stem cells are located below the level of the bulge [72, 101]. The exact location of human hair follicle stem cells remains unclear for now and remains a major obstacle in the further characterization of these cells.

Follicle Stem Cell Niche

Similar to the existence of a sheltered epidermal stem cell 'niche', the follicle stem cells are purported to occupy a niche of their own. The bulge area of the hair follicle has been shown to have a dense vascular as well as neural supply [31]. Merkel cells show a preferential concentration at the region of the bulge [81]. These and other studies, are suggestive of a specially modeled microenvironment for follicular stem cells in the bulge area of the outer root sheath. Ongoing work focuses on elucidating the way these cells are influenced by, and influence in turn, the niche microenvironment.

Markers for Epidermal Stem Cells

Significant controversies in the field of keratinocyte stem cell research arise in relation to identification of markers. Several confounding variables including: different cell isolation techniques, anatomic sites, hairy vs. non-hairy skin, human vs. murine keratinocytes and cultured (as well as the biological state in culture) vs. *in vivo* kerationcytes are all factors which contribute to inconsistencies in reported results among investigators (Lavker and Sun, 2000). Keratinocyte stem cells, as characterized *in vivo* in terms of their slowcycling feature, have been shown to disappear in mitogenic tissue culture environments, with marked changes in integrin expression and other markers (Nguyen 2000, De Luca 1992, Lavker and Sun 2000). While there has been strong evidence pointing to Beta-1 as a marker for epidermal stem cells (both in culture and *in vivo*), a recent series of studies by Kaur and co-workers report different findings: that alpha-6 integrin serves as a better marker than Beta-1 for sorting basal keratinocytes of *in vivo* murine (hairy) skin; that the rapidly adhering keratinocyte stem cell fraction, which are Beta-1 or Alpha-6 positive is far from being pure; and that the use of additional markers is critical to further distinguish between stem cells and TA cells (48, Kaur 2000, Lavker 2000). With the prospects of keratinocytes as carriers for gene therapy, it has become even more imperative to find ways of reliably identifying epidermal stem cells.

Beta –1 Integrin

In recent years, the B1 integrin has emerged as the first major marker of cells derived from the epidermis showing superior proliferative potential. The integrins are a family of cell surface proteins important in mediating cell to cell and cell to matrix interactions. They are heterodimer transmembrane glycoproteins with noncovalently bound Alpha and Beta units. The B unit can associate with different A units and this can be used as a basis for classification. A diverse set of surface receptors, the integrins are involved in cell adhesion and regulation of terminal differentiation [2, 103].

Previous immunofluorescence studies had revealed significant integrin expression by the basal layer of proliferating keratinocytes attached to the basement membrane and weak expression by the suprabasal layers of differentiated cells [87]. Adams [2] subsequently showed that cells committed to terminal differentiation have functionally down regulated B1 integrins.

Jones and Watt used a fluorescence-activated cell sorter (FACS) to separate viable basal cells from terminally differentiated cells on the basis of their light scattering characteristics. These cells were stained for the different surface integrins expressed by keratinocytes (Alpha 2,3,5,v,6 and B1) [112]. Using flow cytometry to fractionate cells into groups based on integrin expression, each group was seeded in vitro to check growth potential. The results revealed that cells sorted on the basis of B1 expression had the highest growth potential in culture. A linear relationship was obtained between the logarithm of B1 fluorescence and growth potential as measured by colony forming efficiency (CPE) [38].

Further work by Jones [40] measured in vivo integrin expression in human scalp, foreskin and palm skin by using indirect immunofluorescent techniques. This involves using a primary antibody specific for integrin of interest and a secondary antibody conjugated to fluorescein isothiocyanate (FITC) raised against the primary.

Thin uniform sections were stained and examined using a confocal microscope. A patterned distribution of A2 and A3 integrin bright basal cells was seen in a non-random distribution. In skin from the scalp and foreskin, the bright patches were found in regions overlying the dermal papilla, whereas in palm skin they were at the tips of the rete ridges. No differences were seen in skin stained with antibody against A6.

Foreskin was then harvested and rapidly adhering cells separated in vitro. These cells were stained and subsequently shown to have high levels of B1 expression as well as superior growth potential in vitro as compared to the late adhering cells. Grafting the rapid adhering cells onto nude mice yielded a normal complete epidermis [38, 39]. Finally, S-phase analysis of the integrin bright, rapidly adhering cells revealed infrequent cycling events [39].

Although the studies discussed identify B1 as a useful first marker of stem cells, they also reveal that the proportion of integrin bright basal cells is 25–50% depending on the body site [39], yet estimates of stem cells range from 1–10% [76, 86]. This suggests the need for more markers to increase sensitivity of stem cell pick up.

Keratin 19

Keratins are epithelial skin cell proteins and important constituents of the cytoskeleton. There are about 20 different types, with a wide range of distribution in the body [73]. Minor keratins such as K19, constitute a subset which are present in a small proportion of cells. Cells positive for K19 have been restricted to various epithelia [13]. Furthermore, K19 positive cells have been identified in the bulge area of the hair follicle, which led to the suggestion that it could be used as a marker for epithelial progenitor cells [49, 81, 82].

Michel et al used the mouse model to identify stem cells as label retaining cells. An antibody against K19 was raised and found to label the bulge area of the outer root sheath, an area known to contain a stem cell reservoir (see earlier discussion). Double labeling revealed the K19 positive cells and the thymidine retaining cells to be the same population.

In hairy skin, K19 was found only in the hair follicles and absent from interfollicular epidermis. At glabrous (hairless) sites however, the K19 positive cells were present in the deep epidermal rete ridges, a proposed location for stem cells in the epidermis [50, 51]. These cells were also shown to have a high level of B1 expression.

In the same experiment, it was observed that K19 does not label interfollicular thymidine label retaining cells which raises the question whether K19 labels all stem cells in the epidermis. Thus K19 cells can be seen to constitute a subset of B1 expressing cells. Furthermore, K19 is not entirely specific for stem cells and has also been found to label Merkel cells [74].

Keratin 15

The C8/144B monoclonal antibody is specific for Keratin 15. Using this antibody, Lyle et al stained human hair follicle stem cells. Cells positive for C8/144B as wel as B1 integrin are localized to the bulge area and have a stem cell phenotype. These cells as well as more differentiated cells present in the lower follicle, stain positively for K19. Cells positive for K15 and B1 only, are restricted to the upper permanent region of the bulge. The investigators suggest that K15 positive cells could represent a subset of the K19 cell population and represent the true stem cell population. Thye also suggest that loss of K15 expression may be an early sign of transition from stem cell to TA cell [58].

Cadherins and Catenins

Cadherins are a family of cell surface glycoproteins involved in calcium dependent cell to cell adhesion. They are single chain transmembrane polypeptides whose adhesive function depends on the interaction with proteins known as catenins. The catenins link cadherins to the intracellular actin cytoskeleton [45, 80].

Cadherins were targeted as possible markers because of evidence to suggest involvement in loss of adhesiveness during keratinocyte differentiation and progress from the basal to the suprabasal layers [121]. A role in regulation of terminal differentiation and modulation of integrin expression has also been suggested by recent studies [33, 130].

Human palm and foreskin were stained with antibodies to a variety of cadherins and catenins concurrently with B1integrin. In the basal layer patches, the integrin bright cells are also positive for E-cadherin, B-catenin, and Gamma-catenin. Strong staining is seen for Gamma catenin and weak staining for the others. A similar pattern as has been previously reported using B1-integrin is seen, ie, in foreskin, tips of dermal papillae, and in the palm where the troughs of the rete ridges are positive. Gradients of fluorescence rather than discrete patches are seen and furthermore not all the B1 cells are cadherin or catenin positive. More research will be necessary to realize the significance of these observations [68].

Alpha 6

Alpha 6/Beta 4 is an integrin which is most strongly expressed on the basal region of stratified squamous epithelium. Immuno-electron microscopy localizes the A6/B4 complex to hemidesmosomes, suggesting a role in basal cell to basement membrane attachment [110]. Li [48] showed that A6 was highly expressed (A6 bright) in the 10% of an epidermal cell population which is not cycling as shown by cell cycle analysis, and also has the greatest regenrative capacity of any basal cells. This population was designated the stem cell and transient amplifying cell population. The post-mitotic cells had low expression of A6 (A6 dim). Interestingly, a significant population of the A6 dim cells were B1 integrin positive. This suggests that cells which are differentiating first lose adhesion to the basement membrane, mediated by A6, yet retain ce-cell adhesion mediated by B1.

The same group of investigators had earlier identified a cell surface protein (10G7 antigen) which is detectable only in proliferating culture and not *in vivo*. Upon differentiation, the 10G7 antigen is downregulated [43]. An antibody to this antigen was raised and the A6 bright cells were co-stained for the antibody to the 10G7 proliferation associated cell surface marker. A subpopulation among the A6 cells was stained and put forward as representing a putative stem cell population by the investigators [48].

Keratinocyte Gene Therapy

The dawn of molecular medicine promises almost unlimited therapeutic possibilities. Gene therapy has exploded as the hope for diseases that involve inherited defects or lack of essential body proteins.

In principle, successful therapy requires that genes be delivered efficiently to a target cell population using a non-toxic vector. The product should be expressed for a prolonged period and be regulated appropriately. This may be done by direct transduction *in vivo* or *in vitro* followed by subsequent transfer back to the host.

At present, the theoretical ideal is beginning to be realized but there are still problems which researchers must overcome. Transient gene expression, concern about vector safety and efficiency, limites survival of transplanted cells and difficulties in targeting stem cells limit effective clinical application at present.

Several features of epidermal keratinocytes make them attractive candidates for gene therapy. Foremost is the presence of stem cells which, if stably transduced, theoretically should show prolonged expresssion. Large surface area, easy accessibility for *in vivo* and *in vitro* transfection, and knowledge of keratinocyte promoters are all factors encouraging investigators to target these cells [28]. Potential value of keratinocytes for gene therapy adds the incentive for researchers to identify specific markers.

Vectors

A variety of vectors have been used by researchers to transduce keratinocytes both *in vivo* and *in vitro*. Replication deficient retroviral vectors have been widely used in research and clinical trials. Retroviri are RNA viruses that integrate a copy of their DNA into the host genome and use the cell machinery to synthesize virally encoded proteins. Retroviral constructs incorporating gene sequences of the proteins of interest, and missing sequences for essential viral proteins, can be used to deliver missing functional DNA to host cells. A high efficiency of transduction of stem cells has been seen in culture [27]. In vivo, using the porcine model, the transduction efficiency is much lower. Problems with the retroviral vector include transient expression, transduction of replicating cells only, poor in vivo transduction and persistent concerns about mutagenesis in the host genome due to random integration [65].

Replication deficient adenovirus has shown promise for transduction of keratinocytes *in vivo* and *in vitro*. Advantages of the adenovirus vector include minimal risk for mutagenesis and transduction of non-replicating cells. However, expression has remained transient at present [109].

Other methods include direct transfer by intradermal injection of purified DNA [19, 32], topical application of a liposome DNA complex [5] and particle bombardment [17]. Transfer rates by these methods are low and expression limited. There has been significant strides made towards improvements in the application of cutaneous gene therapy. These include improved vector design and optimized transduction protocols. The combination of these approaches will make it possible to overcome the major obstacle which has impeded continued progress in this fieldsustaining expression of the transduced gene in a large population of keratinocytes after grafting (Watt, 2000).

Advances in Keratinocyte Gene Therapy

Progress has been made in terms of successful expression of several beneficial proteins by keratinocytes. A summary of significant work follows.

Factor IX

Hemophilia B is an X-linked inherited bleeding disorder caused by decreased levels of the coagulation factor IX in the blood. Therapy of hemophilia involves the transfusion of factor IX derived from human plasma or recombinant factor IX. Gene therapy provides a safer alternative and the potential to avoid repeated transfusions. White et al [123] used a retroviral vector to transduce human keratinocytes and then graft them onto nude mice. They showed that factor IX was present in the serum of the mice for up to one year later.

Human Growth Hormone (hGH)

A mouse model was used to show that retroviral transfer of human growth hormone DNA into keratinocytes was possible. Not only was biologically active hormone secreted into the culture medium, but also when the cells were grafted onto nude mice [69]. Similar results were obtained using the pig model [120]. Using plasmids as vectors and athymic mice as hosts, Teumer [116] demonstrated hGH in mouse blood for up to four weeks.

Interleukin 10 (IL-10)

An inhibitor of pro-inflammatory cytokines, IL-10 is thought to play an impor- tant role in the regulation of inflammatory responses, especially contact and delayed type of hypersensitivity [23, 108]. Kerati-nocytes transduced by the phIL-10 plas-mid vector were injected into the dorsal skin of sensitized rats. Circulating IL-10 released from the treated keratinocytes was shown to suppress the effector phase of contact mediated hypersensitivity at a distant area of the skin [67]. The authors provide evidence that it may be possible to treat systemic disease using keratinocyte gene therapy.

Interleukin 6 (IL-6)

Another cytokine, IL-6 has many diverse effects in the body: growth and differentiation of B lymphocytes, differentiation and activation of B lymphocytes, differentiation and activation of T lymphocytes, stimulation of hematopoietic colony formation and induction of acute phase proteins in the liver [3]. Increased IL-6 production in inflammatory skin diseases like psoriasis and lichn planus may be related to pathogenesis [30, 126]. The same group of investigators working with IL-10 also showed that in vivo transfer of the IL-6 gene to keratinocytes induces keratinocyte proliferation and lymphocytic infiltration in the skin. They suggest that inflammatory diseases in which IL-6 has been implicated may be treated by the transfer of mutant IL-6 genes, whose products act as antagonists at the IL-6 receptor [105].

Wound Healing

Gene therapy can be used to expedite wound healing by the delivery of growth factors or cytokines. Sun et al [114] used an acidic fibroblast growth factor (aFGF) cDNA containing plasmid to show acceleration of healing in wounds.

Gene Therapy in Skin Disease

The genodermatoses are skin diseases caused by genetic deficiency or dysfunction of proteins in the skin. Many of these diseases remain incurable by pharmacotherapy. With progess in gene therapy, there is hope of replacing defective genes to correct the underlying defect.

Recessive ichthyoses

The ichthyotic disorders are a heterogeneous group of skin disorders due to defects in structural and enzymatic proteins involved in epithelial maturation. They are characterized clinically by hyperkeratosis [46, 124]. Lamellar ichthyosis is associated with the TGM1 gene which encodes TGase 1 or keratinocyte transglutaminase. This is a membrane enzyme responsible for the formation of the cornified layer in differentiating keratinocytes and is important for normal terminal differentiation and barrier formation in the outer epidermis. Mutations in the TGM1 gene produce enzymatically inactive Tgase 1 [34, 104, 117].

High efficiency transfer of the normal Tgase 1 gene to affected cells was accomplished by using a retroviral vector. The cells showed normal transglutaminase activity and reconstituted normal epidermis when grafted onto nude mice [18].

A similar approach has also been successful for X-linked ichthyosis [24].

Epidermolysis Bullosa

This is a group of inherited blistering skin disorders due to defects in the structural proteins important in mediating adhesion [118]. Basal keratinocytes firmly adhere to the epidermal basement membrane by means of hemidesmosomes, which are multiprotein complexes linking the epithelial intermediate filament network to the dermal anchoring fibrils. Hemidesmosome-mediated adhesion is dependent upon the binding of the alpha-6 beta-4 integrin to laminin 5, a major basal lamina component formed by three distinct polypeptides, alpha-3, beta-3 and gamma-2, encoded by the LAMA3, LAMB3, and LAMC2 genes, respectively (Christiano and Uitto 1996). Laminin 5 binds to the cell surface of the basal keratinocyte through the alpha-6 beta-4 integrin, and tightens the dermal epidermal junction by binding to the amino terminal NC-1 domain of Type VII collagen as well (Rousselle 1997). Laminin 5 and its alpha-6 beta-4 receptor play a crucial role in maintaining the integrity of the skin. This is clinically evidenced in patients suffering from junctional epidermolysis bullosa (JEB), a disorder marked by devastating blistering which is accompanied by debilitating chronic pain, and often results in severe disfigurement, or even a lethal outcome. JEB is a group of autosomal recessive diseases in either LAMA3, LAMB3, or LAMC2 (Aberdem 1994; Pulkkinen 1994; Vidal 1995a), or in the genes encoding the two subunits of the alpha-6 beta-4 integrin (Vidal 1995b; Ruzzi 1997) or the hemidesmosome component 180-kDa bullous pemphigold antigen (McGrath 1995). To date, human epidermal stem cells have been cultivated and stably transduced with replication-defective retroviral vectors, allowing full phenotypic correction of the adhesion defects which characterize JEB keratinocytes (Dellambra 2000). The demonstration of sustained transgene expression in vitro and in vivo by epidermal stem cells has now led the way to the development of a proposal for the implementation of a phase I/II clinical trial aimed at ex vivo gene therapy of selected JEB patients (Dellambra 2000).

Xeroderma pigmentosum

This disorder is characterized by defects in DNA repair which lead to accumulation of UV induced DNA damage and a high incidence of skin malignancy [47]. Two of the genes implicated in the pathogenesis of this disease are the XPA and the XPD genes. Restoration of these two genes to cells lacking them has been shown to restore DNA repair capacity after ultraviolet injury towards normal [63, 79].

Stem Cell Neoplasia

Stem cells have long been recognized as potential targets for neoplastic induction [16]. Early experiments on carcinogenesis involved the induction of skin tumors in mice by topical application of carcinogens. Initially an 'initiator' or substance damaging to DNA, is applied followed by repeated application of a 'promoter', which induces replication of the damaged cell. A time lapse of at least one year was noted between initiation and the commencement of promotion, indicating that the cells which had been transformed are long lived [113]. Further studies using benz(o)pyrene, a known carcinogen, detected persistence in the epidermis and bulge region up to a month after application. The carcinogen label retaining cells made up approximately 2% of the interfollicular basal cells, most of which were at the center of the epidermal proliferative units. Such cells constituted 4–5% of the population of the basal cells in the infundibulum and external root sheath as well, with few detected in in the dermal papilla and matrix [77].

The hair follicle too has been shown to play a role in skin carcinogenesis. Investigations on the carcinogenic effect of ionizing radiation revealed that when the depth of penetration was limited to the epidermis (<0.3 mm), few skin tumors were formed. However, if the radiation reached deeper to the follicles (0.4–1.4 mm), many skin tumors were observed. This led observers to conclude that hair follicle damage is directly related to skin tumor formation in rats [4]. Further studies on rats revealed that many of the chemically induced basal cell carcinomas arose from portions of the hair follicles whereas squamous cell carcinomas arose from the interfollicular epidermis [129]. In humans, basal cell carcinomas have been found to arise from both follicular and interfollicular epidermis [66]. Another type of skin tumor possibly arising from the hair folicle is the keratocanthoma [29].

More supportive evidence comes from studies that show the stage of the hair cycle can affect tumor yield. Application of a complete carcinogen (one that acts as both an initiator and a promoter) during the growing phase of the hair cycle, or anagen, produces few tumors. Conversely, mice treated during the resting or telogen phase develop many papillomas [6, 14].

References

[1] Adami, JG: The causation of cancerous and other new growths. Br. Med J I:621–628, (1901)
[2] Adams JC, Watt FM: Changes in keratinocyte adhesion during terminal differentiation: reduction in fibronectin binding precedes A5B1 integrin loss from the cell surface. Cell 63:425–435, (1990)
[3] Akira S, Taga T, Kishimoto T: Interleukin-6 in biology and medicine. Adv Immunol 54:1, (1993)
[4] Albert RE, Phillips ME, Bennett P, Heimbach R: The morphology and growth characteristics of radiation induced epithelial skin tumors in the rat. Cancer Res 29:658–668, (1969)
[5] Alexander MY, Akhurst RJ: Liposome-mediated gene transfer and expression via the skin. Hum Mol Gen 4:2279–2285, (1995)
[6] Andreasen E, Engelbreth-Holm J: On the significance of the mouse hair cycle in experimental carcinogenesis. Acta Pathol Microbiol Scand 32:165–169, (1953)
[7] Argyris TS, Kurman M: The proliferative response to epidermis of hairless mice to full thick-ness wounds. Am J Pathol 79 (2) 301–310, (1975)
[8] Al-Barwari SE, Potten CS: Regeneration and dose response characteristics of irradiated mouse dorsal epidermal cells. Int J Radiol Biol Relat Stud Phys Chem Med 30(3):201–216, (1976)
[9] Albers KM, Setzer RW, Taichman LI: Heterogeneity in the replicating population of cultured human keratinocytes. Differentiation 31:134–140, (1986)
[10] Barrandon Y, Green H: Cell size as a determinant of the clone forming ability of human keratinocytes. Proc Natl Acad Sci 82:5390–5394, (1985)
[11] Barrandon Y, Green H: Three clonal types of keratinocytes with different capacities for multiplication. Proc Natl Acad Sci 84:2302–2306, (1987)
[12] Bassukas ID, Hornstein OP: Effects of plucking on the anatomy of the anagen hair bulb. A light microscopic study. Arch Dermatol Res 281(3):188–192, (1989)
[13] Bartek J, Bartkova J, Taylor-Papadimitriou J, Rejthar A, Kovarik J, Lukas Z, Vojtesek B: Differential expression of keratin 19 in normal human epithelial tissues revealed by monospecific monoclonal antibodies. Histochem J 18:565–575, (1986)
[14] Berenblum I, Haran-Ghera N, Trainin N: An experimental analysis of the 'hair cycle effect' in mouse sin carcinogenesis. Br J Cancer 12: 402–413, (1958)
[15] Bickenbach, JR: Identification and behavior of label retaining cells in oral mucosa and skin. J Dent Res 60:1620–1622, (1981)

[16] *Cairns J:* Mutational selection and the natural history of cancer. Nature (Eng) 255:197–200, (1975)

[17] *Chang L et al.:* In vivo promoter activity and transgene expression in mammalian somatic tissues by using particle bombardment. Proc Natl Acad Sci USA 90:4455, (1993)

[18] *Choate KA, Medalie DA, Morgan JR, Khavari PA:* Corrective gene transfer in the human skin disorder lamellar ichthyosis. Nat Med 2:1263–1267, (1996)

[19] *Choate K A, Khavari P A:* Direct cutaneous gene delivery in a human genetic skin disease. Hum Gene Ther 8:1659–1665, (1997)

[20] *Christophers E:* Cellular architecture of the stratum corneum. Invest Dermatol 56:165–169, (1971)

[21] *Cotsarelis G, Sun TT, Lavker RM:* Label retaining cells reside in the bulge area of pilosebaceous unit: implications for follicular stem cells, hair cycle and skin carcinogenesis. Cell 61(7):1329–1337, (1990)

[22] *Fenjves ES, Schwartz PM, Blaese RM, Taichman LB:* Keratinocyte gene therapy for adenosine deaminase deficiency: a model for inherited metabolic disorders. Hum Gene Ther 8:911–917, (1997)

[23] *Ferguson TA, Dube P, Griffith TS:* Regulation of contact hypersensitivity by interleukin-10. J Exp Med 179:1597–1604, (1994)

[24] *Freiberg RA, Choate KA, Deng H, Alperin ES, Shapiro LJ, Khavari PA:* A model of corrective gene transfer in X-linked ichthyosis. Human Mol Genet 6:933–937, (1995)

[25] *Furstenberger G, Gross M, Schweizer J, Vogt I, Marks F:* Isolation, characterization of subfractions of neonatal mouse keratinocytes: effects of phorbol esters. Carcinogenesis 7(10) 1745–1753, (1986)

[26] *Gagnoux-Palacios L, Vailly J, Durand-Clement M, Wagner E, Ortonne JP, Meneguzzi G:* Functional re-expression of laminin-5 in laminin-gamma2-deficient human keratinocytes modifies cell morphology, motility and adhesion. J Biol Chem 271:18437–18444, (1996)

[27] *Garlick JA, Katz AB, Fenjves ES, Taichman LB:* Retrovirus-mediated transduction of cultured epidermal keratinocytes. J Invest Dermatol 97:824–829, (1991)

[28] *Garlick JA, Fenjves ES:* Keratinocyte gene transfer and gene therapy. Crit Rev Oral Biol Med 7(3):204–221, (1996)

[29] *Ghadially FN:* The role of hair follicle in the origin and evolution of some cutaneous neoplasms of man and experimental animals, (1961)

[30] *Grossman RM, Krueger J, Yourish A, Granelli-Piperno DP, Murphy LT, May LT, Kupper PB, Sehgel PB, Gottlieb:* Interleukin 6 is expressed in high levels in psoriatic skin and stimulates proliferation of cultured human keratinocytes. Proc Natl Acad Sci 86:6367, (1989)

[31] *Halata Z:* In Hair and Hair Diseases. Eds CE Orfanos and R Happle. pp 149–164. Springer-Verlag, Berlin, (1988)

[32] *Hengge UR, Chan EF, Foster RA, Walker PS, Vogel JC:* Cytokine gene expression in the epidermis with biological effects following injection of naked DNA. Nature 10:161–166, (1995)

[33] *Hodivala KJ, Watt, FM:* Evidence that cadherins play a role in the downregulation of integrin expression that occurs during keratinocyte terminal differentiation. J Cell Biol 124:589–600, (1994)

[34] *Huber M, Rettler I, Bernasconi K et al:* Mutations of keratinocyte transglutaminase in lamellar ichthyosis. Science 267:525–528, (1995)

[35] *Irvin TT:* In "Wound Healing, Principles and Practice." (Chapman and Hall, Eds) 25–28. University Press, Cambridge, (1981)

[36] *Iverson OH, Bjerknes R, Devik F:* Kinetics of cell renewal, cell migration and cell loss in the hairless mouse dorsal epidermis. Cell Tissue Kinet 1:351–367, (1968)

[37] *Jensen PK, Pederson S, Bolund L:* Basal cell subpopulations and cell-cycle kinetics in human epidermal explant cultures. Cell Tissue Kinet 18(2):201–15, (1985)

[38] *Jones PH, Watt FM:* Separation of human epidermal cells from transit amplifying cells on the basis of differences in integrin function and expression. Cell 73:713–724, (1993)

[39] *Jones PH, Harper S, Watt FM:* Stem cell fate and patterning in human epidermis. Cell 80:83–93, (1995)

[40] *Jones PH:* Isolation and characterization of human epidermal stem cells. Clinical Science 91:141–146, (1996)

[41] *Kabayashi K, Rochat A, Barrandon Y:* Segregation of keratinocyte colony-forming cells in the bulge of the rat vibrissa. Proc Natl Acad Sci 90:7391–7395, (1993)

[42] *Kam E, Watt FM, Pitts JD:* Patterns of junctional communication in skin: studies on cultured keratinocytes. Exp Cell Res 173(2): 431–438, (1987)

[43] *Kaur P, Paton S, Furze J, Wrin J, Olsen S, Danks J, Scurry J:* Identification of a cell surface protein with a role in stimulating human keratinocyte proliferation, expressed during development and carcinogenesis. J Invest Dermatol 109(2):194–199, (1997)

[44] *Keller G:* Hematopoietic stem cells. Curr Opinion Immunol 4:133–139, (1992)

[45] *Kemler R:* From cadherins to catenins: cytoplasmic protein interactions and regulation of cell adhesion. Trends Genet 9:317–321, (1993)

[46] *Khavari PA:* Gene therapy for genetic skin disease. 110(4):462–467, (1998)

[47] *Kraemer KH, Seetharam S, Seidman MM et al.:* Defective DNA repair in humans:clinical and molecular studies of xeroderma pigmentosum. Basic Life Science 53:95–104, (1990)

[48] *Li A, Simmons PJ, Kaur P:* Identification and isolation of candidate human keratinocyte stem cells based on cell surface phenotype. Proc Natl Acad Sci 95:3902–3907, (1998)

[49] *Lane EB, Wilson CA, Hughes BR, Leigh IM:* Stem cells in hair follicles. Cytoskeletal studies. Ann NY Acad Sci 642:197–213, (1991)

[50] *Lavker RM, Sun TT:* Heterogeneity in epidermal basal keratinocytes: morphological and functional correlations. Science 215(4537): 1239–1241, (1982)

[51] *Lavker RM, Sun TT:* Epidermal Stem Cells. J Invest Dermatol 81:121S–127S, (1983)

[52] *Lavker RM, Cotsarelis G, Wei ZG, Sun TT:* Stem cells of pelage, vibrissae and eyelas follicles: the hair cycle and tumor formation. Ann NY Acad Sci. 642:214–24, (1991)

[53] *Lavker RM, Miller S, Wilson C, Cotsarelis G, Wei ZG, Yang JS, Sun TT:* Hair follicle stem cells: their location, role in hair cycle, and involvement in skin tumor formation. J Invest Dermatol 101(Suppl 1) 16S–26S, (1993)

[54] *Lajtha LG:* Stem cell concepts. Differentiation 14:23–24, (1979)

[55] *Leblond CP, Meisser B, Kopriwa B:* Thymidine-3H as a tool for the investigation of the renewal of cell populations. Adv Biol Skin 5:39–67, (1959)

[56] *Lenoir MC, Bernard BA, Paytrat G, Darmon M, Shroot B:* Dev Biol 130(2) 610–620, (1988)

[57] *Limat A, Breitkreutz D, Hunziker T, Boillat C, Wiesmann U, Klein E, Noser E, Fusenig NE:* Restoration of the epidermal phenotype by follicular outer root sheath cells in recombinant culture with dermal fibroblasts. Exp Cell Res 194(2):218–227, (1991)

[58] *Lyle S, Christofidou-Solomidou M, Liu Y, Eler D E, Albeda S, Cotsareliss G:* The C8/144B monoclonal antibody recognizes cytokeratin 15 and defines the location of human hair follicle stem cells. J Cell Sci 111:3179–3188, (1998)

[59] *Jahoda CAB:* In vovi and *in vitro* studies of rat vibrissa follicle components in relation to hair growth. Doctoral thesis, University of Dundee, (1982)

[60] *Mackenzie IC:* Ordered structure of the stratum corneum in mammalian skin. Nature 222:881–882, (1969)

[61] *Mackenzie IC:* Relationship between mitosis and ordered structure of the stratum corneum in mouse epidermis. Nature 226 (246) 653–655, (1970)

[62] *Mackenzie IC:* Retroviral transduction of murine epidermal stem cells demonstrates clonal units of epidermal structure. J Invest Dermatol 109(3):377–383, (1997)

[63] *Marionnet C, Quillet X, Benoit A, Armier J, Sarasin A, Stary A:* Recovery of normal DNA repair and mutagenesis in trichothiodystrophy cells after transduction of the XPD human gene. Cancer Res 56:5450–5456, (1993)

[64] *Menton DN, Eisen AZ:* Structure and organization of mammalian stratum corneum. J Ultrastruct Res 35:247–264, (1971)

[65] *Miller DG, Adam MA, Miller AD:* Gene transfer by retrovirus vectors occurs only in cells that are activel replicating at the time of infection. Mol Cell Biol 10:4239–4242, (1971)

[66] *Miller S J:* Biology of basal cell carcinoma (Part 1). J Am Acad Dermatol 24(1) 1–13, (1991)

[67] *Ming X, Sawamura D, Tamai K, Hanada K, Ishida H, Hashimoto I:* Keratinocyte gene therapy for systemic diseases. J Clin Invest 101(6):1462–1467, (1998)

[68] *Moles JP, Watt FW:* The epidermal stem cell compartment: variation in expression levels of E-cadherin and catenins within the basal layer of human epidermis. J Histochem Cytochem 45:867–874, (1997)

[69] *Morgan JR, Barrandon Y, Green H, Mulligan RC:* Expression of an exogenous growth hormone gene by transplantable human epidermal cells. Science (US) 237(4821): 1476–9, (1987)

[70] *Miller SJ, Lavker RM, Sun TT:* Hair follicles, stem cells and skin cancer. J Invest Dermatol 100:288s–294s, (1993a)

[71] *Misumi Y, Akiyoshi T:* Consistently nonoverlapping distribution of epidermal growth factor receptors in adult human skin detected by various monoclonal antibodies. Acta Anat 137(3):202–207, (1990)

[72] *Moll I:* Proliferative potential of different keratinocytes of plucked human hair follicles. J Invest Dermatol 105:14–21, (1995)

[73] *Moll R, Franke WW, Schiller DL, Geiger B, Krepler R:* The catalog of human cytokeratins: patterns of expression in normal epithelial tumors and cultured cells. Cell 31:11–24, (1982)

[74] *Moll R, Moll I, Frank WW:* Identification of Merkel cells in human skin by specific cytokeratin antibodies: changes of cell density and distribution in fetal and adult plantar epidermis. Differentiation 28(2):136–154, (1984)

[75] *Montagna W, Van Scott EJ:* The anatomy of the hair follicle. In The Biology of Hair Growth, eds W Montagna and RA Ellis. (New York Academic Press) 39–64, (1958)

[76] *Morris RJ, Fischer SM, Slaga TJ:* Evidence that the centrally and peripherally located cells in the murine epidermal proliferative unit are two distinct cell populations. J Invest Dermatol 84(4):277–281, (1985)

[77] *Morris RJ, Fischer SM, Slaga TJ:* Evidence that a slowly cycling subpopulation of adult murine

epidermal cells retains carcinogen. Cancer Res 46:3061–3066, (1986)

[78] *Morris RJ, Fischer SM, Klein-Szanto AJ, Slaga TJ:* Subpopulations of primary adult murine epidermal cells retains carcinogen. Cell Tissue Kinet 23(6):587–602, (1990)

[79] *Myrand SP, Topping RS, States JC:* Stable transformation of xeroderma pigmentosum group A cells with an XPA minigene restores normal DNA repair and mutagenesis of UV-treated plasmids. Carcinogenesis 17:1909–1917, (1996)

[80] *Nagafuchi A, Ishidara S, Tsukita S:* The roles of catenins in the cadherin-mediated cell adhesion: functional analysis of E-cadherin-alpha catenin fusion molecules. J Cell Biol 127:235–245, (1994)

[81] *Narisawa Y, Hashimoto K, Nakamura Y, Kohda H:* A high concentration of Merkel cells in the bulge prior to the attachment of the arrector pili muscle and the formation of the perifollicular nerve plexus in human fetal skin. Arch Dermatl Res 285(5):261–268, (1993)

[82] *Narisawa Y, Hashimoto K, Kohda H:* Immunohistochemical demonstration of keratin 19 expression in isolated human hair follicles. J Invest Dermatol 103:191–195, (1994)

[83] *Oliver RF:* Whisker growth after removal of the dermal papilla and lengths of follicle in the hooded rat. J Embryol Exp Morphol 15(3) 331–347, (1966)

[84] *Oliver RF:* Ectopic regeneration of whiskers in the hooded rat from implanted lengths of vibrissa follicle wall. J Embryol Exp Morphol 17:27–34, (1967)

[85] *Pavlovitch JH, Rizk-Rabin M, Gervaise M, Metezeau P, Grunwald D:* Cell subpopulations within proliferating and differentiating compartments of epidermis. Am J Physiol 256 (5 Pt 1):C977–986, (1989)

[86] *Pavlovitch JH, Rizk-Rabin M, Jaffray P, Hoehn H, Poot M:* Characteristics of homogeneously small keratinocytes from newborn rat skin: possible epidermal stem cells. Am J Physiol 261(6 Pt 1):C964–972, (1991)

[87] *Peltonen JH, Larjava S, Jaakkola H, Gralnick SK, Akiyama SS, Yamada KM, Utto J:* Localization of integrin receptors for fibronectin, collagen and laminin in human skin. J Clin Invest 84:1916–1923, (1989)

[88] *Penneys NS, Fulton JE, Weinstein GD, Frost P:* Location of proliferating cells in human epidermis. Arch Dermatol 101:323–327, (1970)

[89] *Philpott MP, Green MR, Kealet T:* Human hair growth in vitro. J Cell Sci 97:463–471, (1990)

[90] *Potten C S, Hendry J H:* Clonogenic cells and stem cells in epidermis. Int J Rad Biol 24:537–540, (1973)

[91] *Potten CS:* The epidermal proliferative unit: the possible role of the central basal cell. Cell Tissue Kinet 7:77–78, (1974)

[92] *Potten CS, Allen TD:* Fine structural identification and organization of the epider-mal proliferative unit. J Cell Sci 15(2):291–319, (1974)

[93] *Potten CS, Allen TD:* A model implicating the Langhans cell in keratinocyte proliferation control. Differentiation 5(1):43–47, (1976)

[94] *Potten CS:* Cell replacement in epidermis (keratopoiesis) via discrete units of proliferation. Int Rev Cytol:(69)271–318, (1981)

[95] *Potten CS, Morris R J:* Epithelial stem cells in vivo. J Cell Sci Suppl 10:45–62, (1988)

[96] *Regauer S, Compten CC:* Cultured keratinocyte sheets enhance spontaneous re-epithelialization in a dermal explant model of partial thickness wound healing. J Invest Dermatol 95(3):341–346, (1990)

[97] *Reynolds AJ, Jahoda CA:* Hair follicle stem cells? A distinctive germinative epidermal cell population is activated *in vitro* by the presence of hair dermal papilla cells. J Cell Sci 99(Pt2):373–385, (1991a)

[98] *Reynolds AJ, Jahoda CA:* Inductive properties of hair follicle cells. Ann NY Acad Sci 642:226–241, (1991b)

[99] *Rheinwald JG, Green H:* Serial cultivation of strains of human epidermal keratinocytes: the formation of keratinizing colonies from single cells. Cell 6:331–334, (1975)

[100] *Rheinwald JG, Green H:* Epidermal growth factor and the multiplication of cultured human epidermal keratinocytes. Nature, Lond 265:421–424, (1977)

[101] *Rochat A, Kobayashi K, Barrandon Y:* Location of stem cells of human hair follicles by clonal analysis. Cell 0076:1063–1073, (1994)

[102] *Roberts D, Marks R:* The determination of regional and age variations in the rate of desquamation: a comparison of four techniques. J Invest Dermatol 74:13–16, (1980)

[103] *Ruoslathi E:* Integrins. J Clin Invest 87(1):1–5, (1991)

[104] *Russell LJ, DiGiovanna JJ, Rogers GR, Steinert PM, Hashem N, Compton JG, Bale SJ:* Mutations in the gene for transglutaminase 1 in autosomal recessive lamellar ichthyosis. Nat Genet 4: 1875–1881, (1995)

[105] *Sawamura D, Meng X, Ina S, Sato M, Tamai K, Hanada K, Hashimoto I:* Induction of keratinocyte proliferation and lymphocytic infiltration by in vivo induction of the IL-6 gene into keratinocytes and possibility of keratinocyte gene therapy for inflammatory skin diseases using IL-6 mutant genes. J Immunology 161:5633–5639, (1988)

[106] *Schmidt GH, Blount MA, Ponder BA:* Immunochemical demonstration of the clonal organization of chimaeric mouse epidermis. Development 100(3): 535–541, (1987)

[107] *Schofield R:* The relationship between the spleen colony forming cell and the hematopoietic stem cell. Blood Cells 4(1–2):7–25, (1978)

[108] *Schwarz AS, Grabbe H, Riemann Y, Aragane M, Simon S, Manot S, Andrade TA, Luger A, Zlotnik, Schwarz T:* In vivo effects of interleukin-10 on contact hypersensitivity and delayed type hypersensitivity reactions. J Invest Dermatol 103:211–216, (1994)

[109] *Setoguchi Y, Jaffe HA, Danel C, Crystal RG:* Ex vivo and in vivo transfer to the skin using replication deficient recombinant adenovirus vectors. J Invest Dermatol 102:415– 421, (1994)

[110] *Sonnenburg A, Calafat J, Janssen H, Daams H, van der Raaij-Helmer LM, Falconi R, Kennel SJ, Aplin JD, Baker J, Loizidou M:* Integrin alpha 6/beta 4 complex is located in hemidesmosomes, suggesting a major role in epidermal cell basement membrane adhesion. J Cell Biol 113(4):907–917, (1991)

[111] *Spangruade GJ:* Biological and clinical aspects of hematopoietic stem cells. Annu Rev Med (US) 45:93–104, (1994)

[112] *Staiano-Coico L, Higgins PJ, Darzynkiewicz Z, Kimmel M, Gottlieb AB, Pagan-Charry I, Madden MR, Finkelstein JL, Hefton JM:* Human keratinocyte culture. Identification and staging of epidermal cell subpopulations. J Clin Invest 77:396–404, (1986)

[113] *Stenbeck F, Peto R, Shubik P:* Initiation and promotion at different stages and doses in 2200 mice. I. Methods and apparent persistence of initiated cells. Br J Cancer 44:1–14, (1981)

[114] *Sun L, Xu L, Chang H, Henry FA, Miller FA, Harmon JM, Nielsen TB:* Transfection with aFGF cDNA improves wound healing. J Invest Dermatol 108:313–318, (1997)

[115] *Sun TT, Green H:* Differentiation of the epidermal keratinocyte in cell culture: formation of the cornified envelope. Cell 9(4 Pt 1) 511–521, (1976)

[116] *Teumer J, Lindahl A, Green H:* Human growth hormone in the blood of athymic mice grafted with cultures of hormone-secreting human keratinocytes. FASEB J (US) 4(14); 3245–3250, (1990)

[117] *Thacher SM, Rice RH, Greenberg CS, Birckbichler PJ:* Keratinocyte specific transglu-taminase of cultured human epidermal cells: relation to cross-linke denvelope formation and terminal differentiation. Transglutaminases: multifunctional cross-linking enzymes that stabilize tissues. Cell 40:685–695, (1985)

[118] *Uitto J, Pulkkinen L, Christiano AM:* Molecular basis of the dystrophic and junctional forms of epidermolysis bullosa: mutations in the type VII collagen and kallinin (laminin 5) genes. J Invest Dermatol 103:39s–46s, (1994)

[119] *Van Scott EJ, Ekel TM, Auerbach R:* Deter-minants of rate and kinetics of cell division in scalp hair. J Invest Dermatol 41:269–273, (1963)

[120] *Vogt P M, Thompson S, Andree C,, Liu P, Breuing K, Hatzis D, Brown H, Mulligan R C, Erikkson E:* Genetically modified keratinocytes transplanted to wounds reconsititute the epidermis. Proc Natl Acad Sci 91:9307–9311, (1994)

[121] *Watt, FM:* Selective migration of terminally differentiating cells from the basla layer of cultured human epidermis. J Cell Biol 98:16–21, (1984)

[122] *Watt, FM, Jones PH:* Expression and function of the keratinocyte integrins. Development (suppl) 185–192, (1993)

[123] *White SJ, Page P, Margaritis P, Brownlee GG:* Long term expression of human clotting factor IX from retrovirally transduced primary human keratinocytes *in vivo.* Hum Gen Ther 9:1187–1195, (1998)

[124] *Williams ML, Elias PM:* Genetically transmitted generalized disorders of cornification. The ichthyoses. Dermatol Clin 5:155–178, (1987)

[125] *Withers HR:* Recovery and repopulation in vivo by the mouse skin epithelial cells during fractionated irradiation. Radiat Res 32:227–239, (1967)

[126] *Yamamoto Y, Osaka T:* Characteristic cytokines generated by keratinocytes and mononuclear infiltrates in oral lichen planus. J Invest Dermatol 104:784, (1995)

[127] *Yang JS, Lavker RM, Sun TT:* Upper human hair follicle contains a subpopulation of keratinocytes with superior *in vitro* proliferative potential. J Invest Dermatol 101(5): 652–659, (1993)

[128] *Yuspa SH, Ben T, Hennings H, Lichti:* Divergent responses in epidermal basal cells exposed to the tumor promoter 12-O-tetradecanoyl-phorbol-13-acetate. Cancer Res 42(6):2344–2349, (1982)

[129] *Zackheim HS:* Evolution of squamous cell carcinoma in the rat. J Invest Dermatol 77:434–444, (1986)

[130] *Zhu AJ, Watt FM:* Expression of a dominant negative cadherin mutant inhibits proliferation and stimulates terminal differentiation of human epidermal keratinocytes. J Cell Sci 109:3013–3023, (1996)

Organotypic Keratinocyte-Fibroblast Cocultures: In Vitro Skin Equivalents to Study the Molecular Mechanisms of Cutaneous Regeneration

H.-J. Stark, N. Maas-Szabowski, H. Smola, D. Breitkreutz, N. Mirancea, N. E. Fusenig

Summary

Transplantation studies represent indispensable experimental tools to test functional capabilities of epithelial cells under optimal , i.e. more physiologic conditions. In the adult organism connective tissue influences have been shown to be essential for epithelial tissue homoestasis, i.e. the regular balance of growth and differentiation. In transplantation studies using mixtures of malignant and normal keratinocytes a crucial role of surrounding cells for the development of tumor cells within the epidermis was demonstrated. Proceeding tissue reconstruction has been studied *in vitro* and *in vivo*. This transplantation approach produced results which are relevant for the characterization of the wound healing process and, in consequence, may lead to the improvement of clinical wound management. Findings in organotypic cocultures to monitor the differentiation potential of keratinocytes have shown that keratinocytes and fibroblasts cooperate in basement membrane formation and that paracrine interactions regulate proliferation and differentiation.

Introduction

Epithelial tissue reconstruction during regenerative processes as well as maintenance of tissue homeostasis require continuous epithelial-mesenchymal interactions in a well orchestrated and fine tuned fashion. Earlier findings in developmental biology had demonstrated that the histogenesis of epithelial organs during embryogenesis strictly depends on epithelial-mesenchymal interactions [1–3]. Moreover, also in the adult organism connective tissue influences have been shown to be essential for epithelial tissue homoestasis, i.e. the regular balance of growth and differentiation [4–6].

Therefore, it is not surprising, that the manifestations of epithelial differentiation observed in simple *in vitro* systems are largely reduced. In particular, an organized tissue architecture has not been reproduced in those cultures. This is obviously caused by the absence of mesenchymal influence operating *in vivo* as has been demonstrated in transplantation studies with cultured keratinocytes transferred back into animals (for review see [7, 8]). Those studies have clearly shown (i) that epidermal homeostasis and differentiation programs are regulated by diffusible factors provided by the local mesenchyme and systemically by the circulation, and (ii) that isolated and cultured epithelial cells are able to sustain their intrinsic potential for tissue specific differentiation and their responsiveness to external stimuli. Based on these important discoveries, advanced cell culture models have been developed to study epithelial-mesenchymal interactions *in vitro* in order to identify the diffusible factors involved and elucidate their mechanism of action (reviewed in [9]).

Transplantation Assays to Monitor the Differentiation Potential of Keratinocytes

Transplantation studies represent indispensable experimental tools to test functional capabilities of epithelial cells under optimal, i.e. more physiologic conditions (for review see 9, 10]).

The surface transplantation method exploited in our laboratory utilizes an intermediate matrix separating preformed cultures of human keratinocytes from the underlying muscle fascia of nude mice and allows the formation of regular human neoepidermis under mesenchymal influence in vivo [11]. The intermediate layer of a type I-collagen gel serves as a growth supporting dermal substitute and carrier for transferring intact keratinocyte cultures to the animal providing optimal take rates. Additionally, this interposed matrix prevents direct contact between the cellular compartments so that only diffusible factors can contribute to the initial interactions between keratinocytes and mesenchyme. Transplants of normal epidermal keratinocytes prepared by this method exhibited complete differentiation, including regular keratinization, and tissue reorganization. In particular, time course and dynamics of basement membrane restoration could be characterized in detail during recovery of epidermal homeostasis [9, 12]. Furthermore, a large body of evidences stresses the role of connective tissue and extracellular matrix for the morphogenesis not only of normal but also of transformed keratinocytes [10]. In recent transplantation studies using mixtures of malignant and normal keratinocytes a crucial role of surrounding cells for the development of tumor cells within the epidermis was demonstrated [13].

Last but not least, this transplantation approach produced results which are relevant for the characterization of the wound healing process and, in consequence, may lead to the improvement of clinical wound management.

Organotypic Cultures and Tissue Reconstruction *in Vitro*

Despite excellent renormalization of epidermal morphogenesis, transplantation models remain problematic for the accurate analysis of the detailed molecular mechanisms of epithelial-mesenchymal interactions due to the unpredictable variability of ill defined parameters encountered in the living organism. Therefore, we designed an organotypic *in vitro* skin model to circumvent the obscure *in vivo* conditions. These cultures have a configuration identical to that described above for our surface transplantation method: keratinocytes are cultivated air exposed on collagen gels positioned on a porous support which allows directional supply of growth medium from underneath. To generate dermal equivalents mesenchymal cells are incorporated into the collagen gels or seeded onto the bottom surface when a defined distance to the epithelial cells is required. Optionally, these dermal equivalents can be refined by adding further mesenchymal cell types such as endothelial cells [14]. After the methodology has evolved and significantly improved in the last few years, this culture model has proved a very suitable tool for the characterization of fundamental events in epithelial-mesenchymal interaction controlling epidermal tissue reorganization and differentiation as well as tissue homeostasis.

Quite a variety of organotypic *in vitro* models has been described in the literature (reviewed in [9]). The vast majority of these utilizes conventional, serum containing culture media. However, there have been attempts to use either serum reduced or serum-free media formulations in order to exclude ill defined components. Recently, we have demonstrated that organotypic cocultures consist-

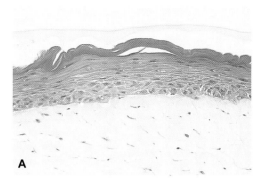

Fig. 1: Epidermal morphogenesis of organotypic keratinocyte-fibroblast cocultures. Keratinocytes are cultivated air-exposed on fibroblast containing collagen gels for 2 wk in serum containing **(A)** and serum-free medium **(B)**. While in both cases the epidermis displays features of differentiation (ortho-keratinization, keratohyalin granula), in the presence of serum epidermal hyperplasia becomes evident **(A)**. Hematoxylin-eosin staining. Scale bar 50 μm.

ing of normal skin keratinocytes and dermal fibroblasts equally well reconstitute a normal epidermal tissue architecture when grown in a fully defined medium as compared with conventional serum containing medium [15]. It should be mentioned, however, that under defined conditions the performance of organotypic cocultures is subjected to higher variability as consequence of a less supportive and limiting nutritional situation.

Independent of the kind of medium used the epidermal morphogenesis in organotypic cocultures faithfully recapitulates the situation in native epidermis. Ortho-keratinized epithelia with regularly stratified organization evolved and persisted up to four weeks in culture with concomitantly thickening of the *stratum corneum*. After two weeks features of hyperplasia became more evident in cultures with serum containing medium (Fig. 1) which is apparently attributed to the larger increase of the fibroblast population. Thus, one desirable feature of a fully defined state of organotypic cocultures is a stable population of mesenchymal cells in the dermal equivalent. This could be achieved by applying human dermal fibroblasts rendered postmitotic, but being still physiologically active, by high-dose X-irradiation [16, 17]. These postmitotic fibroblasts resemble more closely the resting state exhibited by the ma-

jority of fibroblasts in upper dermis and are equally capable of maintaining normal keratinocyte proliferation and differentiation in skin equivalents.

Continued keratinocyte proliferation is the central driving force for epidermal morphogenesis and as such target of regulatory events by external signals (growth factors/cytokines/hormones) as well as intrinsic programs (determined differentiation). The keratinocyte proliferation kinetics observed in organotypic cocultures are very similar to the proliferative responses during cutaneous tissue regeneration [12, 14, 15, 17, 18]. After an initial outburst mitotic activity declines sharply and attains a basal level after two weeeks. Concomitantly, dividing cells become regularly confined to the epidermal basal layer indicating that consolidation of tissue organization and homeostasis is being approached in these tissue engineered skin equivalents [15].

The analysis of differentiation markers confirms the histological finding that organotypic cocultures perform by and large a regular epidermal maturation. Thus, keratin 10 indicative for the early phase or onset of regular differentiation occupies the suprabasal part of the epidermis (Fig. 2a) while transglutaminase 1 and loricrin – both late stage markers and involved in the formation of the

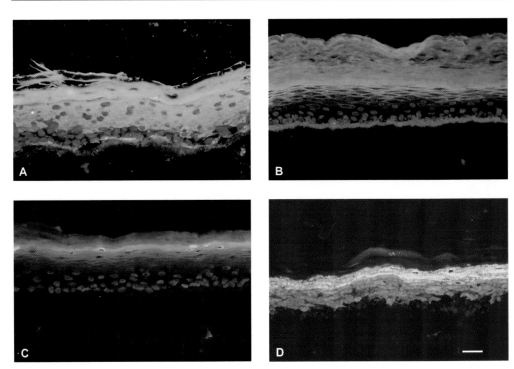

Fig. 2: Localization of keratinocyte differentiation markers in organotypic cocultures at 2 wk (A, C, D) and 3 wk (B). Cultivation in serum containing medium; immunofluorescence detection of **(A)** keratin 10 (green) and collagen IV (red), demarcating the basement membrane zone, **(B)** transglutaminase 1 (green) and laminin-1 (red), **(C)** loricrin (red). In **(D)** double staining of keratin 1 (green) and keratin10 (red) with yellow coloration in the area of colocalization indicates marked uncoupling of their expression. In all images nuclei are counterstained with bisbenzimid (in blue). Scale bar 50 μm.

cornified envelope – are located in the zone immediately underneath the *stratum corneum* (Fig. 2b, c). Further proteins expressed in the course of keratinocyte differentiation such as filaggrin, involucrin and keratin 2e exhibit an *in vivo* like distribution as well (not shown here, see [15, 19]). However, certain deviations from the normal epidermal phenotype usually occur such as the persistence of the 'hyperplastic' keratins K 6 and 16 and the uncoupling of the suprabasal keratins K1 and 10 which normally are coexpressed (Fig. 2 d). This resembles the wound situation and indicates a not yet fully established tissue homeostasis. Nevertheless, the observed features together with an ultrastructure characteristic of normal epidermis (keratohyalin gran-

ules, membrane coating vesicles etc. [15]) prove the potential of this organotypic coculture model to generate skin substitutes capable to recapitulate a normal epidermal morphogenesis *in vitro*.

However, not only keratinocytes from the interfollicular epidermis are suitable targets in organotypic coculture. Similarly, keratinocytes from the outer root sheath of the hair follicle can be used to reconstitute skin *in vitro* [20]. Further development of that system has brought up a technique to produce epidermal autografts which is much less inconvenient for the patient as it needs just few plucked hairs instead of excised skin biopsies. This method is now being applied with a high success rate in leg ulcer treatment [21].

Keratinocytes and Fibroblasts Cooperate in Basement Membrane Formation

Basement membranes are highly specialized structures of extracellular matrix, separating epithelia from the underlying connective tissue. In addition to their mechanical function they participate in mediating and modulating epithelial-mesenchymal interactions [9]. They also play a role in various pathological processes, e.g. wound healing and tumor cell invasion. Several macromolecules have been assigned to individual ultrastructural components of the cutaneous basement membrane zone including collagen type IV, the laminins, the crosslinking nidogen, proteoglycans such as perlecan, and the bullous pemphigoid antigens, but also collagen type VII which is the major constituent of anchoring fibrils [22]

Exploiting *in vitro* reconstituted skin we observed that the process of basement membrane formation itself is strictly dependent on keratinocyte-fibroblast interactions [23]. To elucidate the cellular origin and synthesis dynamics of basement membrane constituents, *de novo* synthesis, deposition, and ultrastructural assembly of its components were analyzed in organotypic cultures of skin keratinocytes with or without fibroblasts in the collagen gels. In the absence of fibroblasts no significant deposition of basement membrane components becomes immunohistochemically detectable with the exception of laminin-5. With fibroblasts present, however, all components are deposited and accumulate with culture time. For this cooperative effect no direct contact of keratinocytes and dermal cells is required as evidenced in a culture configuration where the fibroblasts are separated from the epithelium by an acellular collagen gel. This clearly indicates that both cell compartments interact via diffusible factors or components (i) in mutually inducing the production of basement membrane constituents, and (ii) in delivering their products at the place of basement membrane assembly.

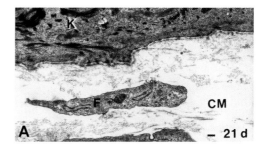

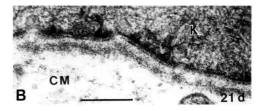

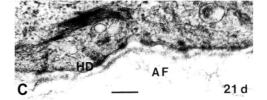

Fig. 3: Basement membrane ultrastructure in organotypic cocultures after 3 wk. (A; B) The basal aspect of keratinocytes (K) on a collagen matrix (CM) with embedded fibroblasts (F) is lined with a continuous lamina densa and bears numerous mature hemidesmosomes (HD). **(C)** In addition, anchoring fibrils (AF) have established after prolonged culture time. Scale bars 200 nm. (from [23], © 1998 Academic Press).

As it becomes obvious at the ultrastructural level, a complete basement membrane structure emerges in organotypic cocultures only after prolonged cultivation (3 weeks). Stringent maturation criteria are a continuous lamina densa, hemidesmosomes and anchoring fibrils (Fig. 3 a–c). Although the corresponding constituents are presumably present in sufficient amounts already early, as confirmed by immunohistochemical detection, the structural organization of the basement membrane occured considerably later. This may be explained by conditions in the early stages which are not appropriate for the spontaneous assembly of the base-

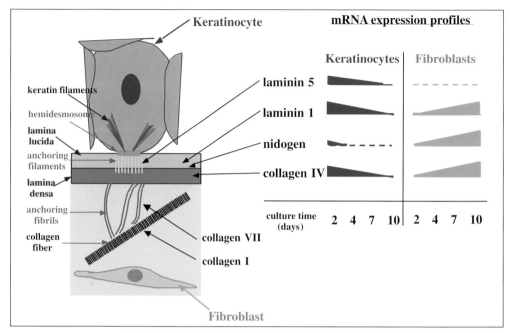

Fig. 4: Basement membrane components: their ultrastrucural distribution and cell type specific differential mRNA expression. The time course illustrates largely reciprocal induction patterns for mRNAs of basement membrane components in keratinocytes and fibroblasts.

ment membrane's supramolecular aggregate structure, such as imbalanced concentrations or insufficient processing and binding properties of key components (see [23] for further discussion).

In order to discover the contribution of keratinocytes and fibroblasts in the production of basement membrane constituents the expression kinetics of basement membrane protein genes were monitored by Northern blot analysis. These results, summarized schematically in Fig. 4, reveal a reciprocal induction pattern with the abundance of specific mRNAs shifting gradually from the keratinocytes to the cocultured fibroblasts. There are few exceptions from this general pattern: the mRNA of the laminin β3 chain indicative for laminin-5 is restricted to epidermal cells in early organotypic cocultures while almost completely downregulated later. Similarly, also collagen VII seems to be expressed solely in the basal keratinocytes in slightly increasing

amounts, as is concluded from immunohistochemical detection of the protein, nevertheless the respective mRNA data are not available yet. In contrast, the mRNA of nidogen, which plays a key role in basement membrane assembly due to its capacity to cross-link collagen IV and laminin-1, is almost exclusively confined to the mesenchymal cells and strongly upregulated with culture time. Experiments interfering with the cross-bridging effectivity of nidogen in the organotypic coculture model further suggest that it is one of the major players in the regulation of organized basement membrane formation (Breitkreutz and coworkers, unpublished data).

Taken together, the potential of organotypic cocultures to reconstitute a complete basement membrane *in vitro* made it possible to investigate the dynamics of a process that is of fundamental importance for skin regeneration during wound healing.

Paracrine Interactions Regulate Proliferation and Differentiation

Since the feeder layer coculture method to grow keratinocytes reproducibly *in vitro* has been elaborated by Rheinwald and Green [24] paracrine stimulation was suggested to be exerted by the mesenchymal feeder cells. First evidences about the nature of paracrine signals in two-dimensional cocultures indicated that KGF, IL-6 and GM-CSF as fibroblast derived factors are involved in the interplay between keratinocytes and fibroblasts [23]. In subsequent studies it could be shown that in two-dimensional cultures postmitotic fibroblasts arrested by X-radiation (same pretreatment as for feeder cells [25]) are inducible to express among others KGF, HGF, and IL-8, but also the IL-1 receptor when challenged with exogeneously added IL-1 [16]. In consequence, two-dimensional cocultures of keratinocytes and postmitotic fibroblasts were investigated for expression and functionality of IL-1 disclosing a double paracrine mechanism for keratinocyte growth regulation [17]. In this scenario, keratinocyte derived IL-1 (IL-1α as well as IL-1β) represents a major inducer of KGF in cocultured fibroblasts that in turn stimulates and maintains keratinocyte proliferation. This mechanism could be confirmed by inhibition experiments: interfering with both directions of the double paracrine signalling pathway by means of neutralizing antibodies or inhibitors of IL-1 and/or KGF, respectively, suppressed the proliferation of keratinocytes to the same extent. Furthermore, it was demonstrated that in the medium of cocultures KGF persisted at a significantly higher level and steadily increased compared to fibroblast monocultures, which suggests a continuous induction in the cocultured fibroblasts by permanent interaction with the keratinocytes. This also explains why fibroblast conditioned medium can not substitute for the feeder effect.

Anticipating a more comprehensive insight into the relevance of epithelial-mesenchymal interactions for skin organization, the corresponding analytical methodology was applied to defined, serum-free organotypic cocultures [19]. The novel double paracrine pathway characterized for monolayer cocultures proved to be operative also under the more physiologic conditions of three-dimensional skin equivalents. A KGF expression in fibroblasts was induced by keratinocytes via release of IL-1. The functional significance was again documented by interference with IL-1 signalling as well as by complementation experiments in skin equivalents containing suboptimal fibroblast numbers not sufficiently supporting epidermal morphogenesis (see [19] for details). Blockade of IL-1 action inhibited not only KGF secretion by fibroblasts, but also keratinocyte proliferation and epidermal tissue formation, and this was comparable to the effects of KGF blocking antibodies. Thus, the effectivity of the IL-1/KGF mechanism could be confirmed and its impact on tissue morphogenesis – an important biological parameter only accessible in such a three-dimensional coculture model – could be properly evaluated.

Due to the excellent recapitulation of *in vivo* like features in these organotyic cocultures those findings can be directly extrapolated to the *in vivo* situation. This assumption that the double paracrine IL-1/KGF circuit plays an essential role in skin regeneration and control of homeostasis, was also underlined by studies on wound healing [26].

Furthermore, in order to discriminate the regulatory mechanisms on growth and on differentiation, signal transduction challenged by IL-1 in fibroblasts was studied using mouse fibroblast lines from AP-1 component knockout mice. Transcription factors of the AP-1 family have been proposed to be key regulators of cell proliferation, differentiation and apoptosis based on loss of function approaches [27]. Whereas *c-jun*[-/-] fibroblasts did not support keratinocyte growth in organotypic cocultures, *junB*[-/-] fibroblasts caused enhanced keratinocyte proliferation and differentiation resulting in epidermal hyperplasia [28]. Detailed analysis discovered KGF and GM-CSF as responsible

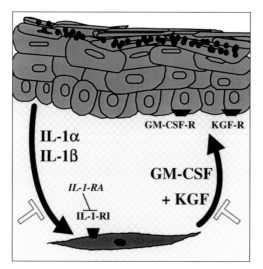

GM-CSF-R   KGF-R

IL-1α

IL-1ß

IL-1-RA

GM-CSF

+ KGF

IL-1-RI

Fig. 5: Schematic illustration of keratinocyte growth regulation in organotypic cocultures with fibroblasts by the double paracrine pathway involving IL-1 and KGF/GM-CSF. IL-1-RA, IL-1-receptor antagonist; IL-1-R1, IL-1 receptor type1; KGF-R, KGF- receptor; GM-CSF-R, GM-CSF-receptor. The posibility to inhibit each branch of the circuit specifically with neutralizing antibodies or receptor antagonist, respectively, is indicated by ⊥.

target genes of AP-1 in fibroblasts: their constitutive and, above all, their IL-1 induced expression was lacking in *c-jun*^-/- cells but largely increased in *junB*^-/- cells. While KGF already had been characterized as paracrine mediator, GM-CSF represents a novel candidate, although this was not unexpected (see [14]). KGF and GM-CSF expression in fibroblasts triggered by keratinocyte released IL-1 is regulated actively by AP-1. Therefore, AP-1 is essential for keratinocyte-fibroblast interaction in organotypic cocultures, and thus critically involved in the double paracrine loop regulating epidermal growth and differentiation (Fig. 5). In addition to the fact, that KGF and GM-CSF are antagonistically regulated by *c-jun* and *junB*, it could be demonstrated that they exert distinct effects on keratinocyte proliferation and differentiation. This implies that fibroblasts regulate the coordinated epidermal morphogenesis via a fine

tuning of the AP-1 transcription factor complex resulting in the balanced expression of cytokines among which KGF and GM-CSF are major players.

Concluding Remarks

As reported herein, organotypic cocultures have proved their usefulness as advanced tools for the investigation of the molecular mechanisms underlying different aspects of cutaneous regeneration. The information about epithelial-mesenchymal interactions collected so far might not be complete, and most likely, further paracrine circuits engaged in the regulation of tissue formation will be found soon. In this respect, *in vitro* skin equivalents open the access to a more accurate analysis with improved practicability. As exemplified above, heterologous coculture systems with cells from transgenic or loss of function mutations bearing animals represent a promising straightforward approach to elucidate in depth the molecular mechanisms in the control of tissue formation.

On purpose, the outlined composition of the organotypic coculture model displays an extremely simplified paradigm of skin. However, in order to understand the influences or responses of further cutaneous cell types of interest, those can be incorporated in addition, as it has been reported for endothelial as well as for Langerhans cells and melanocytes [14, 29]. Also modifications of the dermal equivalent in regard to the extracellular matrix composition have demonstrated some beneficial effects, but in general at the expense of practicability [30].

Furthermore, the characterization of *in vitro* skin equivalents has yielded a data base which now can provide standards for the validation of tissue engineered skin substitutes prepared for clinical application. Having profound knowledge of those biologically meaningful parameters, the design and production of composite grafts, for instance consisting of keratinocytes on top of a dermal substitute made up by a biodegradable scaffold with integrated fibroblasts [31], can be competently controlled and further optimized.

Paracrine crosstalk in epithelial-mesenchymal interactions is supposedly also subjected to pathological alterations. Therefore respective informations, as can be collected in *in vitro* models, are desirable to develop adequate concepts of medical treatment. Other fields of promising application of relevant *in vitro* models are pharmacological and toxicological testing where the increasing legal constraints on animal assays are provoking the search for advanced *in vivo* like systems [32].

In general, *in vitro* models such as organotypic keratinocyte-fibroblast cocultures represent a topic of modern biotechnology which gains growing impact on basic biological research as well as medical sciences, in particular tissue engineering.

Acknowledgements

We would also like to thank our collaborators A. Limat, G. Thiekötter and M. Baur who contributed significantly to the establishment and characterization of the organotypic culture system. Expert technical assistance of Heinrich Steinbauer, Gabi Blaser, Iris Martin, Silke Haid is gratefully acknowledged as well as expert typing by Martina Kegel. The studies summarized in this contribution have been supported by grants of the Deutsche Forschungsgemeinschaft (DFG-Fu 91/4-1), the European Commission (BIO4-CT 96-0036 and BRPR-CT 96-0227) and from Wella Cosmital SA, Marly Switzerland and Beiersdorf AG, Hamburg.

References

[1] *Sawyer, RH, Fallon, JF:* Epithelial Mesenchymal Interactions in Development. New York: Praeger, p. 252, (1983)

[2] *Sengel, P:* Epidermal-dermal interaction. In: Bereiter-Hahn, I, Matoltsy, AG, Richards, KS (eds.). Biology of the integument, Part 2 Vertebrates, Springer-Verlag, Berlin. pp. 374–408, (1986)

[3] *Kedinger, M, Simon-Assman, P, Alexandre, E, Haffen, K:* Importance of a fibroblastic support for *in vitro* differentiation of intestinal endodermal cells and for their response to glycocorticoids. Cell Differentiation 20, 171–182, (1987)

[4] *Mackenzie, IC, Dabbelsteen, E:* Connective tissue influences on the expression of epithelial cell surface antigens. Cell Tissue Res 248, 137–141, (1987)

[5] *Cunha, GR, Bigsby, RM, and Cooke, PS:* Stromal-epithelial interactions in adult organs. Cell Differentiation 17, 137–148, (1985)

[6] *Mackenzie, IC:* Epithelial-mesenchymal interactions in the development and maintenance of epithelial tissues. In: The Keratinocyte Handbook, Leigh, I., Lane, B., and Watt, F.M., eds. Cambridge University Press, Cambridge, pp. 243–258, (1994)

[7] *Holbrook, KA, Hennings, H:* Phenotypic expression of epidermal cells *in vitro*. A review. J Invest Dermatol 81, 11s–24s, (1983)

[8] *Fusenig, NE:* Mammalian epidermal cells in culture. In: Bereiter-Hahn, I., Matoltsy, A.G., Richards, K.S. (eds.). Biology of the integument, Part 2 Vertebrates, Springer-Verlag, Berlin. pp. 409–442, (1986)

[9] *Fusenig, NE:* Epithelial-mesenchymal interactions regulate keratinocyte growth and differentiation *in vitro*. In: The Keratinocyte Handbook, Leigh, I., Lane, B., and Watt, F.M., eds. Cambridge University Press, Cambridge, pp. 71–94, (1994)

[10] *Fusenig, NE, Breitkreutz, D, Boukamp, P, Bohnert, A, Mackenzie, IC:* Epithelial mesenchymal interaction in tissue homeostasis and malignant transformation. In: Oral Cancer: Detection of Patients and Lesions at Risk. Johnson, N.W., ed. Cambridge University Press, Cambridge, pp. 218–256, (1991)

[11] *Fusenig, NE:* Cell interaction and epithelial differentiation. In: Culture of Epithelial Cells, Freshney, R.I., ed. Wiley-Liss Inc., New York, pp. 25–57, (1992)

[12] *Breitkreutz, D, Stark, H-J, Mirancea, N, Tomakidi, P, Steinbauer, H, Fusenig, NE:* Integrin and basement membrane normalization in mouse grafts of human keratinocytes – implications for epidermal homeostasis. Differentiation 61, 195–209, (1997)

[13] *Jahaverian, A, Vacchariello, O, Fusenig, NE, Garlick, JA:* Normal keratinocytes suppress early stages of neoplastic progression in stratified epithelium. Cancer Res 58, 2200–2208, (1998)

[14] *Smola, H, Thiekötter, G, Fusenig, NE:* Mutual induction of growth factor gene expression by epidermal-dermal cell interaction. J Cell Biol 122, 417–429, (1993)

[15] *Stark, H-J, Baur, M, Breitkreutz, D, Mirancea, N, Fusenig, NE:* Organotypic keratinocyte co-cultures in defined medium with regular epidermal morphogenesis and differentiation. J Invest Dermatol 112, 681–691, (1999)

[16] *Maas-Szabowski, N, Fusenig, NE:* Interleukin-1-induced growth factor expression in post-mitotic and resting fibroblasts. J Invest Dermatol 107, 849–855, (1996)

[17] *Maas-Szabowski, N, Shimotoyodome, A, Fusenig, NE:* Keratinocyte growth regulation in fibroblast cocultures via a double paracrine mechanism. J Cell Science 11, 1843–1853, (1999)

[18] *Matoltsy, AG, Viziam, CB:* Further observations on epithelialization of small wounds: An autoradiographic study of incorporation and distribution of ^{3}H-thymidine in the epithelium covering skin wounds. J Invest Dermatol 55, 20–25, (1970)

[19] *Maas-Szabowski, N, Stark, H-J, Fusenig, NE:* Keratinocyte growth regulation in defined organotypic cultures through IL-1-induced KGF expression in resting fibroblasts. J Invest Dermatol 114, 1075–1084, (2000)

[20] *Limat, A, Breitkreutz, D, Hunziker, T, Boillat, C, Wiesmann, U, Klein, E, Noser, F, Fusenig, NE:* Restoration of the epidermal phenotype by follicular outer root sheath cells in recombinant culture with dermal fibroblasts. Exp Cell Res 194, 218–227, (1991)

[21] *Limat, A, Mauri, D, Hunziker, T:* Successful treatment of chronic leg ulcers with epidermal equivalents generated from cultured autologous outer root sheath cells. J Invest Dermatol 107, 128–135, (1996)

[22] *Timpl, R:* Macromolecular organization of basement membranes. Curr Opinion Cell Biol 8, 618–624, (1996)

[23] *Smola, H, Stark, H-J, Thiekötter, G, Mirancea, N, Fusenig, NE:* Dynamis of basement membrane formation by keratinocyte-fibroblast interactions in organotypic skin culture. Exp Cell Res 239, 399–410, (1998)

[24] *Rheinwald, JG, Green, H:* Serial cultivation of strains of human epidermal keratinocytes: the formation of colonies from single cells. Cell 6, 331–344, (1975)

[25] *Limat, A, Hunziker, T, Boillat, C, Bayreuther, K, Noser, F:* Post-mitotic human dermal fibroblasts efficiently support the growth of human follicular keratinocytes. J Invest Dermatol 92, 758–762, (1989)

[26] *Werner, S:* Keratinocyte growth factor: a unique player in epithelial repair processes. Cytokine Growth Factor Rev 9, 153–165, (1998)

[27] *Schorpp-Kistner, M, Wang, ZQ, Angel, P, Wagner, EF:* Jun B is essential for mammalian placentation. EMBO J 18, 934–948, (1999)

[28] *Szabowski, A, Maas-Szabowski, N, Andrecht, S, Kolbus, A, Schorpp-Kistner, M, Angel, P:* c-Jun and JunB antagonistically control cytokine-regulated mesenchymal-epidermal interaction in skin. Cell 103, 745–755, (2000)

[29] *Regnier, M, Staquet, MJ, Schmitt, D, Schmidt, R:* Integration of Langerhans cells into a pigmented reconstructed human epidermis. J Invest Dermatol 109, 510–512, (1997)

[30] *Contard, P, Bartel, L, Jacobs II, L, Perish, JS, MacDonald, ED, Handler, L, Cone, D, Fleischmajer, R:* Culturing keratinocytes and fibroblasts in a three-dimensional mesh results in epidermal differentiation and formation of a basal-lamina anchoring zone. J Invest Dermatol 100, 35–39, (1993)

[31] *Rennekampf, HO, Kiessig, V, Hansbrough, JF:* Current concepts in the development of cultured skin replacements. J Surg Res 62, 288–295, (1996)

[32] *Fusenig, NE:* Cell Culture Models: Reliable Tools in Pharmacotoxicology? In: Fusenig, N.E., Graf, H. (eds.). Cell Culture in Pharmaceutical Research. Springer Verlag Berlin-Heidelberg, pp. 1–7, (1994)

Clinical Results of Cultured Epithelium and Skin Substitutes

Use of Cultured Epidermis for the Treatment of Extensive Burns in Children.
The Edouard Herriot Burn Center Experience, Lyon, France

F. M. Braye, P. Pascal, A. F. Black, E. Venet, O. Damour

Summary

In this study of the combination of widely meshed autograft and autologous cultured keratinocytes was used in the face of the lack of allogenic skin, as an alternative to the well known Cuono method. Fifteen children suffering extensive burn injuries (deep burns of 62 ±18 % of the total body surface [BSA] (42 range to 90)) underwent this grafting procedure.

The surgical treatment consisted of an early surgical excision, with an immediate coverage by autografts as much as possible. When cultured epithelium was available, a large mesh autograft was applied and covered with cultured epidermis sheets during the same operative procedure. The average take rate was 84 % (+/– 12) without any secondary graft loss. This specific approach to cover excised burn wounds appears to be reliable and produces resistant results. On average, this method allowed the reepithelialization of 30 % (+/–9) of the total body surface of the children. The average hospital stay of the children was 50 +/– 20 days. All the children recovered to lead a normal life. Absence from school was one year after the trauma following rehabilitation programs. The use of widely meshed autograft associated with cultured autologous epithelium is an alternative to Cuono's method in the absence of skin allografts. The combination of autograft and autologous cultured epidermis sheets appeared more effective than one of these techniques applied alone, suggesting the induction of a synergy by coupling these two procedures.

Introduction

Extensive burns in children, over 60% of the total body surface, represent a rare but tremendous problem. For the anaesthesiologists, the specificities of the paediatric treatment are represented by the importance of fluid losses, high metabolic demands, and the frequency and severity of respiratory complications. Moreover, pain must be treated, all the more as it may be hidden by silence and apathy in children. The anatomic structures are smaller than in adults, which require specific material and make any procedure more difficult. Paradoxically, for the surgeon, burns in children are easier to treat than in adults at different levels. The manipulations of a small body are easier, the changing of dressings is rapid and easy, and subsequently local infection is rare. The rate of engraftment for any kind of graft is notoriously much higher in children than in adults. For skin substitutes and especially for cultured epithelia, small surfaces are required.

In our centre epidermal cultures are provided by an iso 9002 certified hospital laboratory. In these conditions, the cost of production of cultured epidermis depends on the infrastructure of the laboratory. That is why we have the opportunity to largely use this means of coverage. The cultivation of the epidermis is planned from to deep burns involving more than 60 % of the total body surface or front to specific problems, such as secondary admission for a failure of treatment in an other unit. A hundred children a year is admitted in our Centre. On average two children a year require cultured epidermis.

A skin biopsy is harvested as soon as the patient arrives in our unit. Keratinocytes are cultivated on a nutrient layer, in the presence of a special medium containing foetal calf serum and growth factors according to Green [1]. In our centre the nutrient layer consists of irradiated human fibroblasts [2]. The younger the patient, the faster the growth of the keratinocytes. More over in children, small surfaces are required, so that sufficient amounts of cultured epidermis are available within 2 to 3 weeks.

Surgical Procedure

General Principles

In our experience the surgical preparation of the patient is the key for the success of cultured epidermis. We do not bath the patients. The surgical treatment lays on early excision and immediate temporary skin substitution for obviously deep third degree burns. On the other hand, for deep se-cond degree burns, in so far the outcome is often unforeseeable, especially on the back, a conservative treatment with silver sulfadiazine dressings is applied for 15 days. In any case autografting remain the method of choice. It is used for the face and hands, and on the limbs according the sandwich technique which associates widely meshed autograft and cadaver skin overlay [3]. For patients planned for cultured epidermis, weekly wound bacteriological cultures are performed. Adapted topical antimicrobial therapy is applied for

any colonisation, which is rarely necessary for children.

It is essential to design a program when cultivation is decided: the areas and the means of grafting of cultured epidermis must be planned to optimise the different means of grafting and to prepare these areas properly. The engraftment of cultured epidermis is optimum on the anterior trunk and anterior legs. The engraftment is uncertain on the posterior areas (excepted with the combined technique) and on articulatory regions. On the day of grafting the handling of epidermal sheets must be carefully performed. The transfer gauzes are stapled on the wound bed. Some sterile tulle gauze can be stapled as an overlay to avoid any slipping of the graft. After grafting, the local aspect is controlled every two days by the surgeon. The sheets of epithelium normally appear dry and adherent to the wound bed. In this case, simple Vaseline gauzes are used for the dressing. In case of local infection, topical anti-microbial agents are applied daily onto the epithelium sheets according to the last bacteriological results. The "take off" of the sheets is performed at day six. The removal of the transfer gauzes must be very careful because it is adherent. During the following days the cleaning of the patient is problematic because rubbing is forbidden. Steroid gauzes and anti-microbial topical agents can be used to stabilise the epithelialization. Antibacterial topical agents must be largely used to avoid bacterial lysis of the cultures, all the more that they appear to be better tolerated in physiological conditions than on epidermis culture alone [4].

In our centre, thanks to a close co-operation with the skin substitutes laboratory, it is possible to obtain successive small quantities (one to five thousand cm²) of cultured epidermis, whereas with private laboratory, a single delivery is the rule. This versatility allows to adapt the use of cultured epidermis according to the evolution of the state of the patient. In such conditions, it is possible to use cultured epidermis differently on the same patient.

CUONO's Method

The reference technique for the use of cultured epidermis was set out clearly since 1984 by Gallico and Cuono [5, 6]. The presence of a dermal sub-layer appears fundamental for the take of epidermal layers. In this technique, the preparation of the patient lays on an early excision, followed by an immediate application of the donor skin. On the day of the CEA grafts, the epidermis of the donor skin is carefully removed, leaving an allogenic dermal sub-layer. The epidermis of the homograft must always be removed on the day that the CEA's are placed, since keratinocytes are major carriers of histocompatibility antigens which induce rejection of the homograft. Cultured epidermis keep fragile during several months because the maturation of the dermo-epidermal junction takes 6 to 12 months to occur [7]. Clinically may result in secondary loss of grafts and blistering, so cultured epidermis require specific nursing in order to avoid any mechanical traumatism. Retraction of the grafted areas is substantial in spite of the dense dermal network brought by the allogenic skin, which is contradictory. Rehabilitation is troublesome because splinting and massages can cause wounds which are difficult to cure. Positioning and compression are often the only possibilities for these patient [8]. It is the means of grafting which has the best yielding in so far theoretically all the body surface can be covered with only a few cm^2 biopsy. Meanwhile, this method depends on the availability of homograft which is, in our Centre, taken from brain-dead donors to avoid the risk of infectious transmission. Its use has been therefore greatly limited by the lack of suitable donors.

Combination of Autograft and Cultured Epidermis (Fig. 1)

The lack of allogenic skin led us to develop the combination of widely meshed autograft and autologous cultured epidermis overlay [9, 10]. Since 1990, twenty one children un-

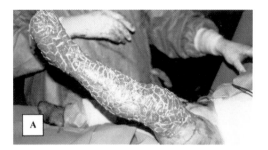

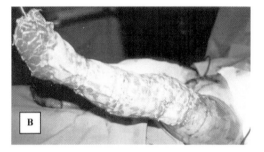

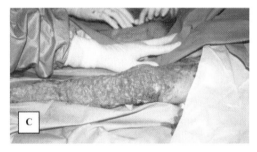

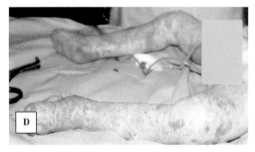

Fig. 1: Combination of autograft and cultured epidermis. **A** – 18 months old boy suffering 80 % TBSA burns (52 % deep burns). 19 days after the burn, an excision deep to fat was performed and the wound bed was grafted with 1x6 meshed autograft. **B** – During the same operative procedure, autologous cultured epidermis is grafted overlay. **C** – Day 5 post grafting, the control of the graft take shows a continuous epidermisation. A thin epidermal layer fills the holes of the mesh. **D** – Day 10 post grafting, the grafts thicken, complete and definitive coverage is achieved. Hospital stay 46 days.

der 15 years old were planed for cultured keratinocytes, for deep burns involving more than 50 % of their body surface (18 cases) or for a critical status at admission (3 cases, with an infection of the burn wound and of the skin donor sites). Among them one died the day following admission and one died of septicemia before the availability of the CEA. For the 19 remaining patients the average age was 8 years, ranging from 1 to 15 years. Thirteen boys and six girls were concerned. The average deep burns concerned 62 ±18 % BSA (42 range to 90).

This technique alone led to the complete healing of 32 % (+/− 10) of the total body surface on average, with a rate of take of 85 %. The association of the culture epidermis and of widely meshed autograft resulted, on the take off day, in a continuous epidermisation. Only one secondary loss of the cultures was noticed. We obtained a definitive coverage of the back in 7 cases.

For 15 children, additional stamp grafts were applied to complete the coverage, but no re-application of cultured epidermis was necessary. The average hospital stay was 50+/− 20 days. It seems to us that the combined technique leads to a good take rate of the cultured epidermis, even on granulation tissue or on an infected bed. The coverage seems more resistant to infection or traumatism than with one of the techniques, even on the back, which is specially difficult to graft. It happens as if a synergy existed between the two means of grafting. The cultured epidermis, by bringing an immediate coverage impairs the development of the granulation tissue through the mesh of the widely expanded autograft. The cultured epidermis is also known to secrete growth factors [11] which may stimulate the development of the autograft. In the same way, the meshed autograft, even when widely expanded, provides a thin living dermis network which may play a key role for the engraftment of cultured epidermis and perhaps to prevent secondary retraction. The average stay in the rehabilitation centre was 11 months. From the point of view of the phys-

iotherapist, the areas which received combined technique appeared more resistant during physiotherapy and seem to present less retraction than areas grafted with cultures alone or CUONO's method. From a biologic point of view, this technique is safe in so far only autologous tissues are grafted. A recent study compared the combination of autografts and allogenic cultured keratinocytes to the usual sandwich method [12]. It shows comparable results for the definitive coverage with the two means of grafting, but higher costs with allogenic cultured epidermis. Our strategy when using the combined method is radically different: it is devoted to patients suffering extensive burns which do require the use of cultured epidermis for their definitive coverage. The few available healthy skin is widely meshed to bring a dermal network which is necessary for the good engraftment of cultured epidermis. The combined technique must not be considered as a substitution for sandwich. At the opposite it has been developed as a substitution for Cuono's method because of the lack of human allograft. The efficiency of this technique in terms of coverage, functional results and security make it the choice in our unit.

Allogenic Cultures on Extensive Deep Second Degree Burns (Fig. 2)

Allogenic cultures are effective on extensive deep second degree burns [13, 14, 15]. In our opinion they are especially useful when burns involve more than 80% of the total body surface. Extensive burns are responsible of hypercatabolism and deterioration of the general condition of the patient. This impairs the healing of burns which would may be achieved if they were less extensive. In such cases, faced with the lack of autograft donor sites, we have usually used autologous cultures. But the delay in obtaining autologous epidermis has been a problem, as it allowed the deterioration of the general condition of the patient and the infection of the burn wound, which greatly jeopardise the

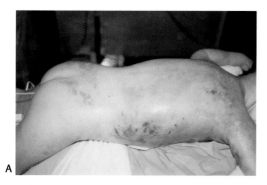

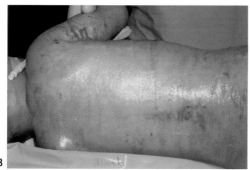

Fig. 2: Allogenic cultured epidermis on extensive deep second degree burns. **A** – 18 months old boy suffering 70 % scalds. The healthy skin is located on the face and the forearms. On day 10 post burns, the second degree burns underwent a thin tangential excision. Cultured epidermis were applied on these areas. (here back and buttocks). **B** – Day 5 post grafting, the control of the graft shows a complete healing of the excised areas. No secondary loss of the epidermis was observed. Hospital stay: 22 days.

allows the treatment of numerous burn patients, as a 8 x 10 cm square of skin, 0.6 mm thick, harvested from one skin donor, is sufficient to obtain 30 m^2 of cultured epidermis. Allogenic cultured keratinocytes are available within one week, thus two weeks earlier than autologous cultures.When applied to second degree burns, allogenic keratinocytes provide temporary coverage and produce growth factors [11] which stimulate epidermisation from healthy epidermal appendages present in the deep second degree burn wound. They are progressively replaced by the keratinocytes of the patient [17] but no acute rejection is observed.

Skin Donor Sites

Likewise, the wound healing effect of allogenic or autologous cultured epidermis onto autograft donor sites has been reported [18]. Indeed, the treatment of extensive burns requires iterative harvesting of skin donor sites. Repeated harvesting is responsible of progressive deepening of the donor sites and subsequently of a delay or a failure of healing. Immediate grafting of split thickness autograft donor sites with autologous or allogenic cultured epidermis speed the healing of the donor sites. Complete healing is obtained within a week (unpublished data), which allows a better turn over of these donor sites and subsequently accelerates the burn wound closure. This is interesting for the treatment of extensive burns and also when, for aesthetic purpose, one wants to restrict the skin donor sites to hidden areas.

engraftment of cultured keratinocytes. The risk of lethal complication dramatically increases with the time required for healing. Furthermore, the functional and aesthetic outcomes of the treatment of deep second degree burns depend mainly of the delay before grafting. That is why, in order to bring to these patients an early temporary coverage, we have created a bank of allogenic keratinocytes obtained from organ donors [16]. Serological profiles were, of course, determined for the organ donor and, three months after transplantation, for the organ recipients. Use of the keratinocytes is possible only after all these tests have been performed. One culture

Discussion

Faced with extensive burns in children, one must consider different factors for therapeutic strategy. Survival is the priority and is correlated to the rapidity of coverage. The quality of long term life has also to be considered. Hence the way of coverage is important. Particularly for children, the evaluation of functional and aesthetic results in the case of extensive burns has to take into account not only the performance in the years following burn, but overall, skin compliance to growth. For this, the puberty period is critical and wide scars may impair a normal physical development. The rapidity and the resistance of the coverage are the best guarantees not only for immediate survival but also for an early rehabilitation in order to obtain good functional results.

From this point of view, cultured epidermis represented a great progress for the treatment of extensive burns, making possible the life saving of patients burnt over 80 % of the total body surface [7, 19, 20]. But the limits of this means of grafting rapidly appeared. The most frequent criticism concern the take rate, the fragility and the cost.

The engraftment of cultured epidermis appears hazardous, greatly dependant of the general state of the patient and of local infection. In our experience in adults we observe a good engraftment of cultured epidermis only when the general state of the patient is satisfying and when the patient underwent a proper preparation. For children the clinical course is more quiet and all the issues report high take rates of cultured epidermis [15, 19, 21, 22, 23].

Cultured epidermis do not replace the "organ" skin. The replacement of epidermis achieves the restoration of the physiological function of skin such as impairing fluid losses and bacterial invasion. But even in CUO-NO's method, where a dense allogenic dermis mesh is grafted, cultured epidermis leads to wide scar areas. The dermis, which is responsible of the functional and cosmetic aspect of skin, appears critical for the life quality of the patients. That is why dermal substitutes have been developed and may put into question the place of cultured epidermis for the treatment of extensive burns [24]. Nevertheless, it must be kept in mind that at the moment dermal substitute do not give a definitive solution for epidermal replacement and may lead to a deadlock.

Further more the cost of dermal substitutes must also be considered.

The cost of cultured epidermis is extremely high when provided by a private laboratory. In our centre, keratinocytes are cultivated in an hospital laboratory. In these conditions, the cost of production of cultured epidermis depends on the infrastructure of the laboratory: The more we use cultured epidermis, the cheaper they are, about 5 \$/cm^2. In these conditions, each time it appears as an advantage for the patient, we use cultured epidermis. When used simultaneously at the different levels of the surgical treatment, such as deep burns, deep second degree burns and autograft donor sites, cultured keratinocytes are a precious tool to accelerate burn wound coverage. In our opinion cultured epidermis clearly shortens the hospital stay of the patients, but it is difficult to perform a randomised study, in so far we can not imagine to deliberately deprive some patients of this treatment. Furthermore, the price of this means of grafting is counter balanced by the shortening of the hospital stay.

As a conclusion cultured epidermis is a means of grafting whose handling is difficult and which requires an experienced burn team. It saves patients by restoring the barrier function of skin, but it is unsatisfactory in so far the non replacement of dermis leads to rehabilitation difficulties and subsequent poor aesthetic and functional results. Cultured epidermis must be considered as the first step to full thickness skin reconstruction. The combination of cultured epidermis and dermal substitutes [25] or in vitro reconstruction of living skin equivalent [26, 27] are probably the future for burn treatment. But till the development of the ideal means of grafting, in our opinion, cultured epidermis remain indispensable for the rapid coverage of extensive burns over 80 % of the total body surface. Thanks to their high take rate, they appear particularly beneficial for the extensive burns of children which represent a distressing position either for the hospital team and for the parents.

References

[1] *Rheinwald JG, Green H:* Serial cultivation of strains of human epidermal keratinocytes: the formation of keratinizing colonies from single cells. Cell; 6: 331–44, 1975

[2] *Limat A, Hunziker T, Boillat C, Bayenther K, Noser F:* Post mitotic human dermal fibroblasts efficiently support the growth of human follicular keratinocytes. Proc Natl Acad Sci USA; 82: 5390–4, 1985

[3] *Alexander JW, Mac Millian BG, Law E, Kittur DS:* Treatment of severe burns with widely meshed skin autograft and meshed skin allograft overlay. J Trauma; 21: 433–8, 1981

[4] *Damour O, Hua SZ, Lasne F, Villain, Rousselle P, Collombel C:* Cytotoxicity evaluation of antiseptics and antibiotics on cultured human fibroblasts and keratinocytes. Burns; 18: 479–85, 1992

[5] *Gallico GG, O'Conner NE, Compton CC, Kehinde O, Green H:* Permanant coverage of large burn wounds with autologous cultured epithelium. N Engl J Med; 311: 448–51, 1984

[6] *Cuono C, Langdon R, Birshall N:* Composite autologous-allogenic skin replacement: development and clinical application. Plast Reconstr Surg; 80: 626–35, 1987

[7] *Compton CC:* Current concepts in pediatric burn care: the biology of cultured epithelial autografts: an eight year study in pediatric burn patients. Eur J Pediatr Surg, 1992; 2: 216–22.

[8] *Weekly R, Klein R:* Clinical nursing experience with cultured epidermal autografts. J Burn Care Rehabil; 13: 138–41, 1992

[9] *Teepe RGC, Kreis RW, Koebrugge EJ, Kempenhaar JA, Vloemans AF Hermans RP, Boxma H, Dokter J, Hermans J, Ponec M:* The use of autologous cultured human epithelium in the treatment of extensive burns wound. J Trauma; 30: 269–75, 1990

[10] *Braye F, Oddou L, Bertin-Maghit M, Belgacem S, Damour O, Spitalier P, Guillot M, Bouchard C, Gueugniaud PY, Goudeau M, Petit P, Tissot E:* Cultured autologous epidermis associated with large mesh autografts for the coverage of extensive burns. About 12 children. Eur J Ped Surg; 10: 35–40, 2000

[11] *Myers S, Navsaria H, Sanders R, Green C, Leigh I:* Transplantation of keratinocytes in the treatment of wounds. Am J Surg; 170: 75–83, 1995

[12] *Monstrey S, Beele H, Kettler M, Van Landuyt K, Blondeel P, Matton G, Naeyert JM:* Allogenic cultured keratinocytes versus cadaveric skin to cover wide-mesh autogenous split thickness skin grafts. Ann Plast Surg; 43: 268–72, 1999

[13] *Madden MR, Finkelstein JL, Staiano-Coico L, Goodwin CW, Shires GT, Nolan EE, Hefton JM:* Grafting of cultured allogenic epidermis on second and third degree burn wounds on 26 patients. J Trauma; 26: 955–62, 1986

[14] *Hefton JM, Madden MR, Finkelstein JL, Shires GT:* Grafting of burn patients with allografts of cultured epidermal cells. Lancet; 20: 428–30, 1983

[15] *De Luca M, Bandanza S, Cancedda F, Tamisani A, Di Noto C, Muller L, Diogardi D, Brienza E, Calvario A, Zeramni R, Di Mascio D, Papadia F:* Permanent coverage of full skin thickness burns with autologous cultured epidermis and reepithelialization of partial skin thickness lesions induced by allogenic cultured epidermis : a multicenter study in the treatment of children. Burns; 18: S16–S18, 1992

[16] *Braye F, Pascal P, Bertin-Maghit M, Colpart JJ, Tissot E, Damour O:* Advantages of using a bank of allogenic keratinocytes for the rapid coverage of extensive and deep second-degree burns. Med. Biol. Eng. Comput.; 38: 248–252, 2000

[17] *Aubock I, Irschick E, Romani N, Kompatscher P, Hopfl R, Herold M, Schuler G, Bauer M, Huber C, Fritsch P:* Rejection, after a slightly prolonged survival time, of Langerhans cell-free allogenic cultured epidermis used for burn coverage in humans. Transplantation. 45: 730–8, 1988

[18] *Phillips TJ, Provan A, Cobert D:* A randomized single blind trial on cultured epidermal allografts in the treatment of split thickness skin graft donor sites. Arch Dermatol; 129: 879–882, 1993

[19] *Sheridan RL, Tompkins RG:* Cultured autologous epithelium in patients with burns of ninety per cent or more of the body surface. J Trauma.; 38: 48–50, 1995

[20] *Carsin H, Ainaud P, Le Bever H, Rives JM, Le Coadou A, Stephanazzi J:* Objectifs, résultats et perspectives du traitement des brûlés en 1997. Bull. Acad. Natl Méd.; 181: n°7, 1307–1320, 1997

[21] *Chalumeau M, Saulnier JP, Ainaud P, Lebever H, Stephanazzi J, Lecoadou A, Carsin H:* Initial general management and surgery of six extensively burned children treated with cultured epidermal autografts. J. Ped. Surg; 34: 602–5, 1999

[22] *Krupp S, Benathan M, Meuli M, Deglise B, Holzer E, Wiesner L, Delacretaz F, Chiolero R:* Current concept in pediatric burn care: management of burn wounds with cultured epidermal autografts. Eur J Pediatr Surg; 2: 210–215, 1992

[23] *Coleman JJ, Siwy BK:* Use of cultured epidermal autografts: life saving and skin saving

technique in children. J Ped Surg; 27: 1029–32, 1992

[24] *Burke JF:* Current concepts in pediatric burn care. Artificial skin: its place in the system of pediatric burn care. Eur J Pediatr Surg; 2: 205–206, 1992

[25] *Buttler, CE, Orgill, DP, Yannas, IV, Compton, C:* Effects of keratinocytes seeding of collagen-glycosaminoglycan membranes on the regeneration of skin in a porcine model. Plast. Rec. Surg.; 101: 1572, 1998

[26] *Bell E, Ehrlich HP, Sher S, Merril C, Sarber R, Hull B, Nakatsuji T, Church D, Buttle DJ:* Development and use of a living skin equivalent. Plast. Reconstr. Surg.; 67: 386–392, 1981

[27] *Coulomb B, Friteau L, Baruch J, Guilbaud J, Chretien-Marquet B, Glicenstein J, Lebreton-Decoster C, Bell E, Dubertret L:* Advantages of the presence of living dermal fibroblasts within an in vitro reconstructed skin for grafting in humans. Plast. Reconstr. Surg.; 101: 1891, 1998

Cultured Epidermal Allografts Strongly Stimulate Reepithelialisation in Deep Dermal Burns

P. Brychta, J. Adler, H. Rihova, I. Suchanek, Y. Kaloudova, J. Koupil

Summary

This study summarizes the Brno Burn Center experience with the application of cultured epidermal allografts in the treatment of deep dermal burns. In a prospective, randomised, clinical trial on 30 patients with deep dermal burns cultured epidermal allografts (CEAl) obtained from young healthy and examined donors and fixed on tule grass carrier (Grasolind) were compared with empty Grasolind as a lowest layer of dressing. All other layers were identical.

Both kinds of dressing were applied simultaneously on the same deep dermal burn wound between 6th and 10th day after burn. Six days later the non healed wound areas were recorded through painting on cellophane membrane and scanned in the computer. The percentage wound reduction was calculated and statistically evaluated.

The recuction of the non-epithelialized wound area was 86,5% when covered through cultured epidermal allografts and only 71,2% when covered with tule grass (Grasolind) only. This difference is statistically significant.

In conlusion it can be stated that cultured epidermal allografts strongly stimulate the reepithelialisation in deep dermal burns.

Introduction

Exciting reports describing in vitro preparation and clinical use of transplantable human skin epithelium [1, 2] encouraged us to establish the Skin culture laboratory in 1992. Since that time this laboratory has been producing the sheet cultured epidermal grafts. The total amount of sheets produced to date is 58 660 cm^2. Due to much bigger capacity of the laboratory than the real need of cultured epidermal autografts for severe burn patients (2–3 cases per year), we started to use them also as allografts for treatment of deep dermal burn wounds, residual wound areas after dermoepidermal grafting and donor sites in special cases. Besides of burned patients donors became also some plastic surgery patients [otapostasis, blepharoplasty].

461 patients received the cultured epidermal allografts [CEAl] between January 1, 1993 and December 31, 1999. We have observed very good stimulating effects of this sheets namely on deep dermal burn wounds in almost [virtually] all patients. In 1996 we decided to perform the prospective clinical study comparing the efficacy of these grafts with conventional dressing and later on with some other forms of dressing (freeze-dried cultured allografts etc.) according to unified protocol.

Material and Methods – Skin donors

Donors of skin for the cultivation were recruited from the patients of Brno Burn and Reconstructive Surgery Centre. Alltogether 40 donors were employed. Their age ranged from 2 to 47 years and their repeated clinical and serological examination was negative. The interval between the examinations was 6 months. The serologic examination protocol is summarised in Table 1.

Table 1: Scheme of examining skin donors

Screening	Examination
AIDS	HIV 1/2
Syphilis	TPHA, RRR
Hepatitis B	HBsAg
Hepatitis C	HCV
Other hepatopathies	ALT

Preparation and Storage of Cultured Epidermal Allografts

Skin samples were harvested under strongly sterile conditions during the operations with subsequent washing out the disinfection agent [Betadine] and positioning in the transport medium.

The processing consisted of:

– removal of the subcutaneous fat and cutting the sample to pieces 2x2 mm using scissors and forceps,
– incubation in 0,2% Trypsin solution for 16–20 hours in temperature + 4°C,
– dividing the dermis and epidermis and separation of keratinocytes mechanically using two forcepces,
– centrifugation and suspension of keratinocytes in culture medium,
– 3T3 fibroblast feeder-layer preparation
– establishing of keratinocytes primocultures according to slightly modifed Rheinwald-Green procedure,
– freezing of keratinocytes suspension

For six months the samples were stored in form of keratinocytes suspension in temperature –150°C.

If repeated examination of the donor was negative, following steps were done:

– in vitro expansion via coculture of keratinocytes and 3T3 fibroblasts
– preparation of cultured epidermal grafts

Completed grafts were either immediately used in the fresh form or cryopreserved in special envelopes in temperature –150°C. Their thawing and releasing was done on demand of a clinician.

Clinical Use of Cultured Epidermal Allografts

The grafts were put into the transport medium in the Petri dishes after thawing and used as soon as possible (within 30 minutes).

The burn wounds were cleansed and for 24 hours the silver-sulfadiazine ointment was avoided. The antibiotic solution was applied in the form of wet soaks in 4 hours intervals. Proper surgical toilette and repeated rinsing of the wound with Ringer's solution were mandatory parts of the wound conditioning prior to grafting. The grafts were then put onto the wound upside-down with the carrier (Grassolind) protecting the multilayer of keratinocytes. The next layer of dressing was also soaked with Ringer's solution, followed by several layers of dry cotton gauze.

Rebandage connected with removal of the carrier was conducted on day 2–4 after application. Another tulle grass and soaks were applied for next 2 days. Two days after application the cultured allogeneic graft was usually firmly attached to the wound surface.

In the period of 1993 through 1999 a total of **461 patients** with deep dermal burns became recipients of the cultured epidermal allografts.

Study Design

According to the guidelines described below the prospective clinical trial in 30 patients was performed in the period of years 1996 through 1999.

Inclusion Criteria

Men/women aged 10–67 years suffering from deep dermal burns were included into the study. The patient had to present with the following:

– deep dermal burns of the non life-threatening extent
– the time between injury and application of CEAl had to be 6–15 days.
– informed consent had to be obtained from all the patients.

Exclusion Criteria

Patient presenting with any of the following were not included into the study:

– multiple burns
– pregnancy
– history of hypersensitivy to any component of carrier media
– concomitant therapy with:
  – immunosuppressive and/or antineoplastic drugs
  – glucocorticoids

Treatment Protocol

The study treatment consisted of:

a/ application of CEAl fixed to Grasolind
b/ application of Grasolind only
c/ application of 1 of others studied dressings

onto the deep dermal burn preferably all the three dressings on one wound

d/ the dressings were covered with transparent sterile cellophane membrane and their shapes were outlined on this membrane
e/ the paintings were transfered into the computer using the scanner and stored in its memory
f/ using the special computer programme the areas covered by different dressings were measured
g/ photographs were taken during the procedures
h/ the wounds were covered with protective dressing soaked with Ringer solution

i/ rebandages were made on 2nd and 4th days leaving the carriers on the wound surface
j/ the carriers were removed on 6th day after application and the rests of wound area
were measured at the same manner as described in points d–g
k/ protocols were stored with clinical comments of the treatment
l/ the duration of each experiment was 6 days
m/ measurement of the wounded area healed was performed by an investigator who was blind with respect to the treatment applied (the appearance of CEAl and Grasolind is almost the same).

The cultured epidermal grafts were prepared and supplied by Tissue Bank, University Hospital, Brno.

Statistical Evaluation

The statistical evaluation of wound recovery was based on the mean of the two separate measurement of the proportion of the area healed performed by a researcher blinded with respect to the treatment used. As each patient in the study received several different treatments, the comparison of the efficaccy of the respective treatments was performed based on *within* patient comparisons.

In each case the observed effects were described by statistical characteristics [e.g. mean values including the appropriate confidence intervals, ranges, etc.]. Whenever the assumption of normally distributed data failed appropriate nonparametric methods were used. The endpoint analysis of difference between the respective treatment groups yielded consistent results, when repeated with the baseline extent of wounded area as a covariate.

For each treatment, we measured the wound area (in mm^2) before [area1] and after [area2] the application of treatment, using an automated procedure. In the analysis, we calculated the proportion of the wound area that was healed after treatment [(area1–area2) area1]. If the whole wound area was healed, we considered this as a complete success.

The results of this trial are unusual in that a considerable proportion of treatments resulted into a complete success (100% healed), while the remaining part showed various levels of success. In those without a complete success, the proportions healed showed a very skewed distribution. We tried to deal with this in two ways: 1. We used logaritmically transformed proportions healed as the outcome variable in t-tests and 2. We applied a non-parametric test for comparing the results of treatment between the treatment groups. As will be shown later, both strategies led to consistent results.

The analysis of efficacy was done by "Intention to treat". All recruited patients completed the study.

Results

The group of patients is presented in Table 2.

Table 2: Group of Patients and Wounds

No.	Name	Dg.	Types of carriers	cm² of wound area
	M. K.	Combustio multipl.	grasolind	5 355,0 ® 0
1.	1945	gr.IIb, 10%, gr.III, 3%	CEG – CP	3 897,9 ® 686,5
	J. S.	Combustio multipl.	CEG – CP	5 457,6 ® 2 265,7
2.	1967	gr. IIb, 8%	Grasolind	5 866,9 ® 3 644,3
	M. V.	Combustio pedis dorsi	CEG – CP	4 991,9 ® 2 956,7
3.	1943	gr.IIb 2,5%,gr.III 1,5%	Grasolind	5 903,0 ® 2 400,0
	V. A.	Combustio multipl.,	grasolind	5 053,0 ® 7132
4.	1986	gr. IIb 3%	CEG – CP	4 583,0 ® 0
	K. M.	Combustio multipl.,	Grasolind	4 988,2 ® 0
5.	1933	gr. IIb, 3%	CEG – CP	6 689,7 ® 0
	J. N.	Combustio reg. femoris	CEG – CP	5 437,6 ® 5 095,4
6.	1941	gr. IIb, 5%	Grasolind	4 249,6 ® 4 122,4
	A. M.	Combustio manus bilat	CEG – CP	2 628,5 ® 34,4
7.	1949	gr. IIb, 1,5%	Grasolind	5 082,5 ® 414,8
	G. L.	Combustio extr.inf.l.dx	Grasolind	5 625,5 ® 0
8.	1976	gr. IIb, 6%	CEG – CP	5 538,1 ® 0
	J. S.	Combustio reg. glutei	CEG – CP	5 446,2 ® 3 739,3
9.	1945	gr. IIb 3%	Grasolind	5 771,5 ® 1 977,3
	M. L.	Combustio ext.inf. l.sin	Grasolind	6 029,5 ® 0
10.	1940	gr. IIb, 10%	CEG – CP	6 048,1 ® 0
	M. L.	Combustio ext.inf.l.sin.	Grasolind	5 750,1 ® 1 890,0
11.	1940	gr. IIb, 10%	CEG – CP	6 267,8 ® 0
	L. M.	Combustio multipl.	Grasolind	6 058,1 ® 4 660,4
12.	1979	gr. IIb, 30%	CEG – CP	5 929,3 ® 1 491,4

Table 2: Continued

No.	Name	Dg.	Types of carriers	cm² of wound area
	L. M.	Combustio multipl.	CEG – CP	5 874,4 ® 0
13.	1979	gr. IIb, 30 %	Grasolind	5 880,9 ® 4 289,7
	V. N.	Combustio reg. glutei	CEG – CP	5 969,0 ® 0
14.	1960	l. dx., gr.IIa–b, 4 %	Grasolind	5 885,9 ® 0
	L. R.	Combustio multipl.,	CEG – CP	5 939,1 ® 0
15.	1948	gr. IIa,b, 40 %	Grasolind	6 231, 5 ® 0
16.	L. B.	Combustio ext. inf.	CEG – CP	5 537,2 ® 3 018,5
	1948	l.dx., gr. IIb–III, 6 %	grasolind	5651,1 ® 4902,0
	M. K.	Combustio ext. inf. bilat	grasolind	4160,7 ® 0
17.	1972	gr. IIb, 5 %	CEG – CP	5462,3 ® 0
	E. CH.	Combustio ext. inf. l.dx.	grasolind	5547,9 ® 1287,4
18.	1955	gr. IIb, 6 %	CEG – CP	4403,8 ® 151,4
	A. H.	Combustio ext. sup.	grasolind	5305,5 ® 4 125,6
19.	1938	l. sin., gr. IIb, 4 %	CEG – CP	4460,2 ® 0
	L. V.	Combustio ext. inf. bilat	grasolind	5106,3 ® 139,2
20.	1981	gr. II–III, 10 %	CEG – CP	5201,1 ® 0
	E. CH.	Combustio ext. inf. l.dx.	grasolind	5218,4 ® 4452,0
21.	1955	gr. IIb, 6 %	CEG – CP	4318,1 ® 0
	R. F.	Combustio dorsi,	grasolind	5110,1 ® 465,9
22.	1953	gr. IIa,b, 15 %	CEG – CP	3867,0 ® 0
	R. N.	Combustio reg. femoris	CEG – CP	4897,1 ® 0
23.	1964	l. sin., gr. IIb, 5 %	grasolind	5453,9 ® 519,9
	E. W.	Combustio antebrachii	grasolind	5098,4 ® 2892,1
24.	1980	l.dx., gr. IIb, 4 %	CEG – CP	5135,5 ® 133,1
	L. V.	Combustio ext. inf. bilat	grasolind	5305,4 ® 0
25.	1981	gr. II–III, 10 %	CEG – CP	4879,7 ® 45,9
	E. W.	Combustio antebrachii	grasolind	5601,1 ® 0
26.	1980	l. dx., gr. IIb, 4 %	CEG – CP	4899,0 ® 0
	V. H.	Combustio reg. abdom.	grasolind	4108,2 ® 272,8
27.	1963	l. sin., gr. IIb, 5 %	CEG – CP	4851,3 ® 1744,4
	J. H.	Combustio multipl.,	grasolind	4360,7 ® 0
28.	1941	gr. IIb, 10 %	CEG – CP	4637,9 ® 0
	P. H.	Combustio multipl.,	grasolind	5192,6 ® 4788,2
29.	1968	gr. IIb–III, 40 %	CEG – CP	5795,5 ® 5025,5
	P. H.	Combustio multipl.,	grasolind	4780,6 ® 3107,7
30.	1958	gr. IIb–III, 40 %	CEG – CP	5832,4 ® 0

Table 3: All 30 patients with cryopreserved cultured epidermal allografts /C/ and grasoling /G/

Treatment	Mean area before treatment (mm²)	Mean area after treatment (mm²)	Mean proportion of area healed (%)	Proportion (%) of patients with complete success	Mean proportion of area healed (%) in patients without complete success
C	5154	712	86.5	56.7	68.9
G	5352	1548	71.2	23.3	62.4

Statistical evaluation is summarised in Tables 3 and 4

Table 4: Differences between treatments

Test	p-value
C×G Complete success, McNemar's exact test	0.013*
Mean proportion healed – paired t-test	0.011*
Mean log proportion healed – paired t-test	0.008**
Wilcoxon signed-ranks test	0.018*

Summary

In this study, there is evidence that the effect of treatment C was better than the effect of treatment G.

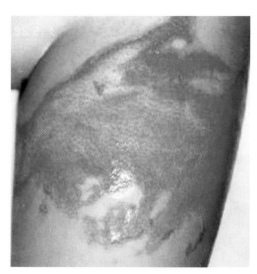

Fig. 1: A 10 year-old girl with deep dermal scald burn on the left lower extremity.

Case Reports

Patient No. 1:

A 10-year-old girl with deep second degree scald burn on 3 % of the body surface area on the left lower extremity (Fig. 1). Scald resulting from spilling of hot water. The wound was treated using topical chemotherapeutic agents [silver sulfadiazine] from 4th to 6th day after injury. Then the burn wound was covered with CEAl + Grasolind as described above (Fig. 2).

After following six days we removed the carriers (Fig. 3). We didn't find out any colonization by bacteria.

The result was better on lateral part of the wound [native multilayer of human keratinocytes] than medial part [Grasolind]. Two weeks after injury deep dermal burn was healed.

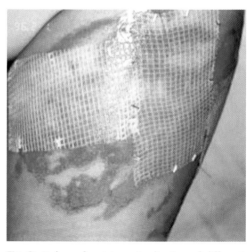

Fig. 2: 6 days after injury. Application of different types of dressing.

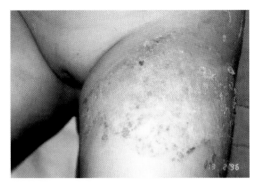

Fig. 3: 14 days after injury burn area was healed. We can see the different quality of skin surface.

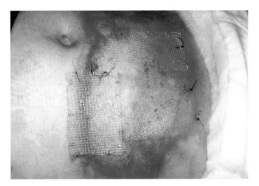

Fig. 5: 11 days after injury. Application of wound dressings.

There was well documented evidence that deep dermal burn wound treated with CEAl was less painful then with conventional dressing [Grasolind].

Patient No. 2:

A 50-year-old woman with flame burn injury 13% of the body surface area (deep dermal burn 10%, full thickness 3%). Full thickness burns was necrectomized and grafted. Antibacterial cream [Dermazin] was applied from 4th day onto the deep dermal burn of abdomen.

The devitalised tissue has covered the wound on day 11 after accident and it did not show proper tendency to heal (Fig. 4). Staphylococcus aureus was detected on the wound surface. Onto this tissue we applied different types of dressing as described above (Fig. 5). The patient described relief of pain in the wound. After six days dressings were removed (Fig. 6). The remaining area was marked and planimetrically measured.

The wound treated by native multilayer had better appearance than that one treated with Grasolind [see pictures].

Discussion

There is general opinion that cultured epidermal grafts improve the wound healing.

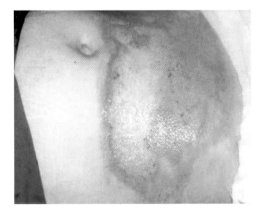

Fig. 4: 50-year-old women with dermal burn. The wound did not show proper tendency to heal.

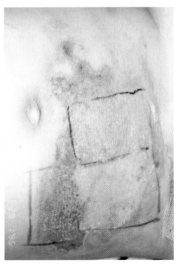

Fig. 6: 6 days after application of CEAl +Grasolind. The healing process is apparently slower on the lower left part.

At the beginning it was demonstrated, that the cultured epidermal autografts **replace the lost epidermis or even the full thickness skin** and function similarly as a conventional epidermal autografts [3–9].

Later on very good engraftment of this sheets has been shown in some kinds of wound bed of other individuals and some researcher postulated permanent take of cultured epidermal allografts in this way. [Thivolet et al., 1986, Kanitakis et al., 1987 and others]. This was denied however by Gielen in 1987, Burt, Brian and Fabre in 1989, who using the Y-probe or anti-class I MHC monoclonal anibodies respectively didn't find any donor cells on the wound surface 9–14 days after grafting.

On this manner the fact was disclosed that cultured epidermal grafts besides of the temporary „take" also **stimulate the wound reepithelialisation** in cases where there is any potential for healing either from wound edges (leg ulcers), or from wound bed (deep dermal burns). This action is similar in both auto- and allografts. Cultured epidermal allografts of course are not successful in large full thickness wounds such as full thickness burns excised down to subcutaneous fat or the muscle fascia, where there are no target cells (remaining keratinocytes in the bases of skin appendages such as hair folicles or skin glands, or marginal keratinocytes in the edges of the wound).

The present study as well as authors previous observations based on hundreds of patients [Brychta, Acta, Medit.] document this fact and are in full concordance with other above mentioned authors.

Another question is, however, what particular mechanism is responsible for such a stimulation.

Is it only physical action of confluent multilayer of keratinocytes creating an optimal wound microenvironment or is it either a biologic interaction between allogeneic cells and the wound bed which causes the stimulation of recipient's own wound cells to proliferate and migrate? The bioactive stimulation seems to be much more important. According to this theory many cytokines and growth factors are released by temporarity engrafted allogeneic keratinocytes such as EGF, bFGF, IGF, TGF-family etc. There has been shown a stimulating effect of these substances on the wound healing.

There are some questions however connected with bioactive stimulation of wound healing which are not completely cleared.

1. Must the cells be confluent? Keratinocytes suspensions in fibrin glue or other fluids seems to act similarly than sheet grafts [Stark, 12/95, Hafeman].
2. Are there fully differentiated or either less differentiated keratinocytes more suitable for normal healing stimulation. Or even are the living cells necessary for this action?

Using an in vitro assay, Schermer and colleagues demonstrated that grafts prepared from more post-confluent epidermal cell cultures, containing a higher proportion of differentiated keratinocytes, yielded higher growth rates than those from younger cultures [personal communication].

In addition, they isolated the basal and suprabasal fractions of a cultured graft and showed that an intact graft prepared from the suprabasal fraction accounted for most of the growth promoting activity. They concluded that differentiated cells in the graft may contribute significantly to the wound-healing effect of cultured epidermal grafts. This was in sharp contradiction to the dogma in the field which dictated that living basal cells in the cultured graft were largely responsible for the wound-healing effect. These results led them to propose, as early as 1999, that freeze-dried sheets of cultured grafts may be a suitable alternative to living grafts.

Freeze-drying of skin cells could facilitate the supply and storage of the grafts/dressings substantially. Some authors postulate the effectiveness of freeze-dried keratinocytes as an overlay over the meshed autografts [Duinslaeger]. Our pilot trial comparing the freeze-dried multilayers with native and/or cryopreserved ones on one side and Grasolind on the other side indicates that the freeze-dried allografts are causing the wound area reduction much closer to living multilayer than to Grasolind (83 % wound reduction in six days). Unfortunately, this result was statistically not significant in our first 11 patients to date.

3. Can a similar degree of stimulation be reached using only one or more of those cytokines in the purified form?
4. Could cultured fibroblasts alone or in the mixture with keratinocytes also be effective?

Studying this mechanism can lead to the construction of optimal bioactive wound dressing material in terms of effectivity and easy clinical applicability, as well.

We believe that our data can be used as background for testing of such systems.

Conclusion

In a prospective clinical trial on 30 patients with deep dermal burns we have shown that these wounds heal quicker when covered with cultured epidermal allografts in comparison with conventional dressing using the Grasolind only. The difference (86,5 % wound healing in six days x 71,2% with Grasolind) is statistically significant.

Case Reports

Patient No. 1:

A 34-year-man was admitted to our department with deep second degree scald burns on the abdomen covering 5 % of body surface area. Scald resulted from spilling hot water. The wound was cooled using cold sterile water for two days after accident (Fig. 7). The topical chemotherapeutic agents

Fig. 7: A 34-year-old man with deep dermal scald burn on the abdomen. 10th day after injury. Immediately before application of different types of dressing.

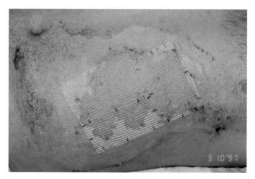

Fig. 8: 16th day after burn injury. Immediately before removal of the carriers.

Fig. 9: 19th days after injury the burn area was healed. We can see the different appearance in quality of skin surface.

[silver sulfadiazine] was applicated from the 4th to 9th day after injury. The burn wound was cleansed with Ringer solution for 24 hours. Then we covered the wound with Cultured Epidermal Allografts (CEAl) + Grasolind (Fig. 8). The wound area was 4108,2 mm² (Grasolind) and 4851 mm² (CEAl) before treatment.

The re-bandage was done 2th, 4th and 6 th days after application. We did not detect any colonisation by bacteria. The carriers were removed on 6 th day (Fig. 9). The rest of unhealed area was measured by the computer using the scanner. The result was better on the part of the wound that was covered by native multilayer sheet of human keratinocytes than on the medial part [Grasolind]. 16th day after injury, the deep dermal burn was healed.

There was well documented evidence that deep dermal burn wounds treated in this way were less painful and healed more quickly than those with conventional dressing [Grasolind].

Patient No. 2:

A 14-month-old girl with no clinically significant part history, sustained scald burns on the thorax covering 4 % of total body surface area. She was immediately admitted to our hospital. The burned area was cooled for 48 hours. The wound was treated with Silver-sulfadiazine on day 4–7 after injury. The Silver-sulfadiazine was removed from the wound surface and the burn wound was cleansed. After 24 hours we covered the wound with multilayer of keratinocytes (Fig. 10a). The Ringer solution was applied on the grafts. The next layer of dressing was dry cotton gauze. The re-bandages were done on the second, the forth and sixth days after application. Then we removed the dressings and evaluated healing of the wound. No bacteria strains were detected on the wound surface. The area was completely healed (Fig. 10b).

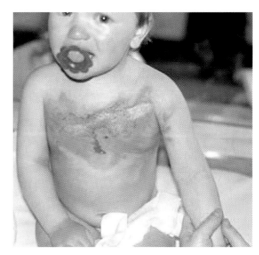

Fig. 10a: A 14-month-old girl with deep dermal scald burn on the chest. Immediately before the application of multilayer of keratinocytes.

Fig. 10b: The dressing was removed 6th days after application. The wound was completely healed.

Addendum

The Scanner

The special computer programme was developed for measurement of burned wounds. The shape and size of the wound was transfered into the memory using scanner and stored. The size was calculated automatically in mm². The measurement of the wounded area was performed in the beginning and in the end of clinical experiment as described above (Fig. 11).

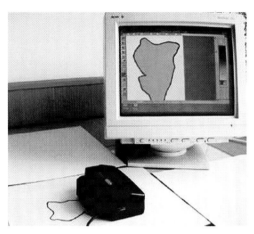

Fig. 11

References

[1] *O'Connor, NE, Mulliken, JB, Banks-Schlegel, S, Kehinde, O, Green H:* Grafting of burns with cultured epithelium prepared from autologous epidermal cells, Lancet; 1:75–8, 1981

[2] *Gallico, GG, O'Connor, NE, Compton, CC., Kehinde, O, Green, H:* Permanent coverage of large burn wounds with autologous cultured human epithelium, N Engl J Med; 311:448–51, 1984

[3] *Eisinger, M, Monden, M, Raaf, JH, Fortner, JG:* Wound coverage by a sheet of epidermal cells grown in vitro from dispersed single cell preparations, Surgery; 88:287–93, 1980

[4] *Kumagai, N, Nishina, H, Tanabe, H, Hosaka, T, Ishida, H, Ogino, Y:* Clinical application of autologous cultured epithelia for the treatment of burn wounds and burn scars, Plast Reconstr. Surg; 82:99–108, 1988

[5] *Munster, AM, Weiner, SH, Spence, RJ:* Cultured epidermis for the coverage of massive burn wounds: a single center experience, Ann Surg; 211:676–80, 1990

[6] *Eldad, A, Burt, A, Clarke, JA, Gusterson, B:* Cultured epithelium as a skin substitute. Burns; 13:173–80, 1981

[7] *Clugston, PA., Snelling C FT, Macdonald, IB, Maledy, HL, Boyle, JC, Germann, E, Courtemanche, AD, Wirtz, P, Fitzpatrick, DJ, Kester, DA, Foley, B, Warren, RJ, Carr, NJ:* Cultured epithelial autografts: Three years of clinical experience with eighteen patients, J Burn Care Rehab; 12:533–9, 1991

[8] *Teepe, RGC, Kreis, RW, Koebrugge, EJ, Kempanaar, JA, Vloemans, AFPM, Hermans, RP, Boxma, H, Dokter, J, Hermans, J, Ponec, M, Vermeer, BJ:* The use of cultured autologous epidermis in the treatment of extensive burn wounds, J Trauma; 30:269–75, 1990

[9] *Compton, CC, Gill, JM, Bradford, DA, Regauer, S, Galico, GG, O'Connor, NE:* Skin regenerated from cultured epithelial autografts on full-thicknessburn wounds from 6 days to 5 years after grafting, Lab Invest; 60:600–12, 1989

[10] *Thivolet, J, Faure, M, Demidem, A, Mauduit, G:* Cultured human epidermal allografts are not rejected for a long period, Archives of Dermatological Research, 278, 252, 1986

[11] *Thivolet, J, Faure, M, Demidem, A, Mauduit, G:* Long-term survival and immunological tolerance of human epidermal allografts produced in culture, Transplantation, 42, 274, 1986

[12] *Kanitakis, J, et al:* Ultrastructural studies of cultured human epithelial sheets used as skin allografts, Virchows Arch A, 410:523–530, 1987

[13] *Gielen, V, Faure, M, Mauduit, G, Thivolet, J:* Progressive replacement of cultured epithelial allografts by recipient cells as evidenced by HLA class I antigen expression, Dermatologica; 175:166–70, 1987

[14] *Burt, AM, Pallett, CD, Sloane, JP:* Survival of cultured allografts in patients with burns assessed with probe specific for X chromosome, British Medical Journal, 298, 915, 1989

[15] *Brain, A, et al:* Survival of cultured allogeneic keratinocytes transplantated to deep dermal bed assessed with probe specific for Y chromosome, Br Med J, 298:917–9, 1989

[16] *Fabre, JW:* Epidermal allografts, Immunology Letters, 29, 161–166, 1991

[17] *Faure, M, Mauduit, G, Schmidt, D, Kanitakis, J, Demidem, A, Thivolet, J:* Growth and differentiation of human epidermal cultures used as auto-and allografts in humans. Br J Dermatol; 116:161–70, 1987

[18] *De Luca, M, Bondanza, S, Cancedda, R, Tamisani, AM, Di Noto C, Muller, L, Dioguardi, D, Brienza, E, Calvario, A, Zermani, R, Di Madcio D, Papadia, F:* Permanent coverage of full skin thickness burns with autologous cultured epidermis and reepithelialisation of partial skin thickness lesions induced by allogeneic cultured epidermis: a multicentre study in the treatment of children, Burns; 18S:16–9, 1992

[19] *Aubock, J, Irschick, E, Romani, N, Kompaktscher, P, Hopfel, R, Herold, M, Schuler, G, Bauer, M, Huber, C, Fritsch, P:* Rejection, after a slightly prolonged survival time, of Langerhans cell-free allogeneic cultured epidermis used for wound coverege in humans. Transplantation; 45:730–7, 1988

[20] *Leigh, IM, Purkis, PE, Navsaria, HA, Philips, TJ:* Treatment of chronic venous ulcers with sheets of cultured allogeneic keratinocytes, Br J Dermatol; 117:591–7, 1987

[21] *Philips, TJ, Gilchrest, BA:* Cultured allogeneic keratinocyte grafts in the management of wound healin; prognostic factor, J Dermatol Surg Oncol; 15:1169–76, 1989

[22] *Teepe, RGC., Koebrugge EJ, Ponec, M, Vermeer, BJ:* Fresh versus cryopreserved cultured allografts for the treatment of chronic skin ulcers, Br J Dermatol; 122:81–9, 1990

[23] *Philips, TJ, Bhawan, J, Leigh, IM, Green, H, Gilchrest, BA:* Cultured epidermal allografts: clinical use, survival, and expression of maturation markers, Clin Res; 36A:684, 1988

[24] *Philips, TJ, Kehinde, O, Green, H, Gilchrest, B:* Treatment of skin ulcers with cultured epidermal allografts, J Am Acad Dermatol; 21: 191–9, 1989

[25] *Hefton, JM, Madden, MR, Finkelstein, JL, Shires, GT:* Grafting of patients with allografts of cultured epidermal cells, Lancet; 2:428–30, 1983

[26] *Brychta, P, Adler, J, Suchínek, I, Komárková, J:* Cultured skin cells for treatment of burns, Ann. Medit Burns Club, Vol. 7, n. 4, December, 206–208, 1994

[27] *Brychta, P, Suchánek, I, Rihová, H, Adler, J, Komárková, J:* Cultured epidermal allografts for the treatment of deep dermal burns, Acta Chir Plast; 37, 20–24, 1995

[28] *Hansbrough, JF:* Wound coverage. R G Landes Company Austin/Georgetown, 1992

[29] *Lamme, EN:* Artificial skin and tissue regeneration, Academic Medical Centre University of Amsterdam, Amsterdam, 1999

[30] *Stark, GB, Kaiser, HW, Horch, R, Kopp, J, Spilker, G:* Cultured autologous keratinocytes suspended in fibrin glue (KFGS) with allogeneic overgraft for definitive burn wound coverage, Eur J Plast Surg 18:267–271

[31] *Horch, RE, Bannasch, H, Andree, C, Kopp, J, Stark, GB:* Fibrin glue as a carrier for cultured human keratinocytes versus cultured epidermal skin grafts in athymic mice full-thickness wounds In: Stark, GB, Horch, R, Tanczos, E: Biological Matrices and Tissue Reconstruction, Springer, 85–95, 1998

[32] *Hafeman, B, Hettich, R, Ensslen, S, Kowol, B, Zühlke, A, Ebert, R, Könix, M, Kikrpatrick, CJ:* Treatment of skin defects using suspensions of in vitro cultured keratinocytes, Burns, 20, 2, 168–182, 1994

The Clinical Use of Cultured Keratinocyte Sheet Grafts: the Milan Experience

L. Donati

Summary

The Institute of Plastic Surgery at the University of Milan started a laboratory on biomaterials and tissue engineering in 1985 mainly devoted to the cultures of human keratinocytes. Since 1986 burn pateints and later on vascular and diabetic ulcers, as well as posttraumatic problem wounds have been treated with cultured keratinocytes. Known difficulties with the handling of the grafts and problems of graft take on the wounds led to technical modifications utilizing esterified hyaluronic acid membranes (HYAFF) to grow and transport human keratinocytes for grafting purposes.

The biomaterial hyaluronan favours cell motility, angiogenesis and it could be also considered as an antiadhesion material, according to its molecular weight showed to be an ideal substrate for human keratinocytes growth, requiring lower inocula, thus allowing a significant reduction of the time required for skin expansion in vitro. From 1993 to 2000 we treated 86 burned patients as well as 97 ulcers and difficult wounds from vascular, diabetic and traumatic origin, with autografts of human keratinocytes, grown on the microperforated sheet of hyaluronan benzylester, with clear advantages in comparison with the patients treated with the classical method, in terms of take rates and clinical performance.

Introduction

We are briefly referring to the last 15 years of experience in tissue engineered skin at the Milan Medical School. The Institute of Plastic Surgery at the University of Milan started a laboratory on biomaterials and tissue engineering in 1985 mainly devoted to the cultures of human keratinocytes. It is only in the last few years that we also studied cultures of human fibroblasts, chondrocytes and semiartificial bone on various scaffolds, mainly esters of hyaluronan.

Materials and Methods

The cultures of keratinocytes have been performed following the technique of Rheinwald and Green [7].

We used this technique in a large number of patients referring to our Institute up to 1993. The main indications were burned patients, vascular and diabetic ulcers, and posttraumatic problem wounds. The first burned patient was grafted with CEA in 1986 [3].

In the majority of cases we used the cultures as autografts, as in other cases keratinocytes cultures were employed as allografts, both in burns as the preparation of the donor sites or intermigled with surgical skin autografts or together with cultured autografts with a very clear effect on tissue repair but without any expectation of permanent take. In all those cases of allografting a meticolous screening of the donors and cultures was done as for what regards TPHA, WDRL, hepatitis markers, HIV I and II, HTLV Herpes Virus, Cytomegalovirus, both serologically and with PCR, RIBA, and Western Blot.

Operative Procedure

The grafted areas were medicated with tulle gras and gauzes imbued with a very diluted solution of the usual local antiseptics (Silver nitrate, Sulfamylon, Cerium Nitrate, Iodophores, Hexaclorophene), choosen after our usual text called topogram, i.e. the identification of the best antiseptic on a culture of germs isolated from the patients.

We used, in principle, a dilution 1/10 or 1/5 of the usual prescriptions searching to avoid the ones which showed the major in vitro toxicity on cells (iodophores, cerium salts, sulphamylon). Notwithstanding this procedure, in most cases the sheets of keratinocytes did not take, apparently for the spread of a local infection. The sheets were usually fixed with catgut on the tulle gras carrying them. In a few cases we also used fibrin glue (Tisseel©, Baxter) or histoacryl for improving the fixation, without obtaining any clear advantage [6].

A modification in our method was introduced in 1993 in order to improve the "surgical compliance" of the sheets of keratinocytes cultivated, i.e. the taking out from the flasks, the handling, the stitching to the receiving beds and even to enhance the take rates. All these factors, as it is well known, are major problems in the current surgical use of those new tissue grafts.

It was clear that there was the necessity of a scaffold or carrier of the keratinocytes permitting good adhesion and growth in vitro, easy surgical handling and good take and the following taking out or its easy biodegradability.

After an accurate screening in search of an appropriate material, where we discarded cellulose, some collagens, fibrin, lactate and glicolate derivatives, silicon, acrilate, carbonium etc., we found out that the best material was the benzylic ester of the hyaluronic acid (HYAFF 11, FAB – Fidia Advanced Biopolymers, Abano Terme, Italy). With the researchers of that company we contributed to the creation of the best form of the carrier, consisting in thin sheets of HYAFF with microperforations (Laserskin©, FAB).

Results

First Treatment Period

The data of our treatment results from the first period of 1986 to 1993, are reported in **Table 1**.

Table 1: CLINICAL APPLICATIONS OF CULTURED HUMAN KERATINOCYTES 1986–1993 Institute of Plastic Surgery – University of Milan Medical School

BURNS						
Autograft	Patients	M.BSA	M.Graft Sess.	M.cmq treated	M:taking	M:healing days
	29	36%	4	598	68%	29
Allografts	12	41%	9	728	–	34
ULCERS/DIFFICULT WOUNDS						
Autografts						
Vascular	12		18	71	58%	72
Diabetics	5		16	63	48%	66
Trauma	21		11	82	81%	59
Allografts						
Vascular	7		21	41	–	88
Diabetics	4		19	98	–	76
Trauma	9		22	73	–	79

M.BSA = mean body surface areas; M.Graft Sess. = mean number of surgical sessions dedicated to CEA grafting or regrafting; M.cmq treated = mean of areas treated in cm²; M:taking = mean of the final taking of the grafts. Differende is covered by spontaneous healing; M:healing days = mean of the days necessary for the complete healing of lesions adding to the CEA taking the mashed skin taking after operation or spontaneous healing from the borders

At the same time, we treated 31 burned patients and 105 ulcers with allografts of CEA, following the same strict indication illustrated before for selecting donors and cells, in order to avoid any risk of infection and controlling the receiving patient, serologically, before and after six months after the grafting, without having any complication or evidence of any transmitted disease. The use of allografts seems actually very useful as a system on advanced wound treatment. Sometimes using those allografts taken from the skin banks was necessary as a preparation of the receiving sites during the couple of weeks necessary for the growing of the autocultures.

Second treatment period

From 1993 to 2000 we treated 86 burned patients as well as 97 ulcers and difficult wounds with autografts of human keratinocytes, grown on the microperforated sheet of hyaluronan benzylester. The origin of these wounds ranged from vascular, diabetic to traumatic genesis. There were clear advantages using this later approach in compari-

son with the patients treated with the classical method. This was mainly true for the take rates, as shown in **Table 2**.

We established only by serendipity that the autocultures on Laserskin© permitted a quicker and better taking with the keratinocytes "up" , migrating through the microholes of the carriers, to colonize the receiving bed. We would like to state that after only 7/10 days, at semiconfluence, when cells have colonized the microholes, the culture on Laserskin© was ready for grafting. Controls with electronic conventional microscopy and histochemistry have shown that the keratinocytes, when migrating from the holes unto the lower surface of the membrane, form a layer with basal morphology and evident hemidesmosomes and physiological adhesion molecules.

That biomaterial showed to be an ideal substrate for human keratinocytes growth, requiring lower inocula, thus allowing a significant reduction of the time required for skin expansion in vitro. Furthermore that carrier is degradated in few days after the implant, releasing hyaluronan of various molecular weight, recreating that embryonal like environment that has been proved to be highly fa-

Table 2: CLINICAL APPLICATIONS OF CULTURED HUMAN KERATINOCYTES 1994–2000 Institute of Plastic Surgery – University of Milan Medical School

BURNS						
Autograft	Patients	M.BSA	M.Graft Sess.	M.cmq treated	M:taking	M:healing days
	86	44%	6	740	80%	13,5
Allografts	30	53%	8	830	–	30
ULCERS/DIFFICULT WOUNDS						
Autografts						
Vascular	34		16	71	60%	49
Diabetics	13		12	88	65%	61,6
Trauma	50		18	92	70%	40,7
Allografts						
Vascular	42		19	80	50%	57
Diabetics	17		15	94	60%	69,2
Trauma	46		22	81	82%	74

M.BSA = mean body surface areas; M.Graft Sess. = mean number of surgical sessions dedicated to CEA grafting or regrafting; M.cmq treated = mean of areas treated in cm2; M:taking = mean of the final taking of the grafts. Differende is covered by spontaneous healing; M:healing days = mean of the days necessary for the complete healing of lesions adding to the CEA taking the mashed skin taking after operation or spontaneous healing from the borders

vourable to tissue repair and regeneration. As it is known, hyaluronan also favours cells mobility, angiogenesis and it could be also considered as an antiadhesion material, according to its molecular weight [2].

In the last three years we have abandoned the use of allografts, following the general principle to avoid the use of not self cultures in products of tissue engineering for avoiding the risk of every potential transmission of infective agents and the necessity of repeated laboratory controls before and after the graftings.

Regarding the vascular ulcers, the diabetic foot and the "difficult wound", we are now following a different protocol. This seems to obtain a consistent advantage. This is particularly true in outpatients or day-care-hospital patients, who represent the majority of the ones suffering from these pathologies, being followed in our so called "difficult wounds unit". That is also keeping in mind that the introduction of the DRG compensation system at present is afflicting the surgical practice in Italy.

The new protocol developed with the help of FAB, consists in the cultivation of the first skin biopsy keratinocytes and fibroblasts from the patients. The fibroblast engineered cultures (dermis-like) are finally grown on a tridimensional scaffold of HYAFF, in a sort of thin sponge or felt. These tissues are ready for grafting after 5 to 7 days. They have consequently to be laid on the donor's bed as a preparation for receiving the keratinocytes a few days later on the usual HYAFF carrier.

The results seem to be very good in terms of rapid healing and better taking of keratinocytes. The fibroblasts, with their growth factors, seem to improve the vascularization and the detersion of the receiving site.

That protocol is now studied in a multicenter trial to be ended at the end of year 2000, focused on diabetic foot ulcers, to confirm the efficacity of that bi-tissual and double scaffolding system.

Although this contribution is focusing on tissue engineered skin substitutes, we would like to say that we are also cultivating chondrocytes, in collaboration with FAB. The aim is to develop nose and ear scaffolds of HYAFF in the near future, which first have to be colonized by autologous cells and in a second phase should be covered by a neo-cartilage. In another field of research we have found out that hyaluronan is a good system to bring BMP in small craniofacial defects inducing new bone formation.

Conclusions

To conclude, we would like to make the following "provisional" statements as a result of our quite large clinical experience, which need however futher confirmation. These statements are meant to be open to suggestions from the scientific environment.

- Cultured human keratinocytes have proved to be surely useful in burns, even if not as much as determinant and efficacious as we first had thought. The reason for this fact, in our opinion, is to be seen in the difficult taking due to infections, even with the use of truly engineered skin i.e. with a biodegradabile carrier. On the other hand the CEA on a carrier has proven to be excellent and essential in the advanced wound care more than we first supposed.
- The expanded human keratinocytes (CEA) became more useful when transformed in a real engineered tissue, with the use of a biocompatible and biodegradable scaffolds or carriers, both for surgical easier handling and for quicker laboratory work.
- The scaffolds we used, based on hyaluronan esters proved to be excellent in the clinical practice and also after estensive biological studies.
- The release of hyaluronans mimicking the "foetal" environment favours the tissue repair and the transformation of staminal-like cells and the angiogenesis and could possibly modulate the scar evolution.
- The stereophysical form of the scaffold is critical in as much as many aspects wait to be elucidated: for instance we have seen

keratinocytes growing well only on a bidimensional microperforated sheet as fibroblasts grow easily only in a tridimensional scaffold. The use of the two cultures with the two scaffolds (bi-tissual, bi-scaffolded system) has proven clinically efficacious if applied in two subsequent times, permitting a total skin engineering. The contemporary application of the two cultures, one on the other, a real total skin, was quite easy to be realized in laboratories, has not proven efficacious in surgical situations, for unclear reasons probably related to poor perfusion.

- The problem of the use of systemic antibiotics and local antiseptics remains open, regarding the quality and quantity of the drugs. In fact, the in vitro level of toxicity of those drugs does not easily maintain any local antibacterial concentration. In any case it should be advisable for the future that the clinical reports, particularly the ones which are not referring single or sporadic cases of relatively scarce interest must report also the microbiological state of the wounds as much as the systemic treatment of the patient.
- And as far as possibile a determination of the immunological status. That is particularly important in burned or trauma patients that have to be considered differently compared to the ones that only have small, localized "dermatological" conditions.
- Notwithstanding the good results obtained with the use of allografts and even in the absence of adverse reactions or complications we are now recommending, where possibile, the use of autografts. As such, autografts are avoiding known and unknown risks of bacterial, viral and prions origin, as well as the need of many protracted exams and even medico-legal implications [1]
- In terms of tissue engineering laboratories security we decided in the first instance not to make cultures of patients HIV positive, but as for ethical reasons that will not make it possibile in the next future. The current production of tissue engineered

products should rely on only certified laboratories, following the guidelines provisionally established by the FDA, the EEC, and for Italy the ones by the Commissions of the "Istituto Superiore della Sanita" and Regione Lombardia as much as the ISO certificatone [5]

- After 15 years of this very exciting experience in that new promising field of surgery, we are going on to develop chondrocytes on scaffolds prepared with CAD/CAM techniques for nose and ear reconstruction. This is based on hyaluronan derivatives, which have also proved to be excellent carriers in some case of cranio-facial bone reconstruction [4] in collaboration with FAB.
- In the near future we believe that the necessity for a larger amount of CEA and other engineered tissues will make it mandatory to rely on a production guaranteed by specialized companies, operating in a controlled and authorized situation, leaving the academic laboratories the task of study and research.

References

[1] Aspetti normativi e medico legali nellÖuso di prodotti dellÖIngegneria Tissutale. Giuffre Editorc Milano 1997
[2] *Abatangelo G, Weigel PH:* Redefining Hyaluronan. Excerpta Medica 2000; International Congress Series Elsevier, Amsterdam: 1196; 2000
[3] *Andreassi L, Donati L:* Esperienze preliminari sullÖimpiego delle colture cellulari nella riparazione del danno cutaneo da ustioni. Procedings 35th Congress Italian Society of Plastic Surgery: 105–109, 1968
[4] *Donati L:* Biomateriali e ingegneria tissutale. Coll Chir Plast Ital; Monduzzi Editore Bologna. 2000
[5] *Donati L, Donati V:* Tissue Engineering: applicazioni e prospettive. Universita di Milano; Progetto CNR (Cont Ric 9700874 PF 3411511589). 1999
[6] *Donati L, Magliacani G, Bormioli M, Signorini M, Preis FW:* Clinical experiences with keratinocyte grafts. Burns; 18 Suppl1: S 19–26, 1992
[7] *Rheinwald JG, Green H:* Serial cultivation of strains of human epidermal keratinocytes: the formation of keratinizing colonies from single cells. Cell; 6(3): 331–343, 1975

Modified Sandwich Technique Using Allogeneic Keratinocyte Cultures: The Brussels Experience

L. Duinslaeger

Summary

Grafting with allogeneic keratinocyte cultures has been used successfully as a wound-healing therapy both by us and by many other groups for many years. Since the survival time of allogeneic cells is limited after the grafting, the effect of these cultures may be generally explained by the production of wound repair-stimulating factors that promote proliferation and migration of resident cells. Burn wounds were tangentially excised and autografted with one to three (or larger mesh ratio) meshed conventional skin transplants. Additional fresh keratinocyte allocultures were applied as sheet grafts on top of these autografts. From 1989 until the year 2000, a total of 656 graft procedures on 622 patients was performed using this modified sandwich technique in the burn centre of Brussels. Results show a significant stimulation of epithelialization.

Introduction

The use of cultured epithelium autografting (CEA) is an established tool in the management of extensive burns. Since the first introduction of keratinocyte culturing techniques by Rheinwald and Green in 1975, multiple reports have been published [1–5, 12–16, 20, 21] on the use of CEA as a permanent wound coverage technique and a life-saving procedure in specific cases [4, 5]

However, the use of autologous cultured epithelium has several important drawbacks: one has to wait for three weeks to 30 days be-

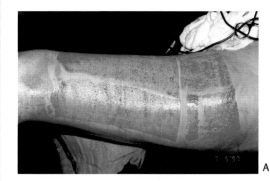

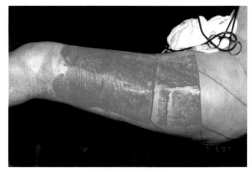

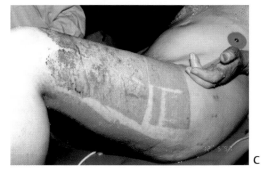

Fig. 1: A to C = use on donor sites

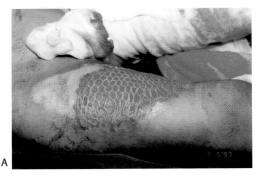

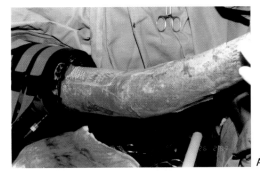

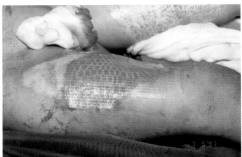

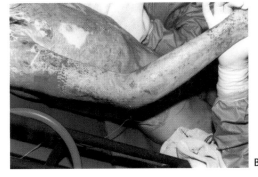

Fig. 3: A and B = use on deep dermal burn

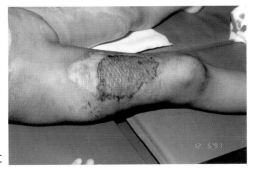

Fig. 2: A to C = modified sandwich technique + donor site (left leg)

fore a CEA consisting of 5 to 6 cell layers thick is available, even with state-of-the-art techniques. Secondly, the surface of the CEA can be limited by technical problems during culturing (contamination, low growth potential, etc.). Thirdly the CEA have to be used at a certain moment that does not necessarily correspond with the ideal timing for the patient, and considerable logistics and technique are required to prepare the CEA immediately before grafting, leading to high costs for per-

sonnel and infrastructure. Finally, average take rates of CEA are definitely lower than conventional split-skin autografting.

Due to the mentioned drawbacks, an increasing tendency arised to use allogeneic cultured keratinocytes [1, 6, 13, 17–20, 22, 23].

In view of the fact that convincing evidence exists that these transplanted cultured cells do not survive very long at the graft site [7–11, 23], it is assumed that they enhance wound reepithelialization by producing factors that stimulate the remaining keratinocytes (e.g. at the wound edge or from residual epidermal appendages in deep dermal burns) to proliferate and/or migrate.

In order to combine the reliable and good take of conventional split-skin grafting with the stimulatory effect on reepithelialization of allogeneic cultured keratinocytes, an alternative sandwich-technique is used currently at the Brussels burn centre of the Military Hospital Queen Astrid.

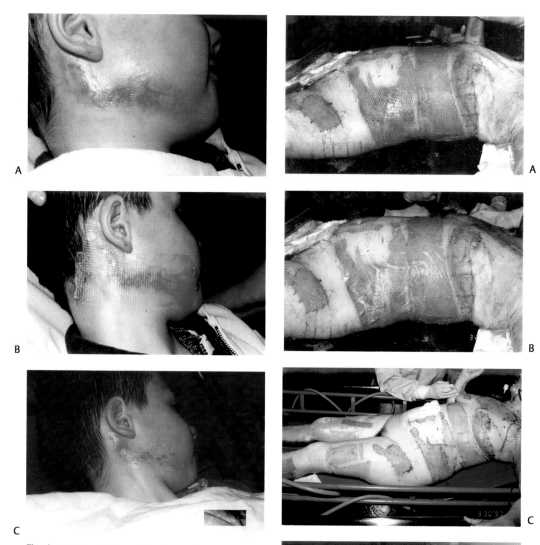

Fig. 4: A to C = use on residual wounds

Modified "Sandwich" Technique

Early excision is of the utmost importance when treating extensive burns: it will provide a good wound surface, ready to accept a skin graft, it will lower infection risks and diminish inflammatory cascade and circulating cytokines. This results in better mortality rates.

The problem however, when donor sites are lacking, is to close the excised wound in *a permanent* way as quickly as possible. Con-

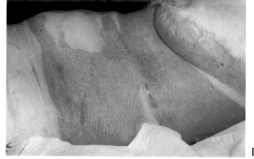

Fig. 5: A to D = modified sandwich technique on large surface. All post-op pictures are on day 5 after grafting (see dates), except photo 5 D = result after day 12 (5 C = day 5)

ventionally, the excised burn wounds are closed *temporarily* with split thickness human allograft from skin banks.

In the modified "sandwich" technique the excised wounds are closed by using widely meshed split thickness autografts covered with fresh or cryopreserved sheets of cultured allogeneic keratinocytes.

Standard treatment regimen of burns over 60 % TBSA in adult or 45 % TBSA in children or elderly patients (over 60 years) is performed as following:

- Biopsy for autologous keratinocyte culturing on admission.
- Tangential excision starting from day 3 to 5 after admission twice a week until total surface of burn is excised.
- Immediate definitive wound closure using large meshed autograft from available donor site **covered with allogeneic cultured keratinocyte sheets**.
- Treatment of donor site with **allogeneic cultured keratinocyte** sheets.
- Temporary closure with cryopreserved human allografts if donor site is lacking.
- Cuono's method or modified sandwich technique using **autologous** cultures as soon as autocultures are available.
- Treatment of small residual defects with cultured keratinocyte sheets.

From 1989 to 2000, 656 graft procedures on 622 patients were performed using this modified sandwich technique in the burn centre of Brussels. Clinical results showed similar take rates and infection risks compared to conventional split thickness grafting, but significantly better wound closure on day 5 post-grafting [26]. A quantification study of the effect on reepithelialization on 1 to 3 meshed autografted wounds showed enhancement of reepithelialization by 80 % on day 5 [24]. The healing time of donor sites was significantly reduced compared to polyurethane dressing treatment [25].

Conclusion

The modified sandwich technique allows the surgeon to excise earlier and more aggressively extensive burns with a safety that is comparable to conventional grafting and with the advantage of a quicker wound closure. It combines the possibilities offered by biotechnology with conventional surgical techniques.

In view of the related costs and needed infrastructure this technique is only indicated for the treatment of extensive burns or in the case of high mortality risk patients.

References

[1] *De Luca M, Albanese E, Bon anza S et al.:* Multicentre experience in the treatment of burns with autologous and allogeneic cultured epithelium, fresh or preserved in a frozen state. Burns 15 : 303–309 (1989).

[2] *Cuono C, Langdon R, McGuire J:* Use of cultured autografts and dermal autografts as skin replacement after burn injury. Lancet II : 1123–1124 (1986).

[3] *Gallico GG O'Connor NE, Compton CC, Kehinde O, Green H:* Permanent coverage of large burn wounds with autologous cultured human epithelium. N Engl J Med311 : 448–451 (1984).

[4] *O'Connor NE, Mulliken JB, Banks-Schlegel S, Kehide O, Green H:* Grafting of burns with cultured epithelium prepared from autologous epidermal cells. Lancet I : 75–78. (1981)

[5] *Hefton JM, Madden MR, Finkelstein JL, Shire GT:* Grafting of burn patients with autografts of cultured epidermal cells. Lancet II : 428–430 (1983).

[6] *McGuire J, Birchall N, Langdon R:* Successful engraftment of allogeneic keratinocytes. Clin Res 35 : 720 a (1987).

[7] *Brain A, Purkis P, Coates P, Hackett M, Navsaria H, Leigh I:* Survival of cultured allogeneic keratinocytes transplanted to deep dermal bed assessed with probe specific for Y chromosome. Br Med J 298 : 917–919 (1989).

[8] *Bettex-Galland M, Slongo T, Hunziker T, Wiesmann U, Bettex M:* Use of cultured keratinocytes in the treatment of severe burns. Z Kinderchir 3 : 224–228 (1988).

[9] *Phillips TJ, Gilchrest BA:* Cultured allogeneic keratinocytes grafts in the management of wound healing : prognostic factors. J Dermatol Surg Oncol 5 : 1169–1176 (1989).

[10] *Deglize B, Benathan M, Krupp S:* Resultats préliminaires du traitement des brûl&ea ute;s d'épiderme de culture. Schweiz Med Wochenschr 117 : 1380–1393 (1987).

[11] *Roseeuw D, De Coninck A:* Epidermal DNA analysis of chronic ulcers grafted with allogeneic cultured epidermis. J Invest Dermatol 92 : 509A (1989).

[12] *Braye F., Oddou, L, Bertin-Maghit M., et al:* Widely meshed autograft associated with cultured aut logous epithelium for the treatment of major burns in children: report of 12 cases. Eur.J.Pediatr.Surg; 10:35 – 40, 2000.

[13] *Foyatier JL, Faure L, Latarjet J:* Cultured epithelium: Clinical use in burned patients.Third congress of European Burn Association, Prague, Czechoslovakia, p 54 (1989).

[14] *Teepe RG, Kreis RW, Koebrugge EJ et al.:* The use of cultured autologous epidermis in the treatment of extensive burn wounds. J Trauma 30 : 269–275 (1990).

[15] *Herzog SR, Meyer A, Woodley D, Peterson HD:* Wound c verage with cultured autologous keratinocytes: use after burn wound excision, including biopsy follow up.J Trauma 28 : 195–198 (1988).

[16] *Munster AM, Weiner SH, Spence RJ:* Cultured epidermis for the coverage of massive burn wounds. Ann Surg 211 : 676–680 (1990).

[17] *Specht BU, Strittmatter B, Bohm N:* Allogeneic cultured epidermals for wound grafting. J Invest Dermatol 191 : 379A (1988).

[18] *Faure M, Demidem A, Maudit G, Chabanon M, Thivolet J:* Immunological aspects of epidermal allografts. In : Clinical use of cultured epithelium in surgery and dermatology. Medical and Scientific Conferences Ltd., Wheathamstead, Herts. UK pp 53–57.

[19] *Boliva Flores J, Poumian E, Marche-Moreno M, Montes de Oca G, Kuri-Harcuch W:* The use of cultured human epidermal keratinocytes for allografting burns and conditions for temporary banking of cultur d allografts. Burns 16 : 3–8 (1990).

[20] *Eldad A, Burt A, Clarke JA, Gusterson B:* Cultured epithelium as a skin substitute. Burns 13 : 173–180 (1987).

[21] *O'Connor NE, Gallico GG, Compton CC, Briggs S, Remensnyder J:* Long term results in major paediatric burns treated with cultured epithelial auto rafts. Proceedings of the American Burn Association meeting, p 174 (1990).

[22] *Teepe RG (ed):* Clinical use of cultured epithelium in surgery and dermatology (Leiden March 1987). Medical and Scientific Conferences Ltd, Birmingham, UK (1988).

[23] *Phillips TJ, Bhawan L, Leigh IM, Baum HJ, Gilchrest BA:* Cultured epidermal autografts and allografts : a study of differentiation and allograft survival. J Am Acad Dermatol 23 : 189–198 (1990).

[24] *Duinslaeger, L, Erbeken G, Reper P et al.:* Lyophilised keratinocyte lysates contain multiple mitogenic activities and stimulate closure of meshed autograft-covered burn wounds with similar efficiency a fresh keratinocyte cultures. Plast. Reconstr.Surg., Jul; 98(1) : 110–117, 1996.

[25] *Duinslaeger, L, Verbeken G, Van Halle S et al.:* Cultured allogeneic keratinocyte heets accelerate healing compared to Op-Site treatment of donor sites in burns. J. Burn. Care Rehabil. 1997 Nov–Dec;18(6) : 545–51

[26] *Duinslaeger L, Delaey B nd Vanderkelen A:* Short- and long-term results of application of allogeneic cultured keratinocytes on burn wounds and burn scar, Eur. J. Plast. Surg; 21 : 14–18, 1998.

The Use of Cultured Epidermal Autografts and Serial Autografting in Massive Pediatric Burns

M. Spies, J. P. Barret, D. N. Herndon

Summary

Our experiences with severely burned pediatric patients (> 90% TBSA full thickness burns) show that patients treated with cultured epidermal autografts had a significantly longer hospital stay, resulting in higher hospital costs than patients treated with conventional widely expanded meshed autografts. There were no differences in mortality. Patients in both groups had similar rates of acute readmissions for open wounds, but patients in the cultured epidermal autografts group developed more contractures and required a higher number of reconstructive procedures. Compared to conventional autografting cultured epidermal autografts showed better quality of scars, with smoother and thinner surfaces and hypopigmentation.

Balancing the advantages and disadvantages, CEA usage should currently still be restricted to defined situations and wound areas. Future research needs to be done to improve the dermal replacement with the ultimate goal of producing a bilayered composite dermal-epidermal graft. Shortening of the culture time to allow earlier CEA grafting should be persued. Advances in this area would allow for a quicker recovery and rehabilitation of severly burned patients leading to a shorter length of hospital stay and a good and durable skin quality. Both would permit an earlier return into society and decrease the need for reconstructive procedures, leading to overall decrease of health care costs in severely burned patients.

Introduction

Severe thermal trauma remains a major challenge. The burn injury is not only a localized event restricted to the damaged integument, the whole organism reacts with a severe inflammatory and metabolic stress response. Unlike other trauma, the physiologic response to burn injury can be correlated to the exact percentage of the body surface area burned.

Many advances in the treatment of major burns have resulted in a decreased mortality during the past three decades. The most singular advance has been the introduction of early excision and closure of the burn wound. The rationale behind this strategy is that the removal of damaged tissue in larger burns will decrease the source of infection and mediator release. The approach used to cover and close the excised burn wound depends on the type and extent of the injury. Usually burn wounds smaller than thirty percent TBSA can be completely covered with skin autografts from available donor sites. In larger burns, donor sites are not sufficient to cover the patient in a single operative procedure. Thus alternatives to autograft skin coverage are necessary. The importance of this problem increases with massive burns greater 50 or 70 percent TBSA. In these patients scarce donor sites usually require the use of cadaver skin and other biological or artificial temporary skin coverage in combination with the use of widely expanded autograft skin. Over the last two decades patients with burns over 60% TBSA have been successfully treated with methods involving excision and grafting with widely expanded meshed autografts with an overlay of homografts [1, 2]. With the advent of tissue engineering in the last years, cultured epidermal autografts have been used more frequently for wound closure in extensive burn injuries. Despite the early excitement about this technique several issues have restricted and questioned its common use. Culture and expansion of a small skin biopsy to a clinically significant expansion commonly takes around 3 to 4 weeks. The characteristics of cultured epidermal autografts (CEA) still include the lack of skin appendages (sweat glands and hair) and an unfavorable long-term fragility partially caused by decreased attachment to underlying tissues and insufficient development of a dermal layer beneath the cultured epidermal autografts [3, 4]. Long term skin fragility, leading to recurrent open wounds, an increased rate of burn scar contractures, and thus troublesome rehabilitation are unsolved problems related to its use. Some good results have been reported in patients with greater than 50 percent total body surface area (TBSA) burns [5]. However the usefulness and efficacy of cultured epidermal autograft even in massive burns is still not clearly established.

The Use of Cultured Epidermal Autograft in Burn Care

Total excision of the burn wound with temporary cadaver skin coverage in larger burns has resulted in decreased mortality and morbidity and has been established as standard burn care over the last decades. Total burn wound excision in the first 24 hours after admission and temporary wound closure with homografts reduces morbidity and/or mortality in severely burned patients most effectively, as shown by Herndon, Desai et al. [2, 6]. The lack of suitable donor areas has been a significant problem especially in burns of greater than 90% TBSA. With recent developments in tissue engineering other possibilities emerge but still have to prove their efficacy and superiority. Currently, the use of

cultured epidermal autografts for the closure of burn wounds is controversial [5]. The feasibility of keratinocyte culture and their clinical applications were explored in the early eighties [7]. After initial case reports larger series of patients treated with CEA techniques have been studied, although with inconsistent results [8]. Major problems in the usage of cultured epidermal autografts include patient selection [5, 8, 9], graft take [3, 10], dermis replacement [3, 12, 13], and long-term durability [4, 13].

In major burns the acute extensive skin loss aggravated by the concomitant acute physiological derangements requires repeated procedures for debridement and grafting. This results in a prolonged recovery process until complete restoration of skin coverage is achieved. Available donor sites are limited by the extent of the burned surface area. Thus delayed wound closure can be anticipated, which leads to a prolongation of the metabolic stress reaction and increases the chance of burn wound infection and sepsis. Therefore temporary wound coverage materials are clearly needed [14].

The availability and the successful clinical application of cultured epithelial autografts in burned patients lead to an initially enthusiastic acceptance of CEA among clinical practitioners [7, 15, 16]. But the resulting quest for multiple clinical applications yielded only small patient populations with difficult to compare results [13, 14]. The mean burn size in different study populations averaged 60% TBSA [5, 8, 9, 14, 17], all with a wide range in graft take rates and long-term results. Only few clinical trials have been carried out in order to compare autografting techniques to CEA engrafting. Munster et al [9] found in their initial experience with CEA a reduction in morbidity and mortality compared to an historical control group. In a prospective, controlled trial [5] these findings were corroborated, with a significant reduction in mortality in the CEA group. The major criticisms on this study have been the specifics of patient selection and the relatively low mean burn size of 69% TBSA for this particular patient population. In this study the hospitalization costs for CEA patients was significantly higher than in the control group. The question remains if the use of CEA is justified in this patient population, when complete wound closure could also be achieved with otherwise less expensive techniques. In our experience with burns over 90 % TBSA, treatment with cultured epidermal autograft caused significantly higher hospitalization costs, without leading to significantly decreased morbidity and/or mortality.

Thirty-eight pediatric patients (6.8 ± 0.9 years, all data presented as means ± SEM) with full thickness burns over 90 % TBSA were treated at the Shriners Burn Hospital in Galveston, Texas between March 1988 and March 2000. Thirteen patients died before day 28 (estimated day of CEA grafting), and only three patients died after day 28 resulting in a mortality of 42 %. All thirty-eight patients presented with inhalation injury diagnosed by bronchoscopy on admission. Of twenty-two patients who survived until post burn day 28, eleven patients were treated with CEA, and eleven with serial 4:1 autografting with cadaveric homograft overlay technique as described by Alexander [1]. Demographic characteristics of the CEA group and the autografting group were not different as shown in Table 1. All but one patient in the CEA group survived, two patients in the autografting group died on day 36 and 123 due to pulmonary thromboembolism and respiratory failure (survival 91 % vs. 82 %, ns).

Table 1: Demographics of study groups including patients surviving more than 28 days (day of CEA application)

	CEA group (n = 11)	Autografting group (n = 11)
Age (years)	8.5 ± 1.5	7.0 ± 1.6
TBSA-full thickness (%)	94.1 ± 1.1	90.5 ± 1.1
Inhalation injury	100 %	100 %
Mortality (in hospital)	9 %	18 %

Data presented as mean ± SEM
No significant differences between groups

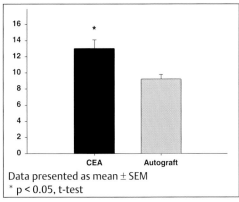

Data presented as mean ± SEM
* p < 0.05, t-test

Fig. 1a: Total number of surgical procedures performed during acute hospitalization.

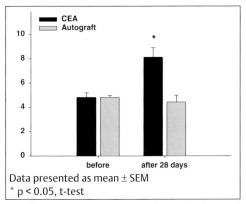

Data presented as mean ± SEM
* p < 0.05, t-test

Fig. 1b: Surgical procedures performed before and after day 28 during acute hospitalization [average time of CEA application].

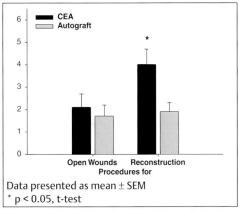

Data presented as mean ± SEM
* p < 0.05, t-test

Fig. 1c: Total number of surgical procedures performed during 2 years after acute burn treatment shown as procedures for re-coverage of open wounds and reconstructive procedures for burn scar and contracture treatment.

Table 2: Characteristics of treatment course for surviving patients in CEA and serial autografting groups

	CEA group (n = 10)	Autografting group (n = 9)
Acute Care **Number of procedures** **Length of hospital stay (days)**	13.0 ± 1.1 135.8 ± 12.2	9.2 ± 0.6 * 92.6 ± 8.7 *
Acute Care **Hospital cost per patient (x1000 USD)**	Including CEA cost 519 ± 43	305 ± 28 *
2 years after burn **Number of procedures for open wounds** **Number of reconstructive procedures** **Length of hospital stay (days)**	2.1 ± 0.6 4.0 ± 0.7 78.0 ± 17.8	1.7 ± 0.5 1.9 ± 0.4* 39.0 ± 8.7
Total hospital cost **per patient in first 2 years (x1000 USD)**	775 ± 79	439 ± 36 *

Data presented as mean ± SEM
* p < 0.05, t-test

In the CEA group the mean time between the skin biopsy taken for culture and application of CEA grafts was 26.2 ± 2.0 days. Before day 28, patients in the CEA and autografting groups had the same number of procedures (4.8 ± 0.4 vs. 4.8 ± 0.2). However after day 28 (estimated day of CEA grafting) the number of procedures was significantly higher in the CEA group (8.1 ± 0.8 vs. 4.4 ± 0.6; p < 0.01) as shown in Table 2 and Fig. 1c. Donor site healing times showed no differences between groups (7.0 ± 0.1 days for CEA vs. 6.6 ± 0.2

days for autograft). Patients with CEA had a significantly longer length of acute hospital stay (135.8 ± 12.2 days vs. 92.6 ± 8.7 days, p < 0.05, Fig. 2a). This in addition to the cost of CEA caused significantly greater costs compared to the conventional treatment group (US$ 519,000 ± 43,000 vs. US$ 305,000 ± 28,000, p < 0.05, Figs. 3a–b, Table 2).

Patients were grafted with CEA on day 26 ± 2.0 after complete burn wound excision. A mean of a 39 ± 5 % of body surface area was covered with CEA, with an initial CEA "take"

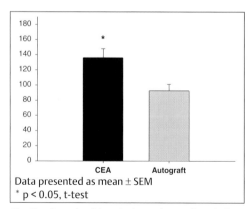

Data presented as mean ± SEM
* p < 0.05, t-test

Fig. 2a: Length of hospital stay [acute hospitalization] in CEA and serial autografting group.

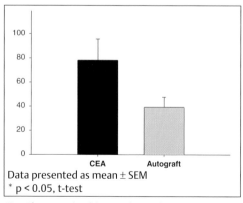

Data presented as mean ± SEM
* p < 0.05, t-test

Fig. 2b: Length of hospital stay for reconstructive procedures during 2 years after burn in CEA and serial autografting group.

Table 3: Comparison of burn scars two years after the injury using the Seattle Burn Scar Rating Scale

	CEA group (n = 7)	Non-CEA group (n = 7)	Kappa test
Surface	2.5 (2–3)	3 (3–4) *	0.65
Border height	3 (3–4)	3 (2–4)	0.45
Thickness	2.5 (2–3)	3 (2–4)	0.60
Color	2.5 (2–3)	3 (3–4) *	0.68

Data presented as median and range
* $p < 0.05$ Non-CEA vs. CEA group, Mann-Whitney rank sum test
Strength of inter-rater agreement (Kappa test):
0.61–0.80 = Good
0.81–1.00 = Very Good

of 74 ± 9 %. Sixty-two percent (62 ± 8 %) of all areas covered with CEA needed to be autografted later in the hospital course to achieve definitive coverage. We noticed no differences in "take" and re-grafting required for different anatomic locations or different ages. When CEA take and re-grafting rates were compared in different burn-wound beds, CEA take was significantly better in wounds excised to fascia with CEA placed directly on the fascia than tangentially excised wounds or when CEA was placed on allodermis (78 % vs. 45 % "take" rate, p < 0.001). However, CEA grafts on fascia were more vulnerable and presented with a higher rate of blistering and need for re-grafting (66% re-grafting in fascial excision vs. 34 % in tangential excision and placement on allodermis, p < 0.001).

Patients in the CEA group experienced a prolonged and clinically more challenging rehabilitation. However acute readmission for open wounds and rehabilitation problems were similar in both groups. The number of procedures performed during a two-year period after burn injury for open wounds (2.1 ± 0.6 vs. 1.7 ± 0.5, ns) showed no significant differences between groups (Fig. 1c). However, the number of reconstructive procedures for burn scar contractures was significantly higher in the CEA group (4.0 ± 0.7 vs. 1.9 ± 0.4, p < 0.05, Fig. 1c). The associated length of hospital stay for both types of procedures showed no signifi-

cant difference (78.0 ± 17.8 days vs. 39.0 ± 8.7 days, ns, Fig. 2b).

When comparing the quality of scars between both treatment groups using the burn scar scale described by Yeong et al [18], patients treated with CEA had scars with a significantly smoother surface and less pigmentation than traditional 4:1 meshed autografts. Scar border height and thickness presented no significant differences between the two groups (see Table 3).

In our hands the overall mortality in the population with burns greater 90% TBSA has dramatically improved. We have shown that the determinants of mortality in massive pediatric burns are inhalation injury, delayed resuscitation and burn-associated sepsis or multiorgan failure [19]. The type of surgical wound closure did not affect outcome. The available area of donor sites did influence the outcome. CEA seems ideal for the treatment of patients with a near total loss of skin, such as burns greater 90 % TBSA. However, others and ours experiences clearly show that there still remain several problems to be solved before CEA can be considered a safe and effective standard technique for treatment of large burns. Sheridan et al [13] reported five pediatric burn patients with a successful initial CEA take rate of 51% and delayed loss of 60 % (like in our group). They concluded that CEA techniques might play an important role in the management of massive burns. However, as its use should be limited to restricted areas, the main area of the burn wound should still be covered with traditional autografting techniques. Similarly Rue et al [20] also failed to demonstrate the advantages on wound closure in extensively burned patients mainly because of low long-term durability of CEAs. In our study graft take on fascial wounds was best, but these areas showed the lowest long-term durability. This reflects the findings of McAree et al [14] with a final take rate on fascia of 72% compared to 95% in deep dermal excised wounds. As CEA are definitively more fragile during the initial postburn period than widely expanded autografts, these areas are more prone to blistering, recurrent open wounds, and contractures [5, 13, 20]. Histological examination shows that as early as 6 days after surgery the epithelial graft has differentiated into a fully stratified epithelium. All four skin layers are present in normal proportion, but a basal lamina is not continuous until four weeks post-grafting. Maturation with a functional dermal-epidermal junction is complete at five months after grafting [21]. During this time any minimal trauma exerting shear forces on skin will result in blistering and skin instability with recurrent open wounds. This situation delays and slows down the early rehabilitation program, making these patients more prone to developing

burn scar contractures. The application of hydrophobic pressure garments could beneficially reduce surface maceration and shearing forces on skin [22], so that this might be a way to protect the fragile CEA derived skin and allow institution of early rehabilitation. Our study showed a significantly higher incidence of contractures and consequent reconstructive procedures with CEA. The start and maintenance of an active and aggressive rehabilitation program is difficult and often delayed due to the fragility of CEA grafts and the tendency of blister under minimal mechanical trauma [4, 14].

Approaches to improve take rate, shorten long-term fragility, and reduce hypertrophy and contracture of CEA grafts include the use of dermal substitutes. Cuono et al. [23] and Hickerson et al. [3] used engrafted allodermis for dermal replacement underneath CEA grafts. Initial take was consistently over 80%, resulting in a supple skin that was stable and resistant to trauma and infection. The problems and difficulties of initial engrafting and the removal of the alloepidermis in the second stage procedure begged for new dermal substitutes that would provide long lasting skin with an easy and quicker means of application. Bilaminate bioengineered artificial skin substitutes consisting of a dermal and an epidermal layer have been developed to

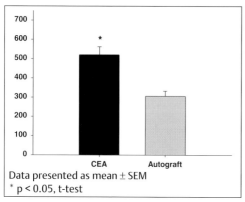

Data presented as mean ± SEM
* p < 0.05, t-test

Fig. 3a: Total estimated cost of acute hospital stay per patient.

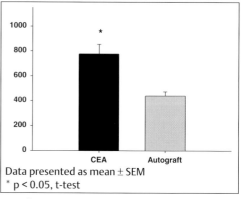

Data presented as mean ± SEM
* p < 0.05, t-test

Fig. 3b: Total estimated cost of hospital treatment per patient from acute hospitalization to 2 years after burn.

address these issues [24]. A collagen and chondroitin-6-sulfate matrix (Integra®) has allowed good direct regeneration of normal skin morphology [25]. Fibroblasts easily integrate into this collagen-glycosaminoglycan matrix [26], and cultured autologous keratinocytes [27] as well as cultured epidermal autografts [28] attach to the formed neo dermis. This provides a good dermal-epidermal junction and a quality of skin comparable to autograft [29]. The optimal dermal substitute still needs to be defined.

Despite the problems with long-term durability of the culture skin and the tendency to contractures due to delayed and slowed rehabilitation, the quality of scars of the CEA grafts appeared to be significantly better than in the 4:1 autograft group. Hypertrophy, thickness and raised surface were more obvious in 4:1 autografts. The wounds covered with CEA eventually show formation of a true dermis. Unlike the reepithelialized interstices of mesh grafts, the underlying connective tissue is remodeled resulting in a bilayered structure with collagen and elastic fibers, and vascularization in a normal pattern over a five-year period after grafting [21, 29].

References

[1] Alexander JW, MacMillan BF, Law E, et al.: Treatment of severe burns with widely meshed skin autograft and meshed skin allograft overlay. J Trauma; 21: 433–438, 1981.

[2] Herndon DN, Barrow RE, Rutan RL et al.: A comparison of conservative versus early excision – Therapies in severely burned patients. Ann Surg; 209: 547–553, 1989.

[3] Hickerson WL, Compton C, Flechall S, Smith LR: Cultured epidermal autografts and allodermis combination for permanent burn wound coverage. Burns; 20 Suppl 1: S52–S55, 1994.

[4] Desai MH, Mlakar JM, McCauley RL, et al.: Lack of long-term durability of cultured keratinocyte burn-wound coverage: a case report. J Burn Care Rehabil; 12: 540–545, 1991.

[5] Munster AM: Cultured skin for massive burns. A prospective, controlled trial. Ann Surg; 224: 372–377, 1996.

[6] Desai MH, Herndon DN, Broemeling L, Barrow RE, Nichols RJ Jr, Rutan RL: Early burn wound excision significantly reduces blood loss. Ann Surg; 211: 753–759, 1990.

[7] O'Connor NE, Mulliken JB, Banks-Schlegel S, et al.: Grafting of burns with cultured epithelium prepared from autologous epidermal cells. Lancet; 1: 75–78, 1981.

[8] Odessey R: Addendum: multicenter experience with cultured epidermal autograft for treatment of burns. J Burn Care Rehabil; 13: 174–180, 1992.

[9] Munster AM, Weiner SH, Spence RJ: Cultured epidermis for the coverage of massive burn wounds. A single center experience. Ann Surg; 211: 676–680, 1990.

[10] Blight A, Mountford EM, Cheshire IM, et al.: Treatment of full skin thickness burn injury using cultured epithelial grafts. Burns; 17: 495–498, 1991.

[11] Compton CC, Hickerson W, Nadire K, Press W: Acceleration of skin regeneration from cultured epithelial autografts by transplantation to homograft dermis. J Burn Care Rehabil; 14: 653–662, 1993.

[12] Hansbrough JF, Dore C, Hansbrough WB: Clinical trials of a living dermal tissue replacement placed beneath meshed, split-thickness skin grafts on excised burn wounds. J Burn Care Rehabil; 13: 519–529, 1992.

[13] Sheridan RL, Tompkins RG: Cultured autologous epithelium in patients with burns of ninety percent or more of the body surface. J Trauma; 38: 48–50, 1995.

[14] McAree KG, Klein RL, Boeckman CR: The use of cultured epithelial autografts in the wound care of severely burned patients. J Pediatr Surg; 28: 166–168, 1993.

[15] Rheinwald J, Green H: Serial cultivation of strains of human epidermal keratinocytes: The formation of keratinizing colonies from single cells. Cell; 6: 331–344, 1975.

[16] Gallico G, O'Conner N, Compton C, et al.: Permanent coverage of large burn wounds with autologous cultured human epithelium. N Engl J Med; 311: 448–451, 1984.

[17] Paddle-Ledinek JE, Cruickshank DG, Masterton JP: Skin replacement by cultured keratinocyte grafts: an Australian experience. Burns; 23: 204–211, 1997.

[18] Yeong EK, Mann R, Engrav LH, et al.: Improved burn scar assessment with use of a new scar rating scale. J. Burn Care Rehabil.; 18: 353–355, 1997.

[19] Wolf SE, Rose JK, Desai MH, Mileski JP, Barrow RE, Herndon DN: Mortality determinants in massive pediatric burns. An analysis of 103 children with > or = 80% TBSA burns (> or = 70% full-thickness). Ann Surg; 225: 554–565, 1997.

[20] Rue LW 3rd, Cioffi WG, McManus WF, Pruitt BA Jr: Wound closure and outcome in extensive-

ly burned patients treated with cultured autologous keratinocytes. J Trauma; 34: 662–668, 1993.

[21] Compton C, Gill J, Bradford D, et al.: Skin regenerated from culture epithelial autografts on full thickness burn wounds from 6 days to 5 years after grafting. Lab Invest; 60: 600–612, 1989.

[22] Wood F, Liddiard K, Skinner A, Ballentyne J: Scar management of cultured epithelial autograft. Burns; 22: 451–454, 1996.

[23] Cuono C, Langdon R, Birchall N, et al.: Composite autologous-allogenic skin replacement: development and clinical application. Plast Reconst Surg; 80: 626–637, 1987.

[24] Boyce ST, Hansbrough JF: Biologic attachment, growth, and differentiation of cultured human epidermal keratinocytes on a graftable collagen and chondroitin-6-sulfate substrate. Surgery; 103: 421–431, 1988.

[25] Boyce ST: Skin substitutes from cultured cells and collagen-GAG polymers. Med Biol Eng Comput; 36: 791–800, 1998.

[26] Pandya AN, Woodward B, Parkhouse N: The use of cultured autologous keratinocytes with Integra in the resurfacing of acute burns. Plast Reconst Surg; 102: 825–828, 1998.

[27] Boyce ST, Kagan RJ, Meyer NA, et al.: Cultured skin substitutes combined with Integra Artificial Skin to replace native skin autograft and allograft for the closure of excised full thickness burns. J Burn Care Rehabil; 20: 453–461, 1999.

[28] Rennekampff HO, Kiessig V, Griffey S, Greenleaf G, Hansbrough JF: Acellular human dermis promotes cultured keratinocyte engraftment. J Burn Care Rehabil; 18: 535–544. 1997

[29] Aihara M: Ultrastructural study of grafted autologous cultured human epithelium. Br J Plast Surg; 42: 35–42, 1989.

Technical Advances in the Utilization of Cultured Epidermal Autografts: Dermal Augmentation for Wound Bed Preparation

W. L. Hickerson, S. R. King

Summary

Cultured epidermal autografts (CEA) have been demonstrated to be an effective permanent skin replacement for major burn injuries. However, they are more sensitive to adverse conditions than split thickness grafts. The introduction of engrafted allodermis as a wound bed for cultured grafts by Cuono and coworkers in 1986 has ever since then become a standard tool to enhance the take of keratinocytes to the wound. A review of 1994–1999 is also underway, but the existing records are not as thorough as to bed preparation and are not included in this report. From 1988 through March 1994, BioSurface Technology, Inc. (Cambridge, MA) had supplied grafts to 422 burn patients.

We report on a method of preparing allodermis and grafting CEA in patients with major burns (48–70 per cent TBSA, average 59.6 per cent). The average age was 38.8 years (20–60 years). All full thickness wounds were excised down to fat within 7 days of admission, and covered with meshed split thickness cryopreserved homograft. Over the ensuing 2–3 weeks, the homograft became engrafted. At surgery, the allo-epidermis was removed, leaving the dermal components as a viable bed for the CEA. Keratinocytes derived from a full thickness biopsy were grown to confluence by the method of Rheinwald and Green, and 25 cm² sheets were stapled to Vaseline gauze backings and applied to freshly excised wounds. Seven to 10 days after surgery, the gauze backings were removed. The average take ranged from 87–100 per cent (average 93.6 per cent). Follow-up for up to 4 years shows supple skin that has been durable, and resistant to trauma and infection.

Introduction

Wound closure continues to be a major problem in patients who have sustained large thermal injuries. With the advent of improved methods of fluid resuscitation, early burn wound excision, and advanced intensive care techniques, patients with larger burns are surviving for longer periods of time. Infection becomes the major cause of death in these patients. This problem is even more pronounced when skin coverage is not available. Widely meshed grafts, postage stamp grafts, allografts, synthetic skin substitutes and cultured epidermal autografts (CEA) have all been used to obtain this closure. The technology of growing CEA in amounts large enough to cover major wounds was developed by Rheinwald and Green in 1975 [15] but not reported for clinical use until 1981 [11] when O'Conner reported CEA use in two children with greater than 90% total body surface area (TBSA) burns. In the past, major problems with the utilization of CEA have been the poor quality of skin, poor take, and expense [9].

Cultured Epidermal Autografts (CEA) have been either heralded as an excellent adjunct and life saving technique for wound coverage in massive burns, or as the "Emperor's Clothes" [13]. Most criticism of CEA has been based upon the application of the cells on fat, fascia, or muscle and seems to be the result of abnormal anchoring fibrils [16]. The application of CEA on an allodermis base, however, has been shown to accelerate normal skin architecture and anchoring fibrils [3].

This article describes the technique we employ at the Firefighters Regional Burn Center in Memphis, Tennessee with CEA, discusses the results of CEA application provided by a single commercial source (Genzyme Tissue Repair, Cambridge, Mass), and the future consideration in burn wound coverage. The records of Genzyme Tissue Repair, formerly Biosurface Technology, was reviewed from 1988 through March 1994.

Surgical Technique

Major burn injures with greater than 50% third degree burns undergo a full thickness biopsy from available sites within 24–48 hours post admission. The skin is prepared by washing with chlorhexidine or betadine soap, rinsed with sterile saline and treated with betadine 0.1% solution that is then allowed to dry. The betadine is then removed with alcohol and a full thickness elliptical skin biopsy is obtained. The biopsy site is closed as a single layer.

Total wound excision is obtained as quickly as possible. If the patient has no pre-existing medical problems, wound excision is often started on the day of admission. In areas of questionable depth, tangential excision is performed to determine if a dermal base may be preserved. Other areas are excised with sharp dissection into viable tissue. The fascial plane is chosen as the base only in very deep burns that involve the adipose tissue. In very deep burns and in the elderly patients excision to muscle must also be considered when adequate vascularity of the fascia is in question. I do not limit excision to the customary 15–20% total body surface area as long as the patient is stable and the anesthesiologist is having no problems with fluid replacement, the vital signs are normal, urine output maintained, and pulmonary function adequate. A constant discussion with the anesthesiologist is mandatory during such large excisions.

Fresh allograft would be ideal, but is normally unavailable. Therefore, frozen allograft is obtained, thawed, meshed 1:1.5 or 1:2 and applied in a minimally expanded fashion. This technique has allowed the best allograft taken in my hands. The allograft is thawed in warm saline and the saline changed when the temperature of the water falls. The maintenance of the water temperature prevents ice crystallization within the skin and helps maintain maximum viability of the allograft. The skin is also not allowed to soak in the saline once it has thawed. It is immediately meshed and placed in saline moistened gauze.

Allograft is applied to the excised wound bed in a minimally expanded fashion and secured with surgical clips. The skin is applied similar to autograft and seams are avoided over joints. Adequate range of motion is assured without movement of the allograft at the time of application. Proper placement is essential for long-term function as the dermis is to remain intact at the time of CEA application. The allograft is then covered with Adaptic* X (Johnson & Johnson Medical, Arlington, Texas) or Acticoat antimicrobial dressing (Westaim Biomedical, Exeter, New Hampshire).

The patient is returned to the operating room every 2–3 days until the wound is totally excised and covered with allograft. Nonadherent allograft is removed, the bed re-excised and the new allograft reapplied. In the interim, autograft is applied to the hands, face and neck when available. If enough autograft is available, joints are also covered. The dermis of the allograft is also

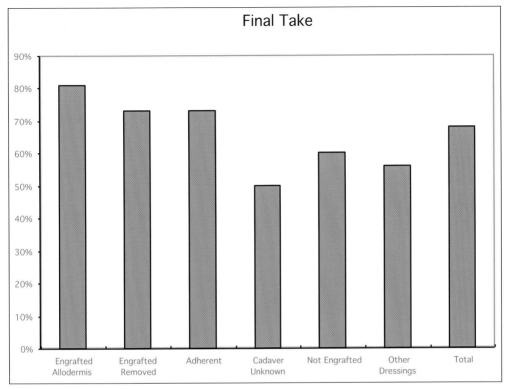

Fig. 1: Percentage of "Final Take" of transplanted CEA

used when possible as a base for the autograft. In this case, the autograft is harvested thinner than normal and re-harvesting is possible in a shorter time span as the donor site heals more readily. The patient undergoes routine physical and occupational therapy during this time span.

Close communication with the commercial company is vital to our success. Wound bed problems, such as infection, or the overall condition of the patient delays the application of the CEA. In this situation the cells are delayed and supplied when the wound bed and patients conditions allows. The wound bed is also biopsied 48–72 hours prior to CEA application and appropriate antibiotics started prior to CEA placement.

When "all systems are go", the cells are placed on their backing in the lab and shipped to the hospital via carrier. The patient is taken to the operating room after the cells arrive

and wounds prepared and draped in a sterile fashion. The allograft often has a separation of the epidermis from the dermis at this phase. Biopsies we have performed (non-published data) show this separation is not due to rejection. Often granulation tissue will also grow through the interstices of the allograft. A dermatome, Weck knives and/or dermabraders are used to produce a smooth wound bed with petechial bleeding visible in the allograft dermis. Hemostasis is then obtained with thrombin, epinephrine, hydrogen peroxide and/or electrocautery. Once precise wound bed preparation is obtained (Fig. 1), the CEAs are precisely applied (Fig. 2). The cells are held in place with surgical clips. Currently we are attempting to decrease the number of staples required by utilizing fibrin glue prior to cell application. The cells are then covered with bridal veil or interface dressing this is stapled in place to decrease the incidence of shearing.

Adaptic* X (Johnson & Johnson Medical, Arlington, Texas) gauze is used to cover the bridal veil. The extremities are wrapped with kerlex and ace and the trunk covered with Exudry (Smith & Nephew, Largo, Florida)

Physical and occupational therapy is withheld for 5 days post CEA application. At this time gentle passive range of motion is started and performed daily. The new grafts are examined daily and allowed to air dry for an hour. The Adaptic* X (Johnson & Johnson Medical, Arlington, Texas) and outer wraps are then reapplied. The cells are kept as dry as possible and no antibiotic solutions are utilized unless the cells become moist and cultures are positive. The bridal veil backing on the cells are removed between the seventh and tenth day post application. Patients are then placed in routine dressings and begin active physical and occupational therapy. If the cells are moist, they are allowed to air dry for an hour or two each day. To date, less than 10% of our patients have had to have release of contractures (Z plasty technique).

I agree with Pruitt that the "epidermis alone is not the answer". The allodermis-CEA technique, first described by Cuono [5] is one method that increases the take of the cultured epidermal autografts and provides a durable skin substitute. The technique is based upon the finding of Medawar (Medawar P. A second study on the behavior of the fate of skin hemografts in rabbits. J. Anatomy 1945; 79, 157), which showed that the dermis was relatively nonimmunogenic.

Methods

A retrospective review of all patients who received CEA provided by BioSurface Technologies, Inc. was performed. The total number of grafts, their initial and final take, and the method of bed preparation was determined. A review of 1994–1999 is also underway, but the existing records are not as thorough as to bed preparation and are not included in this report.

Findings

From 1988 through March 1994, BioSurface Technology, Inc. (Cambridge, MA) had supplied grafts to 422 burn patients. These grafts were supplied to 110 different hospitals world wide. The average full thickness total body surface area burn was 60/3%. The type of wound bed preparation was divided into the following categories:

- allodermis bed;
- allograft engrafted and then removed;
- allograft that was adherent but had not had time to engraft and then was removed;
- allograft that was not adherent;
- other dressings, such as heterograft, Biobrane™, etc;
- cadaver unknown;
- other unknown.

A patient could be classified in more than one category, depending upon how the recipient bed in different anatomic areas was

Table 1: Distribution of CEA grafts according to type of bed preparation.

Bed Preparation	# Sites	# Grafts	% Use
Allodermis	95	8715	20.7%
Engrafted/removed	129	9982	23.7%
Adherent	54	3943	9.4%
Non-Adherent	80	7182	17.0%
Other Dressings	182	12075	28.6%

Table 2: Final take of CEA grafts according to type of bed preparation.

Bed Preparation	Percent Final Take
Allodermis	82%
Engrafted/Removed	73%
Adherent	72%
Non-Adherent	56%
Other Dressings	57%

prepared. A total of 42,123 grafts were applied to the 422 patients. Table 1 shows the distribution of grafts according to the type of bed preparation. The majority of the grafts, 28.6 %, were applied to a bed prepared by excision and the application of pigskin, Biobrane™, or another dressing while awaiting the in vitro growth of the CEA. The take rate shows the lack of a suitable bed for the CEA, a very fragile skin substitute, when compared to the allograft prepared beds. Table 2 shows the results of the take rates for the various groups. A chi square test was used to compare the groups and due to too small a number of grafts in Groups VI and VII, the statistical significance was not meaningful and they have not been considered for the bulk of this paper. All beds prepared with an allograft that was at least adherent prior to the application of CEA produced a much more suitable bed and take rate than other techniques. The takerate between Groups I, II, III and Group V is significant at the $p > 0.001$ level for each comparison group. When Group I was compared to groups II, III, and IV, the take rate difference was again significant at the $p > 0.001$ level. As shown in table III, there was on the average 166 grafts applied to each of the 422 patients. The final take averaged 67 % for the entire patient population, and CEA was used for permanent coverage of 18.6 % of the total body surface area. On the other hand, when the allodermis group was viewed separately, and even greater success was seen. An average of 190 grafts were used in this subgroup and permanent coverage obtained for 23 % of the total body surface area. The composite graft had a final take of 83 %. The wound beds prepared without allograft sustained only a 57 % take rate of the CEA. The overall mortality rate for patients grafted with CEA was 6.4 %.

Discussion

O'Connor [11] showed in 1981 that CEA could be utilized for a permanent skin sub-

Table 3: Multi-center results of CEA grafts applied from a single source from 1988–1994.

Total number of patients	422
Average number CEA grafts	166
Average TBSA grafted	26.2 %
Average final take	71.0 %
Permanent TBSA coverage	18.6 %

Table 4: Multi-center results of CEA grafts applied from a single source over an allodermis bed from 1988–1994.

Average # CEA Grafts	190
TBSA Grafted	28 %
Average Final Take	83 %
Average Permanent Coverage	23 %

stitute. We agree with Arons [1] that CEA can be a lifesaving measure when utilized in severe thermal injuries but, unfortunately, the technique is associated not only with a variable take rate, but also with variable functional and cosmetic results. The average take rate varies from zero to 100 % [6, 7, 8, 10, 12]. This review shows an improved take rate when CEA is applied to an allodermis base. These findings on a large scale, international basis, confirms our earlier report [8] in a much smaller number of patients that the allodermis technique provides an excellent base for CEA. In a separate study [3] it has been shown that both rete ridge formation and the normalizing keratin patterns occurred months earlier for CEA placed on a dermal matrix. Furthermore, the anchoring fibrils at the dermoepidermal junction was 35–50 % greater than that of CEA grafted on granulation tissue and the anchoring fibrils comparable to that of normal skin. The cumulative effects of these events leads to a durable skin substitute.

Allograft also has the capability of early closure of the wound bed while awaiting the growth of the CEA. Pruitt [14] discussed the utilization of allograft for temporary wound coverage and noted the following benefits: its adherence to the wound bed decreases bacterial count, prevents desiccation, decreases heat and evaporative water loss, and prevents further contamination of the wound. Thus early wound excision to decrease bacterial count, perhaps one of the most important items responsible for increased survival in larger burn, combined with allograft coverage of the wound allows the burn surgeon to wait for second degree burns to heal, previous donor sites to re-epithelialize, or CEA to become available.

Patients with major thermal injuries are immunosuppressed and we have found that the allograft does not undergo rejection in the three weeks that it takes for the production of the CEA. The epidermis of the CEA is often seen to slough but there is no cellular infiltration seen in histological specimens nor a systemic eosinophilia. This epidermolysis may be due to the fact that the epidermis does not withstand cryopreservation as well as the dermis. This review shows a definite improvement in overall CEA take when placed on an allodermis bed to provide a composite graft. Take is also improved by preparation of the recipient bed with allograft as long as adherence of the graft to the underlying bed occurs. This finding is significant at the $p < 0.001$ level when compared to the "other dressing" group. The basis for improved take in this situation is felt to be due to an infection free bed that is more suitable for CEA. Infection has been shown to be the number one enemy of CEA and the elimination of this problem leads to an improved take [6, 12]. In addition, the anchoring fibrils and early rete ridge formation leads to a more durable graft.

This technique utilized at the Firefighters' Regional Burn Center in Memphis, Tennessee has led to a 94.6 % take rate of CEA on an allodermis base [8]. Thus we agree with Pruitt [13] that the "Epidermis alone is not the answer" and feel, as does Cuono, that the dermis seems to be the missing piece to the CEA

puzzle [4]. The majority of our patients have been manual laborers that have returned to work and these grafts have withstood the rigors of their employment without undue sequela [9].

Conclusion

In summary, CEA take and durability is technique specific and the composite method is a technical improvement for the armamentarium of the burn surgeon. Further work on CEA/artificial dermis such as Integra Artificial Skin (Johnson & Johnson Medical, Arlington, Texas) is warranted as the supply of high quality allograft diminishes, and the concerns of viral transmission increases.

References

[1] *Arons JA, Wainwright DJ, Jordan RE:* The surgical applications and implications of cultured human epidermis: a comprehensive review. Surgery; 111:4, (1992).
[2] *Bartlett RH:* Skin substitutes. Journal of Trauma; 21(8) S731, (1981).
[3] *Compton CC, Hickerson W, Nadire K, Press W:* Acceleration of skin regeneration from cultured epithelial autografts by transplantation to homograft dermis. Journal of Burn Care and Rehabilitation; 14:653–62, (1993).
[4] *Cuono C, Langdon R, Birchell N, et al.:* Composite autologous-allogenic skin replacement: development and clinical application. Plastic and Reconstructive Surgery; 80:626, (1987).
[5] *Cuone C, Langdon R, McGuire J:* Use of cultured epidermal autografts and dermal allografts as skin replacement after burn injury. Lancet; 1:1123, (1986).
[6] *DeLuca M, Albanse E, Bandaza S, et al.:* Multicenter experience in the treatment of burns with autologous and allogenic cultured epithelium, fresh or preserved in a frozen state. Burns; 15:303, (1989).
[7] *Gallico GG III:* Biologic skin substitutes. Clinics of Plastic Surgery; 17:519, (1990).
[8] *Hickerson WL, Compton CC, Fletchall S, Smith LR:* Cultured epidermal autografts and allodermis combination for permanent burn wound coverage. Burns; 20 (1): S52, (1994).
[9] *Hickerson WL, Love RT Jr, Bishop JF:* Cultured epidermal autografts: the current status.

Problems in General Surgery, Volume 11 (4) (pp 747–752), 1994.

[10] *Nave M:* Wound bed preparation: approaches to replacement of dermis. Journal of Burn Care and Rehabilitation; 13:174, (1992).

[11] *O'Connor NE, Mulliken JB, Banks-Schlegel S, et al.:* Grafting of burns with cultured epithelium prepared from autologous epidermal cells. Lancet; 1:75, (1981).

[12] *Odessey R:* Addendum: multi-center experience with cultured epidermal autograft for treatment of burns. Journal of Burn Care and Rehabilitation; 13,174, (1992).

[13] *Pruitt BA Jr:* Epidermis alone is not the answer. ABA Meeting, Plenary Session I, 1995.

[14] *Pruitt BA Jr, Levine NS:* Characteristics and uses of biologic dressings and skin substitutes. Arch of Surgery; 119:312, (1984).

[15] *Rhinewald JG, Green H:* Serial cultivation of strains of epidermal keratinocytes: the formation of keratinizing colonies from single cells. Cell; 6, 331, (1975).

[16] *Woodley DT, Peterson HD, Hergog SR, et al.:* Burn wounds resurfaced by cultured epidermal autografts show abnormal reconstitution of anchoring fibrils. JAMA; 259:2566, (1988).

Clinical Results of Cultivated Keratinocytes to Treat Burn Injuries – A Metaanalysis

C. Freising, R. E. Horch

Summary

This study was aimed towards the collection of all available published literature concerning clincial resutls of burn treatment with cultured human keratinocytes between 1981 and 2000. The topics investigated were the coherence of take rates and clinical criteria like age, extent of injury (percent TBSA), depth of the injury, and percentage of body surface that received cultured epidermal autografts (CEA). Size of patient collective, duration of hospitalization, and long-term-results were also taken into consideration. Reported keratinocyte take rates varied considerably between 5% and 90%. Although no standardized evaluation of treatment data was possible, this meta-analysis was able to show the effectiveness of keratinocyte transplantation in severe burns in principal. Analyzising all available clinical results of this procedure it becomes clear that future studies should be optimized towards a standardized protocol of data acquisition.

Introduction

The improving survival rates of severely burned patients (Fig. 1) are a result of the enormous progress both in intensive care medicine and surgical treatment. Letality rates have been shifted from 50% mortality in a 30% surface burn towards 50% letality with 70% TBSA (= Total Burn Surface Area) today within the last 50 years [18]. However, new problems were encountered facing the need of temporary and definitive wound coverage after early burn excisional strategies (Fig. 2). One of the most exciting technical advancements was the introduction of cultured keratinocytes to cope with the large wounds despite the obvious lack

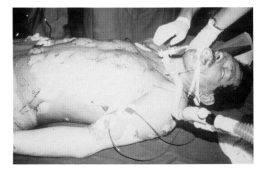

Fig. 1: 35 year old patient with 75 % TBSA deep second and third degree burns at the time of delivery into the burn unit.

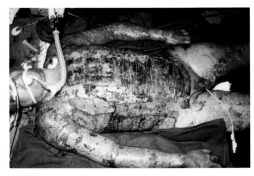

Fig. 2: 78 % TBSA deep second and third degree burn wounds partially covered with cultured autologous keratinocytes in fibrin sealant (right trunk and right arm) with overgrafted allogenic split thickness skin.

of graftable skin in severe burns [17, 37, 40]. Many of the outstanding pioneers of this exciting development present their expertise with cultured skin substitutes in this book. Detailed information on the technique can therefore be found in their contributions.

Today the use of cultivated keratinocytes has become an undispensable tool within the treatment of severely burned patients. However, data from the literature are inconsistent and differ greatly regarding take rates, clinical results and longterm outcome. In this article we therefore tried to analyze the currently available data in a metaanalysis to evaluate the true value of this method.

Aim of the Study

We intended to collect the information available and to investigate the coherence of take rates and clinical criteria like age, extent of injury (percent TBSA), depth of the injury, and percentage of body surface that received cultured epidermal autografts (CEA). Size of patient collective, duration of hospitalization, and long-term-results were also taken into consideration.

Methods

The article is based on a databank research in refer to keratinocyte transplantation, using Medline, Pub Med databank and the Cochrane Library. The studies included were patient examinations between 1981 and 2000.

The patients suffered from skin defects due to severe burn injuries. To close the defects autologous keratinocyte cultures were employed. The cultivated epithelium was either transplanted as sheet grafts or as a fibrin glue suspension. The cultivation method used was the Rheinwald and Green technique [40] or further developments using standardized media.

All publications were reviewed following the same scheme:

- Size of the patient collective (number of patients)
- Take rate
- Method of transplantation
- Percent of burned body surface area (TBSA)
- Long-term results

The Treatment of Burn Injuries with Cultivated Keratinocytes

Reviewing all relevant publications from 1981 to now, it turned out that there was no standardization to measure the exact amount of take rates and even the estimation of the take rates was not clearly defined in the articles. Therefore, all data were compiled, but consistent statistical analysis was not to be used due to the inconsistency of data. Despite this fact we tried to summarize all data available in order to reveal any graspable guidelines if possible.

Table 1 shows that the size of patient groups varied from 1 to 141, depending more on the research effort and size of the hospital than on the time span of the study.

"Take Rate"

Regarding the worldwide published results, the take rate of CEA for burning injuries is significantly lower than the average skin graft take rate (75% versus 92%). Munster [31] and Latarjet [27] explain this by a higher vulnerability of the CEA grafts with regard to the metabolic state of the patient.

The results shown in table 1 represent the large variability (0% to 88%) of take rates. Though most take rates range between 30% and 85%. Overall it can be summarized that those studies which were carried out under the best clinical conditions all came out with a take rate of 50% ore more. There were no data revealing if the number of repeated transplantations had been taken into account when the take ra-

Table 1: Literature data published on the transplantation of keratinocytes (CEA = cultured autologous epidermis) (KFGS = Keratinocyte Fibrin Glue Suspension).

Investigators (First author, Date)	Burn unit	No. of Patients	Kind of trans- plantation-	Take rate	Time of hospitalisation (d)
Archer (1998)	Cincinnati, USA	105	CEA (n=18)		58,3
Barillo (1992)	Allentown, USA	3	CEA	62,50 %	72,3
Bettex-Galland (1988)	Berne, Switzerland	1	CEA		
Carsin (1997)	Clamart, France	30	CEA	69,00 %	114
Caruso (1996)	Phoenix, Arizona	1	CEA		106
Chalumeau (1999)	Cedex, France	6	CEA	84 %	
Clugston (1991)	Vancouver, Canada	18	CEA	33,80 %	
Coleman (1992)	Indianapolis, USA	3	CEA	86,70 %	
De Luca (1989)	Genua, Italy	40	CEA	37,00 %	43,1
Donati (1992)	Mailand, Italy	26	CEA	32,5 %	
Foyatier (1989)	Lyon, France	16	CEA	9 Pat > 50 % 3 Pat < 50 % 4 Pat 0 %	
Gallico (1984)	Boston , USA	2	CEA		157,5
Gobet (1997)	Zürich, Switzerland	6	CEA	56,70 %	
Haith (1992)	Upland, USA	6	CEA	78,00 %	
H.v.Donnersmark (1995)	München, Germany	50	CEA	28,00 %	
Herzog (1988)	Chapel Hill, USA	8	CEA	50,00 %	
Königova (1989)	Prag, Czech Republik	4	CEA	75,00 %	
Krupp (1992)	Zürich, Switzerland	21	CEA	75,00 %	
Kumagai (1987)	Kanagawa, Japan	6	CEA		
Latarjet (1987)	Lyon, France	2	CEA	40,00 %	25,5
Lopez Gutierrez (1995)	Madrid, Spain	4	CEA	80,00 %	80
McAree (1993)	Akron, USA	7	CEA	80,00 %	
Mühlbauer (1995)	München, Germany	141	CEA	39,50 %	
Munster (1990)	Baltimore, USA	7	CEA		60,3
Munster (1992)	Baltimore, USA	10	CEA		64,6
Munster (1996)	Baltimore, USA	22	CEA		96,4
Odessey (1992)	Cambridge, USA	240	CEA	60,00 %	
Petersen (1990)	Stanford, USA	3	CEA		
Rue (1993)	Birmingham, USA	16	CEA	46,70 %	132
Sheridan (1995)	Boston, USA	5	CEA	51,00 %	
Siwy (1992)	Indianapolis, USA	5	CEA	65,00 %	
Stark (1994)	Köln, Germany	3	KGFS	88,30 %	
Still (1994)	Augusta, USA	15	CEA	71,50 %	
Tamisani (1992)	Genua, Italy	17	CEA n=7	57,10 %	
Williamson (1995)	Vancouver, Canada	28	CEA	26,90 %	90,4

Table 1: Transplantation of keratinocytes (CEA) CEA: Cultured autologous epidermis
KGFS: Keratinocyte fibrin glue suspension

te was evaluated. Haith reported on one case [20], for example, that the transplantations had to be repeated 19 times before a success was recorded. Most authors describe that the transplantation procedure had to be repeated twice, the average was 1 to 7 repetitions.

Evaluation of the Transplantation Success

Due to the invariate account of the various data in the reports and the lack of standardized selection criteria the interpretation of the results is very difficult.

Most research groups evaluated their results considering mainly aesthetic aspects, partly also including long-term results. Evaluation often took place after a long time interval after transplantation. The results seem to depend on the date of examination in relation to the operation date. Some authors describe a transplant failure 2, 3, or 4 weeks after the first healing of the keratinocytes. Rejection can be partial or complete (total), it may follow infection or happen without any sign of infection.

Various factors such as wound ground conditions, surgical excision, infection have an influence on the take rate of the transplant, as well as nutritional status, age, and general condition of the patient. This may explain why the results differ strongly amongst the patients, and also from hospital to hospital [13]. Some of those factors are similar to the conditions influencing any organ transplantation. Others are particularly important for CEA transplantation, for example infections or the special handling of the filmy transplant during postoperative wound care [49].

Odessey [38] was the first to standardize treatment parameters and clinical assessment. Within 2 and 1/2 years 240 patients in 79 burning injury care units in the USA and Europe were treated with industrially produced CEA. Odessey analyzed the take rates of 104 patients 3 to 4 weeks after transplantation, following a certain formula for take rate evaluation:

Take rate = 100% × (1-[area requiring regrafting]/[area grafted with CEA])

The average of CEA-transplant-treated body surface was 70% (scattering 25%–99%). 50% of the burning injuries were 3rd grade burns. the average take rate of the 104 patients was 60%.

Percent of Burned Body Surface (TBSA-Total Burn Surface Area)

Donati [14] claimed that patients aged 12 years or younger with a burn of more than 20% BS and adults with more than 30%

burned BS should receive CEA transplants. Until today the indication for CEA has not been restricted to an upper limit of any injury extent. But in cases with a very poor general prognosis, the procedure of in-vitro-keratinocyte cultivation is not advisable. Additional injuries and preexisting other diseases – in particular cardiovascular diseases, diabetes, or liver diseases – must be paid attention to.

Further more Donati and colleagues reported that they obtain a skin biopsy of every patient with burns exceeding 40% TBSA (Total Body Surface Area). The keratinocytes are cultivated, and after 10 days a decision is made up whether the defect receiving the transplant still covers over 30% TBSA. If this is the case, cultivation is continued. If it is not, the procedure is stopped and the keratinocytes are refrigerated.

This guarantees that the laboratory costs are minimized if the treatment had to be changed in the interim, the wound extent had reduced under the transplantation limit described above, or if the patient had died.

Other authors indicate a keratinocyte transplantation if 50% or more of BS are burned. One of the obvious judgement problems is the initial assessment of the depth of the injury. Misjudgement concerning injury depth, in particular when affecting back and thighs, happens frequently because it is a subjective and empirical parameter. Therefore this factor must be taken into account when comparing different reports with unclear statements of the burn depth.

Long-Term Results

Meanwhile long-term results after keratinocyte transplanation have been published [10, 11, 16, 21, 36]. In most of the studies skin biopsies are used to analyze the condition of dermal-epidermal junctions, the invasion of Langerhans cells, the revascularization, and the reconstruction of the neodermis. So far the reported results are not uniform. Assisted by light microscopy, electron microscopy, ultrastructure-immune-markers, and immunohistochemistry, the ultrastructures can be figured. On the one hand it has been described that after about 3 weeks a complete basal membrane and hemidesmosomes was traceable. On the other hand, the first, immature and rare junctions to the bottom of the wound have been found to set in after about 12 months, taking another 4–5 years until the first elastin can be found in the neodermis under the CEA grafted areas. In genereal several observations report that within several years a highly differentiated epidermis develops from the CEA transplants. The regeneration of skin thus can successfully be achieved [7, 10, 11, 12, 16, 23, 30, 35, 36].

Two studies of Carolyn Compton and co-workers seem to be of special importance [10, 11]: In a long-term control study [11] she reported on the histopathological long-term results of 22 children with severe (3rd grade) burning injuries who underwent excisions down to the muscle fascia and keratinocyte transplantation. Within the postoperative 6–12 months the keratinocyte cultures developped anchoring fibrils and a neodermis with a normal stroma architecture and vascularization. 4–5 years after transplantation elastin was produced indicating the maturation of the dermal regeneration process. The normal structure of the epidermis remains over years.

These long-term results show that with keratinocyte cultures the regeneration of a normally structured epidermis and also the induction of regeneration of a normally structured neodermis is possible.

To the contrary Woodley and collegues repeatedly described a deficient quantity and quality of the fibrillary junctions up to 4–5 months after the operation [49]. This instability in the dermal-epidermal contact region was claimed to be responsible for the formation of blisters as soon as shearing forces or pressure is applied to the neodermis [26, 29, 39].

From the aesthetic point of view the long-term results with CEA transplants have been described to be superior to mesh-skin grafted areas. The neo-skin was reported to be smoother, more supple, and more flexible, and the formation of hypertrophic scar tissue is less frequent. However, other authors do not agree with those observations. Warden [47] describes extreme keloid formation, particularly after CEA transplantation onto deep wound. A high growth factor concentration within the wound is discussed as one of the causes.

Conclusions

Although there is much consensus, certain controversies exist regarding the clinical outcome after the transplantation of cultured human keratinocytes. Although no standardized evaluation of treatment data was possible, this metaanalysis was able to show the effectiveness of keratinocyte transplantation in severe burns. Analyzising all available clinical results of this procedure it becomes clear that future studies should be optimized towards a standardized protocol of data acquisition. This should include not only standard data on patient population but also clearly differentiate between burn depth, TBSA, number of keratinocyte transplantations, exact amount of healed areas after transplantation with regard to the time span after keratinocyte delivery, and the modalities of pretreatment. Longterm results with regard to scar assessment, functional outcome, number of reoperations, estimation of the costs and any complications during or after the procedure should be named. By this way future metaanalyzes might more distinctly help to clarify overall clinical performance data of cultured skin substitutes than is possible at present.

References

[1] Archer, SB, Henke, A, Greenhalgh, DG, Warden, GD: The use of sheet autografts to cover extensive burns in patients. J Burn Care Rehabil 19 (1):33–38, 1998.
[2] Barillo, DJ, Nangle, ME, Farell, K: Preliminary experience with cultured epidermal autograft in a community hospital burn unit. J Burn Care Rehabil 13 (1):158–173, 1992.

[3] Bettex-Galland, M, Slongo, T, Hunziker, T, Wiesmann, U, Bettex, M: Use of cultured keratinocytes in the treatment of severe burns. Z Kinderchir 43:224–228, 1988.

[4] Carsin, H, Ainaud, P, Le Bever, H, Rives, JM, Le Coadou, A, Stephanazzi, J: Objectifs, résultats et perspectives du traitement des brûlés en 1997. Bull Acad Natle Méd 181 (7):1307–1319, 1997.

[5] Caruso, DM, Gregory, MW, Schiller, WR: The use of skin from a monozygotic twin combined with cultured epithelial autografts as coverage for a large surface area burn: a case report and review of the literature. J Burn Care Rehabil 17 (5):432–434, 1996.

[6] Chalumeau, M, Saulnier, J-P, Ainaud, P, Lebever, H, Stephanazzi, J,. Lecoadou, A, Carsin, H: Initial general management and surgery of six extensivelx burned children treated with cultured epidermal autografts. J Pediatr Surg 34 (4):602–605, 1999.

[7] Clark, RAF: Biology of dermal wound repair. Dermatol Clin 11 (4):647–666, 1993.

[8] Clugston, P, Snelling, CFT, Macdonalds, IB, Maledy, HL, Boyle, JC, Germann, E, Courtemanche, AD, Wirtz, P, Fitzpatrick, DJ, Kester, DA, Foley, B, Warren, RJ, Carr, NJ: Cultured epithelial autografts: three years of clinical experience with eighteen patients. J Burn Care Rehabil 12 (6):533–539, 1991.

[9] Coleman JJ, Siwy, BK: Cultured epidermal autografts: a life-saving and skin-safing technique in children. J Pediatr Surg 27 (8): 1029–1032, 1992.

[10] Compton, C, Gill, JM, Bradford, DA, Regauer, S, Gallico, GG, O'Connor, NE: Skin regenerated from cultured epithelial autografts on full-thickness burn wounds from 6 days to 5 years after grafting. J Burn Care Rehabil 18 (6):535–544, 1989.

[11] Compton, C: Current concepts in pediatric burn care: the biology of cultured epithelial autografts: an eight-year study in pediatric burn patients. Eur J Pediatr Surg 2:216–222, 1992.

[12] Compton, C, Nadire, K, Regauer, S, Simon, M, Warland, G, O'Connor, NE, Gallico, GG, Landry, DB: Cultured human sole-derived keratinocyte grafts re-express site-specific differentiation after transplantation. Differentiation 64:45–53, 1998.

[13] De Luca, M, Albanese, E, Bondanza, S, Megna, M, Ugozzoli, L, Molina, F, Cancedda, R, Santi, PL, Bormioli, M, Stella, M, Magliacani, G: Multicentre experience in the treatment of burns with autologous and allogenic cultured epithelium, fresh or preserved in a frozen state. Burns 15 (5):303–309, 1989.

[14] Donati, L, Magliacani, G, Signorini, M, Baruffaldi Preis, FW: Clinical experiences with keratinocyte grafts. Burns 18 (Supplement 1): S19–S25, 1992.

[15] Foyatier, JL, Faure, M, Hezez, G, Masson, C, Paulus, C, Chomel, P, Latarjet, J, Delay, E, Thomas, L, Adam, C, Thivolet, J: Application clinique des greffes d'épiderme cultivé chez le brûlé; A propos de 16 observations. Ann Chir Plast Esthét 35 (1):39–46, 1989.

[16] Franzi, AT, D'Anna, F, Zicca, A, Trabucchi, E: Histological evaluation of human cultured epithelium before and after grafting. Burns 18 (S1):26S–31S, 1992.

[17] Gallico, GG, O'Connor, NE, Compton, C, Kehinde, O, Green, H: Permanent coverage of large burn wounds with autologous cultured human epithelium. N Engl J Med 331 (7):448–451, 1984.

[18] Germann, G, Raff, T: Fremdhauttransplantation bei Schwerverbrannten; Grundlagen, Indikationen und Möglichkeiten. Chirurg 66 (260):270, 1995.

[19] Gobet, R, Raghunath, M, Altermatt, S, Meuli-Simmen, C, Benathan, M, Dietl, A, Meuli, M: Efficacy of cultured epithelial autografts in pediatric burns and reconstructive surgery. Surg 1216 (654):661, 1997.

[20] Haith, LR, Patton, ML, Goldman, WT: Cultured epidermal autograft and treatment of the massive burn injury. J Burn Care Rehabil 13 (1):142–146, 1992.

[21] Herzog, SR, Meyer, A, Woodley, D, Peterson, HD: Wound coverage with cultured autologous keratinocytes: use after burn wound excision, including biopsy follow up. J Trauma 28 (2):195–198, 1988.

[22] Henkel v. Donnersmark, G, Mühlbauer, W, Höfter, E, Hartinger, A: Die Verwendung von Kerationcytenkulturen in der Schwerstbrandverletztenbehandlung – bisherige Erfahrungen, Ausblicke zur weiteren Entwicklung. Unfallchirurg 98:229–232, 1995.

[23] Horch, RE, Corbei, O, Formanek-Corbei, B, Brand-Saberi, B, Vanscheidt, W, Stark, GB: Reconstitution of Basement Menbrane after "Sandwich-Technique" Skin Grafting for Severe Burns Demonstrated by Immunhistochemistry. J Burn Care Rehabil 19 (3): 189–202, 1998.

[24] Königová, R, Kapounková, Z, Vogtová, D, Veselý, P, Matoušková, E: First experiences with clinical application of cultured auto-epithelium grafts. Acta Chirurgiae Plasticae 31 (4):193–200, 1989.

[25] Krupp, S, Benathan, M, Meuli, M, Deglise, B, Holzer, E, Wiesner, L, Delacretaz, F, Chiolero, R: Current concepts in pediatric burn care: Management of burn wounds with cultured epidermal autografts. Eur J Pediatr Surg 2:210–215, 1992.

[26] *Kumagai, N, Nishina, H, Tanabe, H, Hosaka, T, Nishida, H, Ogino, Y:* Clinical application of autologous cultured epithelia for the treatment of burn wounds and burn scars. Plast Reconstr Surg 82:99–110, 1988.

[27] *Latarjet, J, Gangolphe, M, Hezez, G, Masson, C, Chomel, P, Cognet, JB, Galoisy, JP, Joly, R, Robert, A, Foyatier, JL, Faure, M, Thivolet,J:* The grafting of burns with cultured epidermis as autografts in man. Two case reports. Scand J Plast Reconstr Surg 21:241–244, 1987.

[28] *López Gutiérrez, JC, Ros, Z, Vallejo, D, Perdiguero, M, Soto, C, Tovar, J:* Cultured epidermal autograft in the management of critical pediatric burn patients. Eur J Pediatr Surg 5:174–176, 1995.

[29] *McAree, KG, Klein, R, Boeckman, CR:* The use of cultured epithelial autografts in the wound care of severely burned patients. J Pediatr Surg 28 (2):166–168, 1993.

[30] *Medalie, DA, Eming, SA, Collins, SA, Tompkins, RG, Yarmush, ML, Morgan, JR:* Differences in dermal analogs influence subsequent pigmentation, epidermal differentation, basement membrane, and rete ridge formation of transplanted composite skin grafts. Transpl 64 (3):454–465, 1997.

[31] *Munster, AM, Weiner, SH, Spence, RJ:* Cultured epidermis for the coverage of massive burn wounds – A single center experience. Ann Surg 211 (6):676–680, 1990.

[32] *Munster, AM:* Use of cultured epidermal autograft in ten patients. J Burn Care Rehabil 13 (1):124–126, 1992.

[33] *Munster, AM:* Cultured skin for massive burns; A prospective, controlled trial. Ann Surg 224 (3):372–377, 1996.

[34] *Mühlbauer, W, Henkel v. Donnersmark, G, Hoefter, E, Hartinger, A:* Keratinozytenzüchtung und -transplantation bei Verbrennungen. Chirurg 66:271–276, 1995.

[35] *Myers, S, Navsaria, H, Brain, AN, Purkis, PE, Leigh, IM:* Epidermal differentation and dermal changes in healing following treatment of surgical wounds with sheets of cultured allogenic keratinocytes. J Clin Pathol 48:1087–1092, 1995.

[36] *Neveux, Y, Rives, JM, Le Breton, C, Gentilhomme, E, Saint-Blancar, P, Carsin, H:* Clinical interest of cutaneous models reproduced in vitro for severe burn treatment: histopathological and ultrastructural study. Cell Biology Toxicology 11:173–178, 1995.

[37] *O'Connor, NE, Mulliken, JB:* Grafting of burns with cultured epithelium prepared from autologous epidermal cells. Lancet:75–78, 1981.

[38] *Odessey, R:* Addendum: Multicenter Experience with Cultured Epidermal Autograft for Treatment of Burns. J Burn Care Rehabil 13 (1):174–180, 1992.

[39] *Peterson, MJ, Lessane, B, Woodley, D:* CharacteriSation of cellular elements in healed cultured keratinocyte autografts used to cover burn wounds. Arch Dermatol 126:175–180, 1990.

[40] *Rheinwald, JG, Green, H:* Serial Cultivation of Stains of Human Epidermal Keratinocytes: the Formation of Keratinizing Colonies from Single Cells. Cell 6:331–344, 1975.

[41] *Rue, LW, Cioffi, WG, McManus, WF, Pruitt, BA:* Wound closure and outcome in extensively burned patients treated with cultured autologous keratinocytes. J Trauma 34 (5):662–668, 1993.

[42] *Sheridan, RL, Tompkins, RG:* Cultured autologous epithelium in patients with burns of ninety percent or more of the body surface. J Trauma 38 (1):48–50, 1995.

[43] *Siwy, BK, Compton, C:* Cultured epidermis: Indiana University Medical Center`s experience. J Burn Care Rehabil 13 (1):130–137, 1992.

[44] *Stark, GB, Kaiser, HW:* Cologne Burn Centre experience with glycerol-preserved allogeneic skin: Part II: Combination with autologous cultured keratinocytes. Burns 20 (1): S34–S38, 1994.

[45] *Still, J, Orlet, HK, Law, EJ:* Use of cultured epidermal autografts in the treatment of large burns. Burns 20 (6):539–541, 1994.

[46] *Tamisani, AM, Ferretti, S, Sangiorgio, L:* Critical reflections on the use of human cultured keratinocytes in children with burns. Eur J Pediatr Surg 2:223–226, 1992.

[47] *Warden, GD:* The fifth quinquennium: 1989 to 1993. J Burn Care Rehabil 14:247–251, 1993.

[48] *Williamson, JS, Snelling, CFT, Clugston, P, Macdonalds, IB, Germann, E:* Cultured Epithelial Autograft: Five Years of Clinical Experience with Twenty-Eight Patients. J Trauma 39 (2):309–319, 1995.

[49] *Woodley, D:* Covering wounds with cultured keratinocytes. JAMA 262:2140–2141, 1989.

The Use of Allogeneic Cultivated Keratinocytes for the Early Coverage of Deep Dermal Burns – the Viennese Experience

R. Koller, B. Bierochs, G. S. Bayer, G. Meissl, M. Frey

Summary

Since 1995 a programme of cultivation of human epidermal cells was established in the the Department of Plastic and Reconstructive Surgery at at the Vienna University Hospital. This study surveys the indications, technical questions and results of approximately 600 sheets of cultured keratinocytes, 75 cm² in size, which had been produced each year since 1997. The majority of these sheets has been used as either fresh or cryopreserved allografts to treat burns. In our unit the share of autografts is only 5%, reflecting the well known problems of the relatively long time until the cultures are ready for grafting and of the significant number of severely burned individuals which succumb to their injuries during this period. Although a long-term presence of the transplanted allogenous cells in the epithelialised wound could never be demonstrated, we have noted a beneficial effect in the treatment of superficial and deep dermal burns using cultured epidermal allografts. This is attributed to the release of growth factors and mediators of wound healing.

Introduction

In the burn unit of the Department of Plastic and Reconstructive Surgery at the Vienna University Hospital a programme of cultivation of human epidermal cells was established in 1995. Since 1997 approximately 600 sheets of cultured keratinocytes, 75 cm² in size, have been produced each year. Like in many centres in Europe the majority of sheets are used as either fresh or kryopreserved allografts [5]. In our unit the share of autografts is only 5%, which is reflecting the well known problems of the relatively long time until the cultures are ready for grafting and of the significant number of severely burned individuals which succumb to their injuries during this period [3, 5].

Due to the release of growth factors and mediators of wound healing, it has been shown that cultured epidermal allografts have a beneficial effect in the treatment of superficial and deep dermal burns [5, 6, 8]. Nevertheless a long-term presence of the transplanted cells in the epithelialised wound could never be demonstrated [1].

Materials and Methods

In our department donor skin samples are mostly acquired from other burn patients. In addition, special methods of skin preservation allow us the use of skin, which has been taken in redundancy for split thickness skin grafting from nonburned patients and is not needed by them any more. Donors are in generally tested for HIV, Hepatitis (HBV and HCV) by polymerase chain reaction (PCR) or repetitive serological tests. Cells are grown into cultures by the method according to Rheinwald and Green

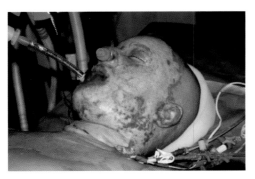

Fig.1: 48 hours old deep dermal burns in the face, ready for debridement and coverage with allogeneic keratinocytes and skin grafts for the neck and chin, where a third degree injury was found.

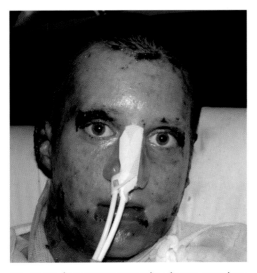

Fig. 2: 10 days postoperatively, almost complete epithelialisation.

[3, 7]. The multilayered sheets of epithelial cells are either used freshly or deep frozen at −170°C.

Indications and Results

At present there are several important indications for the application of cultured epidermal allografts.

Coverage of Donor Sites of Split Thickness Skin

Several authors have shown a significant acceleration of the healing of skin donor sites by the coverage with allogeneic keratinocytes [2]. Therefore patients with burns covering more than 50% TBSA are routinely treated with allogeneic sheets of keratinocytes at their skin donor sites.

Lightning Arch Injuries

These are quite commonly occurring in high voltage injuries. Although large in size, lightning arch injuries are mostly extending to the deep dermis and therefore the coverage with allogeneic keratinocytes is indicated in order to minimize the harvest of skin grafts [4].

Scalds in Children

These injuries are representing an important part of trauma in childhood. The coverage of lesions which have been excised to the dermal layer with keratinocytes is mostly resulting in rapid epithelialisation. In the case of failure, split thickness grafts have to be applied secondarily. Nevertheless the use of split thickness skin grafts can be reduced significantly and large areas can be covered in one operation.

Deep Dermal Burns in the Face

In the Burn Unit of the Department of Plastic and Reconstructive Surgery at the Vienna University Hospital 34 patients with deep partial thickness burns in the face were treated since 1996 according to the following concept: Dermbrasion or tangential excision were performed at a median time of four days following trauma. If viable dermis was present the wounds were covered with sheets of allogeneic cultivated keratinocytes. In cases of deeper defects a combination with autologous skin grafts was applied.

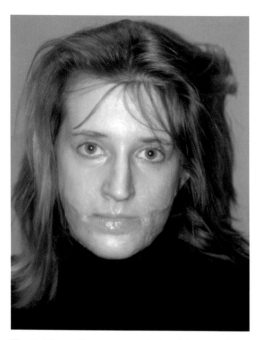

Fig. 3: 18 months postoperatively with a satisfying cosmetic and functional result.

Thus in 27 cases coverage was achieved with keratinocytes alone, in 7 patients split thickness skin grafts were an additional means. The median total burned surface area (TBSA) amounted to 24% [3–8], the median ABSI-score of all patients was 7,5.

In 22 cases complete epithelialisation was achieved within 10 days, in 8 patients a prolonged duration until complete healing was observed. In 5 faces a second operation for coverage of residual defects with skin grafts was necessary. The mentioned problems of wound healing occurred from infection, incomplete excision of burn eschar and a wrong estimation of the depth of the wound which was retrospectively seen too deep for the treatment with keratinocytes. At follow up patients were examined clinically and functionally with Frey 's faciometer®, which is an instrument for quantification of mimic movements. In cases of uncomplicated healing a nearly complete restitution was found whereas in patients sustaining complications the mimic stiffness was objectified.

Conclusions

Due to the three-dimensional architecture of the face the treatment of burns in this area usually requires a lot of skin grafts. According to our experience the great advantage of the application of allogeneic keratinocytes is the possibility of early coverage of the face without sacrificing skin donor sites, especially in large burns. As the final result is influenced by many factors, a lot of experience is necessary to avoid the occurrence of complications which mostly result in prolonged healing and severe scarring.

References

[1] *Brain A, Parkins P, Coates P, Hackett M, Navsaria H, Leigh I:* Survival of Cultured Allogeneic Keratinocytes Transplanted to deep dermal bed assessed by a probe specific for y-chromosomes. Br Med J; 298: 917–919, 1989.

[2] *Fratianne R, Papay F, Housini I, Lang C, Schafer IA:* Keratinocyte allografts accelerate healing of split-thickness donor sites: applications for improved treatment of burns. J Burn Care Rehabil; 14: 148–54, 1993.

[3] *Gallico GG, O'Connor NE, Compton CC, Kehinde O, Green H:* Permanent coverage of large burn wounds with autologous cultured human epithelium. N Engl J Med; 311: 448–52, 1984.

[4] *Koller R, Rath T, Bayer GS, et al.:* Rückblick auf 20 Jahre Erfahrung in der Behandlung von Starkstromverbrennungen – ein Spiegelbild der Entwicklung der Wiederherstellungschirurgie. Acta Chir Austr; 31: 95–103, 1999.

[5] *Mühlbauer W, Henckel von Donnersmarck G, Hoefter E, Hartinger A:* Keratinozytenzüchtung und -transplantation bei Verbrennungen. Chirurg; 66: 271–6, 1995.

[6] *Nunez Gutierrez H, Castro-Munozledo F, Kuri-Harcuch W:* Combined use of allograft and autograft epidermal cultures in therapy of burns. Plast Reconstr Surg 1996; 98: 929–41.

[7] *Rheinwald JG, Green H:* Serial cultivation of strains of human epidermal keratinocytes: the formation of keratinizing colonies from single cells. Cell; 6: 331–43, 1975.

[8] *Rivas-Torres MT, Amato D, Arambula-Alvarez H, Kuri-Harcuch W:* Controlled clinical study of skin donor sites and deep partial-thickness burns treated with cultured epidermal allografts. Plast Reconstr Surg 1996; 98: 278–87.

Use of Allogeneic Human Keratinocytes Cultured on Dried Porcine Dermis in the Treatment of Burns

E. Matoušková, L. Brož , P. Veselý, R. Königová

Summary

The absence of the dermal component pre-disposes cultured keratinocyte sheets to instability, contractibility, and difficult handling. In order to overcome these disadvantages, we developed recombined human/pig skin (RHPS) composed of human keratinocytes cultured on acellular pig dermis. The RHPS is applied "upside-down", with the epidermal cells facing the wound. Thus RHPS serves in this way as an effective keratinocyte delivery system. It has been proved that keratinocytes can migrate from the inverted RHPS, covered with confluent keratinocyte layer, onto the culture dish. RHPS with allogeneic keratinocytes allows early grafting without requiring dispase digestion to release the graft from the dish. The advantage of RHPS, in comparison with cultured keratinocyte sheets, is the skin-like consistency and thus higher resistance, easy handling and optimal adhesiveness resulting in a hemostatic effect. RHPS has been used successfully for the treatment of donor sites and deep dermal burns. Donor sites healed within 6–8 days compared to 14–18 days in controls. In immunodeficient patients with prolonged wound healing donor sites epithelized in 7–10 days under RHPS compared to 32–90 days in areas treated with tulle gras and dry gauze. From 20 deep dermal burns 13 healed completely within 4–14 days after RHPS application, three wounds showed partial healing and in 4 healing was not achieved because of a thin necrotic layer remaining on the wound bed.

Introduction

Traumatic wound management has always been based on the fundamental surgical principle of immediate débridement of necrotic tissue and primary wound closure. Burns have been the exception to this principle. A burn wound and all the subsequent events observed in the patient represent a continuum without any clear points of separation [1]. Although early excision and grafting changed dramatically local care, this procedure is still restricted by difficulty in diagnosing burn depth, by limited donor sites and by technical skills to excise certain areas (face, perineum). The depth of the burn wound is determinant of the late prognosis causing fatal outcome in very extensive burns and influencing quality of life due to scar formation in survivors. Depth is a variable factor being altered by many additional insults. Wound which appears superficial on day one may appear deep on day three or four. Conversion of superficial dermal into deep dermal or even into full thickness skin loss is encountered during the whole course of burn treatment.

Treatment of full thickness burns is based on use of donor sites for split-thickness skin auto-grafting. Treatment of deep dermal burns consists either in the application of antibacterial creams or in gentle laminary excision and immediate coverage of the excised area with biological dressings, synthetic membranes or, most efficiently, by thin split-thickness auto-grafts [2]. Treatment with antibacterial creams prevents development of early infection, but actual healing is prolonged. The reason is that the necrolysis of the thin necrotic layer followed by spontaneous epithelization from residual adnexas has to take place. If the healing is too long it can cause granulation resulting in hypertrophic scars and contractures. On the contrary, excision removes the thin necrotic layer and a suitable immediate coverage of the wound bed prevents dehydration which otherwise would result in microthrombosis followed by conversion to full thickness skin loss. The quality of the cover influences healing decisively.

In the last two decades it has been possible to culture human keratinocytes serially with large expansion factors [3, 4]. Since 1981 cultured human keratinocyte sheets have been used in treatment of burns and other skin defects [5]. Autologous as well as allogeneic keratinocytes can serve as an effective deep dermal burn cover [6], although they do not solve (without allograft skin pregrafting) the problem of full thickness skin loss. However, they may decrease their size by preventing the conversion of deep dermal wounds into full thickness ones. The production of autologous grafts takes about 3 weeks, during which time the patient is susceptible to sepsis and wound deepening. Therefore, in our practice, we prefer using allogeneic keratinocytes because they can be prepared in advance and be ready for immediate usage.

Cultured epidermal sheets are, however, very thin, fragile and retractile, with low adherence to the wound bed and low resistance to mechanical stress and infection [7, 8]. Moreover, before grafting they must be enzymatically released from the dish. This process is rather laborious and may be harmful for the keratinocyte quality, as it removes some of the basement membrane proteins [9] and the support for cell attachment.

In order to overcome some of the disadvantages of multilayered keratinocyte grafts, we developed recombined human/pig skin (RHPS) composed of human keratinocytes cultured on acellular pig dermis [10, 11]. The graft is applied "upside-down", with the epidermal cells facing the wound. In this way RHPS serves as an effective keratinocyte delivery system. The advantage in comparison to cultured keratinocyte sheets is the skin-like consistency and thus easy handling and higher resistance.

Methods

Preparation of the RHPS

Allogeneic keratinocytes were obtained from the redundant skin of healthy donors after mammoplasty. Donors were tested for hepatitis B and C, BWR and repeatedly for HIV. RHPS was prepared as described previously [10]. Briefly, pig skin from slaughtered animals was shaven. Sheets of approximately 7x40 cm in size and 0.2–0.3 mm thick were removed with a Humby knife and bathed in a solution of streptomycin 4 g/l, chloramphenicol 6 g/l and furantoin 2.4 g/l. Skin sheets (xenografts, routinely used in the Prague Burn Centre as temporary cover of burns) were trypsinized overnight at 4°C, then 30 min at 37°C, and then shaken to remove the epidermis and fibroblasts. The dermis was thoroughly washed and macerated in sterile redistilled water. It was cut into pieces, spread on the bottom of a tissue culture dish (epidermal side up) and by drying adhered to it. The dried dermis was stored at room temperature. Prior to seeding the cells, it was washed for 10 min with 70% ethanol and for 5 min with PBS.

The medium for cultivation of 3T3 cells was H-MEM (Eagle's MEM in Hanks' buffered saline) supplemented with all non-essential amino-acids, 0.12 g/l sodium pyruvate, 1 g/l NaHCO$_3$ and 10% bovine serum (pretested for optimal growth of 3T3 cells). For keratinocytes the medium was enriched with 0.5 µg/ml hydrocortisone (Spofa, Czech Republic), 5 µg/ml insulin (NOVO, Denmark), 10^{-10} M cholera toxin (Sigma, USA), 5 ng/ml epidermal growth factor (Sigma, USA) and 2% fetal bovine serum. Primary keratinocytes and 3T3 cells were grown in tightly closed tissue culture bottles. Secondary human keratinocytes were cultured in dishes with the dried pig dermis in a humidified 3.5% CO$_2$ atmosphere. The irradiated 3T3

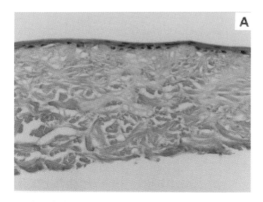

Fig. 1: (A) Vertical section of RHPS. Confluent human keratinocytes form 1–2 layers on the acellular xenodermis. **(B)** RHPS graft lifted from the culture dish.

cells were used as feeders in both, primary as well as secondary keratinocyte cultures, at a concentration of 2.5×10^4 cells/cm^2.

The cell growth was followed on areas not covered by the dermis or on specimens stained by May-Grünwald (10 min) and Giemsa-Romanowski (15 min). The 3T3 cells can be selectively washed off by trypsin or EDTA [10].

The metabolic activity of cultures was measured by the decrease of the glucose concentration in the medium during 24 h using the Beckmann glucometer as described previously [12]. To assess the viability and migrational activity of the reverted keratinocytes, the RHPS (meshed or nonmeshed) was inverted "upside-down" on the culture dish and migration of keratinocytes was followed for 1 week using phase contrast microscopy.

Wound Preparation in Deep Dermal Burns

20 deep dermal wounds in 16 patients were grafted. The wound area treated with RHPS was 35–200 cm^2. The wounds were prepared either by tangential excision or by dermabrasion. Tangential excision – laminar excision with Watson knife, gentle enough to avoid losing deep epidermal cells. Dermabrasion – blunt dermabrasion to the level of capillary bleeding.

Grafting with RHPS

The RHPS grafts were applied "upside-down" (keratinocyte layer facing the wound) to donor sites or deep dermal burns and covered with tulle gras and dry (or in some cases cholera toxin free medium wetted) gauze. Controls were covered with tulle gras and dry gauze.

Three forms of RHPS containing allogeneic keratinocytes were used: (a) *Subconfluent RHPS* – pig dermis covered with a subconfluent keratinocyte layer (4–7 days after cell seeding). The advantage of this type of RHPS is a shorter cultivation period. The disadvantage is the necessity to wash out the rest of the irradiated 3T3 cells with trypsin [10]. (b) *Confluent unmeshed RHPS* (further *confluent*) – pig dermis covered with a confluent or postconfluent keratinocyte layer (8–29 days after cell seeding). (c) *Confluent meshed RHPS* (further *meshed*) – confluent RHPS meshed at the rate of 1.5:1 or 3:1.

Results

The results are based on data published in Matousková et al. [11].

Keratinocyte Growth and RHPS Morphology

Secondary keratinocyte cultures, grown from cryopreserved cell suspension (seeding density 6×10^3 keratinocytes/cm^2) reached confluency within 8–10 days. Freshly confluent keratinocytes produced 1–2 epithelial layers on

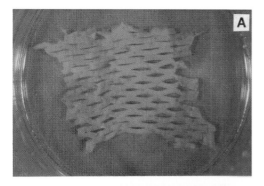

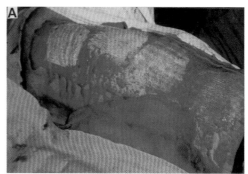

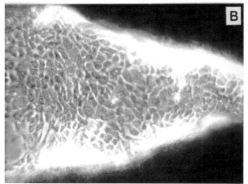

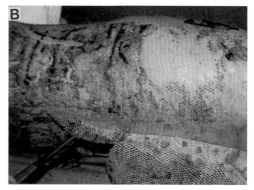

Fig. 2: Migration of keratinocytes from the inverted RHPS to the culture dish. (**A**) Meshed RHPS (3:1), (**B**) the windows of the mesh were covered with epithelial cells in 4 days.

Fig. 3: Healing of a donor site covered with RHPS in a 3-year-old boy burned on 65 % of TBSA. (**A**) Four RHPS grafts applied on donor site, (**B**) dry RHPS grafts peeled off the healed donor site 8 days after application.

xenodermis (Fig. 1); four-week postconfluent keratinocytes created 1–4 cell layers surrounded by spontaneously formed fibres of extracellular matrix. Postconfluent keratinocytes were metabolically fully active up to four weeks after having reached confluency (evident from the rapidly decreasing pH of the medium).

We compared the metabolic activity of RHPS with simple cultured epidermal sheets mounted on tulle gras. After 24 h, the simple epidermal sheets consumed only 64 % of the glucose consumption of the RHPS grafts.

Migration of Keratinocytes From the Inverted RHPS in Vitro

After inverting RHPS upside-down, the keratinocytes (subconfluent, confluent and also postconfluent) migrated from the edges of the graft onto the surrounding free surface of the dish. The windows of the mesh (3:1) were covered with epithelia in 4–5 days (Fig. 2).

The "Take" of RHPS

The "take" of RHPS was visually recognizable. The graft adhered firmly to the underlying wound tissue within 24 h. It appeared as a dry thin brownish membrane (Fig. 3 and 5). The firm attachment of the graft developed only in RHPS grafts applied with the epithelium facing the wound bed. It was not observed if RHPS was applied with normal orientation (dermis down, keratinocytes up), or if acellular xenodermis, or xenodermis covered with autologous or allogeneic

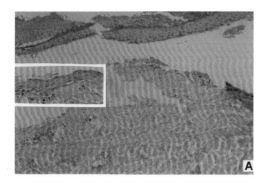

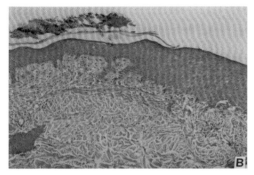

Fig. 4: Histology of a donor site after treatment with RHPS. (**A**) Four days after RHPS application epidermis was stratified but not yet anchored to the dermis (RHPS peeled of the wound during biopsy). *Insert:* epidermis attached to the wound bed. (**B**) Fully stratified epidermis, locally hypertrophic, with shallow rete ridges 8 days after RHPS application.

fibroblasts were used. After 4–8 days, the dry part of the graft was peeled off with forceps, leaving a newly formed epithelium underneath (Fig. 3 and 5).

Donor Sites

Donor sites grafted with RHPS were completely epithelized within 6–8 days (Fig. 3). No significant differences were noted in the healing time of donor sites treated with either confluent, subconfluent, or meshed RHPS. Control donor sites treated with tulle gras and dry gauze healed within 14–18 days.

Donor sites of immunodeficient patients with prolonged wound healing (e.g. over 65

years old patients or patients with extensive over 60 % TBSA burns) epithelized in 7–10 days under RHPS compared to 32–90 days in donor areas treated with tulle gras and dry gauze.

Histological examination of RHPS-treated donor site 4 days after grafting (Fig. 4A) showed a multilayered epithelium which was not yet firmly anchored to dermis (rete ridges missing), but still adherent to dried xenodermis; in this stage there was no epithelization in controls. On day 8, RHPS-treated areas developed well stratified, often hypertrophic epidermis with shallow rete ridges (Fig. 4B). Control areas on day 8 only started epithelization from adnexas.

Deep Dermal Burns

In deep dermal burns (IIb degree) superficial tangentional excision (saving the adnexa) or abrasion to the layer of capillary bleeding appeared to be essential for the "take" of RHPS. The wound bed should resemble the donor site.

From 20 deep dermal burn wounds 13 (65 %) completely healed within 4–14 days (Fig. 5 and 6). Three wounds (15 %) showed partial healing (60 %–70 % wound area reduction). In 4 patients (20 %) the graft did not "take" (probably because a thin necrotic layer remained on the wound) and the wound had to be autografted. Seven days after successful grafting, histological examination of the RHPS-healed deep dermal burn showed well stratified epidermis of variable thickness and irregular morphology, with flatter rete ridges than in the normal skin (Fig. 6B)

From 5 full-thickness burns 4 cases after fascial necrectomy and temporary xenografting were not successful, the grafts did not "take". The only successful case, clinically assessed as a 3rd degree burn wound, required 3 subsequent RHPS grafting and antibiotic treatment. It healed in 18 days presumably due to remaining single deep keratinocytes.

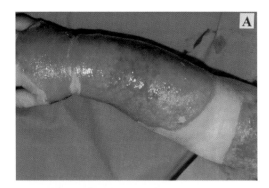

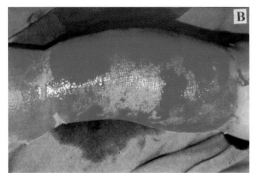

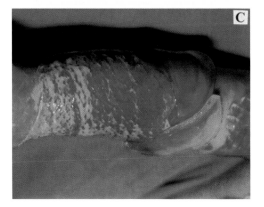

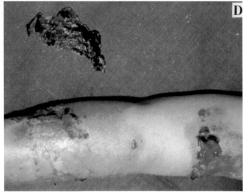

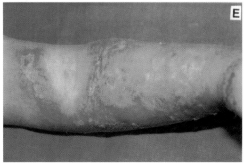

Fig. 5: A 10-month-old boy suffered deep dermal scalds over 26 % of his body surface. On day 3 after the accident the wounded area on the right arm (**A**) was tangentially excised (**B**) and covered with RHPS (**C**), the edge of the wound was covered with Aquagel (Rybus and Rybus, Poland). The left arm, which was evaluated to be analogically scalded, was treated partially with xenografts and partially with silversulfadiazine cream. The right arm healed five days after excision (day 9 after the accident) (**D**), while the burn on the left arm deepened (**E**) and had to be excised and autografted on day 17.

Discussion

The recombined human/pig skin composed of human allogeneic keratinocytes cultured on cell-free pig dermis was used as a keratinocyte delivery system in the treatment of burns. Dried xenodermis was chosen as culture substratum because it had been proved to be a good support for cell growth and its consistency is similar to human dermis, providing the RHPS with biomechanical properties of normal skin. The graft does not need to be enzymatically detached from the dish, is easy to handle, does not shrink, is optimally adhesive, has a haemostatic effect and is more resistant to any kind of stress in comparison with cultured keratinocyte sheets. At the Prague Burn Centre pig skin has been used since 1973 as temporary cover on burn wounds (550–700 patients per year) without any side effects [13].

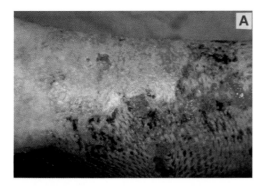

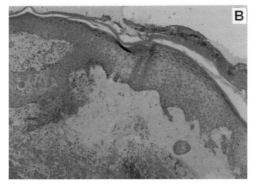

Fig. 6: A 20 year-old male suffered deep dermal flame burn over 11% of TBSA. One part of the wound was grafted with RHPS after tangential excision, the rest was xenografted. The area treated with RHPS appeared to be healed within 4 days, while the area covered with xenografts had to be autografted on day 9. (A) RHPS treated area healed, the rest was autografted. (B) Histology of the RHPS treated area – 7 days after RHPS application (14 days after accident).

To achieve direct contact of keratinocytes with the wound bed, the recombined skin must be applied in the "upside-down" manner. It "takes" poorly in wound beds with full-thickness skin loss. On the other hand, RHPS applied on a deep dermal wound can prevent conversion and save the areas which would otherwise require autografting. RHPS was able to survive under conditions, in which cultured epidermal sheets would probably collapse [11].

The wound preparation is essential for keratinocyte attachment. Donor sites represent an ideal wound bed and their healing with RHPS was always successful in about one week. Deep dermal wounds should be prepared in a manner to resemble donor sites as far as possible. Necrotic tissue must be completely removed, but it is necessary to be careful to preserve the adnexa remnants. The best way of wound preparation was tangential excision, preferably up to 5 days after the accident, while the wound is usually not yet infected. The second alternative was deep dermabrasion to the level of capillary bleeding, which was most effective several days after the treatment with antibacterial creams that accelerated dissolution of the thin necrotic layer. In case of deep burns between deep dermal and full thickness skin loss (but also in infected wounds) it is preferable to repeat grafting in 2–3 day intervals.

Although it has been confirmed that it is possible to use subconfluent or confluent keratinocytes on xenodermis, in practice confluent RHPS grating is the simplest way. Such graft can be simply lifted from the dish and spread on the wound area without dispase release or other procedures (from subconfluent RHPS graft 3T3 cells must be washed off). However, this technique often provokes the question, whether the "upside down" applied confluent keratinocytes can "take" or whether they stimulate epithelization only via the production of growth factors [14]. We have shown that keratinocytes from subconfluent, confluent and even 2 week-postconfluent RHPS placed "upside-down" (keratinocytes down, dermis up) on the tissue culture dish are able to attach to the bottom of the dish, migrate and proliferate (Fig. 2). In a similar way, keratinocytes in vivo could attach to a wound bed that may act as culture substratum. The temporary "take" (incorporation of cells into the newly formed epidermis) of confluent, inverted allogeneic keratinocytes was proved by morphology, immunocytochemistry and fluorescence in situ hybridization for the Y chromosome in female recipient grafted with male cells. These results were presented in The International Symposium and Course on Burns and Fire Disaster Management, held in Jerusalem, Israel, February 13–16, 2000 [15] and will be the subject of our next publication.

It has been considered that RHPS "close" (not only cover) the wound because donor keratinocytes attach to the wound bed, proliferate and form several epidermal layers (Fig. 4A). Early "closure" of the wound with allokeratinocyte-RHPS may be important to span the period before patient's keratinocytes from deep adnexal structures are activated and replace donor cells. Such "closure" may also reduce release of mediators that influence further deepening of burn wounds.

Other types of delivery systems, such as autologous keratinocytes dispersed in fibrin glue [16] or pre-confluent keratinocytes grown on a polymeric membrane in serum free medium [17] have been used for treatment of burns. Lately, laser skin was used, where autologous keratinocytes are grown on a laser-perforated hyaluronic acid membrane and applied with normal orientation [14, 18]. However, to achieve satisfactory stability and mechanical quality on full thickness wounds, these method should also be combined in a two-stage procedure with allogeneic dermis or a dermal substitute, which is a rather complicated and prolonged process. For deep dermal burns and donor sites allokeratinocyte-RHPS grafting remains one of the simplest and most effective treatment methods (quick and easy). One of RHPS greatest advantages consists in its ability to heal the wound soon after injury, a fact that is very important for burns. The second important advantage is optimal adhesiveness resulting in a haemostatic effect (RHPS immediately stops bleeding) and the fact that it needs not be fixed (sutured) to the wound bed. Nuñez-Gutiérez at al. [19] proved that a complex treatment of burns with cultured allo- and autografts shortened hospitalization. RHPS has similar healing effects, but the treatment is simplified. The allogeneic keratinocyte source is actually unlimited, it is possible to get a large amount of cells from one donor, to freeze them in suspension until all donor tests are performed. The transplantation safety is guaranteed by the fact that the skin donors are tested according to the same rules as blood donors. The pig dermis is sterile, completely free from pig cells (see method of preparation), so that infection danger is minimized.

The RHPS delivery system represents a remarkable stimulation for host epithelization. The results in the treatment of burned patients are comparable to those reported for successful grafting with cultured epidermal sheets [7, 20]. However, grafting with the RHPS has been easier and safer with a low level of graft losses because of the graft firmness, optimal adhesivity, keratinocyte support, and wound protection.

Acknowledgments

This work was financially supported by grant No. NC 4368-3 from the Grant Agency of the Ministry of Health of the Czech Republic.

References

[1] Williams WG, Phillips LG: Pathophysiology of the Burn Wound. In: D.N. Herndon: Total Burn Care, W.B. Saunders Company LTD, London, Philadelphia, pp. 63–70 (1996)

[2] Janzekovic Z:A new concept in the early excision and immediate grafting of burns. J Trauma 10:1103–1108 (1970)

[3] Rheinwald JG, Green H: Serial cultivation of strains of human epidermal keratinocytes: the formation of keratinizing colonies from the single cells. Cell 6:331–344 (1975)

[4] Green H, Kehinde O, Thomas J: Growth of cultured human epidermal cells into multiple epithelia suitable for grafting. Proc Nat Acad Sci USA 76: 5665–5668 (1979)

[5] O'Connor NE, Mulliken JB, Banks-Schlegel S, Kehinde O, Green H: Grafting of burns with cultured epithelium prepared from autologous epidermal cells. Lancet 1:75–78 (1981)

[6] Bolivar-Flores J, Poumian E, Marsch-Moreno M, Montes de Oca G, Kuri-Harcuch W: Use of cultured human epidermal keratinocytes for allografting burns and conditions for temporary banking of the cultured allografts. Burns 16:3–8 (1990)

[7] Leigh IM: Keratinocyte autografting, allografting and wound healing. In: The Keratinocyte Handbook (Leigh IM, Lane EB, Watt FM, eds.), Cambridge University Press, pp. 513–526 (1994)

[8] Tamisani AM, Fereti S, Sangiorgio L: Critical Reflection on the use of human cultured ke-

ratinocytes in children with burns. Eur J Pediatr Surg 2:223–226 (1992)

[9] *McKay I, Woodward B, Wood K, Navsaria HA, Hoekstra H, Green C:* Reconstruction of human skin from glycerol-preserved allodermis and cultured keratinocyte sheet. Burns 20 (Suppl 1):S19–22 (1994)

[10] *Matousková E, Vogtová D, Königová R:* A recombined skin composed of human keratinocytes cultured on cell-free pig dermis. Burns 19:118–123 (1993)

[11] *Matoušková E, Buček S, Vogtová D, Veselý P, Chaloupková A, Brož L, Singerová H, Pavlíková L, Königová R:* Treatment of burns and donor sites with human allogeneic keratinocytes grown on acellular pig dermis. Br J Dermatol 136:901–907 (1997)

[12] *Dvořánková B, Matousková E, Vogtová D:* Metabolic activity of cultured skin grafts cryopreserved in different forms. Folia Biol (Praha) 40: 149–159 (1994)

[13] *Moserová J, Houšková E:* The healing and treatment of skin defects. S.Karger AG, Basel,; p.143–151 (1989)

[14] *Harris PA, Leigh IM, Navsaria HA:* Pre-confluent keratinocyte grafting: the future for cultured skin replacement? Burns 24:591–593 (1998)

[15] *Matousková E, Brož L, Pokorná E:* Characterization of wound healing accelerated by up-

side down transplanted human keratinocytes cultured on acellular porcine dermis. In ABSTRACTS of "The International Symposium and Course on Burns and Fire Disaster Management", Jerusalem, Israel, February 13–16, 2000, p.46 (2000)

[16] *Stark GB, Kaiser HW, Horch R, Kopp J, Spilker G:* Cultured autologous keratinocytes suspended in fibrin glue (KFGS) with allogeneic overgraft for definitive burn wound coverage. Eur J Plast Surg 18:267–271 (1995)

[17] *Barlow Y, Burt A, Clarke JA, McGrouther DA, Lang SM:* The use of a polymeric film for the culture and transfer of subconfluent autologous keratinocytes to patients. J Tissue Viability 2:33–36 (1992)

[18] *Harris PA, di Francesco F, Barisoni D, Leigh IM, Navsaria HA:* Use of hyaluronic acid and cultured autologous keratinocytes and fibroblasts in extensive burns. Lancet 353:35–36 (1999)

[19] *Nuñez-Gutiérrez H, Castro-Muñozledo F, Kuri-Harcuch W:* Combined use of allograft and autograft epidermal cultures in therapy of burns. Plast Reconstr Surg 98:929–939. (1996)

[20] *Madden MR, Finkelstein JL, Staiano-Coico L, Goodwin CW, Shires GT, Nolan EE, Hepton JM:* Grafting of cultured allogeneic epidermis on second- and third degree burn wounds on 26 patients. J Trauma 26:955–962 (1986)

Cultured Epithelial Autografts for the Coverage of Massive Burns – the Baltimore Experience

A. M. Munster, R. J. Spence

Summary

We present ten years' experience with cultured epithelial autografts(CEA). There were 39 patients with an average burn size of 67%. These were compared to a group of 48 simultaneous, but not randomized, controls with an average burn size of 61.2%. There was a significant reduction in the mortality rate from 48% in the controls to 18% in the CEA group. Total hospital costs were much higher in the CEA group, but this difference disappeared when the costs were calculated per diem instead of total hospital. The readmission rate for regrafting or reconstruction was significantly higher in the CEA group. Currently, the use of CEA can be optimized by preallografting the excised burn bed, and by minimizing the area grafted with CEA. In the future, composites will improve the functional outcome.

We grafted our first patient with cultured epithelial autografts (CEA) in the summer of 1988. Between 1988 and 2000, at this time of writing, a total of 39 patients have undergone CEA grafting; a matching control group of 48 patients has been created for comparison of results. Our experience is different from most other centers for three reasons: first, all patients were pre-allografted with allograft skin at least once, but often several times, while the CEA was being processed. Second, the prospective control group is unique, as will be explained below. Third, the source of the cells has been exclusively commercial from one source, initially Biosurface Technology Inc., later Genzyme Co., of Cambridge, Mass.

In the 12 years of use of this material, much has been learned, both about the advantages and the limitations of CEA. In this chapter, we present our up-to-date experience and discuss some of what we have learned in the process. Because our early experience and the historical background of the development of commercially available CEA have been previously reviewed [1, 2] detailed discussion of these subjects will be omitted.

Patients and Methods

Patients with total body surface burns of 50% or more admitted to the Baltimore Regional Burn Center became candidates for inclusion in this study. To qualify, the patient had to satisfy the following two criteria:

1. skin biopsy for culture with intent to graft and
2. survival past the first cultured skin grafting operation, or, in case CEA was not used, survival past the first major excision and closure procedure.

The Hospital allocated a certain budget for the purchase of the commercially produced cultured skin, each fiscal year beginning July 1. When the allocation was sufficient for the fiscal year (fewer patients requiring grafting), all eligible patients received cultured skin grafts. When the allocation was insufficient (and in one year, all of the allocation was spent within two months!), the remaining patients during that year received standard

Table 1: Patient Population.

	Cultured	Control	p
N	39	48	–
Age	33.3 ± 2.3	39.6 ± 2.4	N.S.
Burn Size (% BSA)	67.2 ± 2.7 (range 21–91)	61.8 ± 1.5 (range 50–96)	<0.011
3rd Degree %	44.3 ± 3.3 (range 11–86.0)	38.8 ± 2.9 (range 1–93.0)	N.S.
Male / Female	32/7	41/7	N.S.
Smoke Inhalation	35/39 (90 %)	32/48 (67%)	<0.011

grafts using a variety of accepted techniques. Thus, this study was not truly randomized, but it was prospective. As will be shown below, the two groups matched very well.

Patients who were to receive cultured CEA autografts underwent excision and allografting operation of the areas designated for cultured skin at the first sitting with additional excisions and immediate autografting of other areas as conditions permitted. Allografts were removed and replaced, together with light re-excision when indicated, every five to seven days until the cultures were ready for placement. Immediately before cultured skin placement, allografts were removed one final time and again, light re-excision performed where allograft adherence had been less than optimal.

No attempt was made to cover *all* of the excised burn area with cultured skin. Indeed, between one-third and one half of the total burn area was grafted with autograft even in the CEA patients. This was done mainly to reduce costs but also because preferred geographic sites such as the hands, face, and

perineum were always autografted with split-thickness grafts harvested from the patient if at all possible.

The patient population is shown in Table 1. There were no significant differences between the groups as to age, sex, total body surface burn size, and third degree component, although the cultured skin group total burn size was marginally larger. Smoke inhalation injury in our institution is simply defined as the need for endotracheal intubation and respirator support within 24 hours of admission, i.e., these patients have a truly severe injury. By this criterion, the cultured skin group had a statistically significantly higher incidence of inhalation injury than the controls (90 % vs. 66 %, p< 0.01).

Results

Results are summarized in Table 2. There was no statistically significant difference between the groups as to the timing of initial surgery or the occurrence of major complica-

Table 2: Clinical Results.

	Cultured	Control	p
First OR day after burn	4.3 ± 0.5	5.3 ± 0.5	N.S.
Total hospital days	91.7 ± 12.1	51.0 ± 3.2	<0.005
No. of surgical procedures for grafting	6.4 ± 0.4	3.7 ± 0.3	<0.026
Major complications	14/39 (36 %)	25/48 (52 %)	N.S.
Mortality	7/39 (18 %)	23/48 (48 %)	<0.003
Total Cost ($)	350,205 ± 47,565	117,261 ± 13,777	<0.010
Per Diem Cost ($)	4,043 ± 234	4,514 ± 434	N.S.

Table 3: Readmission for Surgery

	Cultured	Control	p
N	14/39 (36%)	6/48 (12%)	<0.01
Mean number of procedures per patient	5.0	3.5	–
Mean time of First re-operation (months)	23.9 (range 1–97)	24.0 (range 0.3–95)	N.S.

tions. The most striking difference is the reduced mortality rate seen in the cultured skin group, 18% vs. control group, 48%. The predicted mortality rate for the control group would be 75% according to the formula of Zawacki [3] and somewhere between 33% and 90% according to the most recent formula of Ryan et al. [4]. Since the mortality rate of the controls matches published national figures, the improvements seen in the CEA group can be considered genuine.

Because breakdown and need for reconstruction are often cited as problems in those patients grafted with CEA without dermal support, we also analyzed the details of readmission for regrafting or reconstructive procedures in all patients, and these results are shown in Table 3.

The total number of patients needing reconstruction was significantly higher in the CEA group than the control group: over a third of patients with CEA required further surgical intervention. Twenty-one operative procedures were performed on control patients and 71 on patients initially covered with CEA. However, a single patient with an original 92% burn required 32 procedures over a period of eight years. If this patient is removed from the analysis, the *average* number of re-operative procedures per patient becomes similar, 3.5 in the controls and 3.3 in the CEA group, p = N.S.

Discussion

The global experience with the "take" rates of CEA is extremely variable. In a database of over 500 patients, if a burn wound is excised and grafted immediately with cultured keratinocytes, or if a nonbiological cover is used as a temporary dressing, the "take" rate is 50 to 60%. If allograft coverage is employed for the initial wound coverage and entirely removed at the time of the CEA placement, which was our technique in this series, the „take"rate is approximately 70%. If a dermal component is left behind and CEA grafted onto a viable dermal bed, that figure can be raised to 80% [5]. Clearly, technical considerations matter a great deal in improving results.

In aftercare, meticulous fixation of the dressings with non-shearing bandages and limb immobilization with splints is also important. It is our custom to moisturize dressings lightly with an antibiotic (polymyxin-bacitracin) solution and not to disturb the dressings for an absolute minimum of ten days, and optimally, even longer.

Often cost is another factor cited which needs to be considered in using this wound coverage methodology. Costs can be reduced and results improved by using CEA only as an *adjunct* to burn wound coverage, i.e., not covering the entire wound with cultured material. We graft as much as possible with the patient's own skin and the remainder with CEA. Analysis of the per diem costs of care show a mean of $4,043 in the cultured group, and $4,514 in the controls, p = N.S. Of course, the total cost of hospitalization is higher because of the expense of the CEA, but this extra expense is neutralized by the increased survival, therefore the increased length of stay, of these patients. We feel that the fairest way to analyze costs is to examine the daily, rather than the total, costs. Our current practice is to save the patient's own donor sites for aesthetically or functionally critical areas (face, hands) and secondarily for areas where the take rate is somewhat lower (perianal area, back). In addition, if at all possible, it is preferable to graft the lower legs with autologous split-thickness skin, even if widely expanded, to better sustain the trauma of dependence and ambulation. All other areas of the body can be grafted quite satisfactorily with CEA.

Experience at other centers has matched ours. Chalumeau et al [6] reported a final take rate of 84 % in a group of children with an average burn size of 82 %. Gober et al[7] reported 60 % take in acute burn, but 100 % take in reconstructive burn procedures with excellent aesthetic and functional results in burned children. Recently, Carsin et al have reported the results from 30 patients with very large burns and a survival of 90 %, with a mean CEA take rate of 69 % [8].

Because many other workers' experience is covered elsewhere in this book, and a wide variety of technologies explored both for the production and application of cultured skin alone or composite with dermal components, these subjects will not be discussed further in this chapter. Suffice to say that the use of cultured epithelial autografts for massive burns has been an excellent adjunct to treatment, and, in one form or another, will remain part of the surgical armamentarium for the foreseeable future.

References

[1] *Munster AM:* Cultured skin for massive burns – A prospective, controlled trial. Ann. Surg.; 224:372–377, 1996

[2] *Rennekampff HO, Kiessig V, Hansborougj JF:* Current concepts in the development of cultured skin replacements. J. Surg. Res.; 62:288–295, 1996

[3] *Zawacki BE, Azen SP, Imbus SH, Chang YT:* Multifactorial probit analysis of mortality in burned patients. Ann.Surg.; 189(1):1–5, 1979

[4] *Ryan CM, Schoenfeld DA, Thorpe WP, Sheridan RL, Cassem EH and Tompkins RG:* Objective estimates of the probability of death from burn injuries. New Eng. J. Med.; 338(6):362–6, 1998

[5] Data from the registry of the Genzyme Corporation, 1999.

[6] *Chalumeau M, Saulnier JP, Ainaud P, Lebever H, Stephanazzi J, Leco A and Carsin H:* Initial general management and surgery of six extensively burned children treated with cultured epithelial autografts. J. Pediatr Surg; 34(4):602–5, 1999

[7] *Gober R, Raghunath M, Altermatt S, Meuli-Simmen C, Benathan M and Meuli M:* Efficacy of cultured epithelial autografts in pediatric burns and reconstructive surgery. Surgery; 121(6): 654–61, 1997

[8] *Carsin H, Ainaud P, Le Bever H, Rives JM, Lakhel A, Stephanazzi J, Lambert F and Perrot J:* Cultured epithelial autografts in extensive burn coverage of severely traumatized patients: A five year single-center experience with 30 patients. Burns; 26:379–87, 2000

Autologous Keratinocytes Combined with a Collagen-GAG Matrix

C. E. Butler, D. P. Orgill

Summary

An optimal tissue engineered skin will have both dermal and epidermal function. We combined autologous keratinocytes with a well-characterized highly porous collagen-GAG matrix in a porcine model. Keratinocytes were either directly seeded into the matrix to proliferate in vivo or grown into multi-layer sheets in cell culture prior to transplant onto a vascularized matrix. In both cases a multi-layer keratinizing epidermis, basement membrane and neodermal structure resulted. Both of these techniques result in a treatment sequence that could be performed in one operative setting. Combining autologous keratinocytes with collagen-glycosaminoglycan membranes may be a useful strategy for skin replacement in reconstructive surgery.

Introduction

Skin protects mammals from the environment by the barrier functions of the epidermis and the mechanical properties of the dermis. Current clinically available skin substitutes focus on either dermal or epidermal replacement. There is controversy as to the optimal method of achieving both epidermal and dermal coverage. Using a porcine full-thickness wound model, a well characterized dermal extracellular matrix analog (DEMA), composed of a highly porous, cross-linked collagen/glycosaminoglycan (CG) matrix, was used to study the temporal and spatial constraints in combining autologous keratinocytes.

Many skin substitutes have been developed in an attempt to circumvent the limited availability of skin graft donor sites with large surface area wounds. These efforts have focused on epidermal replacement, dermal replacement, or composite replacement of both layers. Composite replacement technology holds the promise of providing a single stage closure: providing simultaneous epidermal and dermal coverage of the wound.

Epidermal Replacements

Cultural Epithelial Autografts (CEAs) are confluent stratified epidermal sheets that can be grafted onto a wound. These are reviewed in detail in the other chapters in this book. The quality of the healing achieved by CEA alone, without dermal substrate, has been assessed in burn patients with histologic and immunohistochemical studies at 5 years resurfaced with human CEA. Although the late results show incredible remodeling and development of the dermal-epidermal junction, (DEJ) [1], most clinicians find CEAs difficult to work with and unstable early on.

Dermal Replacements Combined with CEA

The limited success achieved with CEAs grafted alone has encouraged the use of CEA in conjunction with dermal substrates. Cuono, *et al.* [2]. reported a successful transplantation technique in humans that employed cryopreserved allogenic skin for dermal replacement and CEA to generate epidermis. When the highly antigenic epidermis was removed by dermabrasion the remaining transplanted dermis was not rejected. This dermal allograft supported the normal growth and differentiation of the keratinocyte grafts and formation of an intact dermal-epidermal junction, including anchoring fibrils.

Other studies support the use of a dermal substrate with CEA. The percent take of cultured grafts was improved from 4% to 47% by the use of a dermal graft in a porcine model [3]. A survey of the use of CEA on cadaveric dermal allograft substrates indicated a take rate of approximately 90%, which is a considerably higher take rate than that achieved on wound bed granulation tissue [3]. The experimental and clinical evidence to date suggests that a dermal-like substrate promotes the take and stability of CEAs.

Dermal Replacements

Yannas *et al.* [5–7] have developed an array of acellular, biodegradable collagen-glycosaminoglycan (CG) copolymer matrices by co-precipitating type 1 bovine hide collagen and shark chondroitin-6-sulfate. This was then lyophilized to produce a highly porous membrane. Collagen cross-linking was achieved with vacuum dehydration and exposure to glutaraldehyde. Room temperature vulcanizing silicone was applied to the surface. Biologic activity was highly dependent on specific physicochemical properties such as porosity, glycosaminoglycan (GAG) content and cross-link density. Only a small fraction of these matrices demonstrated biologic activity by interacting with wounds to produce a neodermal structure as they were simultaneously degraded. CG matrix that has biologic activity is defined as a Dermal Extracellular Matrix Analog (DEMA). DEMAs posses the strict physiochemical properties which render them biologically active including mean pore diameter of 80 μm, a GAG content of 8% and a mean molecular weight between crosslinks (M_c) of 10,000 daltons.

Studies of DEMAs were conducted in a Guinea pig model. Seeding the DEMAs with uncultured autologous keratinocytes the contraction kinetics and scar morphology of the wound could be altered. After an original decrease in wound area, wound contraction was arrested and reversed such that three months after wounding, grafted areas preserved greater than 70% of their original areas compared with 15% for unseeded controls. This DEMA has been successfully used in human full-thickness wounds when combined with thin autologous epidermal grafts [8, 9]. Grafting in this fashion allows use of epidermal autografts thinner than conventional split-thickness skin grafts. The resulting skin coverage is similar in quality to that achieved by conventional split-thickness grafts, and the donor site is less deeply wounded, allowing more rapid healing. Currently DEMAs are commercially available for human use.

Another commercially available dermal substitute has been prepared from cadaveric allodermis. The method of preparation removes cellular material and immunogenic elements from the dermis. This has been successfully used to treat full-thickness wounds using thin epidermal autografts for coverage. A theoretical advantage of using this product is that portions of the basement membrane are preserved in the processing [10].

Composite Grafts

Composite grafts have consisted of collagen, collagen-GAG or polyglactin polymers seeded with fibroblasts with a multilayered epidermis [11–15]. Despite the theoretical advantages of this approach, these "skin equivalents" have not achieved success in treating burn wounds. It is possible that the nutrient demands of these bilayer tissues are not adequately met during the critical time after grafting before they are vascularized resulting in decreased take.

Keratinocyte seeded DEMAs placed directly onto wounds without an *in vitro* step to allow for keratinocyte confluence has several theoretic advantages [16–18]. By avoiding the *in vitro* step required for keratinocytes to reach confluence, grafts can be placed on wounds immediately after seeding. When uncultured keratinocytes are used for seeding, skin biopsies can be harvested, processed and seeded into the DEMA during one operative procedure. A portion of the harvested keratinocytes can be placed into cell culture and at later times be resuspended and seeded into matrix that may be immediately grafted when wound coverage is needed.

It has been shown that keratinocytes subcultured [19, 20] from confluent epithelial sheets are "growth arrested" whereas keratinocytes resuspended from subconfluent cultures demonstrate logarithmic phase growth. Subconfluent keratinocytes may interact more favorably with the developing dermis than confluent keratinocytes that are growth arrested. This may contribute to enhanced dermal-epidermal interaction and basement membrane formation.

In this study we desired to use composite graft technology that would minimize the nutrient requirements of a thick membrane immediately after grafting on an open wound. The two methods selected was to seed a small number of keratinocytes within the matrix and allow them to proliferate while the matrix was undergoing vascularization. Using this method we compared both fresh keratinocytes and those grown in culture to sub-confluence. The second method allowed the matrix to vascularized prior to placing a CEA.

Materials and Methods

Aultologous porcine keratinocytes were combined with DEMA's using various modalities to produce a bilayer, functional, neoepidermal and neodermal structure in a Yorkshire Pig full-thickness wound. Confluent CEAs were grafted to vascularized DEMA's in full thickness wound. Uncultured keratinocyte seeded

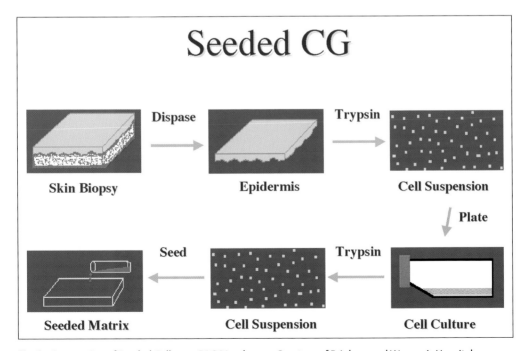

Fig. 1: Preparation of Seeded Collagen-GAG Membrane. Courtesy of Brigham and Women's Hospital.

DEMA's were grafted onto wounds directly. Keratinocytes were cultured to sub-confluence prior to DEMA seeding. An imunohistochemical analysis of seeded DEMA's was performed between days 4 and 35 post-grafting.

Synthesis of Seeded DMEMs

DEMAs were synthesized from bovine hide collagen and chondroiten-6-sulfate as previously described [5–7]. Split thickness skin biopsies, 0.25 mm thick, were taken from the scapular region with a dermatome. The epidermis was separated from dermis with 0.25 % dispase for 2 hours, at 37 °C, shredded and disassociated with 0.1 % trypsin and 0.02 % EDTA for 30 minutes, at 37 °C. The suspension was filtered through a 100-μm filter and placed in Waymouth's medium, supplemented with 20 % fetal calf serum and growth substances [16]. Viable cells were counted using Trypan Blue exclusion. Split thickness skin samples yielded roughly 3 million viable keratinocytes per cm^2.

Vascularized DEMAs covered with a thin silicone film were used as a dermal substrate for CEAs [18]. These were grafted onto full-thickness porcine wounds and allowed to vascularize for 10 days after which the silicone layer was replaced with CEA. CEAs were prepared from split-thickness porcine donor skin. The epidermis was mechanically separated from

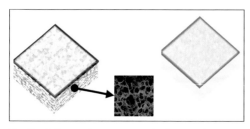

Fig. 2: Collagen-GAG matrix. The bottom layer is a highly porous matrix coated with a silicone elastomer. On the right is a membrane seeded with autologous keratinocytes by centrifugation resulting in most of the cells near the silicone membrane. Courtesy of Brigham and Women's Hospital and Massachusetts Institute of Technology.

the dermis aided by 0.25 % Dispase and the epidermis was disaggregated with 0.1 % Trypsin / 0.02 % EDTA. Cells were primarily cultured to post-confluence in Waymouth's medium, supplemented with 20 % fetal calf serum and growth substances over approximately three weeks. The CEA's were released from the flasks using Dispase and petroleum-impregnated gauze was attached to the outer surface with surgical ligating clips for protection and ease of handling. After removing the silastic layer, any epithelium migrating from the wound periphery was excised prior to C0EA grafting. Gross observations and biopsies were obtained at Days 7, 14 and 21. Freshly excised full-thickness wounds were used as the control graft bed for CEA [16] (Figs. 1 and 2).

Uncultured Keratinocyte Seeded DEMAs

Single-cell keratinocyte solutions were seeded by centrifugation at 50 g for 15 minutes (4 °C) into the porous side of the matrix). A custom reservoir was used to maintain the centrifugal force perpendicular to the DEMA surface, more than 85 % of cells became positioned near the silicone-CG interface.

An "island graft" technique was used to determine the effect of seeding density on epidermal thickness, confluence, and the number of keratinocyte cysts in the neodermis. The 4 x 4 cm full-thickness wounds were grafted with 1.5 x 1.5 cm "island" DEMA grafts with cell seeding densities of 0 to 3 million cells/cm2 and biopsied all at day 14. The time sequence of epitheliali- zation between 0 and 25 days was then studied using DEMAs each seeded with 500,000 cells/cm^2.

Imunohistocheical Sequential Analysis of Seeded DEMAs

DEMAs were seeded with 50,000 uncultured autologus keratinocytes per cm^2 (a 60-fold surface area expansion factor), generated a confluent epidermis by day 19. The temporal sequence of events in epidermal and neodermal formation was analyzed histopathologically and immunohistochemically in uncultured keratinocyte seeded DEMAs between days 4 and 35 [17].

Results

CEA on Vascularized DEMA

By 7 days CEAs placed on vascularized matrices were found to be near completely confluent with a markedly improved take rate when compared to that of controls grafted onto fat that demonstrated blistering of the CEA. Microscopic measurements of confluence from wound cross-sections showed CEA on vascularized DEMA was 98 ± 4%, compared to 8 ± 12% on fat (p< 0.05), and there was not take when grafted directly onto fascia (Fig. 6). Electron microscopy of the CEA/vascularized DEMA construct demonstrated anchoring fibrils at the DEJ.

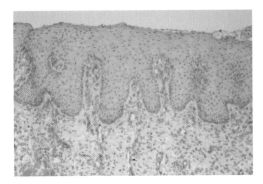

Fig. 3: Immunohistochemistry of seeded membrane, day 35, staining for Factor VIII. Note capillary loops that are close to the basement membrane, Courtesy of Carolyn Compton, M.D., Ph.D.

At 7 days the vascularized DEMA/CEA construct neoepidermis was both hyperplastic (185 ± 30 μm in thickness) with a jagged basal contour, and parakeratotic in comparison to native skin. Significant maturation of the epidermis occurred by 21 days

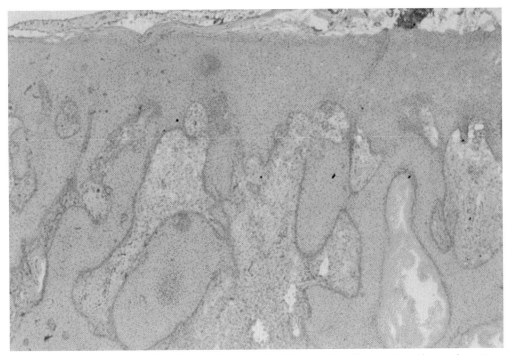

Fig. 4: Immunohistochemistry of seeded membrane, day 12, staining for collagen VII.. Note the multiple epithelial cysts with positive staining at the periphery. Over time these cysts migrate to the surface and extrude.

with disappearance of the basal undulations, resolution of parakeratosis and a decrease in thickness to 94 ± 3 μm. Immunohistochemical staining of the DEMA indicated collagen type VII, the major structural protein of anchoring fibrils, and [alpha]6[beta]4 integrin, a major structural component of hemidesmosomes to be localized at the dermo-epidurmal (DEJ) where they stained continuously. Laminin was observed at the DEJ as well as perivascularly where it stained basement membranes of keratinocytes and endothelial cells, respectively. Grossly, the newly formed epidermis was less fragile and more resistant to tearing when applied to vascularized CG wounds than freshly excised wounds.

Uncultured Keratinocytes Seeded DEMAs

Two critical relationships; effects of seeding density on neoepidermal development and time sequence of neoepidermal formation were established by Butler, et al. [4]. The autologous keratinocytes proliferated and migrated to form a confluent epidermis by two weeks in matrices seeded with at least 100,000 cells/cm² of matrix (Fig. 5). The

neoepidermal thickness and keratinocyte cyst density at two weeks increased linearly with the logarithm of the seeding density. Sequential analysis of neoepidermis developing from matrices seeded with 500,000 keratinocytes/cm² showed that the neoepidermis was hyperplastic, parakeratotic, and lacked a granular layer at two weeks after which it appeared to undergo normal maturation and differentiation.

All seeded DEMAs engrafted to the wound without evidence of infection. Grossly, translucent epidermis was observed in all seeded grafts at the silicone-DEMA interface at day 14. The island graft technique ensured that the resulting neoepidermis formed from the seeded keratinocytes rather than from epithelial wound migration by the presence of a well-defined unepithelialized zone surrounding each graft. Keratin granules were seen at the surface of DEMAs seeded with 20,000 or more cells/cm². These were more abundant with higher seeding densities. No epidermis or surface keratin granules were generated from unseeded DEMAs.

At day 14, the epidermis was hyperplastic in grafts seeded with 50,000 cells/cm² or more cells with focal parakeratosis. The neodermis of all DEMAs was well vascularized and fully infiltrated by cells from the wound base. Neoepidermal confluence neodermis contained keratinocyte cysts with a basal cell layer located peripherally and progressively differentiated cell layers including a stratum corneum in the center. The density of keratinocyte cysts varied increased with seeding

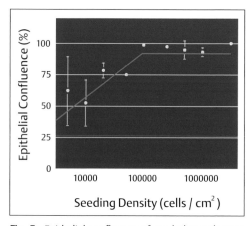

Fig. 5: Epithelial confluence of seeded membranes at 14 days as a function of seeding density. Note excellent confluence at 100,000 cells/cm². Courtesy of Brigham and Women's Hospital

CEA take on freshly wounds versus take on CG: 7 days post-grafting		
	gross take (%)	histologic take (%)
CEA on CG	100 (n = 16)	97± 3 (n = 2)
CEA on fascia	0 (n = 3)	0 (n=1)
CEA on fat	0 (n = 7)	8 (n=1)

Fig. 6: CEAs took well on vascularized CG matrices but not on freshly excised fat or fascia.

density. Unseeded DEMAs were devoid of epidermis and keratinocyte cysts. Neoepidermal thickness decreased from 249 ± 12 μm at day 14 to 108 ± 10 μm at day 25. The epidermis became less hyperplastic and keratinocyte cysts disappeared day 25.

Seeded keratinocytes proliferated, coalesced and differentiated to generate a neoepidermis as well as keratinocyte cysts that unidirectioally migrated and fused with the neoepidermis. A fully differentiated, normally oriented epidermis with rete ridges was formed (Figs. 3 and 4). A neodermis formed simultaneously by endothelial cells, fibroblasts, and macrophages migrating into the DEMA from the wound bed. As the DEMA was degraded it was replaced with extracellular matrix and was vascularized from the wound. Cellular density decreased as collagen deposition and remodeling occurred to form mature neodermis. The DEMA was completely degraded, with no acute inflammation or infection. Many of the structural components of normal skin were regenerated by 4 weeks.

Discussion

Treatment improvements for burns have increased the survival of patients with large surface area skin loss. With more survivors, patients and surgeons will want to have access to better technology to replace skin loss. As new technologies become available, they will be applied to other areas of reconstructive surgery including acute and chronic wounds, hypertrophic scars and keloids, and congenital disorders of the skin. The durability, color, the presence of adnexal organs and overall cosmetic appearance of skin replacements will be important criteria in evaluating new technologies.

We have focused on semi-synthetic porous matrices combined with epithelial cells harvested from small donor areas. Semi-synthetic membranes based on collagen can be made into a wide variety of membranes with an array of physicochemical properties. They

can be manufactured and stored for long periods of time. Cell isolation and culture technology has improved over the last 20 years resulting in faster expansion of keratinocytes and a better understanding of the biology.

These studies demonstrate that autologous keratinocytes can be combined with a well-characterized collagen-GAG membrane to result in a tissue with properties that in many ways simulate normal skin. This can be done either as cell culture or as isolated cells from skin biopsies. Keratinocytes are able to expand, proliferate, migrate to the surface and form a layer with a normal differentiation pattern. The molecular signals that allow this precise spatial and temporal control of these cells within these matrices are not understood.

Further work in this field will need to focus on the differences in keratin expression in keratinocytes derived from different body areas. In addition, work is need to better understand melanocytes and melanin expression so that skin color can be better controlled. Finally, incorporation of adnexal elements such as hair follicles and sweat glands will need to be considered. Ultimately, we hope that advances in this field will result in our ability to reproduce a near normal skin using minimal donor tissue.

References

[1] Compton, CC, Gill, JM, Bradford, DA, Regauer, S, Gallico, G, O'Connor, NE: Skin Regenerated from Cultured Epithelial Autographs on Full-Thickness Bum Wounds from 6 Days to 5 Years After Grafting, Lab. Invest., 60, No. 5, 600–612, (1989).

[2] Cuono, CB, Langdon, R, Birchall, N, Barttelbort, S, McGuire, J: Composite autologous-allogenic skin replacement: Development and clinical application. Plas Reconstr Surg, 80(4):626–37) 1987.

[3] Kangesu T, Navasaria HA, Manek S, Fryer PR, Leigh IM, Green CJ: Kerato-dermal grafts: the importance of dermis for the in vivo growth of cultured keratinocytes, Brit J Plast Surg, 46, 401–9, (1993).

[4] Odessey, R: Addendum: Multicenter Experiences with Cultured Epidermal Autograph for Treatment of Bums, J. Bum Care Rehabil., 13, 174–180. Billingham, RE, and Medawar, PB

(1951) The Technique of Free Skin Grafting in Mammals, J. Exp. Biol. 28:385–394, (1992).

[5] Yannas, IV, Lee, E, Orgill, DP, Skrabut, EM, Murphy, GF: Synthesis and characterization of a model extracellular matrix that induces partial regeneration of adult mammalian Skin, Proc. Natl. Acad. Sci., USA ; 86, 933937, 1989.

[6] Yannas, IV, Burke, JF: Design of an Artificial Skin. 1. Design Principles, J. Biomed. Mat. Res., 14, 65–68, 1980.

[7] Yannas, IV, Burke, JF, Gordon, PL, Huang, C, Rubinstein, RH: Design of an artificial Skin. III. Control of chemical composition, J. Biomed. Mat. Res. 14, 107–13 1, 1980.

[8] Burke, JF, Yannas, IV, Quinby, WC, Jr, Bondoc, CC, Jung, WK: Successful Use of a Physiologically Acceptable Artificial Skin in the Treatment of Extensive Skin Injury, Ann. Surg. 194, 413–428, 1981.

[9] Heimbach, D, Luterman, A, Burke, J, Cram, A, Herndon, D, Hunt, J, Jordan, M, McManus, W, Solem, L, Warden, G, Zawacki, BA: multicenter randomized clinical trial, Artificial dermis for major bums., Ann. Surg. 208, 313–320, 1988.

[10] Wainwright DJ: Use of an acellular allograft dermal matrix (AlloDerm) in the management of full-thickness burns. Burns. Jun;21(4): 243-8, 1995

[11] Boyce, ST, Greenhalgh, DG, Kagan, RJ, et al: Skin anatomy and antigen expression after burn wound closure with composite grafts of cultured skin cells and biopolymers. Plast Reconstr Surg 91:632–641, 1993.

[12] Cooper ML, Hansbrough JF: Use of a composite skin graft composed cultured human keratinocytes and fibroblasts and a collagen-gag matrix to cover full-thickness wounds on athymic mice. Surg 1099: 198–207, 1991.

[13] Hansbrough, JF, Boyce, ST, Cooper, ML, Foreman, TJ: Bum Wound Closure with Cultured Autologous Keratinocytes and Fibroblasts Attached to a Collagen-Glycosaminoglycan Substrate, JAMA 262:2125–2130, 1989.

[14] Hansbrough, JF, Morgan, JL, Greenleaf, GE, Bartel, R: Composite Grafts of Human Keratinocytes Grown on a Polyglactin Mesh-Cultured Fibroblast Dermal Substitute Function as a Bilayer Skin Replacement in Full-Thickness Wounds on Athymic Mice, J Bum Care Rehabil, 14, 485–494, 1993.

[15] Hull, BE, Finley, RK, Miller SF: Coverage of full-thickness bums with bi-layered skin equivalents: a preliminary clinical trial. Surgery, 107, 496–502, 1990.

[16] Butler CE, Orgill DP, Yannas IV, Compton CC: Effect of Keratinocyte Seeding of Collagen-Glycosaminoglycan Membranes on the Regeneration of Skin in a Porcine Model. Plast. Reconst. Surg. 101(6): 1572–1579, 1998.

[17] Compton CC, Butler CE, Yannas IV, Warland G, Orgill DP: Organized Skin Structure Is Regenerated In Vivo from Collagen-GAG Matrices Seeded with Autologous Keratinocytes. J Invet Dermatol 100(6):908–916, 1998.

[18] Orgill DP, Butler C, Regan JF, Barlow MS, Yannas IV, Compton CC: Vascularized Collagen-GAG Matrix Provides a Dermal Substrate and Improves Take of Cultured Epithelial Autografts. Plast. Reconstr. Surg. 102(9): 423–429, 1998.

[19] Butler, CE, Orgill DP, Correia CA, Compton CC, Yannas IV: Comparison of Cultured and Uncultured Keratinocytes used for Cell Seeded Collagen-GAG Matrix Skin Replacements, Br J Plast Surg 52:(2)127–132, March, 1999.

[20] Butler, CE, Orgill, DP, Compton, CC, Yannas, IV: Effects of cell culturing on keratinocyte-seeded collagen-glycosaminoglycan matrix skin replacement in full-thickness porcine model. Surg Forum 47:752–754, 1996.

The Role of Cultured Epithelial Autografts in the Treatment of Extensive Burns: The Paris Experience

J.-M. Rives, D. Cantaloube, A. Lakhel, F. Lambert, P. Ainaud, Y. Barandon, H. Le Bever, J. Stephanazzi, J. Perrot, H. Carsin

Summary

Cultured epithelial autografts have been used in the Paris Burn Center since 1989 until 2000.

Despite initial optimism over CEA application the clinical use has been tempered by subsequent reports asserting that this modality is unreliable and expensive, thus continuing discussions about its role in burn therapy are prevalent in the literature and in the burn community. The experiences in a large, single center series of severely burned and otherwise traumatized patients who received cultured epithelial autografts (CEA) from a single commercial laboratory are reported in this study.

From 1991 to 1996, CEA were applied to a mean 37+/−17% of total body surface area (TBSA) of 30 patients. These patients had 78+/−10% average burn size, 65 +/−16% average third-degree burn size, 90% prevalence of endoscopically confirmed inhalation injury and 37% prevalence of other serious conditions. CEA achieved permanent coverage of a mean 26+/−15% of TBSA, an area greater than that covered by conventional autografts (a mean 25+/−10% of TBSA). Survival was 90% in these severely burned and otherwise traumatized patients. Final CEA take was a mean 69+/−23%. In subset analyses, only younger age was significantly associated with better CEA take (p = 0.0001 in univariate analysis, p<0.04 in multivariate analysis, Student's t-test). Three patients with facial burns treated with CEA on a fibrin substrate offer very interesting prospects of autologous culture epidermal grafts on a fibrin substrate.

Epicel CEA successfully provided extensive, permanent burn coverage in severely traumatized patients, proving an important adjunct to achievement of a high survival rate in a patient population whose prognosis previously had been poor. In our experience CEA appear to be highly beneficial in the treatment of bur n wounds >60% TBSA. From our expereince it can be concluded that in addition in single cases studied it became obvious that CEA proved itself to be a life-saving therapy.

Introduction

The use of autologous cultured epidermal sheets (CEA) has been one of the recent advances in the treatment of burn patients. Facing the absence of sufficient autograft donor sites in large burns as one of the side effects of early eschar excision policies, CEA had been regarded to overcome this donor site shortage and to offer immediate and definitive autologous coverage of burn wounds after the early excision of the eschar since the introduction in the early 1980's [9]. Despite many advantages of this technique, however, the initial optimism had been tempered by subsequent reports of failures, difficulties and high costs of CEA grafting procedures [12].

The single center experiences made in the Paris Burn center over the recent years using a standardized treatment protocol and a commercially available standardized keratinocyte sheet transplant from one source reported in here may help to clarify the ongoing discussion about the true value of CEA in burn wound therapy.

Patients and Methods

The burn center of the Percy Army Teaching Hospital in Paris represents a specialized burn care facility with 20 beds. About 200 severely injured patients are treated each year (> 90 % civilians), including 10 % of patietns with burns of more than 60 % total body surface area burned (TBSA).

From 1991 until 1996 a total of 30 patients were treated with cultured keratinocytes. Two individuals succumbed after biopsy before they received CEA. Informed consent about risks and benefits was obtained by the patient's fdamilies or responsibles.

Burn severity was evaluated according to a standard scoring system (TBSA, amount of full thickness burns, Baux score and abbreviated burn severity index (ABSI). Burn estimation was confirmed by a second physician on the day after initial assessment.

Full thickness burns were excised down to the fascia and burns of uncertain depth were excised tangentially as soon as possible after the admission, while excision was limited to 30 % TBSA at a single time [25]. Local wound treatment was performed with silver-sulfadiazine plus cerium nitrate daily and closed dressings were changed daily.

Preliminary woudn coverage of CEA awaiting areas was achieved with split thickness skin allografts according to Cuono's technique [7]. Weight bearing areas, face and hands were grafted using the "sandwich"-technique [1, 15]. Nonadherent allografts were replaced. Wound bacterial contamination was measured twice per week using quantitative cultures of biopsies.

During the initial days of treatment a 2 to 4 cm^2 biopsy was harvested from the scalp or axillary or retroauricular region and sent off for keratinocyte culture. CEA were delivered between days 18 and 24 by air courier in special transport containers as stratified epidermal sheets of 25 to 30 cm^2 in size, 2 to8 cell layers thick and mounted on petroleum gauze backings strictly oriented with the basal cells away from the backing.

Generally, sites of CEA placement were chosen to minimize exposure to shear and other friction forces and were mainly applied to anterior and non-weight bearing surfaces. Whereas in the first 6 patients CEA had been placed on granulating surfaces, the protocol was soon changed to the allograft pretreatment and removal of allo-epidermis according to Cuono. CEA was fixed with staples and overlaid with sterile gauze, dry compresses and elastic bandage. Dressings were changed daily down to the veil gauze.

Removal of gauze backing (take-down) was performed on day 7 after the grafting procedure in general. Utilizing the aid of a moistener (Shur Clens, Calgon Westol Lab., St. Louis, MO).

Upon the take down the percentage of CEA grafted areas that had developed an epithelium was estimated, since after a few minutes later to exposion to the air, such areas reveil a characteristic "frosted" appearance. Measurements of rgaft take was repeated on the next day by another physician, in an attempt to judge the amount of reepithelialization as good as possible. Complete or near complete loss of CEA was noted in a few occasions only. Tulle gras impregnated with polymyxin, neomycin and corticosteroids plus an elastic bandage were applied daily after the take down.

Statistical evaluation of the obtained results was performed using the SAS statistical package including univariate and multivariate analysis, accepting significance at $p < 0,05$.

Results

The main causes of injuries treated were induced by flame burns of different origins. All

30 patients with CEA treatment needed artificial ventilation therapy (54 +/– 25 days). Artificial nutrition was necessary for a mean of 86 +/– 30 days including enteral nutrition for a mean of 59 +/– 25 days. For detailed data on other treatment parameters see Carsin H et al. [3, 4, 20].

Patients needed an average of 10 +/– 3 skin grafting operations, a mean of 55 +/– 17 dressings and a mean of 61 +/– 19 administrations of general anaesthesia for burn excisions, temporary coverage with sandwich grafts and allograft pretreatment or CEA.

The average TBSA initially covered with sandwich grafts was 25 +/– 10 % (range: 4 to 40 %, median 27 %). Mean TBSA grafted with CEA was 37 +/– 17 % (range 7 to 80 %, median 33 %).

A mean of 210 +/– 103 CEA sheets was applied to each patient, and a total of 6300 were applied to the entire series in a total of 40 operations. 22 (73 %) pateints received CEA in one intervention, six patients in 2 interventions and two patients in 3 interventions.

Initial coverage was achieved by CEA in 26 +/– 14 % of TBSA (range. 6–62 %, median 73 %), reflecting a 69 +/– 19 % (range 25–95 %, median 73 %) mean rate of initial CEA engraftment. Permanent coverage with CEA was seen in an average of 26 +/– 15 % of TBSA (range 5–60 %, median 24 %), reflecting a 69 +/– 23 % (range 9 to 93 %. Median 75 %) mean rate of final CEA take.

Statistically an increased rate of improved initial engraftment was associated with younger patient´s age as the only factor to be significant after uni- or multivariate analysis (p = 0.0001 in univariate analysis, p < 0.04 in multivariate analysis, Student's t-test). Although there was no statistic significance it turned out that subgroups with more extensive overall and third degree burns, inhalation injury and other serious comorbidity showed a better initial take rate. Multivariate analysis revealed that these subgroups consisted of generally younger patietns which may explain these data.

The mean cost of CEA including the biopsy, culture and transportation cost was found to be 89 +/– 8 FF (~ US $ 14 +/– 1,5) per square cm grafted with keratinocyte sheets.

The mean duration of hospitalization was 114 +/– 30 days (range 67–189, median 112) which is equivalent to 1,5 days of hospital stay per percent of TBSA burned.

Discussion

The overall results of the Paris single center experiences are encouraging and show the high efficacy of CEA to prmanently cover excised burn wounds and to add a life-saving tool to the armamentarium of burn surgery. The approach of assessing the final CEA take as the area that did not require regrafting procedures by the time of patient discharging or death has been demanded by others [10, 21]. By actually measuring and not calculating the mean take rate we can assess an average take rate of 69 % +/– 23 %, which compares to other data from the literature [6, 13, 18, 19, 21, 22, 24].

Comparing the severity of the patients treated with a mean burn size of 78 +/– 10 TBSA, an average third degree burn size of 65 % +/– 16 % TBSA, and a mean burn severity index of 12 points +/– 1 point on the ABSI score, as well as a percentage of more than 90 % inhalation injury and 37 % additional serious concomitant traumata the amount of 90 % survival in this group seems to be noteworthy [11, 20]. This becomes especially evident, when considering that the ABSI would have predicted a < 10 % survival for patients similar to those reported in this study. These data resemble the survival rates published by others [22, 23] and especially when comparing CEA treated patients to a historical control when survival rates were in favour of the CEA treated group [18]. In our experience a significant correlation was noted between the timing of CEA culture and take.

Problems encountered with the clinical use of CEA included the fragility of the grafts, hyperkeratosis of grafted areas, considerable scar contractures, labour intensiveness and the high costs [17]. Retarded development of the dermal-epidermal anchoring system [5] may be responsible for the blistering in response to the least friction, beginning around three weeks after the take down and lasting for several months. Physical therapy was delayed by this blistering in our patients as well as was the use of pressure garments. Due to the limited autograft donor sites even in the long term management the resolvement of scar contractures and hyperkeratosis remains to be a considerable surgical challenge in the rehabilitation period.

Further research should concentrate on the improvement of current cell culture techniques to reduce the period until enough CEA is available to cover large excised burn wounds. Keratinocytes with the highest colony forming capacity have to be identified [2, 8], improved feeder layers should be developed, graftable cultures on appropriate substrates and transport materials such as fibrin sealant [14], hyaluronic acid membranes, collagen carriers [16] or other support materials should be established. Another important aim in improving current skin replacement technologies with cultured keratinocytes is the achievement of better dermal reconstitution and better dermal support for the subsequent engraftment of CEA.

In conclusion it can be stated from the Paris experience with CEA that permanent burn coverage can be achieved in extensive burns and that this fact contributes to an overall improvement of severe burn trauma survival altering the hitherto poor prognosis of such injuries. CEA thus can be considered to be a lifesaving tool in the treatment of patients with more than 60% TBSA full thickness burns.

References

[1] Alexander JW, MacMillan BG, Law E, Kittur DS: Treatment of severe burns with widely meshed skin autograft and meshed skin allograft overlay. J Trauma; 21(6):433–438, 1981.

[2] Barrandon Y: [The biology of epidermal stem cells]. Ann Dermatol Venereol; 125 Suppl 2:S5–6:S5–S6, 1998.

[3] Carsin H: [Skin cultures in the treatment of burns]. Pathol Biol (Paris); 47(8):776–779, 1999.

[4] Carsin H, Ainaud P, Le Bever H, Rives J, Lakhel A, Stephanazzi J et al: Cultured epithelial autografts in extensive burn coverage of severely traumatized patients: a five year single-center experience with 30 patients. Burns; 26(4):379–387, 2000.

[5] Compton CC, Gill JM, Bradford DA, Regauer S, Gallico GG, O'Connor NE: Skin regenerated from cultured epithelial autografts on full-thickness burn wounds from 6 days to 5 years after grafting. A light, electron microscopic and immunohistochemical study. Lab Invest; 60(5):600–612, 1989.

[6] Compton CC, Hickerson W, Nadire K, Press W: Acceleration of skin regeneration from cultured epithelial autografts by transplantation to homograft dermis. J Burn Care Rehabil; 14(6):653–662, 1993.

[7] Cuono CB, Langdon R, Birchall N, Barttelbort S, McGuire J: Composite autologous-allogeneic skin replacement: development and clinical application. Plast Reconstr Surg; 80(4):626–637, 1987.

[8] De Luca M, Pellegrini G: The importance of epidermal stem cells in keratinocyte-mediated gene therapy [editorial]. Gene Ther; 4(5):381–383, 1997.

[9] Gallico GG, III, O'Connor NE, Compton CC, Kehinde O, Green H: Permanent coverage of large burn wounds with autologous cultured human epithelium. N Engl J Med; 311(7):448–451, 1984.

[10] Hefton JM, Caldwell D, Biozes DG, Balin AK, Carter DM: Grafting of skin ulcers with cultured autologous epidermal cells. J Am Acad Dermatol; 14(3):399–405, 1986.

[11] Herndon DN, Barrow RE, Rutan RL, Rutan TC, Desai MH, Abston S: A comparison of conservative versus early excision. Therapies in severely burned patients. Ann Surg; 209(5):547–552, 1989.

[12] Herndon DN, Rutan RL: Comparison of cultured epidermal autograft and massive excision with serial autografting plus homograft overlay. J Burn Care Rehabil; 13(1):154–157, 1992.

[13] Hickerson WL, Compton C, Fletchall S, Smith LR: Cultured epidermal autografts and allodermis combination for permanent burn wound coverage. Burns; 20 Suppl 1:S52-5; discussion S55-6:S52–S55, 1994.

[14] Horch RE, Bannasch H, Kopp J, Andree C, Stark GB: Single-cell suspensions of cultured human keratinocytes in fibrin-glue reconstitute the epidermis. Cell Transplant; 7(3):309–317, 1998.

[15] Horch RE, Corbei O, Formanek-Corbei B, Brand-Saberi B, Vanscheidt W, Stark GB: Reconstitution of basement membrane after 'sandwich-

technique' skin grafting for severe burns demonstrated by immunohistochemistry. J Burn Care Rehabil; 19(3):189–202, 1998.

[16] *Horch RE, Debus M, Wagner G, Stark GB:* Cultured human keratinocytes on type I collagen membranes to reconstitute the epidermis. Tissue Eng; 6(1):53–67, 2000.

[17] *Meuli M, Raghunath M:* Burns (Part 2). Tops and flops using cultured epithelial autografts in children. Pediatr Surg Int; 12(7): 471–477, 1997.

[18] *Munster AM:* Cultured skin for massive burns. A prospective, controlled trial. Ann Surg; 224(3):372–375, 1996.

[19] *Nunez-Gutierrez H, Castro-Munozledo F, Kuri-Harcuch W:* Combined use of allograft and autograft epidermal cultures in therapy of burns. Plast Reconstr Surg; 98(6):929–939, 1996.

[20] *Rives JM, Cantaloube D, Ainaud P, Barandon Y, Carsin H:* [Role of autografts of cultured epi-

dermis in the treatment of deep burns of the face. Preliminary results]. Ann Chir Plast Esthet; 40(3):286–292, 1995.

[21] *Rue LW, III, Cioffi WG, McManus WF, Pruitt BA, Jr:* Wound closure and outcome in extensively burned patients treated with cultured autologous keratinocytes. J Trauma; 34(5):662–667, 1993.

[22] *Sheridan RL, Tompkins RG:* Cultured autologous epithelium in patients with burns of ninety percent or more of the body surface. J Trauma; 38(1):48–50, 1995.

[23] *Sheridan RL, Tompkins RG:* Skin substitutes in burns. Burns; 25(2):97–103, 1999.

[24] *Siwy BK, Compton CC:* Cultured epidermis: Indiana University Medical Center's experience. J Burn Care Rehabil; 13(1):130–137, 1992.

[25] *Thompson P, Herndon DN, Abston S, Rutan T:* Effect of early excision on patients with major thermal injury. J Trauma; 27(2):205–207, 1987.

Cultured Epithelial Autograft (CEA) for Burn Wound Care: A 12 Year Review

C. F. T. Snelling, J. S. Williamson, M. Putland, I. Macdonald, V. Tron,
P. A. Clugston, J. C. Boyle, E. Germann

Summary

With cultured epithelial autografts (CEA) available our position has been to initiate it for burns with a full thickness component exceeding 35 % of the body surface. We use all available autograft sites as often as they are available and will only use CEA after all available autograft has been applied. CEA is allowed 2 weeks to engraft. If not adherent or absent, our practice is to re-prepare the wound and cover it either with autograft or if autograft is not available, further CEA or allograft. At present with a mean coverage of 2.4 % body surface achieved in 43 patients, CEA's value in our Unit is equivalent to allograft since both provide coverage which is temporary. If CEA engrafts it is a bonus. It has yet to reduce hospital stay. A larger number of patients will need to be treated to determine if CEA changes mortality. CEA is still an experimental burn tool. To date it has not accelerated wound closure, has not reduced the number of crops of autograft harvested, and has not reduced mortality. The composite epidermal-dermal cultured model is looked forward to.

Introduction

Cultured Epithelial Autograft (CEA) has been available for all burn patients admitted to the Vancouver Hospital & Health Sciences Centre Burn Unit from 1988 to 1999. It has been prepared in-house by the method developed by Rheinwald and Green [1], and Green et al [2]. It has been available as early as 3 weeks post-burn. This report updates our initial experience with 18 patients reported by Clugston et al [3] and expanded to 28 patients treated in 5 years by Williamson et al [4]. The role of CEA in the care of 43 patients in the past 12 years has been reviewed. This includes success of engraftment, short and long term wound stability, longitudinal histological characteristics, the effect on length of hospitalization, and patient survival.

Method

CEA was initiated for 83 patients and available for some as early as 3 weeks post-burn. Some patients received 2 or 3 applications. In preparation wounds destined to receive CEA were excised to fat or fascia and covered with either fresh or frozen allograft which was left until the area was prepared prior to CEA application. Where possible attempts were made to preserve the allograft dermis by thin tangential excision of superficial allograft with the Cobbett dermatome. However in most cases allograft had become soft and avulsed or peeled completely leaving only the granulation tissue below. In some patients a series of saline compresses changed every 4 hours up to 12 hours post-preparation of the wound were used before CEA application on the ward while other patients had CEA applied immediately. After

CEA had been lifted from the culture flasks it was attached to fine mesh Vaseline backing gauze with peripheral vascular clips to facilitate application. CEA was laid on the wound, covered with one layer of coarse mesh Vaseline gauze and either left open or covered with multi-layered dry gauze dressings. Antibiotic solution irrigation post-application was used for 2 patients. When CEA was covered with a single layer of Vaseline gauze the surface was moist with saline at 2 hour intervals. Patients had a bath 7 to 10 days post-application and the gauze dressing was allowed to float off. Fine mesh Vaseline backing gauze which was loose was removed, and that which remained adherent was left and allowed to separate spontaneously up to 14 days post-burn after which residual was removed. After the Vaseline backing gauze initially came off it was some times difficult to know if CEA had taken. Thereafter, the CEA covered wound was protected with coarse mesh Vaseline gauze and moistened with saline to 2 weeks.

Evaluation

Engraftment was evaluated visually at 2 weeks. If an epithelial covering was not visible the CEA application was considered a failure and the wound was prepared for repeat coverage. The area which had epithelial coverage was determined as a percentage of the total area originally grafted with CEA. Take was graded as good when 50% or more of the area covered with CEA was successfully engrafted. Long term stability was evaluated for up to 24 months. Histological biopsy specimens were harvested from 12 days to 5.5 years post-application with 4 patients undergoing serial biopsies from 1 to 3.5 years post-application. These were stained with H and E and van Gieson's stain for elastic fibers. We evaluated the epidermal underlying bed interface including the appearance of rete ridges and dermal papilli, the appearance of elastic fibers in the underlying bed, and the epidermal thickness and other features. CEA

was compared to split thickness skin grafts of similar age. Patient mortality in the 12 years in which CEA was available (1988 to 1999) was compared to that in the 5 preceding years (1983–1987) when only allograft was available for temporary coverage of large burns. The first 27 CEA survivors were matched with patients with a similar age, total extent of burn, and total extent of full thickness burn treated in the preceding 5 years (1983–1987) to compare the number of coverage procedures required and length of hospitalization.

The cases with good take or engraftment > 50% were compared to those with poor or no take in regards to differences in preparation of wound prior to CEA application and organisms cultured. The pattern of usage of CEA in our Burn Unit in the subpopulation with full thickness burns covering more than 34% body surface was reviewed from 1988 to 1999.

Results

Forty-three patients could have had engraftment of CEA evaluated at 14 and more days post-application between 1988 to 1999. These 43 remained from 83 patients for whom CEA initiated and 50 who had CEA applied to their wounds (Table 1). These 43 patients had a mean total body surface burn (TBSB) of 52%, mean full thickness (FTBSB) 43%, and mean age of 33 years. Twenty-six

Table 1: Usage of CEA Initiated from 1988 to 1999

	Patients (No.)	
Patients for whom CEA Initiated	83	
Died or Wound Autografted Before CEA Ready		29
CEA to Donor Sites Only		4
Patients for whom CEA Applied to Wounds	50	
CEA to Deep 2⁰ Burns Which Re-epithelized		3
Patient Died Within 10 Days		4
CEA Engraftment Evaluated	43	

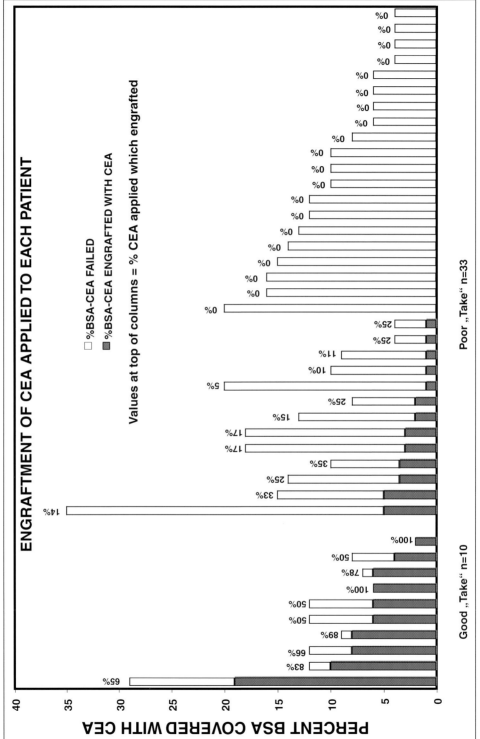

Fig. 1: Extent of body surface covered with CEA and engraftment of CEA in each of 43 patients, 10 with good take (> 50 %), 33 poor or no take.

had associated smoke inhalation injury and 36 survived. During this 12 year period our Burn Unit treated 1662 patients in total. The mean TBSB was 12%, mean total FTBSB 7%, mean age 32 years, and 9% had a smoke inhalation injury. (Table 2)

In the 43 patients evaluated the mean BSA covered with CEA was 11% with a range from 2% to 34%. Some patients received multiple applications to a maximum of 3 from 20 to 50 days post-burn. However only the first application has been evaluated. In no case did the engraftment of a subsequent application exceed that of the first application in that patient.

2. Engraftment was determined at 14 days post-application. Ten patients retained 50% or more of CEA applied and were classified as good take or engraftment with the extent of body surface engrafted with CEA being 19, 10, 8, 8, 6, 6, 6, 6, 4 and 2% respectively. (Fig. 1) One of the patients with 10% body surface successfully covered with CEA died 3 weeks after engraftment of CEA had been confirmed. Nineteen additional patients had zero retention and a further 14 had lesser amounts ranging from 5 to 35% of that applied with the greatest amount of body surface being covered with CEA in this group being 5%. These 33 were classified poor take. Mean final body surface area covered in 43 patients was 2.4%.

When the 10 patients with good take were compared to the 33 with poor or zero take, the two groups were similar for age, and to

Table 3: Comparison of Good and Poor Engraftment Patients

	Good	Poor
Patients (No.)	10	33
Mean Age (Yrs)	36	32
Mean TBSB (%)	55	53
Mean 3° BSB (%)	39*	46*
*(Significant Difference)		
Inhalation Injury (%)	60	60
Mean Interval From Burn to Eschar Excision from Site to Receive CEA (Days)	10	11
Mean Interval Burn to CEA Application (Days)	22	24
Mean Body Surface Covered (%)	11	11
Depth of Eschar Excision (No.)		
Fascia	3	14
Dermis/Fat	1	1
Fat	6	18
Bacterial Colonization 10 Days Before to 10 Days After CEA		
Staph. aureus (%)	30	21
Enterococcus (%)	60	45
E. coli (%)	30	12
Ps. aeruginosa (%)	30	60
Candida albicans (%)	60	42
Interval Allograft (No.)	8	28
Fate of Allograft Dermis Before CEA Applied (No.)		
Preserved	1	2
Avulsed or Sloughed	7	26

Table 2: Comparison of CEA treated Patients Evaluated to All Patients Treated From 1988 to 1999

	All	CEA Evaluated
Patients (No.)	1662	43
Mean Age (Yrs)	31.7	33.4
Mean TBSB (%)	12.3	51.8
Mean 3° BSB (%)	7.2	42.9
Severe Inhalation Injury (%)	8.7	60.0
Survival (%)	95.0	84.0

tal extent of body surface burn but the poor take group had a larger mean FTBSB of 46% compared to a mean FTBSB of 39% in the good take group (Table 3). The mean interval from burn to excision of eschar and interval from burn to application of CEA as similar with the good take group receiving their first crop of CEA on mean day 22 and the poor take group on mean day 24 post-burn. Wound excision was to fat or fascia in equal proportions in both groups. Most received interval allograft although a few underwent eschar excision immediately before CEA application. All of these patients had wounds colonized with organisms at the

Table 4: Comparison Pre-CEA to CEA Treatment Periods.

	1983–1987	1988–1999	
Patients (No.)	934	1662	p Value
Age (Mean ± SD) Yrs	31.0 ± 22.1	31.6 ± 22.1	0.519
Total BSB (Mean ± SD) %	12.3 ± 14.5	12.3 ± 14.0	0.95
Total FT BSB (Mean ± SD) %	5.8 ± 10.9	7.2 ± 11.9	0.002
Severe Inhalation injury (No.)	59	145	0.023
Days Burn to Discharge (Mean ± SD)	27.2 ± 25.6	26.8 ± 24.6	0.64
Days in Hospital (Mean ± SD)	23.5 ± 23.6	23.0 ± 24.6	0.63
Survivors (No.)	890	1584	0.99

Table 5: Comparison of Surviving Patients Treated with CEA to Prior Controls

	CEA 1988–1994	Pre-CEA 1983–1987	p Value
Patients (No.)	27	27	
Age (Mean ± SD) Yrs	33.6 ± 13.1	31.5 ± 14.8	0.57
Total BSB (Mean ± SD) %	51.3 ± 19.3	48.6 ± 15.2	0.57
Total FT BSB (Mean ± SD) %	41.3 ± 16.9	37.0 ± 14.4	0.32
Inhalation Injury (No.)	15	16	0.78
Days Burn to Discharge (Mean ± SD)	90.0 ± 33.4	92.9 ± 36.4	0.77
Days Post Burn to Last Autograft Harvest (Mean ± SD)	60.2 ± 28.5	55.6 ± 27.2	0.55
No. of Autograft Harvests (Mean ± SD)	5.9 ± 2.4	4.9 ± 1.7	0.08
No. of Debridements Without Autograft Harvest (Mean ± SD)	2.0 ± 1.6	0.9 ± 1.1	0.004

time of CEA application. Pseudomonas aeruginosa, Enterococcus, Candida albicans, Staph aureus, and Staph epidermis were the most frequent organisms in both groups with none occurring with significant greater frequency in either group.

3. The profile of patients treated from 1983 to 1987 was similar to that when CEA was available except the mean full thickness burn in the 1983–1987 was 5.8% and in the more recent treated group 7.2% (p =.002). Mortality rate for 1988 to 1999 was similar to that from 1983 to 1987 at 9.5% of patients treated. The availability of CEA in the 12 most recent years did not alter overall mortality. (Table 4)

4. To determine the influence of CEA on treatment of large burns, the first 27 patients who survived with CEA between 1988 and 1994 were matched by age and extent of burn with 27 surviving patients treated in the years 1983 to 1987. (Table 5) The means for

age and extent of burn in the two groups did not differ. The group who received CEA required a mean of 5.9 autograft harvests per patient to achieve complete coverage compared to a mean 4.9 autograft harvest for the patients where CEA was not used (p = 0.08). The CEA patients underwent their last autograft harvest and application at 60.2 days post-burn compared to the non-CEA patients' last autograft harvest at 55.6 days (NS). Both groups of patients were discharged mean day 90 post-burn. The CEA treated patients also underwent a mean 2.0 debridements followed by allograft in addition to the autograft procedures compared to 0.9 debridements in the non-CEA previously treated match patients. This refects our practice to excise sites destined to receive CEA early and cover these with allograft. It was surprising that the use of CEA did not reduce the number of autograft harvests required nor did it shorten the time until the wound was considered closed.

Fig. 2: Patient AS: 31 days after application of CEA to lower abdomen and upper thigh. Oval island of engraftment over inguinal crease (biopsy sites seen within area), surrounded by layer of granulation tissue where CEA failed.

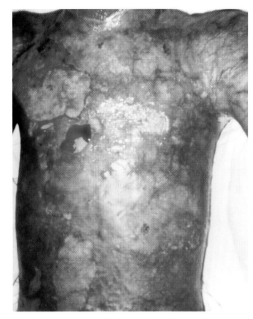

Fig. 4: Patient AK: 77 days after CEA application to rectangle in central chest and abdomen in area bordered by nipples superiorly and laterally and umbilicus inferiorly. CEA lighter in colour than meshed autograft lateral and inferior. Note blisters and breakdown of CEA which was unstable.

Fig. 3: Patient AS: CEA at 31 days after application. H & E stain, magnification x 100. Basal cells columnar, loose contact with underlying bed. Granular cell layer 4 cells thick with prominent keratohyalin granules. Squamous cell layer 8 cells thick. Thick loose keratin layer. Interface between basal cell layer and underlying bed flat.

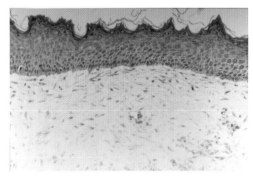

Fig. 5: Patient AK: CEA 77 days after application H & E stain magnification x 100. Basal layer columnar with loose contact with underlying bed. Melanocytes present. Granular cell layer 2 cells thick with less defined keratohyalin granules. Squamous cell layer 6 cells thick. Keratin layer thinner. Interface between basal layer and underlying bed flat.

5. Histology: Biopsies of CEA harvested from 12 days to 5 years post-burn showed distinctive characteristics. These are shown with corresponding patient photographs. At 31 days the squamous layer was 8 to 9 cells thick and the granular layer 3 to 4 cells thick with prominent keratohyaline granules. (Figs. 2, 3) The basal layer was very loosely adherent to the underlying bed. (Figs. 2, 3) After 77 days the basal layer was still columnar, and interface with the underlying bed was flat. Blister formation and ulceration was still occurring. (Figs. 4, 5) The picture at one year was variable. Only 1 of 4 patients serially biopsied showed rete ridge formation by one year, this

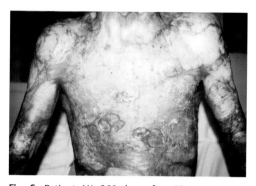

Fig. 6: Patient AK: 360 days after CEA to anterior chest. (The same patient as Figures 4 and 5.) Has demonstrated repeat ulceration which has healed by secondary intention. Remaining CEA has not thickened and is lighter than surrounding skin graft. Subsequently because of continuing breakdown, CEA of anterior chest excised and replacement with split thickness autograft.

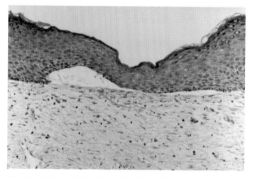

Fig. 7: Patient AK: CEA 360 days after application. H & E stain magnification x 100. Shows area where basal cell layer has lifted off underlying bed. Basal layer poorly organized even where in contact with bed. Squamous cell layer varies from 4 to 7 layers in thickness. Keratin layer thin and poorly organized. No rete rigid formation. Homogeneous underlying bed.

having appeared at 9 months. In some patients the basal layer was disorganized and adherence of the basal layer to the underlying bed was poor and blister formation occurred spontaneously or with mild shearing force. (Figs. 6, 7) In other patients adherence was good. CEA areas were stable. The basal layer was organized but still flat (Figs. 8, 9).

The difference between CEA (Fig. 9) and expanded autograft from the same patient also biopsied at one year (Fig. 10) is evident when the histology is compared. In the expanded autograft rete are present in the graft and in the interstice covered by migrated epidermis. (Fig. 10) The patient in Fig. 11 shown at 1290 days after CEA applied first demonstrated rudimentary rete at 9 months. At 1290 days the rete are still thin and less numerous (Fig.12) than in split thickness skin graft at one year. (Fig. 10) In contrast a biopsy of CEA from the right leg of another patient at 1340 days showed no rete formation. (Figs. 13, 14) The most mature specimen from a thigh at 2100 days shows stable epithelial cover (Fig. 15) but sparse rete ridges (Fig. 16)

The collagen in the underlying bed at one year was quite homogeneous (Figs. 7, 9) while from specimens at 1290 days and later differentiation of the collagen into thinner superficial fibers and thicker deeper collagen bundles suggesting neodermis became evident (Figs. 12, 14, 16). With van Gieson's stain fine elastic filaments were first seen at one year in the bed and became well developed later.

6. Long Term Stability: Blister formation was common up to 3 months post-application. (Fig. 4) Shearing of apparently adherent CEA was observed below dressings or pressure garments after this time. (Fig. 6) Pressure therapy had to be delayed and carefully monitored in these patients. One of the 10 patients in the good take group had persistent breakdown of the anterior chest CEA continuing after one year post-burn and required excision of CEA and replacement with autograft. (Fig. 6) No other patient had this persisting problem. The degree of scar tissue formation was similar in both CEA and meshed split thickness skin graft treated areas of a given patient. CEA could be identified as it was less pigmented than same age meshed expanded autograft.

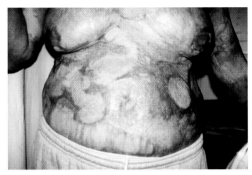

Fig. 8: Patient EC: CEA at 360 days after application to abdomen. CEA ovals less pigmented than surrounding split thickness skin graft. No breakdown.

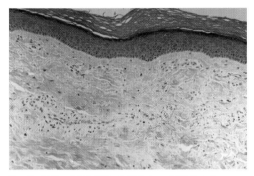

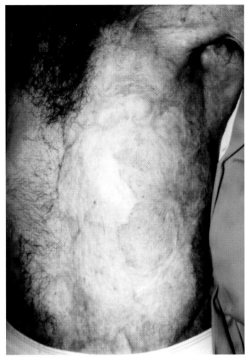

Fig. 9: Patient EC: CEA at 360 days, H & E stain magnification x 100. Basal layer cuboidal, well organized and in close apposition to underlying bed. Squamous layer 5 to 6 cells thick. Granular layer flat. Keratin layer well developed. Interface of basal layer to bed is flat.

Fig. 11: Patient RD: CEA 1290 days after application to left side of trunk, chest and abdomen from level of the nipple superiorly from mid line to left nipple to level of anterior iliac spine inferiorly . Lateral to this meshed split thickness skin graft. CEA slightly paler. Texture and scar formation in CEA and split thickness skin graft similar.

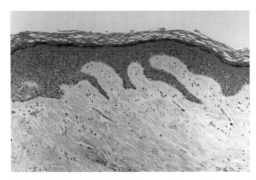

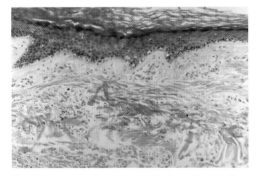

Fig. 10: Patient EC: Split thickness skin graft meshed 1.5:1 and expanded at 360 days after application to abdomen. H & E stain magnification x 100. Skin autograft bridge in middle with thin long rete ridges. On either margin is the interstice bridged previously by migrating epithelium. Interstice epithelium has blunt rete ridges. Robust rete ridge formation distinguishes split thickness skin graft from CEA.

Fig. 12: Patient RD: CEA at 1290 days after application. H & E stain magnification x 100. Basal layer has a few narrow rete ridges penetrating into underlying bed although less numerous than split thickness skin graft of same age. Squamous layer 4 to 5 cells thick. Superficial collagen bundles fine, deeper bundles thicker. This is earliest evidence of collagen reorganization within the underlying bed.

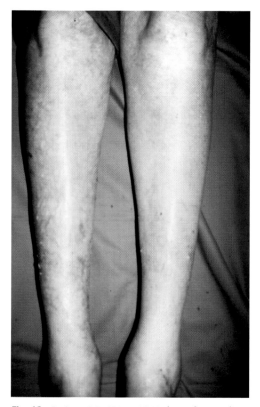

Fig. 13: Patient GC: CEA at 1340 days after application. CEA applied to right leg (on left side in picture). Split thickness autograft to right leg. CEA surface slightly rougher than split thickness skin graft, no difference in pigment.

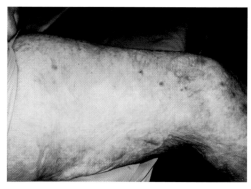

Fig. 15: Patient FB: CEA at 2100 days post application. CEA applied to anteromedial aspect of left thigh from groin to knee. Biopsy sites visible in distal medial thigh. CEA surface smoother than split thickness autograft on posterior and lateral left thigh. Colour and thickness of both equal.

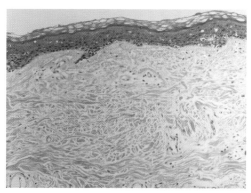

Fig. 16: Patient FB: CEA at 2100 days post application. H & E stain magnification x 100. A few rete ridges penetrate into underlying bed. Superficial underlying bed has fine collagen, deep bed has thick collagen suggestive of neodermis.

Discussion

After 12 years of use CEA engraftment remains unpredictable in our hands. At the time that it is initially available from 21 to 28 days post-burn available donor sites have been cropped once or twice. Most burn eschar has been excised and areas to which CEA is to be applied, usually the anterior trunk or anterior thighs, have been excised and covered with allograft often

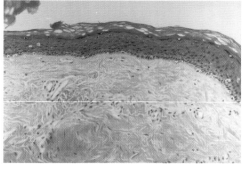

Fig. 14: Patient GC: CEA at 1340 days. H & E stain magnification x 100. Basal layer underlying bed interface still flat without any rete ridge formation. Bed collagen organized with fine superficial fibers and deep thicker bundles.

within 5 days post-burn. About 3 to 4 weeks the initial crop of homograft is usually sloughing. This makes homograft dermis preservation difficult. Perhaps homograft should be excised and replaced 10 days before projected CEA application. If non-frozen allograft is available take is often more prolonged.

If CEA engraftment is good it provides a major advancement towards wound coverage. In a few cases it has contributed to final coverage. (Fig. 1) However, in some patients the extra time necessary to judge engraftment and not dislodge CEA may delay the next steps towards coverage including reharvesting of healed donor sites. Therefore, if CEA is to be used on the anterior trunk and a donor site such as the back is available, it is optimum to harvest the back just before the CEA is applied to the anterior trunk so that the healing of the back is progressing while CEA in engrafting. Otherwise healed donor sites may not be used when available further delaying ultimate coverage.

A second problem is the need to prevent shearing beneath dressings and pressure therapy garments during early patient remobilization. CEA should not be used over joints and should not be used below the knees. CEA usually delays initiation of pressure therapy until at least 4 weeks post-application.

Rue et al [5] noted difficulty in assessing take initially and felt that identification of the actual percent of the body surface ultimately covered was of greater value. In 16 patients treated with CEA, Rue et al [5] reported the mean body surface area finally covered with CEA was 4.7 % which is better than a mean coverage of 2.4 % of the body surface area achieved in our 43 patients. Munster et al [6], compared 7 CEA treated patients to 18 similar extent retrospective controls and found that the use of CEA did not reduce the hospital stay and did not reduce the number of grafting procedures required. This was also our experience. The importance of preserving allograft dermis has been emphasized by Cuono et al [7] and Compton et al [8]. Both have also demonstrated rete ridge formation within the first year after application. We tried to retain homograft dermis utilizing the Cobbett skin graft knife to thinly excise allograft epidermis. Often the allograft was soft and avulsed completely or if solid came away completely despite taking thin slices of allograft. In future it may be advisable to replace allograft 7 to 10 days before CEA is available hoping that it will engraft and be firmly adherent to permit allograft dermis preservation during tangential excision.

A promising advancement in cultured skin is the composite epidermal-dermal model being developed and described by Boyce et al [9] in which a collagen-glycosaminoglycan substrate is populated with the patient's fibroblasts and this latter seeded on one surface with the patient's keratinocytes. After a suitable incubation period this composite is applied. The presence of the dermal equivalent lattice against the underlying bed would facilitate the underlying bed uniting with the composite through fibrin formation, collagen formation and facilitate the ingrowth of capillaries into dermal equivalent lattice. In this model histological studies demonstrated early formation of rete ridges within the composite within 2 weeks of application to the patient. Adherence of this composite should be superior to what we have observed in clinical practice with CEA alone.

Our histological sections demonstrated clearly that with CEA rete ridge formation did not occur until after one year in the patients monitored. Putland et al [10] observed that the ridges were less numerous and thinner than in split thickness autografts of the same age. In one patient rete ridges appeared at 9 months. In two others rete ridges were present at $3\,^1/_2$ years whereas the fourth patient showed no rete at $3\,^1/_2$ years. Compton et al [11] reported rete ridge formation at 9 months in CEA initiated from groin skin and 12 months from axillary skin. Perhaps the rapidity of rete formation is donor site specific. Our cultures were all initiated from abdominal or thigh skin. The flat epidermal underlying bed interface contributed to the instability seen in some patients and served to distinguish CEA which had engrafted from split thickness skin graft.

Our burn population has changed. From 1988 to 1993 54 patients with a third degree component covering greater than 34% of the body surface were treated. Thirty survived and 22 received CEA. From 1994 to 1999 only 39 were treated, 22 survived and 14 received CEA. Since engraftment is still uncertain we reserve CEA for large burns and would favour re-cropping all available donor sites as soon as re-epithelialized rather than delaying their harvest to utilize CEA which is incubating. CEA can be used to dress donor sites if there is sufficient autograft donor sites to cover all recipient sites with autograft.

The number of patients with large burns who would benefit from CEA to supplement insufficient donor sites has decreased in the past 6 years and less CEA has been initiated and used.

Conclusion

With CEA available our position has been to initiate it for burns with a full thickness component exceeding 35% of the body surface. We use all available autograft sites as often as they are available and will only use CEA after all available autograft has been applied. CEA is allowed 2 weeks to engraft. If not adherent or absent, our practice is to re-prepare the wound and cover it either with autograft or if autograft is not available, further CEA or allograft. At present with a mean coverage of 2.4% body surface achieved in 43 patients, CEA's value in our Unit is equivalent to allograft since both provide coverage which is temporary. If CEA engrafts it is a bonus. It has yet to reduce hospital stay. A larger number of patients will need to be treated to determine if CEA changes mortality. CEA is still an experimental burn tool. To date it has not accelerated wound closure, has not reduced the number of crops of autograft harvested, and has not re-

duced mortality. The composite epidermal-dermal cultured model is looked forward to.

Acknowledgements

The authors thank Mosby Inc. Publishing Company for their permission to print the following figures from the Journal of Burn Care and Rehabilitation, 1995, Volume 16: (Nov/Dec) 627-40, Putland M, Snelling CFT, Macdonald I, Tron VA: Histological comparison of cultured epithelial autograft and meshed expanded split thickness skin graft. J. Burn Care Rehabil. 1995;16:627–40. Original Fig. 7, 11, 12, 14, 22, 24 and 28 renumbered and reproduced as Fig. 3, 7, 9, 10, 12, 14 and 16 respectively.

We thank Maureen Bérard for typing the manuscript and Wendy Cannon for preparation of tables and graphics.

We thank British Columbia Professional Fire Fighters Burn Fund for financial support to found the CEA laboratory and finance statistical analysis.

References

[1] Rheinwald JG, Green H: Serial cultivation of strains of human epidermal keratinocytes: the formation of keratinizing colonies from single cells. Cell.;6:331–343, Nov. 1975.
[2] Green H, Kehinde O, Thomas J: Growth of cultured human epidermal cells into multiple epithelia suitable for grafting. Proc Natl Acad Sci USA; 76(11)5665–5668, Nov. 1979.
[3] Clugston PA, Snelling CFT, Macdonald IB, Maledy HL, Boyle JC, Germann E, et al.: Cultured epithelial autografts: three years of clinical experience with eighteen patients. J Burn Care Rehabil.;12(6) 533–539, Nov. 1991.
[4] Williamson JS, Snelling CFT, Clugston P, Macdonald IB, Germann E: Cultured epithelial autograft: five years of clinical experience with twenty-eight patients. J Trauma; 39(2)309–319, Aug. 1995.
[5] Rue LW, Cioffi WG, McManus WF, Pruitt BA: Wound closure and outcome in extensively burned patients treated with cultured autologous keratinocytes. J Trauma. 34(5)662–668, May 1993.

[6] *Munster AM, Weiner SH, Spence RJ:* Cultured epidermis for the coverage of massive burn wounds. Ann Surg.;211(6):676–680, June 1990.

[7] *Cuono CB, Langdon R, Birchall N, Barttelbort S, McGuire J:* Composite autologous-allogeneic skin replacement: development and clinical application. Plast Reconstr Surg.;80(4)626–635, Oct. 1987.

[8] *Compton CC, Hickerson W, Nadire K, Press W:* Acceleration of skin regeneration from cultured epithelial autografts by transplantation to homograft dermis. J Burn Care Rehabil.; 14(6):653–662, Nov. 1993.

[9] *Boyce ST, Greenhalgh DG, Kagan RJ, Housinger T, Sorrell JM, Childress C et al.:* Skin anat- omy and antigen expression after burn wound closure with composite grafts of cultured skin cells and biopolymers. Plast Reconstr Surg.; 91(4)632–641, April 1993.

[10] *Putland M, Snelling CFT, Macdonald I, Tron VA:* Histologic comparison of cultured epithelial autograft and meshed expanded split-thickness skin graft. J Burn Care Rehabil.; 16(6) 627–640, Nov. 1995.

[11] *Compton CC, Gill JM, Bradford DA, Regauer S, Gallico GG, O'Connor NE:* Skin regenerated from cultured epithelial autografts on full-thickness burn wounds from 6 days to 5 years after grafting. Lab Investig.;60(5)600–612, 1989.

Clinical Use of Cultured Keratinocytes

R. L. Sheridan

Summary

This is a brief review of recent experience with cultured keratinocytes alone and in combination with dermal substitutes at the Shriners Burns Hospital, Massachusetts. Overall engraftment rates are now 70 % or better, provided the preparation of the burn bed is meticulous. Limited experience with cultured cells placed on Integra® dermal substitute has, to date, been poor.

Introduction

Although cultured epithelial cells were first used clinically at the Shriners Burns Hospital in Boston [1], they have remained a relatively marginal component of routine care, used principally in patients with massive injuries. However, when used, it seems clear that clinical results have improved, probably reflecting the learning curve that is associated with any new technology. Rather than presenting data on engraftment and contraction rates, the objective of this manuscript is to review what we have learned about cultured epithelial graft use in the environment of our burn unit. These reflections are based on the personal experience of the author with 16 patients managed over ten years.

In our hospital, the clinical use of cultured epithelial cells has generally been confined to those children with massive (more than 70 % full thickness) injuries [2, 3]. The general plan of care for such children includes individualized resuscitation followed, when he-

modynamic stability is achieved, by early identification and excision of full thickness burns and immediate biologic closure of the resulting wounds [4, 5]. In general, the first choice of methods of immediate wound closure is split thickness autograft. When this

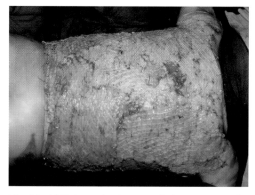

Fig. 1A: Widely meshed autograft does not provide immediate physiologic coverage of wounds.

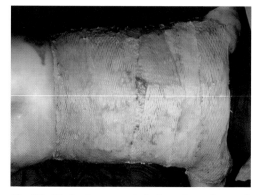

Fig. 1B: Meshed unexpanded allograft can be used to cover meshed and widely expanded autograft to provide immediate physiologic coverage.

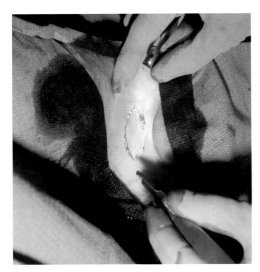

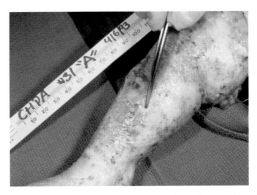

Fig. 3: At the time of surgery, allograft is either stripped off of the bed of excision, or the alloepidermis is excised, leaving behind a layer of allodermis that it is hoped will proved a more flexible and less hypertrophic wound.

Fig. 2: At the time of initial surgery in children with massive injuries, a small full thickness skin biopsy is often taken to allow for separation and culture of keratinocytes.

is exhausted, generally at the time of the first operation, coverage proceeds with cryopreserved human allograft and Integra (Integra Lifescience, Plainsboro, New Jersey). Oftentimes, meshed but unexpanded allograft is used to cover meshed and widely expanded autograft to provide immediate physiologic coverage (Figs. 1A, 1B). At the time of initial surgery in children with massive injuries, a small full thickness skin biopsy is often taken to allow for separation and culture of keratinocytes (Fig. 2). The biopsy is sent to a commercial vendor (Genzyme Tissue Repair, Cambridge, MA) where confluent sheets of autologous keratinocyte are produced. By the time these are ready for clinical use, approximately 2 to 3 weeks later, the child generally has physiologic closure of the large bulk of the wound and is awaiting definitive closure using serial reharvesting of donor sites as they heal. If there is substantial wound area remaining without this definitive coverage, autologous keratinocytes are employed.

I feel that it is important to use cultured keratinocytes as an adjunctive wound clo-

sure strategy. In other words, a defined area of wound should be set aside for keratinocyte use while the remaining wound is definitively covered with serial reharvest of autograft in the traditional manner. If this is not done, and the entire wound is committed to closure with keratinocytes, disastrous problems may follow failure of the keratinocytes to successfully engraft.

The cells seem to do best on a wound bed that has been optimally prepared. In our unit this consists of wounds, ideally on anterior surfaces only, that have previously been successfully engrafted with allograft. At the time of surgery, allograft is either stripped off of the bed of excision, or the alloepidermis is excised, leaving behind a layer of alloepidermis that it is hoped will proved a more flexible and less hypertrophic wound (Fig. 3). This technique, originally described by Cuono [6, 7], results in removal of the basement membrane and epidermal to dermal bonding structures, possibly explaining the mixed clinical results [8]. It is essential that the wound bed is meticulously prepared.

After the vascularized allograft or alloepidermis is removed, careful hemostasis is achieved and the grafts, with their vaseline gauze backings, are placed (Fig. 4). Generally, the grafts are secured with a dry mesh dress-

Fig. 4: After the vascularized allograft or alloepidermis is removed, careful hemostasis is achieved and the grafts are placed.

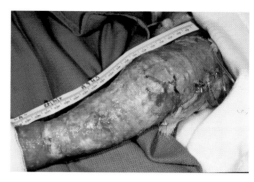

Fig. 6: On occasion, engraftment is spotty, despite well prepared wound beds, particularly in patients during episodes of systemic sepsis.

Fig. 5: Although infrequent, purulence beneath the impermeable vaseline gauze carrier can occur. Prompt recognition and removal will avert systemic sepsis.

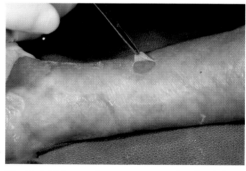

Fig. 7: Initial engraftment rate vary, but lately have been 70 % or better in most cases. However, many children will have coverage that is more fragile than ideal and may later require resurfacing with autograft.

ing and examined for purulence daily at the time of a dry dressing change. Although infrequent, purulence beneath the impermeable vaseline gauze carrier can occur. Prompt recognition and removal will avert systemic sepsis (Fig. 5). On or about the seventh day after surgery, the vaseline gauze backings are removed and the wound inspected. Grafts are then treated with non adherent, dry protective dressings.

Initial engraftment rate vary, but lately have been 70 % or better in most cases. On occasion, engraftment is spotty, despite well prepared wound beds, particularly in patients experiencing episodes of systemic sepsis (Fig. 6). However, many children will

have coverage that is more fragile than ideal (Fig. 7) and may later require resurfacing with autograft [9]. It is tempting to limit physical therapy and physical activity to protect the fragile grafts. However it is important not to compromise long term outcomes by doing this. It is preferable to continue routine rehabilitation efforts and accept some loss of the fragile epithelial grafts that ensure (Fig. 8).

Subsequent care of the wounds is identical to other split thickness autografts, and includes moisturizers massage and compression garments. For at least the first year it is possible to discern areas closed with cultured keratinocytes by visual inspection, these wounds

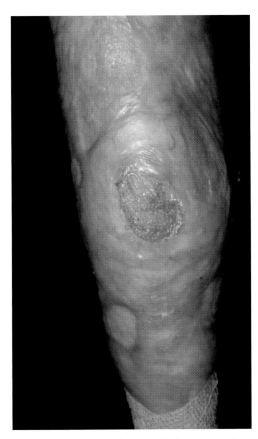

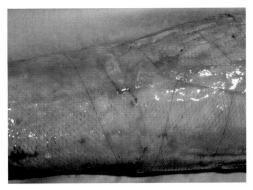

Fig. 9: Integra® is a bilaminate synthetic with an inner layer of bovine collagen that serves as a template for dermal regeneration and an outer layer of silicone that provides a temporary vapor barrier. The silicone is later replaced with an ultrathin epithelial autograft.

Fig. 8: It is tempting to limit physical therapy and activity to protect the fragile grafts. However it is important not to compromise long term outcomes by doing this. It is preferable to continue routine rehabilitation efforts and accept any loss of epithelial grafts that ensures.

having a shiny, smooth appearance and more frequent superficial blister formation.

Innovative Clinical Use of Cultured Epithelial Cells

Although useful in children with very large burns, cultured keratinocytes are an imperfect solution to the problem of the massive wound. The principal imperfection is the fragility of the coverage, probably related to the absence of dermis. Leaving behind a remnant

of allodermis when applying keratinocytes to wounds from which the alloepidermis has been excised does not reliably solve the problem, as initial engraftment rates and graft durability do not seem improved by this maneuver. This may relate to removal of basement membrane after sharp excision of alloepidermis.

There are several efforts underway that attempt to combine keratinocytes with a dermal analog, either on the patient or in the laboratory prior to engraftment. Efforts on the patient prior to engraftment include the technique described above in which the alloepidermis of vascularized allograft is excised and cultured keratinocytes are placed on the resulting bed of remnant vascularized dermis [6, 7]. Clinical results are mixed, but the technique does not seem to compromise initial engraftment and may improve long term results. Another approach is to place the keratinocytes on vascularized Integra® (Integra Life Sciences, Plainsboro, NJ). Integra® is a bilaminate synthetic with an inner layer of bovine collagen that serves as a template for dermal regeneration and an outer layer of silicone that provides a temporary vapor barrier [10, 11]. The silicone is later replaced with an ultrathin epithelial autograft (Fig. 9). Al

Fig. 10a: Our experience with the combination of cultured keratinocytes and Integra® is limited to three children (unreported data).

Fig. 11a: Our own efforts to combine keratinocytes with a dermal analog has involved culturing autologous keratinocytes into allogenic dermis. The dermis is generated from properly screened allograft from which all cellular elements have been removed. Our initial clinical experience with this combination generated successful engraftment rates of approximately 50 %. With changes in culturing technique, successful engraftment has been much more reliable. This photograph illustrates this composite graft at the time of engraftment.

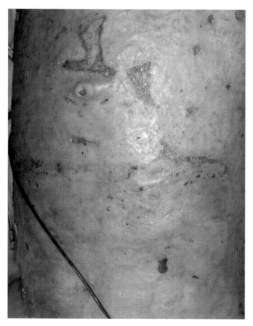

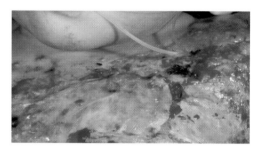

Fig. 11b: The keratinocyte and dermal analog composite at 5 days, illustrating relatively rapid vascularization.

Fig. 10b: In two cases, keratinocyte engraftment was very poor. In one child, pictured here, initial engraftment was good. However, the combination subsequently underwent marked contraction that required staged release.

though there are no reports describing successful clinical use of keratinocytes on Integra®, it has been explored in an animal model [12]. Our experience with this combination is limited to three children (unreported data). In two cases, kertainocyte engraftment was very poor. In one child, initial engraftment was good (Figs. 10A, 10B). However, the combination subsequently underwent marked contraction that required staged release.

The other approach to bring keratinocytes and a dermal analog together is in the laboratory prior to engraftment. This has been explored, without marked clinical success, by a number of research teams. Boyce and coworkers have been working with a combination of keratinocytes and fibroblasts cultured into a bovine collagen scaffold [13–16]. Their early clinical experience was mixed, but their recent reports are more encouraging [17]. Our own efforts in this regard involve culturing autologous keratinocytes into allogenic dermis. The dermis is generated from properly screened allograft from which all cellular elements have been removed. Our initial clinical experience with this combination generated successful engraftment rates of approximately 50 % [18]. With changes in culturing technique, successful engraftment has been much more reliable (Figs. 11A, 11B). This work is currently in progress. The ultimate success of the effort to reliably combine keratinocytes with a dermal analog remains to be seen.

Conclusion

At the time of their first clinical use, cultured keratinocytes as tools in burn surgery were lauded as the ideal solution to the problem of the massive wound. The enthusiasm for their use has been tempered by engraftment rates and durability inferior to standard split thickness autograft. Despite this, the technology has earned a place in the armamentarium of the burn surgeon. At the present time, their utility seems limited to defined areas of anterior, well-prepared wound in patients with very large injuries. However, the future of the technology will likely be brighter when it can be reliably combined with a dermal analog.

References

[1] Gallico GG, 3d, O'Connor NE, Compton CC, Kehinde O, Green H: Permanent coverage of large burn wounds with autologous cultured human epithelium. New England Journal of Medicine; 311:448–51, 1984.

[2] Sheridan RL, Tompkins RG: Cultured autologous epithelium in patients with burns of ninety percent or more of the body surface. Journal of Trauma; 38:48–50, 1995.

[3] Sheridan RL, Tompkins RG: Recent clinical experience with cultured autologous epithelium. Br J Plast Surg 1996 Jan.; 49:72–4, 2000.

[4] Sheridan RL: The seriously burned child: resuscitation through reintegration – 1. Current Problems in Pediatrics; 28:105–27, 1998.

[5] Sheridan RL, Tompkins RG, Burke JF: Management of burn wounds with prompt excision and immediate closure. J Intensive Care Med.; 9:6–19, 1994.

[6] Cuono C, Langdon R, McGuire J: Use of cultured epidermal autografts and dermal allografts as skin replacement after burn injury. Lancet; 1:1123–4, 1986.

[7] Langdon RC, Cuono CB, Birchall N, et al.: Reconstitution of structure and cell function in human skin grafts derived from cryopreserved allogeneic dermis and autologous cultured keratinocytes. Journal of Investigative Dermatology; 91:478–85, 1988.

[8] Rue LW, III, Cioffi WG, McManus WF, Pruitt BA, Jr: Wound closure and outcome in extensively burned patients treated with cultured autologous keratinocytes. J Trauma; 34:662–7, 1993.

[9] Desai MH, Mlakar JM, McCauley RL, et al.: Lack of long-term durability of cultured keratinocyte burn-wound coverage: a case report. J Burn Care Rehabil.;12:540–5, 1991.

[10] Heimbach D, Luterman A, Burke J, et al.: Artificial dermis for major burns. A multi-center randomized clinical trial. Ann Surg.; 208: 313–20, 1988.

[11] Burke JF, Yannas IV, Quinby WC, Jr., Bondoc CC, Jung WK: Successful use of a physiologically acceptable artificial skin in the treatment of extensive burn injury. Annals of Surgery; 194:413–28, 1981.

[12] Compton CC, Butler CE, Yannas IV, Warland G, Orgill DP: Organized skin structure is regenerated in vivo from collagen-GAG matrices seeded with autologous keratinocytes. J Invest Dermatol 1998 Jun.;110:908–16, 2000.

[13] Hansbrough JF, Boyce ST, Cooper ML, Foreman TJ: Burn wound closure with cultured autologous keratinocytes and fibroblasts attached to a collagen-glycosaminoglycan substrate. JAMA; 262:2125–30, 1989.

[14] Harriger MD, Warden GD, Greenhalgh DG, Kagan RJ, Boyce ST: Pigmentation and microanatomy of skin regenerated from composite grafts of cultured cells and biopolymers applied to full-thickness burn wounds. Transplantation; 59:702–7, 1995.

[15] Boyce ST, Hansbrough JF: Biologic attachment, growth, and differentiation of cultured human epidermal keratinocytes on a graftable collagen and chondroitin-6-sulfate substrate. Surgery; 103:421–31, 1988.

[16] *Boyce ST, Goretsky MJ, Greenhalgh DG, Kagan RJ, Rieman MT, Warden GD:* Comparative assessment of cultured skin substitutes and native skin autograft for treatment of full-thickness burns. Annals of Surgery; 222: 743–52, 1995.

[17] *Boyce ST, Kagan RJ, Meyer NA, Yakuboff KP, Warden GD:* The 1999 clinical research award. Cultured skin substitutes combined with Integra Artificial Skin to replace native skin autograft and allograft for the closure of excised full-thickness burns. J Burn Care Rehabil 1999 Nov–Dec.; 20:453–61, 2000.

[18] *Sheridan RL, Morgan JR:* Initial clinical experience with an autologous composite skin substitute. J Burn Care Rehabil.; 21:S214, 2000.

The First 7 Years of the West Australian Skin Culture Laboratory

F. Wood

Summary

The impetus to develop tissue – engineered skin is clinical need. As surgeons we are all too often faced with cutaneous defects from many aetiologies. Current techniques are limited by the availability of suitable donor sites. Tissue engineering is method of extracorporal tissue expansion. From a small donor site sample, site-specific cells can be grown.

Keratinocyte suspensions can potentially treat a variety of epidermal defects and the author has gained wide experience using this technique to treat burn wounds, chronic wounds and donor sites. Based on experimental findings the author's group from expatients has shown that wounds heal of epithelialization when sprayed with cell culture medium alone.

Introduction

As technology advances into the 21st century, medicine is set to progress from organ donation looking towards organ regeneration, for tissue replacement in situations of trauma, malignancy or disease. As the scientist engineer cells into tissues, as clinicians we need to explore the indications of the new technology, and workout how to ensure the best clinical outcome. It is essential that the clinical evolution of care parallel the tissue engineering revolution [1].

The story so far with respect to implementing CEA into clinical burn practice will be presented. Working to bring basic science to the bedside. Striving to give the best cosmetic and functional outcome in the reconstruction of the burn wound [2].

Skin is a complex organ involving all embryological elements. Each cellular type is capable of survival and replication under appropriate laboratory conditions [3].

Since the first reported clinical case in 1982, cultured epidermal cells are increasingly used to treat skin loss with mixed results. The use of this invitro form of tissue expansion allows surface epidermal cover of a burn injury with minimal donor site.

Such cellular expansion is vital when considering early massive burn wound debridement. Clearly as patients with larger body surface area burns survive the available skin donor sites become restricted. It is essential for all aspects of care to progress at pace with Intensive Care technology. As survival from a massive burn becomes more commonplace we must ensure the scar outcome is worth the pain of survival [4–12].

The ultimate reconstruction of the cutaneous defect would of course be in the form of regeneration of all embryological elements within the skin. The ability to manipulate the cellular systems and the wound environment to accept and maintain the viability of such a composite system is not yet possible. However, there is an exciting future ahead of us as we advance towards composite organ regeneration for the reconstruction of cutaneous defects [13].

In Western Australia we have spent the last 7 years exploring the clinical limitations and indications of the current evolving epidermal culture technology. By critical clinical review we have identified areas of concern and potential improvement. In close collaboration between scientist and surgeon we have developed techniques attempting to augment wound healing and optimise scar formation [14].

Development of Skin Culture WA

CEA was introduced into our burns treatment plan in 1990. We were faced with a difficult clinical problem. A fifty-year-old female suffered 75 % body surface area full thickness burn injury. After a five-month period, 50 % BSA remained unhealed. Donor sites had been repeatedly harvested and skin lost due to recurrent infection. The possibility of using CEA was investigated. A sample of skin was sent to Professor Mastertons team in Melbourne for culture 5 months post injury. The CEA was grown and grafted successfully, wound healing being achieved. However, the patient died 5 weeks later due to a mycetoma in the right atrium.

Having seen the potential of CEA, it's use expanded over the subsequent years to a stage where funding was sought to establish a dedicated skin culture laboratory. With our onsite facility we were able to tackle a number of difficulties, most importantly the time taken to culture the epidermis, the cost of the process and establish a reliable clinical system. Having established a rapid cost effective technique we were then in a position to explore the wider indications.

Our current facility opened in February of 1993 with the aid of a Telethon grant. Since then CEA has been used on 851 patients and 1024 biopsies as part of their clinical care.

Process

The clinical provision of CEA commences with clinical examination of the patient. The question to ask is how can CEA improve the quality of the outcome for the patient? Reducing the time taken to achieve healing can influence the issue of scar quality.

The cells are harvested from a thin split thickness skin biopsy using EMLA cream as a local anaesthetic agent. The basal cells are harvested from the dermal epidermal junction subsequent to soaking in trypsin.

The process used is as described by Green [15] until 70 % confluence is achieved. The cells are then harvested as a single cell suspension and delivered to the operating theatre for clinical use from day 5-post biopsy onwards. It is preferable to use primary cultured cells though in cases where a great expansion is needed secondary cultures are used.

Clinical Indications

Initially CEA was used in cases of massive body surface area burns where severe limi-

Table 1: Biopsy sites for CEA

Year	Thin	Glabrous	Post Auric	Respiratory Mucosa	Nail Bed	Labia	Mastoid	Urothelium	Total
1993	40	0	0	0	0	0	0	0	40
1994	59	10	0	0	0	0	0	0	69
1995	109	6	1	0	0	0	0	0	122
1996	129	6	3	1	1	0	0	0	140
1997	187	8	4	2	0	1	0	0	202

last updated 01/01/2001

tation of suitable donor sites was associated with prolonged healing times [16, 17]. The indications have expanded to include:

– acute burn trauma [18, 19]
– Scar manipulation
– Chronic wounds [20–22]
– Giant hairy naevi
– Mastoid cavity reconstruction [23–26]
– Respiratory epithelium reconstruction [27]
– Vaginal reconstruction
– Re-pigmentation [28–32]
– Urothelium [33, 34]

Surgical Preparation of the Wound Bed

In order to optimise the potential of CEA wound bed preparation must be meticulous. Accurate debridement to the level of viable tissue is essential. Infection must be controlled locally and systematically.

Wound preparation uses a combination of techniques including,

– Sharp dissection
– Diathermy
– Ultra sonic scalpel
– Rotating burr

The wounds are then washed with copious quantities of warm normal saline, using the pulse lavage system in large burn cases, prior to applying the CEA.

Application of CEA

Initially CEA was used as a confluent sheet using Vaseline gauze as the carrier dressing. It was placed on the prepared wound and secured with Histoacyly glue and secondary dressings. We evolved to use Surfrasoft as the carrier dressing as it was easier to handle both in the laboratory and clinically.

As we began to explore the use of CEA in suspension, our first method was its introduction under an occlusive dressing e.g. Opsite. Having explored a number of methods of cell suspension delivery our currently favoured method of application is via a spray nozzle, which fits into the syringe. It provides a system that is simple to use, delivering an aerosol of viable cells to the wound surface.

The Issue of Take

The indication for which CEA was developed was the large body surface area burn where donor sites are severely limited. This was our starting point. The results are typically biphasic with "take" rates greater than 80 % or, unfortunately a smaller group (12 patients of the 850) where "take" was less than 20 %.

We consider "take" to be epithelization at 5 days post surgery. On review of the cases, inadequate debridement and infection were the main causes of the poor "take". In the patient with better "take" rates, it became apparent very quickly that we were not dealing with a standard split skin graft in respect of establishing wound cover. The "take" process is dependent on cellular adhesion, which takes time to mature [35–38]. The surface lacks keratin and moisture loss from the surface can cause local maceration and secondary ulceration. It is vital to protect the surface whilst it matures but equally important to mobilize the area. The difficulties

Table 2: The number of biopsies V patients

Year	Total # Patients	Total # Biopsies
1993	35	40
1994	55	69
1995	110	122
1996	104	140
1997	170	202
1998	144	186
1999	135	151
2000	150	170
Total	903	1080

we encountered led us to investigating ways of protecting the surface [39]. We have done so using a custom made hydrophobic fabric garment. Since the introduction of a hydrophobic fabric garment the secondary loss of epithelium has reduced i.e. small blisters due to sheering forces. The fabric transports moisture from the surface. Sheer forces from pressure garments are reduced by transmission of the forces to the layer between the hydrophobic fabric and outer garments. Compliance has also increased as the hydrophobic lining is more comfortable than power net alone.

Full Thickness Skin Loss

In the large full thickness injury we noted that the CEA will certainly "take" onto fascia, but the lack of dermis makes it a less than ideal form of reconstruction, in particular long-term fragility and contraction being the main problem [40–47].

Illustration

The surgical approach has developed to use a 1 to 3 or 1 to 6 meshed split thickness skin graft, or papillary dermal graft to introduce dermis, with CEA in fluid suspension to fill the interstices of the mesh. In this way the wound heals rapidly, reducing granulation formation in the interces. It is of interest to us that the resulting mesh pattern is much less obvious than when using mesh alone resulting in a better quality of scar.

Recent work in a pig model has demonstrated clearly the benefit of augmenting a meshed graft with CEA in order to speed up healing with the potential of improving the quality of the scar [48]. In situations where autologous dermis is unavailable, Integra has been used to reconstruct the dermis. The dermal template forms a reticular dermis with a second stage procedure of thin mesh graft + CEA suspension to complete the reconstruction.

Partial Thickness Skin Loss

In cases if partial thickness burn injury the purpose of surgical intervention is to achieve the best scar possible, reducing overall morbidity. It is in this group of patients where the assessment of the wound us difficult, we are attempting to replace the lost tissue with the most appropriately matched donor tissue CEA [49] making comparison of treatments subjective. We have used a donor site model and trans-epidermal water loss measures to follow the early healing phase of the partial thickness loss showing the benefit of CEA in suspension [50].

It is our belief that timely surgery is associated with hypertrophic scar reduction. In the group of partial thickness injury we planned surgery around day 10 post injury, a compromise to [51]:

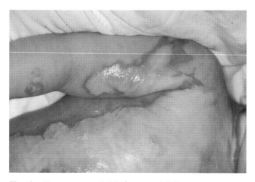

Fig. 1: Pre-surgery at 13 days post injury

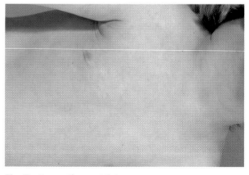

Fig. 2: 3 months post injury

- avoid the risk of unnecessary surgery,
- Avoid undue delay in healing with the associated risk of increasing the hypertrophic scar.

Technique has developed based on clinical judgement and experience. The grafted area is often seen as smooth, appropriately pigmented, without the shiny characterless surface seen with secondary healing. The appropriate pigmentation has lead us to use CEA to manipulate areas of hypopigmentation. Also we use CEA from site-matched areas to further improve the quality of the scar.

Indirect evidence of improved scar in this group of dermal injuries has come from a retrospective review of pressure therapy for scar manipulation. It is a routine part of our burn management to commence pressure as close to 10 days post surgery as the wound will allow. Based on clinical observation that pressure therapy appears to be most effective when introduced early in scar evolution.

Since the introduction of CEA to our surgical program the prescription of garments has fallen in surgical patients from 91% with a 74% compliance to 34% with a 30% compliance, a comparison of 1990 to 1996 figures. We clearly cannot commence pressure therapy when there is no or minimal scar. The 34% of those treated surgically with CEA and pressure is the early cases when pressure was routine, it was removed at 3 months when it became apparent that the hypertrophic scar was not developing. Twelve patients in this 34% did not have 100% "take" at 5 days, small areas were secondarily skin grafted with split skin and these areas were treated with pressure in line with our protocol for split thickness skin grafting. The rate of prescription of pressure therapy has now fallen to 18% of our patients where CEA is used.

The big question when treating a partial thickness injury is the mechanism of healing. Does CEA act by stimulating the remaining adnexal structures within the dermis to heal the wound, or do the cells integrate becoming part of the healed wound surface? To answer the question we need a feature of the cells, which can be identified as donor site and tracked to the recipient site. Past work on allograft used DNA markers i.e. sex chromosome. When using autograft the genetic material is identical, we therefore need to look at phenotypic expression from one site to another. Clinical scientific evidence shows that CEA retains its site-specific character.

We identified cytokeratin 9 from glabrous skin grafted to a thin skin site. Although this demonstrates incorporation of cells in one case, further work would be needed to prove routine "take" as opposed to augmentation of wound healing [55].

Clinically we have seen that as the wound is deeper, into the reticular dermis the take with CEA alone is not reliable. The introduction of a papillary dermal element e.g. thin SSG or dermal graft meshed increases reliability.

The donor site of split thickness graft is often overlooked as a source of morbidity. The intraoperative blood loss, pain of healing, and subsequent scar, are all too often significant. The donor site for CEA is a fraction of the size: from 2cm–10cm of thin split thickness skin we routinely culture sufficient CEA to cover the burn wound in from 5 days. In addition it is routine to use CEA on the donor sites to hasten healing and reduces scar potential.

Properties of CEA

As we developed the culture service we explored the concept that the epithelium retained its site-specific character [57]. Although burns of glabrous skin often heals by secondary intention due to the thickness of the dermis when extending deep the resulting wound is difficult to reconstruct. We have successfully used a glabrous donor site resulting reconstruction using site specific CEA which has resulted in a surface with no subsequent contracture, fissuring or hyperkeratosis, in 29 cases.

In a case of severe injury of full thickness loss Integra, papillary dermis and site specific CEA was used to reconstruct the defect.

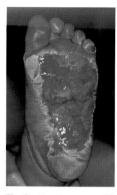 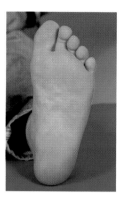

Fig. 3: Pre-Surgery at 20 days post-injury

Fig. 4: 6 months post-operative

The secretory function of the epithelium of the auditory canal is unique to its site. It was used as a donor site and culture techniques facilitated tissue expansion allowing cover of the mastoid cavity in mastoidectomy. The problem of skin grafts producing keratin inappropriately in the area was avoided. The site-specific nature of epithelium relates to the keratins produced and the activity of the reconstruction will need to pay attention, not only of the differences in dermal distribution over the body but also the more subtle epithelial differences.

In cases of severe respiratory injury CEA from a biopsy of epithelium in the maxillary antrum/inferior turbinate have been used to enhance healing. Anecdotally in 3 cases a positive effect was seen clinically.

The influence of the epidermis on the underlying scar development is poorly understood. It is possible that the results seen are due to as interaction with the cyokines produced by the basal cells. With the increased use of CEA and the clinical impression of improved scar in the acute cases and we explored the possibility of modulating established scar.

Scar improvement is possible with dermabrasion and using CEA to resurface the area. The surface is smooth with reduction in contour changes and it is possible to introduce pigment into the area to match surrounding skin tone using CEA from an appropriately matched donor site. Further critical analysis including histology is needed to identify the influence of the cells on the extracellular matrix.

Discussion

To suffer a burn injury is devastating, the initial shock and pain slowly resolving making way for the realisation of the permanent change of body image. It is frequently stated that the outcome of the injury must be worth the pain of survival. The permanent mark of the survival is the scar and it is the scar we should measure both cosmetically, functionally, and psychologically to give an indication of success of treatment. It is the aim of the burn management team to focus on minimising the scar and hence optimising the outcome, using all the technologies available.

Having established that scar minimisation is our primary focus we have explored the technology of cell culture to establish its indications within the burns practice of W.A.

Our aim when establishing the skin culture laboratory was to reliably produce good quality CEA for clinical use. Having a tissue culture laboratory on site has allowed us to pursue ideas and manipulate the CEA to achieve:

1. Rapid growth radically reducing the time between harvest of the biopsy and CEA application. All areas of potential time saving were identified and as a result we currently use CEA, day 5-post biopsy onwards.

2. Ease of use; issues were identified in the laboratory specifically to handling and clinically applying the CEA to the patient, which could be improved. As a result we currently preferentially use CEA in suspension applied in the form of an aerosol.

3. Reducing costs giving the freedom to investigate wider indications in combination with other reconstructive techniques. Overall the use of CEA in partial

thickness burn injury has become routine in our unit. Complications result from inadequate wound bed preparation, infection and post-operative trauma. The best results are seen when 100 % epithelialization is achieved 5 days post surgery. The "take" rate has improved as we have evolved our technique. The reliability increased as we moved to the use of sub confluent culture. The difficulties placing sheet CEA on a carrier in areas of complex contour, with the result of less than 100 % "take" has been solved by the use of sub confluent CEA as a cellular suspension with increased reliability. In addition the technique of harvest of the cells for use as suspension is simple, eliminating the labour intensive harvesting necessary for confluent sheets. The cells are available for use routinely at day 5 onwards post biopsy. Reducing the time to clinical use and the labour involved has reduced the running costs of the laboratory.

4. Consistency of "take" is essential in developing a reliable wound system. Our clinical experience in handling helped. We found that relatively immature preconfluent cells appeared to adhere better giving a more reliable take, rapid healing and hence optimise scar quality [58].

As indicated since 1993, 1080 biopsies have been processed from 903 patients for clinical use of CEA. As technology advances to provide clinicians with composite Tissue Engineering skin we need to be in a position to utilize that technology. At each stage critical clinical appraisal of results identifying strengths and weaknesses will eventually lead us to healing by regeneration rather than repair.

References

[1] *Caplan, AI,* Tissue Engineering for the Future: New Logistics, Old Molecules. J. Tissue Engineering 6: 1–8, 2000.

[2] *Wood FM,* Quality assurance in burn patient care: the James Laing Memorial Essay, 1994. Burns. Dec; 21(8): 563–8, 1995

[3] *Bell E* et al., The Reconstruction of Living Skin. Journal of Investigative Dermatology. 81: 2s–10s, 1983.

[4] *Odessey, R,* Addendum: Multicentre Experience With Cultured Epidermal Autograft for Treatment of Burns. J. of Burn Care & Rehabilitation 13: 174–180, 1992.

[5] *Arons JA, Wainwright DJ, Jordan RE,* The Surgical Applications and Implications of Cultured Human Epidermis: A Comprehensive Review. J. of Surgery. 111: 4–11, 1992.

[6] *Nanchahal J, Ward CM,* New Grafts for Old? A Review of Alternatives to Autologous Skin. British Journal of Plastic Surgery. 45: 354–363, 1992.

[7] *Pittelkov MR, Scott RE,* New Techniques for the In Vitro Culture of Human Skin Keratinocytes and Perspectives on Their Use of Grafting of Patients with Extensive Burns. Mayo Clinic Proceedings, 61: 771–777, 1986.

[8] *Zawacki BE,* et al. A Technique for Autografting Very Large Burns from Very Limited Donor Sites. J. of Surgery, 74: 774–777, 1973.

[9] *Heimbach DM,* A Nonuser's Questions About Cultured Epidermal Autograft. J. of Burn Care & Rehabilitation. 13: 127–129, 1992

[10] *Munster AM,* et al. Cultured Epidermis for the Coverage of Massive Burn Wounds. Ann. Surg. 211: 666–679, 1990

[11] *Herndon DN,* et al. Comparison of Cultured Epidermal Autograft and Massive Excision with Serial Autograft and massive Excision with Serial Autografting Plus Momograft Overlay. J, of Burn Care & Rehab. 13: 154–157. 1992

[12] *Ming-Liang Z,* et al., Microskin Grafting. 11. Clinical Report. J. of Burns. 12: 544–548, 1986.

[13] *Green H,* Cultured Cells for the Treatment of Disease. Scientific American. November 1991.

[14] *Wood FM, Stoner ML.:* Implication of basement membrane development on the underlying scar in partial hickness burn injury. Burns. Sept;22(6): 459–62, 1996

[15] *Shakespeare VA, Shakespeare PG,* Growth of Cultured Human Keratinocytes on Fibrous Dermal Collagen: a Scanning Electron Microscope Study. J. of Burns, 13: 343–348, 1987.

[16] *Hull BE, Finely RK, Miller SF,* Coverage of Full-Thickness Burns with Bilayered Skin Equivalents: A Preliminary Clinical Trial. J. of Surgery. 107: 496–502, 1990.

[17] *Alexander JW, MacMillan BG, Law E,* Kittur. D.S.Treatment of Severe Burns with Widely Meshed Skin Autograft and Meshed skin Allograft Overlay. J. of Trauma. 21: 433–438, 1981.

[18] *Thompson C.,* et al. Transplantation of Cultures autologous Epidermis to a Patient with Burns. The Medical Journal of Australia, 147: 507–510, 1987.

[19] *Blight A,* et al. The Treatment of Donor Sites with Cultured Epithelial Grafts. British Journal of Plastic Surgery, 44: 12–14, 1991.

[20] *Pye RJ,* Cultured Keratinocytes as Biological Wound Dressings. J. of Eye. 2: 172–178, 1988.

[21] *Compton C,* Wound Healing Potential of Cultured Epithelium. . WOUNDS: A Compendium of Clinical Research and Practice. 5: 97–108, 1993

[22] *Wood FM, Griffiths TA., Stoner ML,* Epidermal-derived factors in the treatment of a chronic leg ulcer. J of Wound Care. (6) 256–258, 1997

[23] *Premachandra DJ,* et al. Treatment of Post-Operative Otorrhoea by Grafting of Mastoid Cavities with Cultured Autologous Epidermal Cells. The Lancet 335: 365–367, 1990.

[24] *Veda M, Hata K,* The Potential of Oral Mucosa Cells for Cultured Epithelium: A Preliminaary Report. J. of Plastic Surgery, 35: 498–504, 1995.

[25] *Mackenzie IC, Hill MW,* Connective Tissue Influences on Paterns of Epithelial Architecture & Keratinization in Skin and Oral Mucosa of the adult Mouse. J. of Cell Tissue Res. 235: 551–559, 1984

[26] *Langdon J,* Autologous Kerainocyte Grafting: A New Technique for Intra-Oral Reconstruction. British Dental Journal 171: 87–90, 1991.

[27] *Papini RP, Wood FM,* Current concepts in the management of burns with inhalation injury. Care of the critically ill. April;15(2):61–66, 1999

[28] *Brysk MB,* Repigmentation of Vitiliginous Skin BY Cultured Cells. Pigment Cell Research, 2: 202–207, 1989.

[29] *Plott R,* et al., A Surgical Treatment for Vitiligo: Autologous Cultured-Epithelial Grafts. J. of Dermatol Surg Oncol. 15: 1161–1166, 1989

[30] *Gauthier Y* et al., Autologous Grafting with noncultured melanocytes: A Simplified Method for Treatment of Depigmented Lesions. J. of American Academy of Dermatology, 26: 191–194, 1992.

[31] *Navarro F A, Stoner ML, Lee HB, Park CS, Wood FM, Orgill DP:* Melanocute reproduction in full-thickness wounds using a cell spray apparatus. J burn Care Rehabil. Jan-Feb;22(1):41–6, 2001

[32] *Stoner ML, Wood FM:* The treatment of hypopigmentation lesions with cultured epithelial autograft. J Burn Care Rehabil; Jan-Feb:21(1 pt1): 50–4, 2000

[33] *Hutton KA R,* et al., Urothelial Tissue Culture for Bladder Reconstruction: An Experimental Study. J. of Urology 150: 721–725, 1993.

[34] *Romagnoli G* et al., Treatment of Posterior Hypospacias by the autologous Graft of Cultured Urethral Epithelium. The New England Journal of Medicine. 323: 527–530, 1990

[35] *Woodley, DT,* et al. Burn Wounds Resurfaced by Cultured Epidermal Autografts Show Abnormal Reconstruction of Anchoring Fibrils. Jama. 259: 2566–2571, 1988

[36] *Limova M, Grekin RC, Jordan RE,* Synthetic Membranes and Cultured Keratinocyte Grafts. J. of the American Academy of Dermatol., 23: 713–719, 1990.

[37] *Shakespeare VA, Shakespeare PG,* Growth of Cultured Human Keratinocytes on Fibrous Dermal Collagen: a Scanning Electron Microscope Study. J. of Burns, 13: 343–348, 1987.

[38] *Compton C,* Current Concepts in Paediatric Burn Care: The Biology of Cultured Epithelial Autografts: An Eight –Year Study in Paediatric Burn Patients. Eur J Padiatr Surg 2: 216–222, 1992.

[39] *Wood FM, Liddiard K, Skinner A, Ballantyne J:* Scar management of cultured epithelial autograft. Burns. Sept; 22 96); 451–454, 1996

[40] *Purdue G* et al., Biosynthetic Skin Substitute versus Frozen Human Cadaver Allograft for Temporary Coverage of Excised Burn Wounds. The Journal of Trauma, 27: 155–157, 1987.

[41] *Compton C* et al., Skin Regenerated from Cultured Epithelial Autografts on Full-Thickness Burn Wounds from 6 Days to 5 Years after Grating. Laboratory Investigation, 60: 600–612, 1989

[42] *Heck E L,* et al., Composite Skin Graft: Frozen Dermal Allografts Support the Engraftment and Expansion of Autologous Epidermis. The Journal of Trauma. 25: 106–112, 1985.

[43] *Myers S,* Navsaria et al. Transplantation of Keratinovytes in the Treatment of Wounds. The American Journal of Surgery. 170:75–83, 1995.

[44] *Botce ST,* et al. Skin Anatomy and Antigen Expression after Burn Wound Closure with Composite Grafts of Cultured Cells and Biopolymers. J of Plastic & Recon Surgery. 91: 632–641, 1993.

[45] *Compton C* et al,. Acceleration of Skin Regeneration From Cultured Epithelial Autografts by Transplantation to Homograft Dermis. J. of Burn Care & Rehabilitation, 14: 653–661, 1993

[46] *Heimbach D,* et al,. Artificial Dermis for Major Burns. Ann. Surg. 208: 313–320, 1998.

[47] *Boyce ST,* et al., Reduced Wound Contraction After Grafting of Full-Thickness Burns with a Collagen and Chondroitin-6-Sulfate (GAG) Dermal Skin Substitute and Coverage with Biobrane. JBCR 9: 364–370, 1988.

[48] *Navarro F A, Stoner ML, Lee HB, Park CS, Huertas JC, Wood FM, Orgill DP:* Sprayed keratinocyte suspensions accelerate epidermal coverage in a porcine microwound model. J Burn Care Rehabil. Nov-Dec, 21(6):513–8, 2000

[49] *Madden MR,* et al. Grafting if Cultured Allogenic Epidermis on Second and Third Degree Burn Wounds on 26 Patients. J. of Trauma. 26: 955–966, 1986.

[50] *Ronford V,* et al. Use of Human Keratinocytes Cultured on Fibrin Glue in the Treatment of Burn Wounds. J. of Burns. 17:181–184, 1990.

[51] *Mountford,* EM, Implications for Wound Healing of Patient age and Time Elapsed Since Burn Injury. J. of Wound Care; 4: 32–35. 1995

[52] *Mosher DF,* et al. Assembly of Fibronectin into Extra cellular Matrix. Annals New York Academy of Sciences, 614: 167–180, 1991.

[53] *Rousselle P Kalinin:* An Epithelium – Specific Basement Membrane Adhesion Molecule That is a Component of Anchoring Filaments. J. of Cell Biology, 114: 567–576, 1991

[54] *Marchisio PC,* Polarized Expression of Integrin Receptors ($\acute{\alpha}_6\,\beta_4, \acute{\alpha}_2\,\beta\acute{\alpha}$, and $\acute{\alpha}_v\beta_5$) and their Relationships with the Cytoskeleton and Basement Membrane matrix in Cultured Human Keratinocytes. J. of Cell Biology, 112: 761–773, 1991

[55] *Stoner ML,* Wood FM.: Cultured epithelial autograft "take" confirmed by the pressure of cytokeratin 9. J Invest Dermatol ; Mar; 112(3):391–2, 1999

[56] *May AL, Wood FM, Stoner ML:* Assessment of Adhesion assays for use with keratinocytes. Exp Dermatol. Feb; 10(1):62–9, 2001

[57] *Leigh IM,* et al, Clinical Practice and Biological effects of Keratinocyte Grafting. Annals Academy of Medicine, 20: 449–555, 1991.

[58] *Wood FM, Stoner ML:* Implication of basement membrane development on the underlying scar in partial hickness burn injury. Burns. Sept;22(6): 459–62, 1996

Various Approaches and Different Application Techniques

The Effect of the Tissue Glue Tisseel® on the Grafting of Cultured Human Epidermal Sheets and Their Evolution *in Vivo*

F. A. Auger, C. J. Hayward, C. A. López Valle, R. Guignard, L. Germain

Summary

Since the results of graft take are variable after the commonly used grafting of cultured epidermal sheets, which are currently used for burn wound treatment, this study was designed to evaluate the role and influence of Tisseel, a fibrin sealant, in the take of cultured human epidermal sheets in an athymic mouse model. Histology, electron microscopy and immunofluorescence staining confirmed the presence of a human epithelium and the development of a basement membrane when investigated on days 4, 10 and 21 post-grafting. Tisseel was detectable on day 4 only, but overall treated and untreated grafts were similar. The use of Tisseel enhanced the mechanical stability of these fragile grafts, increased the percentage of graft take, and its innocuity on the in vivo evolution of cultured epidermal sheets was demonstrated. For these reasons, we think that Tisseel may be advantageous in a clinical setting.

Introduction

In recent years the use of cultured human epithelial autografts grown from isolated and serially cultured keratinocytes has led to important breakthroughs in the treatment of human skin defects and trauma [1]. This technique has been particularly successful in the permanent coverage of full-thickness burns over large body surface areas [2–4]. However, there is still a great variability in the success rate of these grafts; in some reports the cultured epidermal sheets displayed a poor level of attachment and vascularisation [5], and the graft take ranges from 0 to 100 % depending on the study [4, 6–9].

There are several factors which influence the success of such grafts; they include the graft site itself, the presence and rate of revascularisation of the wound bed, the stability and thickness of the graft and the quality of adhesion between the implant and the graft bed [10–11]. The survival of the grafted cultured epidermis depends on its being nourished by the underlying wound bed, and this can only occur with the formation of a complete basement membrane zone which physically attaches the graft to the implantation site [12]. In normal skin, this zone ensures the structural and mechanical stability of the junction between dermis and epidermis [13–14]. In some studies, the fragility of the dermo-epidermal junction has been apparent even as long as 7 months after the grafting was performed [15].

The components of the basement membrane zone include hemidesmosomes, the lamina lucida, the lamina densa, and anchoring fibrils [16–19]. Hemidesmosomes are composed of plasma membrane integrins linked to bullous pemphigoid antigens and other extracellular glycoproteins [20–22]. The lamina lucida contains the glycoprotein laminin [16, 19]. The main components of the lamina densa and the anchoring fibrils are collagens of types IV and VII, respectively

[18, 19, 23, 24]. These emerge in a time-dependent manner in the first days and weeks following the grafting procedure [12]. After only two days post-graft, laminin is present as a continuous line under the epidermis; hemidesmosomes are also present and the lamina densa is found sparsely under the hemidesmosomal plaques. Type VII collagen forms a discontinuous layer under the epithelium. After four days all membrane components are present, the lamina densa now extending outwards from the hemidesmosomal plaques. At day 21 a well-organised basement membrane is present [12].

Since the formation of a complete basement membrane takes days if not weeks, an important factor in the success of cultured epithelial sheet grafts would be the immobility of the graft on the wound site. Any shearing movements would presumably disrupt the basal cell layer along with the nascent basement membrane and compromise the graft take [25]. For this reason an adhesive which would temporarily fix the graft to the graft bed during the early formation of the basement membrane complex could be expected to improve the rate of graft take.

In this perspective, our group undertook to evaluate the effect of the tissue glue Tisseel® on the grafting of epidermal sheets *in vivo* [25]. Tisseel® is a fibrin sealant which contains fibrinogen, aprotinin solution, fibronectin, plasminogen, human albumin and factor XIII. Upon activation by thrombin and calcium, it enhances clotting and the adhesion of tissues. The addition of Tisseel® to a graft bed before skin application in the case of mesh graft, split thickness skin and skin flap has been shown to lead to better graft take, haemostasis, and more rapid revascularisation [26–29]. Thus one would hope to find similar results in the case of cultured epidermal skin grafts applied in the presence of Tisseel®.

Materials and Methods

Cultured epidermal sheets produced as previously described [1, 30] were grafted on the dorsal muscular bed of athymic nu/nu CD-1 male adult mice by the following procedure. After anaesthesia of the mice, a 2.5 cm incision was made through the dorsal skin and the panniculus carnosus, and the loose connective tissue under these layers excised in order to provide a muscular graft bed, all work being carried out under a laminar flow hood [30]. A Fusenig's chamber [31] was then implanted and the cultured epidermal sheet grafted on the muscular bed either directly or after the application of Tisseel® (Immuno Canada Ltd., Windsor, Ontario). The glue solutions were reconstituted according to Immuno's recommendations and sprayed with the Tissomat® system (Immuno). After deposition of the graft, the vaseline gauze was detached from the cultured epidermal sheet and the cap of the Fusenig's chamber put in place and held by four cutaneous stitches.

The chamber cap was removed after five days to allow keratinisation of the epidermis. The percentage of graft take was established as the ratio of the surface occupied by grafted cultured epidermis to the surface of the Fusenig's chamber as measured in photographs taken on days 5, 10, and 21. Biopsies were taken 4, 10 and 21 days after grafting, from 2 control and 2 Tisseel®-treated mice. The protocol was repeated twice and gave similar results each time. An initial pilot study was done with 20 mice to test for the toxicity of Tisseel® to cultured grafts. The results reported here are from an experimental group of 12 mice – 6 treated with Tisseel® and 6 controls.

The biopsies were fixed in Bouin's solution, embedded in paraffin and stained with haematoxylin, phloxine and saffron. Those specimens used for electron microscopy were fixed in a solution of 2 % glutaraldehyde in sodium cacodylate buffer for 24 hours and post-fixed with 1 % osmium tetroxide. The tissues were stained with uranyl acetate. After dehydration the samples were embedded in Epon 812, contrasted with uranyl acetate and lead citrate, and observed with a Philips EM300 electron microscope.

Results

The use of the Fusenig's chambers in the grafting procedure allowed an excellent follow-up of the transplanted epidermal sheets. Better graft adherence was observed in the mice where Tisseel® was applied to the muscular surface before deposition of the epidermal sheet. This characteristic of the glue was also made evident when the vaseline gauze was detached from the graft immediately after deposition on the graft bed, as the gauze was more easily freed when Tisseel® was applied to the muscular surface. Furthermore, the percentage of graft take was increased after the application of Tisseel® (Table 1 shows the results obtained with 12 mice, 6 control and 6 treated)

There was no difference in the histological appearance of the epidermis between the two treatment groups, except that the layer of tissue glue could be seen in the Tisseel®-treated grafts on day four after grafting (Fig. 1b). Keratinocytes within the epidermal sheet had begun to organise and stratify into five to eight cell layers by the fourth day after grafting (Fig. 1, a–b). By day 10 the tissue glue had disappeared, and on days 10 and 21 the epidermis was composed of several layers of ke-

Table 1: Percentage of graft take of cultured human epidermal sheets grafted on nude mice with or without Tisseel®

Days after grafting	5	10	21
Tisseel®-treated mice*	70 % ± 3	71 % ± 8	66 % ± 1
Control mice**	52 % ± 10	51 % ± 9	46 % ± 2

Values are the mean of 2 or 3 mice ± standard deviation (total of 12 mice grafted).
* Statistically different from control at 95 % (Mann-Whitney test on all mice).
** Control mice were grafted with epidermal sheet without previous application of Tisseel®
Reprinted from British Journal of Plastic Surgery, Vol. 46, F.A. Auger, R. Guignard, C.A. López Valle and L. Germain, Role and innocuity of Tisseel®, a tissue glue, in the grafting process and *in vivo* evolution of human cultured epidermis, pp 136–142, © 1993, by permission of the publisher Churchill Livingstone.

ratinocytes at different stages of their normal terminal differentiation (Fig. 1, c–f). The stratum corneum was thicker on day 21 than on day 10, and the entire epidermis was stratified in a very satisfactory manner in both groups of mice (Fig. 1, e–f).

The human nature of the transplanted epidermis was verified by immunofluorescent labelling of the major histocompatibility complex (MHC) molecules of class 1 (HLA-A, B, C) which are present on viable human skin cells. The epidermis taken in the biopsies was labelled by the anti-HLA-A, B, C antibody (Fig. 2, b–c) but not by the anti-H_2D antibody (against mouse MHC molecules) (Fig. 2d), thus confirming its human nature.

The expression of keratins, the intermediate filaments present in keratinocytes, was normal in the cultured epidermis grafted with or without tissue glue as shown by immunofluorescence labelling with AE2 and AE3 (data not shown). The characteristic staining of all keratinocyte layers with AE3 and of suprabasal layers only with AE2 was observed.

The progressive emergence of the basement membrane macromolecules laminin and type IV collagen was also studied in the transplanted cultured epidermis. No basement membrane was present in cultured epidermal sheets released with Dispase (Boehringer Mannheim, Laval, Quebec, Canada) before grafting. The presence of type IV collagen in the basement membrane was observed by immunolabelling on day four after grafting (Fig. 3, a–b). The fluorescence of the basement membrane was slightly diminished in the presence of Tisseel® (Fig. 3b) as compared to the control (Fig. 3a). However, type IV collagen labelling was identical in both groups of mice (Fig. 3, c–d) on days 10 and 21, and its distribution was ubiquitous as it is in the dermal-epidermal junction of normal human skin (Fig. 3e). The pattern of immunofluorescent staining of laminin in the cultured epidermis was similar to that of type IV collagen (Fig. 4).

To better evaluate the formation of the basement membrane after grafting, the biopsies harvested 4, 10 and 21 days after grafting were analysed by electron microscopy. The structure of the basement membrane with its 3 characteristic regions (plasma membrane, lamina lucida and lamina densa) was observed on day four in the mice grafted without Tisseel® (Fig. 5a). However, the

lamina densa was still discontinuous, and present mainly under the hemidesmosomes. In the mice treated with Tisseel®, the tissue glue was seen as an electron-dense structure this soon after grafting. Consequently, the lamina densa of the basement membrane was difficult to distinguish (Fig. 5b). By day 10, the Tisseel® had disappeared and the lamina densa, with slight discontinuities,

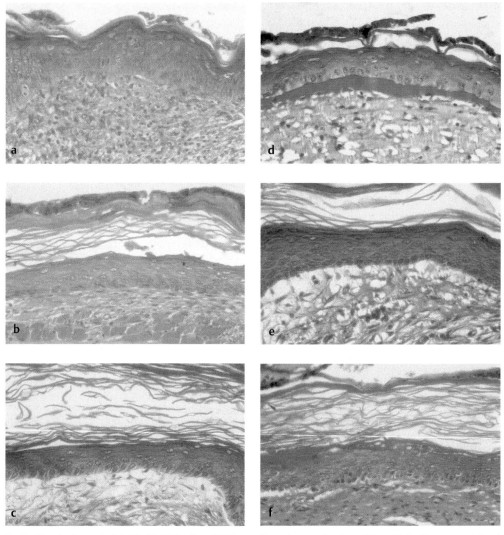

Fig. 1: Biopsies harvested at 4 (a, b), 10 (c, d) and 21 (e, f) days after grafting of human cultured epidermis on a mouse muscular graft bed without (a, c, e) or with (b, d, f) previous application of Tisseel®. Sections were stained with haematoxylin, phloxine and saffron. The presence of the tissue glue can be noted at day 4 (b). x140.

was visible under the epidermal cells of both groups of mice. The basement membrane components were well defined and the lamina densa continuous on day 21 (Fig. 5, c–d); hemidesmosomes and anchoring filaments were also observed. The ultrastructural appearance of the transplanted tissue was similar in both groups of mice. Therefore, the

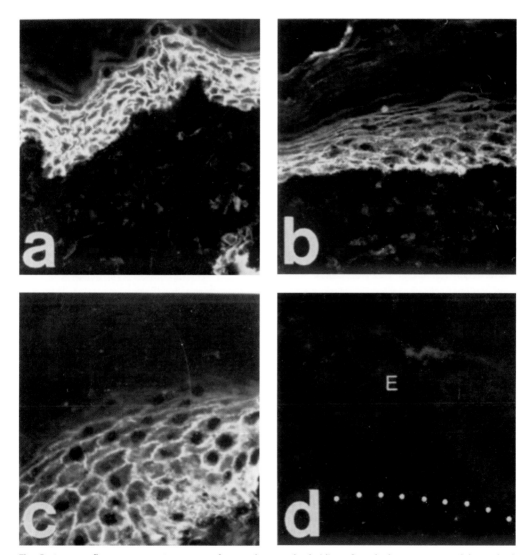

Fig. 2: Immunofluorescence microscopy of normal human skin (a) and of human cultured epithelium grafted on nude mice with previous Tisseel® application (b, day 10 post-transplantation; c–d, day 21) using mouse monoclonal anti-HLA-A,B,C (a–c) or anti-H$_2$D (d) antibodies. The anti-HLA-A,B,C antibody labelled the cell membranes of all strata (except stratum corneum). The positive staining with anti-HLA antibody (b,c) and negative staining with anti-H$_2$D antibody (d) confirm the human nature of the grafted epidermis (E). The dotted line represents the epidermal-connective tissue junction (d). x180. Reprinted from British Journal of Plastic Surgery, Vol. 46, F.A. Auger, R. Guignard, C.A. López Valle and L. Germain, Role and innocuity of Tisseel®, a tissue glue, in the grafting process and *in vivo* evolution of human cultured epidermis, pp 136–142, ©1993, by permission of the publisher Churchill Livingstone.

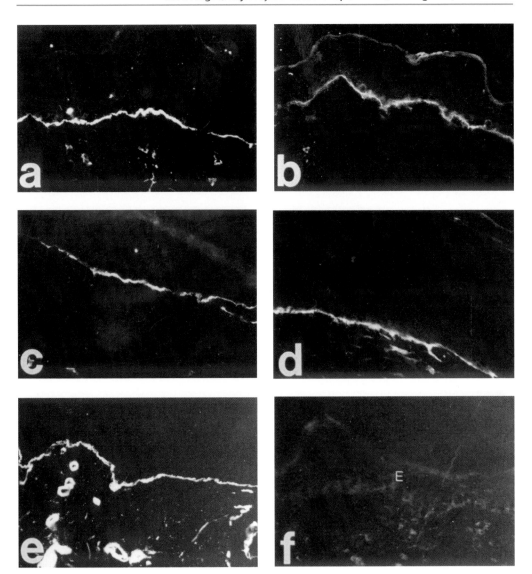

Fig. 3: Immunofluorescence staining with sheep polyclonal anti-human type IV collagen antibodies of human cultured epithelium grafted on nude mice without Tisseel® (a, day 4; c, day 21) or with previous Tisseel® application (b, day 4; d, day 21). Positive control of normal human skin (e). Negative control (primary antibody omitted) (f). Note the linear staining of the basement membrane. The fluorescence was slightly lower when Tisseel® was present at day 4 (b). E, epidermis. X180. Reprinted from British Journal of Plastic Surgery, Vol. 46, F.A. Auger, R. Guignard, C.A. López Valle and L. Germain, Role and innocuity of Tisseel®, a tissue glue, in the grafting process and *in vivo* evolution of human cultured epidermis, pp 136–142, ©1993, by permission of the publisher Churchill Livingstone.

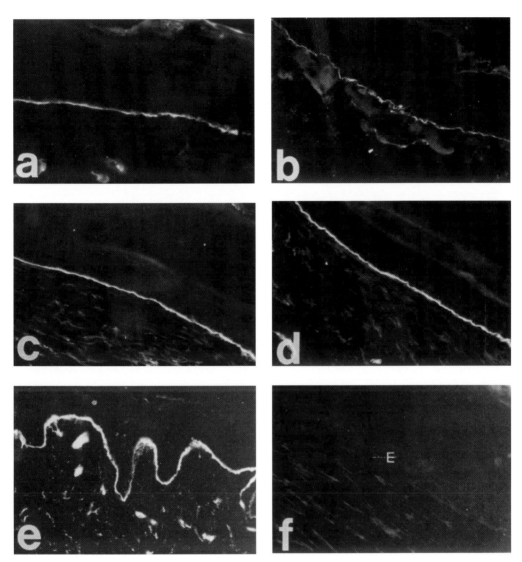

Fig. 4: Immunofluorescence staining with rat monoclonal anti-laminin antibody of human cultured epithelium grafted on nude mice without Tisseel® (a, day 4; c, day 21) or with previous Tisseel® application (b, day 4; d, day 21). Positive control of normal human skin (e). Negative control (primary antibody omitted) (f). Note the linear staining of the basement membrane. The fluorescent line was thinner when Tisseel® was present at day 4 (b). E, epidermis. X180. Reprinted from British Journal of Plastic Surgery, Vol. 46, F.A. Auger, R. Guignard, C.A. López Valle and L. Germain, Role and innocuity of Tisseel®, a tissue glue, in the grafting process and *in vivo* evolution of human cultured epidermis, pp 136–142, ©1993, by permission of the publisher Churchill Livingstone.

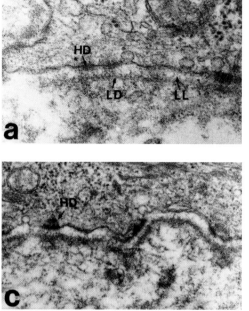

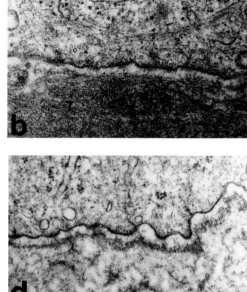

Fig. 5: Transmission electron microscopy of cultured human epithelium grafted on nude mice without Tisseel® (a, day 4; c, day 21) or with previous Tisseel® application (b, day 4; d, day 21). The regions of the basement membrane zone, lamina lucida (LL) and lamina densa (LD) were already observed at day 4 post-transplantation in the control group (a). The basal cell plasma membrane contained numerous electron-dense plates characteristic of hemidesmosomes (HD). Note the presence of Tisseel® (T) at day 4 (b) which impedes the observation of the lamina densa (LD). The ultrastructure of the basement membrane is better defined 21 days post-transplantation (c,d). Bar represents 250 nm. x29 000. Reprinted from British Journal of Plastic Surgery, Vol. 46, F.A. Auger, R. Guignard, C.A. López Valle and L. Germain, Role and innocuity of Tisseel®, a tissue glue, in the grafting process and *in vivo* evolution of human cultured epidermis, pp 136–142, ©1993, by permission of the publisher Churchill Livingstone.

tissue glue did not affect the formation of the basement membrane structure.

Discussion

The treatment of severely and extensively burned patients has benefitted enormously from the production by tissue engineering of autologous cultured epithelial sheets for transplantation [1, 2, 4]. However, there are drawbacks to this method: the cultured grafts are thin and fragile and there is always the possibility of membrane damage after sheet separation from the culture flask surface [34] and upon deposition on the burn wound. This damage and the abnormal formation of anchoring fibrils [8, 15] have been suggested as causes of the failure of cultured epidermal sheets to attach and vascularise sufficiently well to close the wound routinely as reported in some studies [5]. These phenomena are perhaps transient, as others have described a time-dependent formation of anchoring filaments [35–36].

There is a large variation in the reported percentage of take for cultured epidermal grafts, from 0–100% depending on the study [7, 9, 37, 38]. There are many factors which must be taken into account when considering this variability, including the lack of graft adherence caused by insufficient immobilisation or the collection of blood or serum, the presence of virulent bacteria on the wound, and any shearing movements, which would destroy the basal cell layer and thus prevent the formation of a basement membrane. A tissue glue such as Tisseel® should help avoid some of these problems by providing extra, though temporary, stability to the newly grafted epidermal sheet. Another fibrin sealant, Hemaseel™ HMN, has been shown to increase the graft take over the bony spinal region in a similar mouse model [39].

The improved adherence of the cultured epidermal sheet to the graft bed is the main benefit of Tisseel®, as demonstrated in our animal model. The use of Tisseel® on the wound bed led to at least a 20% increase in the graft take, even though in our model the amount of graft movement was limited to begin with (Table 1). It would be reasonable to expect a similar improvement in graft take for burn patients with the use of Tisseel®, as these grafts are strongly affected by any movement and the additional immobilisation of the grafted cultured epidermis would be beneficial.

There is no apparent toxic effect in the epidermal sheets grafted in the presence of Tisseel®; indeed, normal epidermal stratification, keratin distribution and basement membrane formation were seen in both the control and treatment groups of mice. A complete basement membrane is essential for prolonged graft stability and the maintenance of a proliferating basal layer [17]. In our immunofluorescent staining and electron microscope analyses, the presence of basement membrane components was observed as early as day four after grafting, and a well-defined structure was seen on day 21. The usual sequence of basement membrane formation was not impeded by Tisseel®, as shown by the absence of significant differences between the control and Tisseel®-treated grafts on days 10 and 21. On day four, the electron-dense tissue glue prevented the observation of the lamina densa, but the immunofluorescent labelling of type IV collagen, a component of the lamina densa, indicated its presence in the treatment group. Thus, considering that by day 10 the Tisseel® had disappeared, it can be concluded that the pres-

ence of Tisseel® had no deleterious effect on the epidermal graft. Further clinical evaluation of the role of Tisseel® in epidermal sheet transplantation would certainly be warranted in view of these promising results.

References

[1] *Green H, Kehinde O, Thomas J:* Growth of cultured human epidermal cells into a multiple epithelia suitable for grafting. Proc Natl Acad Sci USA; 76: 5665–5668, 1979.

[2] *Gallico GG, O'Conner NE, Compton CC, Kehinde O, Green H:* Permanent coverage of large burn wounds with autologous cultured human epithelium. New Engl J Med; 311: 448–452, 1984.

[3] *Auger FA:* The role of cultured autologous human epithelium in large burn wound treatment. Transplant Implant Today; 5: 21–26, 1988.

[4] *Donati L, Magliacani G, Bormioli M, Signorini M, Baruffaldi Preis FW:* Clinical experiences with keratinocyte grafts. Burns; 18 (suppl 1): S19–S26, 1992.

[5] *Kumagai N, Nishina H, Tanabe H, Ishida, H, Ogino Y:* Clinical application of autologous cultured epithelia for the treatment of burn wounds and burn scars. Plast Reconstr Surg; 82: 99–110, 1988.

[6] *Woodley DT, Peterson HD, Herzog SR, Stricklin GP, Burgeson RE, Briggaman RA, Cronce DJ, O'Keefe EJ:* Burn wounds resurfaced by cultured epidermal autografts show abnormal reconstitution of anchoring fibrils. J Am Med Assoc; 259: 2566–2571, 1988.

[7] *Hunyadi J, Farkas B, Bertényi C, Oláh J, Dubozy A:* Keratinocyte grafting: a new means of transplantation for full-thickness wounds. J Derm Surg Onc; 14: 75–78, 1988.

[8] *Desai MH, Mlakar JM, McCauley RL, Abdullah KM, Rutan RL, Waymack JP, Robson MC, Herndon DH:* Lack of long-term durability of cultured keratinocyte burn-wound coverage: a case report. J Burn Care Rehabil; 12: 540–545, 1991.

[9] *Clugston PA, Snelling CTF, Macdonald IB, Maledy HL, Boyle JC, German E, Courtemanche AD, Wirtz P, Fitzpatrick DJ, Kester DA, Foley B, Warren RJ, Carr NJ:* Cultured epithelial autografts: three years of clinical experience with eighteen patients. J Burn Care Rehabil; 12: 533–539, 1991.

[10] *Xu W, Li H, Brodniewicz T, Auger FA, Germain L:* Cultured epidermal sheet grafting with Hemaseel™ HMN fibrin sealant on nude mice. Burns; 22 (3): 191–196, 1996.

[11] Xu W, Germain L, Goulet F, Auger FA: Permanent Grafting of Living Skin Substitutes: Surgical Parameters to Control for Successful Results. J Burn Care Rehabil; 17: 7–13, 1996.

[12] Germain L, Guignard R, Rouabhia M, Auger FA: Early basement membrane formation following the grafting of cultured epidermal sheets detached with thermolysin or Dispase. Burns; 21 (3): 175–180, 1995.

[13] Furthmayr H: Basement Membrane. In: Clark R.A.F., Henson D.M. (eds) The Molecular and Cellular Biology of Wound Repair. New York: Plenum; pp 525–558, 1988.

[14] Timpl R, Wiedemann H, Ban Delden V, Furthmayr H, Kühn K: A network model for the organization of type IV collagen molecules in basement membranes. Eur J Biochem; 120: 203–211, 1981.

[15] Woodley DT, Peterson HD, Herzog SR, Stricklin GP, Burgeson RE, Briggaman RA, Cronce DJ, O'Keefe EJ: Burn wounds resurfaced by cultured epidermal autografts show abnormal reconstitution of anchoring fibrils. JAMA; 259: 2566–2571, 1988.

[16] Woodley DT: The molecular organization of basement membrane. Biochem Dis; 12: 141–158, 1987.

[17] Briggaman RA, Wheeler CE: The epidermal-dermal junction. J Invest Dermatol; 65: 71–84, 1975.

[18] Yaoita H, Foidart JM, Katz SI: Localization of the collagenous component in skin basement membrane. J Invest Dermatol; 70: 191–193, 1978.

[19] Stanley JR, Woodley DT, Katz SI, Martin GR: Structure and function of basement membrane. J Invest Dermatol; 79: 69s–72s, 1982.

[20] Marchisio PC, Bondanza S, Cremona O, Cancedda R, De Luca M: Polarized expression of integrin receptors (α6β4, α2β1, α3β1, αVβ5) and their relationship with the cytoskeleton and basement membrane matrix in cultured human keratinocytes. J Cell Biol; 112: 761–773, 1991.

[21] Westgate GE, Weaver AC, Couchman JR: Bullous pemphigoid antigen localization suggests an intracellular association with hemidesmosomes. J Invest Dermatol; 84: 218–224, 1985.

[22] Carter WG, Kaur P, Gil SG, Gahr RJ, Wayner EA: Distinct functions for integrins α3β1 in focal adhesions and α6β4 bullous pemphigoid antigen in a new stable anchoring contact (SAC) of keratinocytes: relation to hemidesmosomes. J Cell Biol; 111: 3141–3154, 1990.

[23] Pruniéras M, Régnier M, Fougère S, Woodley D: Keratinocytes synthesize basal lamina proteins in culture. J Invest Dermatol; 81: 74s–81s, 1983.

[24] Burgeson RE: Type VII collagen, anchoring fibrils, and epidermolysis bullosa. J Invest Dermatol; 101: 252–255, 1993.

[25] Auger FA, Guignard R, López Valle CA, Germain L: Role and innocuity of Tisseel®, a tissue glue, in the grafting process and in vivo evolution of human cultured epidermis. Brit J Plast Surg; 46: 136–142, 1993.

[26] Blümel G, Ascherl R, Haas S, Geibdörfer K, Stemberger A, Schäfer G, Erhardt W, Petrowicz O: Fibrin sealant in burn injuries – experimental study. In: Schlag G., Redl H. (eds) Fibrin Sealant in Operative Medicine. Vol. 4 Plastic Surgery, Maxillofacial and Dental Surgery. Berlin: Springer-Verlag; p.98, 1986.

[27] Grabosch A: Fibrin sealant in the treatment of burn wounds. In: Schlag G., Redl H. (eds) Fibrin Sealant in Operative Medicine. Vol. 4 Plastic Surgery, Maxillofacial and Dental Surgery. Berlin: Springer-Verlag; p.110, 1986.

[28] Hettich R: Skin grafting with fibrin sealant in burns. In: Schlag G., Redl H. (eds) Fibrin Sealant in Operative Medicine. Vol. 4 Plastic Surgery, Maxillofacial and Dental Surgery. Berlin: Springer-Verlag; p.104, 1986.

[29] Zohar Y, Shwilli Y, Schimberg R, Buler N: [Human fibrin glue in head and neck surgery] Harefuah; 126 (10): 567–70, 628, 1994.

[30] López Valle CA, Glaude P, Auger FA: Tie-over dressings: surgical model for in vivo evaluation of cultured epidermal sheets in mice. Plast Reconstr Surg; 89: 139–143, 1992.

[31] Worst TK, Valentine EA, Fusenig NE: Formation of epidermis after reimplantation of pure primary epidermal cell cultures from perinatal mouse skin. J Natl Cancer Inst; 53: 1061–1064, 1974.

[32] Woodcock-Mitchell J, Eichner R, Nelson WG, Sun TT: Immunolocalization of keratin polypeptides in human epidermis using monoclonal antibodies. J Cell Biol; 95: 580–588, 1982.

[33] Sun TT, Eichner R, Nelson WG, Tseng SC, Weiss RA, Jarvinen M, Woodcock-Mitchell J: Keratin classes: molecular markers for different types of epithelial differentiation. J Invest Dermatol; 81: 109s–115s, 1983.

[34] Merrick P, Meyer AA, Herzog S, Woodley D: Scanning electron microscopy of cultured human keratinocytes. J Burn Care Rehabil; 11: 228–236, 1990.

[35] Aihara M: Ultrastructural study of grafted autologous cultured human epithelium. Br J Plast Surg; 42: 35–42, 1989.

[36] Compton CC, Gill JM, Bradford DA, Regauer S, Gallico GG, O'Conner NE: Skin regenerated from cultured epithelial autografts on full-thickness burn wounds from 6 days to 5 years after grafting. A light, electron micro-

scopic and immunohistochemical study. Lab Invest; 60: 600–612, 1989.

[37] *DeLuca M, Albanese E, Bondanza S, Megna M, Ugozzoli L, Molina F, Cancedda R, Santi PL, Bormioli M, Stella M, Magliacani G:* Multicentre experience in the treatment of burns, with autologous and allogenic cultured epithelium, fresh or preserved in a frozen state. Burns; 15: 303–309, 1989.

[38] *Herzog SR, Meyer A, Woodley D, Peterson HD:* Wound coverage with cultured autologous keratinocytes: use after burn wound excision, including biopsy follow-up. J Trauma; 28: 195–198, 1988.

[39] *Xu W, Li H, Brodniewicz T, Auger FA, Germain L:* Cultured epidermal sheet grafting with Hemaseel™ HMN fibrin sealant on nude mice. Burns; 22 (3): 191–196, 1996.

Post Burn Keloid Treated With Keratinocyte Cell Suspension and Fibrin Glue

A. Burd, E. S. Y. Chan, P. K. Lam

Summary

The full spectrum of scar response after initial treatment from the 'scar less' donor site, through normal and hypertrophic scarring to the most extreme form of keloid scarring is not yet understood. One evolving hypothesis is that the keloid scar response, whilst being associated with a genetic predisposition, is a local manifestation of cell matrix imbalance. Based on the clinical observations in a patient with keloid scarring treated with cultured epithelial keratinocyte suspensions in fibrin sealant it is postulated that the effect of the cultured cell suspensions may be one tool to influence this imbalance. Reduction of abnormal matrix and the introduction of normal cells seems to positively modulate the subsequent scar formation. The case reported here is still at an early stage of clinical evaluation but it does lend support to this postulate. Another empirical finding has been that cell suspensions are more resistant to infection than mature cultured epithelial autograft. This is another area that needs further study.

Introduction

Post burn hypertrophic scarring is a frequent but not absolute sequelae of deep dermal burns in children. This scarring goes through a variety of stages of maturation but for a prolonged period it is associated with a vas-cular matrix clinically obvious as a raised, red and firm scar. It has been recognized that there is a spectrum of scar response and the most extreme form of scarring is keloid scarring. In the keloid scar, normal cellular growth patterns and control of matrix production appear to be lost with a massive overproduction of tissue resulting in thick, red, raised scar tissue that proliferates outwith the original zone of injury. Such scarring can cause profound and prolonged morbidity with contraction causing functional loss leading to disability and distortion of normal anatomical features leading to deformity. Treatment of established scarring involves the application of a variety of therapeutic modalities including prolonged application of pressure using custom designed garments, the empirical application of silicone and other elastomers, laser therapy and reconstructive surgery. Ultimately, however, it has to be acknowledged that there is no currently available treatment for keloid scar that has a predictable outcome. In large part this is because, despite extensive research covering many aspects of the cell and matrix biology of scar tissue the fundamental control mechanisms of keloid scarring remain elusive [1].

It is evident that some individuals are susceptible to keloid scarring irrespective of body site or mechanism of induction. There are other individuals, however, who demonstrate a variable response to trauma and develop keloid scar reactions in some sites of trauma but not in others. It is this later group of patients which fascinates us because it would appear that local control mechanisms are at fault rather than a widely expressed genetically predicted wound healing response. The presentation of a child with massive keloid scar reaction adjacent to normal scar, thus raised intriguing possibilities to modulate the repair response. In this chapter we outline our strategy and report our preliminary results of what has to be regarded as a pilot study of the clinical application of a suspension of cultured normal keratinocytes delivered to a keloid scar tissue bed and 'fixed' with fibrin glue.

Clinical Detarts

The patient is a six year old girl who sustained approximately 40% BSA burns from hot soup when she was four years old. She was initially admitted to a hospital in Mainland China and subsequently transferred to the Prince of Wales Hospital in Hong Kong. She had sustained burns to her right arm, right and left buttocks and posterior thighs and the right lateral thigh. She was treated with skin grafting procedures to the right hand and right forearm and was treated conservatively with biological (pig skin) dressings to the other burns. Fig. 1a shows the appearance of the posterior aspects of the buttocks and thighs eighteen months post-burn. For the previous twelve months the child had been wearing pressure garments and also had trials of laser therapy and silicone gel. The scar on the right buttock was remarkable in that it was out growing the original area of burn and was forming an overhanging lip of 2–3 cm on the medial margin. The scar on the left buttock/trunk area however was softening and becoming paler as would be expected from more normal post-burn hypertrophic scar. The scar in the region of the right popliteal fossa was very rigid and horizontal fissures were forming when the knee joint was flexed and extended causing open wounds and discomfort. The scars in the natal cleft were enlarging forming tail-like appendages that were interfering with personal hygiene. It became apparent then, for a number of reasons, that a more aggressive approach to the scar was needed. After extensive discussions both with the child and the mother an initial trial phase of surgery was commenced.

First Surgical Episode

At the first sitting of surgery the linear scar in the left gluteal cleft was excised with direct closure of the wound. The medial half was excised leaving a 2 mm rim of scar tissue whilst the lateral aspect was excised to macroscopically normal skin. The wound was closed in layers.

The thick, broken scar that extended across the right popliteal fossa was excised down to the underlying subcutaneous fat and Integra, artificial dermal regeneration template [2], was used to fill the excisional defect.

A split thickness piece of skin was taken from the posterior left thigh. This was used to initiate cell culture lines of normal skin keratinocytes and fibroblasts. The child kept a knee extension splint on the right leg but was allowed to mobilize and all wounds healed satisfactorily.

Second Surgical Episode

The nature of Integra dermal regeneration template is such that a second procedure is required three to four weeks after the initial placement of the material. During this period, the tissue engineered dermal matrix is bio-degraded and a new vascularized dermal matrix is formed from the patients own fibroblasts and collagen. The silicone sheet covering the tissue engineered matrix has to be removed and replaced with the patients own epidermal cells. The delivery of epidermal cells to the Integra-formed neo-dermis is a focus of both clinical and laboratory research [3] and our group has had experience of using both the conventional sheet and meshed autografts as well as cultured epithelial autografts delivered on a commercially available cell carrier, laser skin. This latter technique had been developed by Dr P K Lam and involves the 'priming' of the laser skin with human fibroblasts prior to the seeding with cultured keratinocytes. A composite skin equivalent is formed for clinical application. Experimental work with this model had involved the used of allogenic fibroblasts. Subsequently two clinical studies had been undertaken on patients with very extensive burns using both allogenic and autologous fibroblasts to good effect [4, 5].

During the initial discussions with the mother of the young girl the question of using the composite laser skin graft to resurface the Integra had been raised. The mother had agreed and this was why the split skin biopsy was taken from the left thigh. Laboratory culture of keratinocytes and fibroblasts were established but the rate of establishing keratinocyte culture exceeded that of establishing the fibroblast culture.

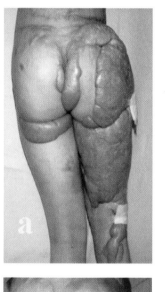
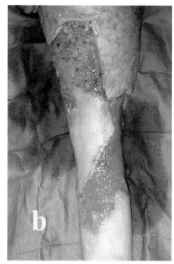
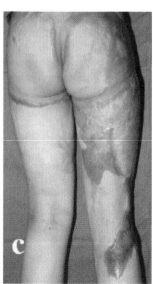
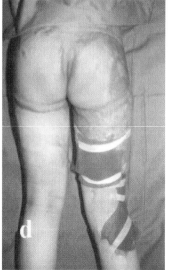

Fig. 1: (a) View of scarring before any procedure. (b) Right popliteal fossa with neodermis from Integra and shaved area on lower medial thigh for cell suspension trial. (c) Hyperpigmented epidermis five months after application of meshed epidermal autograft to poplited fossa and cell suspension to thigh. (d) Three months after application of cultured cells to right buttock the scar remains flat and the contour of the buttock is retained.

This was the background to the second surgical procedure: the silicone cover of the Integra had to be replaced and we had a good culture of keratinocytes but the composite laser-skin was not ready. In view of this the neodermis was covered in a conventional manner by a meshed epidermal autograft. What then, to do with the keratinocyte culture?

In 1989 whilst working in Boston, USA the senior author (AB) was shown a clinical photograph of a patient who had an extensive keloid on the dorsum of his hand. In an experimental procedure this had been shaved tangentially so that the exposed bed of scar tissue was level with the surrounding normal skin and the wound covered with a sheet of cultured epithelial autograft. The initial response in terms of the lack of recurrence of the keloid was very promising (personal communication Dr Carolyn Compton). We are not aware that this was subsequently reported but the clinical observation does concur with our evolving hypotheses regarding keratinocyte-scar interactions.

This then was the rationale behind the further trial procedure undertaken at the second operation which involved excising an area of the three centimeter thick scar tissue to leave a wound bed six by nine centimeters in dimension on the right lower medial thigh. This bed contained residual scar tissue and some subcutaneous fat (Fig. 1b).

The question then arose how to deliver and 'fix' the keratinocyte cell suspension to the wound bed? The role of Tisseel© (Baxter, Vienna) was raised with regard to published studies of cell suspensions in fibrin glue [6, 7]. We decided, however, to pipette the cell suspension on the wound bed and spray fibrin glue over the wound to fix the keratinocyte suspension. Cells were dispersed at a concentration of 8.3×10^4 cells per cm^2. This was covered with Mepitel, which is a silicone dressing, which promotes re-epithelialization [8, 9] and has a bacteriostatic effect [10]. The surrounding skin was smeared with the light covering of Mupirucin ointment, which is active against MRSA, our most common pathogen in the Reconstruc-

tive Unit. To date we have not identified any resistant strains [11]. The Mepitel© was covered with dressing gauze that was held in place with an adhesive dressing. The wound was left undisturbed for one week and then inspected. At this stage there was a 'matt' film of tissue covering the wound that appeared otherwise clean and healthy. The wound was redressed as before and left for a further week. At this stage it was apparent that the transparent film on the wound surface had become opaque and was dry to the touch. Mepitel© was still used as a dressing for a further two weeks by which time it was obvious that the covering of the wound was keratinised epidermis with the uniform pink colour and a smooth surface contour. At this stage it was felt prudent to observe the behaviour of the tissue for several months before deciding whether to undertake a further excision. Four months later the surface of the trial wound remained pink, smooth and flat. It did demonstrate some patchy hyperpigmentation.

Third Surgical Episode

The mother and patient both strongly requested further treatment. Using cells prepared from the initial skin biopsy, the procedure was repeated. This time a larger area of gross keloid scarring was excised from the right buttock. The excision was performed using a fethering technique with needle point diathermy set on coagulation mode which left a completely dry wound which again consisted of haphazard scar matrix and some islands of fat tissue (Fig. 2a). The cells were pipetted on using a concentration of 8.3×10^4 mls per cm^2, to give an even distribution on the wound. One ml of Tisseel was sprayed, taking care not to allow the air current to blow the liquid suspension off the wound area. The wound was allowed to dry for five minutes then covered as before with Mepitel and Bactroban (Fig. 2b). The wound went through the same process of healing is described above although it was more patchy and small moist areas were treated with Gentian violet. By one month after initial ap-plication of the culture cells the entire wound was completely healed (Fig. 2c) and at this stage punch biopsies were taken of the three areas (Fig. 3):

1. Integra©, neo-dermis, treated with meshed epidermal autograft at five months,

2. wound treated with cell suspension at five months,

3. wound treated with cell suspension at one month.

The microscopy, all at 100x magnification shows that in all three cases rete ridge for-mation had not developed. There was a strat-ified, keratinized epidermis, in all three biop-

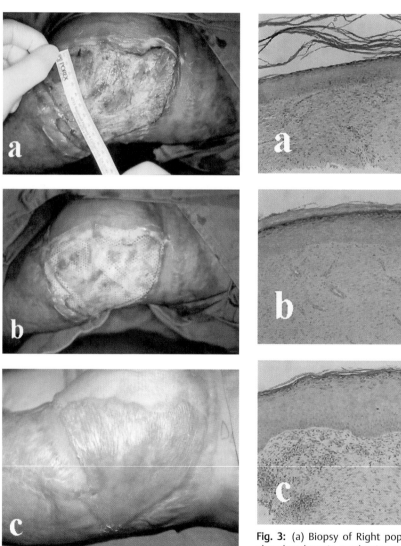

Fig. 2: (a)The excised buttock wound showing scar in the wound bed. (b) The cell suspension covered with Mepital (silicon) dressing. (c) Close up of re-epi-thelialised wound at four weeks post cell application.

Fig. 3: (a) Biopsy of Right popliteal fossa showing abundant keratin production and no rete ridge for-mation in epidermis over Integra derived neo-dermis (x100). (b) Cell suspension derived epidermis at five months (x100). (c) Cell suspension derived epidermis at one month (x100).

sies. The epidermal cell layer was very much thickened in the four week biopsy. The dermis in this case demonstrated an abundant infiltration of inflammatory cells.

The patient has been followed up for a further three months. The excisional wounds which were closed directly have developed some hypertrophy and silicone gel has been applied. The area resurfaced with Integra© has become hyperpigmented and a hypertrophic rim did develop around the resurfaced area (Fig. 1c). The new dermis, however, remains supple and there is no restriction of knee flexion/extension and no linear cracking of the skin. The contour of the left buttock remains flat and there is no evidence of recurrence of the keloid at this stage (Fig. 1d).

Discussion

This case raises several important issues regarding cell matrix interactions. One difficulty for the Reconstructive Burns Surgeon is how to monitor the progress of the post burn scar and how long to persist with conservative treatment. This patient exhibits a full spectrum of scar response after initial treatment from the 'scar less' donor site, through normal and hypertrophic scarring to the most extreme form of keloid scarring. Why was there this spectrum of response and how much is determined by the initial trauma and the treatment and how much by genetically determined responses? It is established that there are varying populations of fibroblasts within individuals but the mechanisms of the variation are unclear.

Our evolving hypothesis is that the keloid scar response, whilst being associated with a genetic predisposition, is a local manifestation of cell matrix imbalance. If this imbalance can be altered by the reduction of abnormal matrix and the introduction of normal cells then the subsequent scar formation will be positively modulated. The case reported here is still at an early stage of clinical evaluation but it does lend support to this postulate.

Of clinical interest is the observation that the healing of the buttock wound occurred without any infection. It is been observed that human fibrin glue does have potential anti-infection function [13]. In addition to this are the local effects of Mepital and Mupirocin. A final factor to be considered is the effect of the cultured cell suspension. An empirical finding has been that cell suspensions are more resistant to infection than mature cultured epithelial autograft. This is another area that needs further study.

References

[1] *Niessen FB, Spauwen PHM, Schalkwijk J, Kon M:* On the nature of hypertrophic scars and keloids: a review. Plastic and Reconstructive Surgery; 104(5):1435–1458, 1999.

[2] *Schulz JT 3rd, Tompkins RG, Burke JF:* Artificial skin. Annual Review of Medicine; 51:231–44, 2000.

[3] *Boyce ST, Kagan RJ, Meyer NA, Yakuboff KP, Warden GD:* The 1999 clinical research award. Cultured skin substitutes combined with Integra artificial skin to replace native skin autograft and allograft for the closure of excised full-thickness burns. Journal of Burn Care & Rehabilitation; 20(6):453–61, 1999.

[4] *Lam PK, Chan ES, Yen RS, Lau HC, King WW:* A new system for the cultivation of keratinocytes on acellular human dermis with the use of fibrin glue and 3T3 feeder cells. Journal of Burn Care & Rehabilitation; 21:1–4, 2000.

[5] *Lam PK, Chan ES, To EW, Lau CH, Yen SC, King WW:* Development and evaluation of a new composite Laserskin graft. Journal of Trauma-Injury Infection & Critical Care; 47(5):918–22, 1999.

[6] *Kaiser HW, Stark GB, Kopp J, Balcerkiewicz A, Spilker G, Kreysel HW:* Cultured autologous keratinocytes in fibrin glue suspension, exclusively and combined with STS-allograft (preliminary clinical and histological report of a new technique). Burns; 20(1):23–29, 1994.

[7] *Siedler S, Schuller-Petrovic S:* Allogenic keratinocytes suspended in human fibrin glue used for wound healing support in chronic leg ulcers. Arch Dermatol; 136(5):676–678, 2000.

[8] *Gotschall CS, Morrison MI, Eichelberger MR:* Prospective, randomized study of the efficacy of Mepitel on children with partial-thickness scalds. Journal of Burn Care & Rehabilitation; 19(4):279–83, 1998.

[9] *Bugmann P, Taylor S, Gyger D, Lironi A, Genin B, Vunda A, La Scala G, Birraux J, Le Coultre C:* A silicone-coated nylon dressing reduces healing

time in burned paediatric patients in comparison with standard sulfadiazine treatment: a prospective randomized trial. Burns; 24(7): 609–12, 1998.

[10] *Troshev K, Kolev Z, Zlateva A, Shishkov S, Pashaliev N, Raycheva-Mutafova E:* Bacteriostatic and biological stimulation effect of Mepitel on experimental burns on the skin of rats. Acta Chirurgiae Plasticae; 39(3):97–102, 1997.

[11] *Eltringham I:* Mupirocin resistance and methicillin-resistant Staphylococcus aureus (MRSA). Journal of Hospital Infection; 35(1):1–8, 1997.

[12] *Boemi L, Allison GM, Graham WP, Krummel TM, Ehrlich HP:* Differences between scar and dermal cultured fibroblasts derived from a patient with recurrent abdominal incision wound herniation. Plastic and Reconstructive Surgery; 104(5):1397–1405, 1999.

[13] *Fabrizio T, Nava M, Arioli N, Calabrese L, Parise O, Molinari R, Savani A:* Use of fibrin glue in reconstructive plastic surgery. In G Schlag J Holle (Eds), Plastic Surgery Nerve Repair Burns Berlin Heidelberg, Springer-Verlag 1995.

Epithelialization of Porcine Wounds With an Aerosol of Epidermal Cells

M. Cohen, A. Bahoric, H. M. Clarke

Summary

The delivery of epithelial suspensions using an aerosolization apparatus was examined in a standardized pig wound model. Full-thickness pig skin was harvested, and an epithelial suspension was created using standard techniques of dispase and trypsin. Twenty-four hours after skin harvest, four full-thickness wounds were created on the flanks of the pig. Control wounds were sprayed with a solution without epithelial cells. The three experimental wounds were sprayed with epithelial cell suspensions (10^6 cells/suspension). Weekly evaluation with photographs, biopsies, and tracings were done for 4 weeks. At 10 weeks, the entire process was repeated with new wounds on the pig's back. Control wounds healed by contraction alone, with epithelium at the edges only. Central epithelial islands developed in experimental wounds at 2 weeks. These islands coalesced to close the wounds by 4 weeks. Histology at 1 week showed groups of epithelial cells deeply embedded in granulation tissue. These groups became immature epithelial layers on the surface by 2 weeks, and all layers of epithelium were present by 4 weeks. Overall, flank experimental wounds epithelialized sooner, but contracted at the same rate as control wounds.

In conclusion, epithelial cells can be delivered by an aerosolization apparatus and remain viable and proliferative in a pig model.

Introduction

Since the early nineties we have used at the Hospital for Sick Children in Toronto an aerosol of epidermal cells to epithelialized full thickness porcine wounds. We have found this technique to be cheaper and more simple to use compared with cultured epithelial autografts. We initially found that autotransplantation of a mixture of epidermal cells via an aerosol vehicle is effective *in vitro* [1]. In that study, we were able to consistently deliver a uniform distribution of suspended epidermal cells onto culture plates using a pump action aerosol nozzle. By day 4 there was evidence of cell proliferation, and by day 7 to 9 a confluent layer of cells was achieved on the plates [1]. This was followed by an *in vivo* study that evaluated the usefulness of this technique for epithelialization of full thickness porcine wounds [2]. This study showed the development of central epithelial islands and complete wound closure two weeks and four weeks respectively after application of keratinocyte aerosol to full thickness porcine wounds [2]. Overall aerosolized wounds epithelialized sooner but contracted at the same rate as control non-treated wounds [2].

In the following paragraphs we describe in detail the technique of wound aerosolization with epidermal cells and specifically concentrate on the different harvesting techniques, processing protocols, epidermal cell application techniques and dressing types, which have been evaluated by our group.

Material and Methods

The animals used in all studies described in this chapter were Yorkshire piglets 6 weeks of age. The animals were housed at the Animal Laboratory facilities of the Hospital for Sick Children, and the study protocols met the standards and approval of the hospital's Animal Ethics Committee. All procedures were carried out while the pigs were under general anesthesia.

Overview Of The Technique

The technique of wound epithelialization with epidermal cell aerosol includes 6 stages:

1. *Skin processing.* Two techniques have been evaluated: a long (24H) processing protocol of full thickness skin grafts and a short (2H) processing protocol of split thickness skin grafts. Different time intervals between epidermal cell suspension preparation and aerosolization were also tested.
2. *Creation of full thickness wounds.*
3. *Transfer of the epidermal cells to the wound.* The effects on wound healing of a spray containing cell medium (without keratinocytes), a spray of cell medium with keratinocytes and a spray of cell medium with keratinocytes and fibrin glue were evaluated. Different aerosolization devices were tested, a single compartment device for aerosolization of a suspension of cell medium and keratinocytes and a three-compartment device for aerosolization of cell suspension and fibrin glue to the wound. We also evaluated wound healing after we applied a suspension of cells and fibrin glue to a two layer silicone dressing and then applied the dressing to the wound.
4. *Wound dressing.* Three methods of wound dressing were evaluated – a single layer silicone dressing, a two-layer silicone dressing and Biobrane.
5. *Macroscopic wound assessment.* Epithelialization and wound contraction were

initially evaluated by conventional photography and tracings and followed by digital photography.
6. *Microscopic evaluation.* This included descriptive evaluation of wound biopsies stained with hematoxylin and eosine. Correlation between the macroscopic and microscopic observations was also evaluated.

Donor Skin Graft

Preparation of keratinocyte aerosol from full thickness skin graft

A 9-cm² ellipse of full thickness skin was harvested from each hind leg groin. This site was chosen because the skin is thin, it is distant from the site of the cell spray, and can be closed primarily. The skin was then cut into 5 mm strips, placed in a lactated Ringer's solution, gentamycin (200 µg/ml), penicillin (100 units/ml), and streptomycin (100 µg/ml), and refrigerated for 6 hours at 40 °C.

The full thickness strips were then placed in dispase solution, (24 units/ml, Boehringer-Mannheim, Munich, Germany) for 12 hours at 40 °C. The epidermis was mechanically peeled off the dermis with forceps and cut to 1 mm² pieces with a scalpel blade (Fig. 1). The pieces were then treated with trypsin (0.25 % in EDTA, Life Technologies, Rockville, Maryland) and incubated for 45 minutes at 37 °C. This process separates epidermal cells from one another in preparation for aerosolization. Next, the cells are suspended in RPMI 1640 transport medium (BioWhittaker, Walkersville, Maryland), 30 % fetal calf serum (Cansera, Rexdale, Ontario), penicillin (50 units/ml), and streptomycin (50 µg/ml). At the end of the process an 8 cc suspension containing about 2×10^6 cells/ml is produced. The suspension contains keratinocytes at different stages of proliferation and a few fibroblasts and dendritic cells (presumed to be Langerhan's cells) [1]. Most of the suspension consists of individual cells with few aggregates of cells [1]. The ratio of donor size to recipient wound area is 9 cm² to 224 cm² or approximately 1 to 25.

Fig. 1: The epidermis was mechanically peeled off the dermis and cut to 1–2 mm² pieces.

Preparation of Keratinocyte Aerosol from Split Thickness Skin Graft

A disadvantage of the full thickness protocol was the prolonged processing time (24 hours) and the need to anesthetize the animal twice one day after the other. We were recently able to make the same suspension of cells from partial thickness skin grafts using a short, 2-hour processing protocol. The same suspensions and procedures were used except incubation in Ringer's lactate for 15 minutes and in dispase for 60 minutes. Separation of the dermis of split thickness grafts was not found to be mandatory and preservation of the small amount of dermis present in split thickness grafts was possible.

Creation of Full Thickness Wounds

In order to find the optimal timing for wound aerosolization we evaluated wound healing following wound aerosolization with suspension of cells made from full thickness skin immediately at the end of the skin processing (24 hours after skin harvesting) or 24 hours following completion of skin processing (48 hours after skin harvesting).

Bilateral pairs of full thickness 6 cm by 7 cm wounds were created over the pig's back. This was done approximately 24 hours following the full thickness skin graft harvesting and approximately two hours after split thickness skin graft harvesting. The wounds were located 3 cm lateral to the vertebral column and created at a plane superficial to the muscle fascia.

Immediately following wound creation retraction of the edges was observed and the actual size of the wounds increased to 7 cm by 8 cm. Calculations done by us to evaluate wound healing referred to wound size following retraction.

Transfer of the Epidermal Cells to the Wound

Porcine Model for Evaluation of the Effect of Epidermal Cell Suspension on Wound Healing

In this model the left sided wounds are sprayed with a suspension of epidermal cells (4 cc) and the right sided wounds are sprayed with Ringer's lactate (4 cc).

Porcine Model for Evaluation of the Effect of Fibrin Glue on Wound Healing

In this model the right-sided wounds are sprayed with a suspension of epidermal cells (4 cc) and the left sided wounds are sprayed with cells (4 cc) and fibrin glue (1 cc) (Tisseel VH, Hyland Immuno, Baxter Corporation, Illinois).

Aerosolization Devices

During our initial studies on the effect of epidermal cells on wound healing we have used a single compartment device for aerosolization of a suspension of cell medium and epidermal cells (Fig. 2A). The device was connected to a syringe or an air compressor (Tissomat, Hyland Immuno, Baxter Corporation, Illinois). When fibrin glue was added to the epidermal cells we have used a three-compartment aerosoli-zation device connected to an air compressor (Fig. 2B).

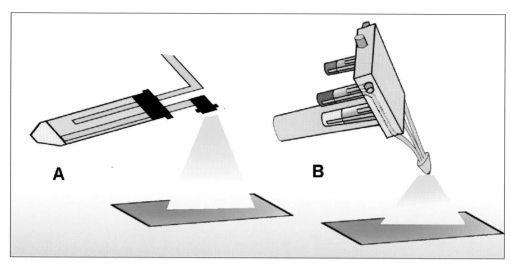

Fig. 2: Schematic drawing of the aerosol devices: A – a single compartment device for cell suspension aerosolization. B – a three-compartment device for cell suspension and fibrin glue aerosolization. Compressed air was injected into sterile fibrin glue vials (blue and red vials) and epidermal cell suspension vial (yellow vial). A second silicone tubing system was used to spray the contents of the vials trough a nozzle. The cell suspension vial is located inside a larger non-sterile plastic tube, which is used to support and aim the device.

Wound Dressing

One Layer Silicone Dressing

Ten minutes after aerosolization, the wounds were covered with a direct contact single layer of silicone dressing, (Silastic, Dow Corning, Midland, Michigan) a tie over dressing and a circumferential cotton sleeve. These protective measures were necessary because the pigs are left unrestrained in their cages. This dressing was chosen because it is non permeable, pliable and does not adhere to the wound.

Biobrane Dressing

Ten minutes after aerosolization, the wounds were covered with a direct contact single layer of Biobrane (Mylan Laboratories Inc., Pittsburgh, PA) a tie over dressing and a circumferential cotton sleeve. This dressing was tested due to it frequent use in burn wound care.

Two Layer Silicone Dressing

This dressing was composed of two glued silicone layers (Silastic, Dow Corning, Midland,

Michigan). One layer was a single untouched silicone sheet and the other was a fenestrated silicone sheet (Fig. 3). The two layers created wells, which served to house the suspension of cells. When this dressing was used the suspension and fibrin glue were poured on the dressing rather than aerosolized on the wound. We felt that this meth-

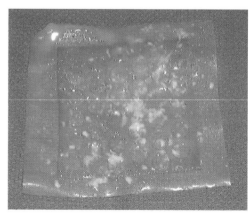

Fig. 3: Two layer silicone dressing with wells which house the suspension of cells and fibrin glue.

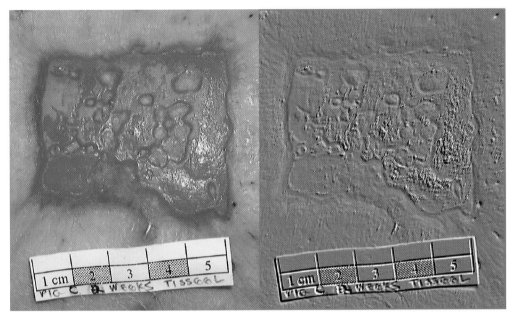

Fig. 4: On the left side is a digital photograph of a wound two weeks after treatment with aerosolized cells and fibrin glue. To facilitate delineation of the epi- thelialized areas a gray emboss digital effect was used (right). This effect helped to differentiate between the epithelial islands and the light reflection of the flash.

od of application decreased by 25 % the amount of suspension required.

Macroscopic Wound Assessment

Wound Evaluation

The dressing was changed after 7, 14, 21 and 28 days under general anesthesia. The wounds were gently washed and digital photographs were taken with a scale. The pictures were printed and traced. To delineate the epithelialized and non-epithelialized areas a gray emboss digital effect was used (Photo-Pro, Kodak, gray color, right upper shadow, depth grade 5). This technique assisted in delineating the different wound areas and to differentiate epithelialized areas from areas with a flash reflection (Fig. 4). The shiny flash areas tended to produce a distinctive bright signal when the emboss effect was applied.

Three areas were outlined on the printouts, the total size of the wound, areas covered with epithelium and areas without epitheli- um. By the use of a scale-adjusted grid the total wound size, epithelialized areas and non epithelialized areas are measured. The values were recorded as area (cm²), percent of original wound size and percent of epithelialization by the use of the following formulas:

$$\% \text{ of original wound size} = \frac{\text{Current total wound size}}{\text{Original total wound size}} \times 100$$

$$\% \text{ epithelialization} = \frac{\text{Current total epithelialized area}}{\text{Current total wound size}} \times 100$$

Microscopic Evaluation

To verify the macroscopic evaluation, 10 punch biopsies were taken from the areas marked as epithelialized and 10 biopsies from areas marked as non-epithelialized. The biopsies were stained with hematoxylin and eosin and assessment of the correlation between the macroscopic and microscopic observations was done. The presence of epithelial cells as well as the microscopic arrangement was recorded.

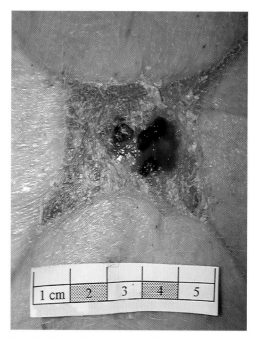
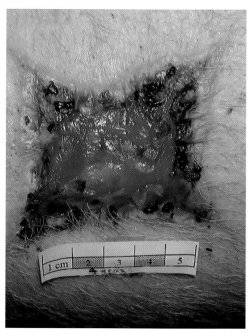

Fig. 5: Effect of epidermal cell aerosol on wound healing in one animal. On the left side, a full thickness wound four weeks after treatment with epidermal cell aerosol. The wound has almost completely epithelialized. The open areas are the biopsy sites. On the right side, a same size wound which was sprayed with Ringer's lactate. Peripheral epithelialization could be seen but overall the wound was mostly open and covered with exudate at 4 weeks.

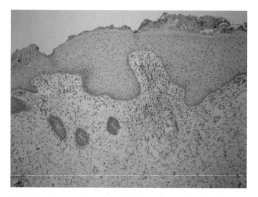
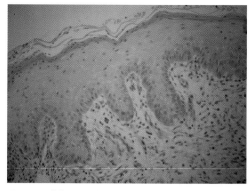

Fig. 6: Groups of epithelial islands embedded deep in granulation tissue and immature epidermis were found 7 days after aerosolization with epidermal cell suspension (Hematoxylin and eosin stain, original magnification 40x).

Fig. 7: All layers of the epidermis and rete ridges were observed 14 days after aerosolization with epidermal cell suspension. The epithelium is reactive with parakeratosis on surface (Hematoxylin and eosin stain, original magnification 40x).

Results

Feasibility of the Technique

Our initial studies concentrated on the effect of epidermal cell aerosol made from full thickness skin graft on full thickness porcine wounds [2]. We have found that the aerosol enhanced wound epithelialization but had no effect on wound contraction (Fig. 5). Representative microscopy slides after 1 week and 2 weeks are presented in Figs. 6 and 7. This shows epithelial islands deep in the dermis after one week and complete coverage of the surface with epidermis after 2 weeks.

Donor Skin

The effect of donor skin thickness and processing protocol on the average percentage of epithelialization in two animals (two wounds in each group) is presented in Fig. 8. This shows a similar rate of epithelialization following aerosolization of a suspension made within 2 hours from a split thickness graft or of a suspension made within 24 hours from a full thickness skin graft.

Optimal Timing for Aerosolization

The average percentage of wound epithelialization obtained following wound aerosolization with a suspension of fibrin glue and

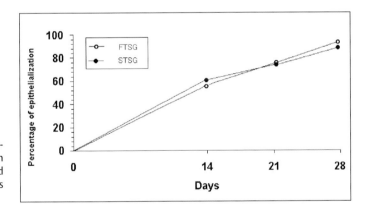

Fig. 8: Effect of donor skin thickness and processing protocol on the average percentage of wound epithelialization in two animals (two wounds in each group).

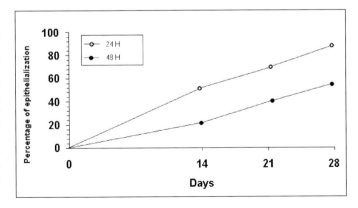

Fig. 9: The average percentage of wound epithelialization in two animals (two wounds in each group) following wound aerosolization with fibrin glue and suspension of cells made from full thickness skin: 24H curve – the aerosol was applied immediately at the end of the skin processing (24 hours after skin harvesting). 48H curve – the aerosol was applied 24 hours following completion of skin processing (48 hours after skin harvesting).

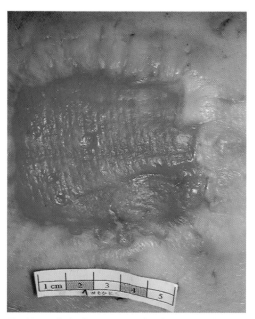

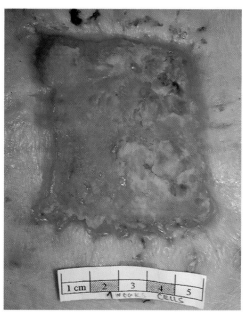

Fig.10: Full thickness wounds after 1 week. The wound on the left was sprayed with epidermal cells mixed with fibrin glue. There are few central epithelialization islands and very little fibrinous crust. The wound on the right was sprayed with epidermal cell suspension without fibrin glue. It was covered with substantial amount of fibrinous crust at 7 days.

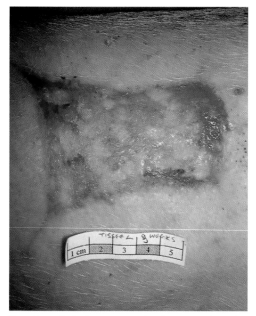

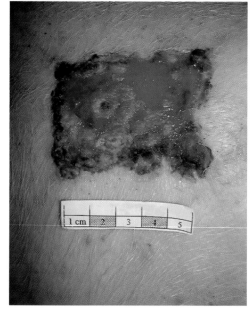

Fig. 11: Full thickness wounds after 3 weeks. The wound on the left was sprayed with epidermal cells mixed with fibrin glue. There was central epithelialization with almost complete wound closure at 3 weeks. The wound on the right was sprayed with epidermal cell suspension without fibrin glue. At 3 weeks, it was still covered with substantial amount of fibrinous curst with some peripheral epithelialization.

cells made from full thickness skin immediately at the end of the skin processing (24 hours after skin harvesting) or 24 hours following completion of skin processing (48 hours after skin harvesting) in two animals (two wounds in each group) is presented in Fig. 9. This shows that wound epithelialization was decreased when the suspension of cells was applied 24 hours after the end of the skin processing compared with immediate aerosolization.

Effect of Fibrin Glue on Wound Healing

Representative pictures of wound healing in one animal after 1 week and 3 weeks are presented in Figs. 10 and 11. The effect of epi-

dermal cell aerosol mixed with fibrin glue on wound epithelialization and wound contraction in one animal is presented in Figs. 12 and 13. This shows that the addition of fibrin glue enhanced wound epithelialization but did not have effect on wound contraction.

Wound Dressing

The effect of wound dressing (following application of keratinocytes and fibrin glue) on epithelialization is presented in Fig. 14. This shows similar epithelialization rate when the single sheet or two sheet silicone dressing were used. Biobrane was associated with decreased epithelialization compared with the silicone dressings.

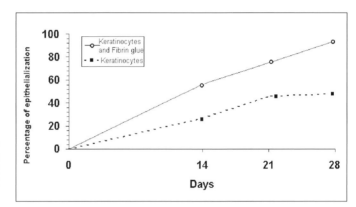

Fig. 12: Wound epithelialization – Effect of fibrin glue on the average percentage of wound epithelialization in one animal (two wounds in each group).

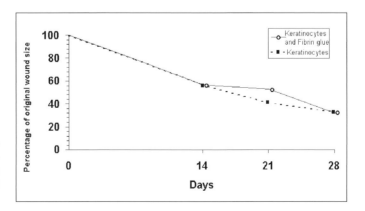

Fig. 13: Wound contraction – Effect of fibrin glue on percentage of original wound size in one animal (two wounds in each group).

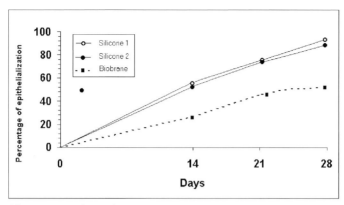

Fig. 14: Effect of dressing type on the percentage of wound epithelialization in three animals (two wounds in each group).

Silicone 1 – one layer silicone.
Silicone 2 – two layer, fenestrated silicone dressing.

Cost Analysis

When an aerosol of cells and commercial fibrin glue is used to epithelialize a 2 x 2 inch area, the costs are around US $ 20 dollars. This technique is much cheaper compared with a 2 x 2 inch cultured epithelial graft that costs approximately US $ 400 dollars [3].

Discussion

Several strategies have evolved during our on-going exploration of the keratinocyte aerosol technique which may be important when this technique is adjusted for use in humans: Firstly, the suspension of fibrin glue and cells should optimally be applied immediately at the end of the skin processing. Incubation for additional 24 hours decreases the beneficial effect of the keratinocytes. Secondly, we have found out that a suspension of cells could be made from split thickness skin graft by a short 2-hour processing protocol. This may allow the surgeon to harvest a split thickness skin graft, make cell suspension and spray the wounds within less than 3 hours. Technically this may enable us to undertake skin harvesting and wound aerosolization within one operating room session while the patient is kept under general anesthesia. Thirdly, our results indicate that the

most suitable dressing tested by us is a non-permeable and non-adhesive silicone sheet. Biobrane has pores that may allow a shift of cells through the dressing and therefore was associated with inferior results compared with non-permeable silicone [4]. Another option is that the adhesive properties of Biobrane caused the cells to stick to the dressing instead of adhering to the wound.

The technique has several disadvantages: Firstly, the aerosol of keratinocytes does not decrease early wound contraction in pigs. It is believed that wound contraction is dependent on the dermal component of skin grafts [5]. Therefore this finding is probably due to the lack of a significant dermal component in the aerosolized cell suspension [2]. We are aware of this disadvantage of epidermal autotransplantation and therefore believe that the method presented may be most useful for partial thickness wounds such as scald burns in which the dermis survives [6]. Another option would be to use the cells along with a dermal graft or dermal substitute [7, 8]. Secondly, the follow-up was limited to four weeks. Long term effects of early wound closure could not be evaluated in our studies. Thirdly, commercial fibrin glue is associated with a low risk of disease transmission and anaphylactic reaction [9, 10]. Both patients and physicians should be aware of this risk. The use of autogenous fibrin glue and epidermal cells is a possible alternative that requires further evaluation [11, 12].

To conclude, our series of studies on wound epithelialization with epidermal cell aerosol show that this technique is simple, effective and inexpensive. Nine cm^2 of full thickness or split thickness donor skin were used within 24 hours or 2 hours respectively to resurface an area of 224 cm^2 which represents a promising ratio of 1 to 25 donor skin to recipient wound areas. We believe that this technique is a significant step in the development of an autogenous skin grafting methodology free from some of the disadvantages of cultured epithelial autograft sheets such as 2 to 3 weeks of growth in culture, fragility, unpredictable results and high costs [13–16].

References

[1] Bahoric, A, Harrop, AR, Clarke, HM, Zuker, RM: Aerosol vehicle for delivery of epidermal cells – an in vitro study. Can. J. Plast. Surg. 5(3): 153–56, 1997.

[2] Fraulin, FOG, Bahoric, A, Harrop, AR, Hiruki, T, Clarke, HM: Autotransplantation of epidermal cells in the pig model via an aerosol vehicle. J. Burn. Care. Rehabil. 19: 337–45, 1998.

[3] Kelton, PL: Skin grafts. Selected Read Plast Surg. 7: 20–21, 1992.

[4] Tavis, MJ, Thornton, JW, Bartlett, RH, Roth, JC, Woodroof, EA: A new composite skin prosthesis. Burns. 7: 123, 1980.

[5] Brown, D, Garner, W, Young, VL: Skin grafting: dermal components in inhibition of wound contraction. South. Med. J. 83: 789–95. 1990.

[6] Fratianne, R, Papay, F, Housini, I, Lang, C, Schafer, IA: Keratinocyte allografts accelerate healing of split thickness donor sites: applications for improved treatment of burns. J. Burn Care Rehabil. 14:148–54, 1993.

[7] Navsaria, HA, Kangesu, T, Manek, S, Green, CJ, Leigh, IM: An animal model to study the significance of dermis for grafting cultured keratinocytes on full thickness wounds. Burns. 20 Suppl 1:S57–60, 1994.

[8] Orgill, DP, Butler, C, Regan, JF, Barlow, MS, Yannas, IV, Compton, CC: Vascularized collagen-glycosaminoglycan matrix provides a dermal substrate and improves take of cultured epithelial autografts. Plast. Reconstr. Surg. 102(2):423–9, 1998.

[9] Tisseel properties from Baxter, Immuno. http://www.baxter.com/doctors/blood_therapies/hyland_immuno/index.html

[10] Mitsuhata, H, Horiguchi, Y, Saitoh, J, et al.: An anaphylactic reaction to topical fibrin glue. Anesthesiology. 81: 1074, 1994.

[11] Buckley, RC, Breazeale, EE, Edmond, JA, Brzezienski, MA: A simple preparation of autologous fibrin glue for skin graft fixation. Plast. Reconstr. Surg. 103(1): 202–6, 1999.

[12] Kjaergard, HK, Weis-Fogh, US: Important factors influencing the strength of autologous fibrin glue; the fibrin concentration and reaction time – comparison of strength with commercial fibrin glue. Eur. Surg. Res. 26(5): 273–6, 1994.

[13] Rheinwald, JG, Green, H: Serial cultivation of strains of human epidermal keratinocytes: The formation of keratinizing colonies from single cells. Cell. 6: 331–44, 1975.

[14] O'Connor, NE, Mulliken, JB, Banks-Schlegel, S, Kehinde, O, Green, H: Grafting of burns with cultured epithelium prepared from autologous epidermal cells. Lancet. 1: 75–8, 1981.

[15] Gallico, GG, O'Connor, NE, Compton, CC, Kehinde, O, Green, H: Permanent coverage of large burn wounds with autologous cultured human epithelium. New Engl. J. Med. 311: 448–51, 1984.

[16] DeLuka, M, Albanese, E, Bondanza, S, et al.: Multicenter experience in the treatment of burns with autologous and allogenic cultured epithelium, fresh or preserved in a frozen state. Burns. 15: 303–9, 1989.

Keratinocyte Allografts Act as a "Biologic Bandage" to Accelerate Healing of Split Thickness Donor Sites

R. Fratianne, I. A. Schafer

Summary

Grafting with split-thickness autograft skin remains the most effective method for treating burn wounds. When insufficient donor sites are present, decreasing the time required for healing of available donor sites permits more frequent reharvests to continue the grafting process. Cultured human keratinocytes speed wound healing by providing cover and by producing growth factors and extracellular matrix proteins. In this study we compare the rates of healing induced by allografts of cultured keratinocytes applied to split-thickness donor sites with healing by a standard treatment. Sheets of cultured human keratinocytes derived from neonatal foreskins are applied to a portion of a split-thickness donor site while the remainder is covered with a temporary skin substitute. The wound is inspected at 5, 7, 9, 11, 14, 17, 20, and 23 days. Biopsies are obtained at 7 days for light and electron microscopy. A total of ten patients admitted to the Burn Center at MetroHealth Medical Center were studied (age from 21 to 86 years, 3 females and 7 males). The average time to healing for sites covered with keratinocytes was 6.6 +/– 1.96 days compared with 12.6 +/– 4.32 days for control sites (p < 0.002). By day 7 most keratinocyte-covered sites showed reepithelization with the formation of a basement membrane and hemidesmosomes at the dermal-epidermal junction. Control areas were unhealed without epithelial coverage.

The reepithelized donor sites from three patients treated with cultured keratinocytes were reharvested. In each case these grafts took, and they were equivalent to skin used from donor sites harvested for the first time. Keratinocyte allografts speed healing of split-thickness donor sites, thereby increasing the availability of autograft skin for burn wound coverage.

Introduction

Survival rates for burn injuries have improved dramatically in the past two decades. The cited reasons for this improvement are better understanding of the resuscitation process [1–5], improved antibiotics, both systemic and topical [6, 7], improved nutritional support for the hypermetabolic-catabolic effects of burn injuries [8–15] and, perhaps most importantly, the recognition that early excision of devitalized tissue and prompt closure of the burn wound is the most effective method of reducing the size of the burn wound, thereby decreasing the hypermetabolism and systemic inflammatory response. Closure of the burn wound also aids in preventing sepsis and multiple organ system failure [16–18]. Despite these advances, the mortality rate for patients suffering greater than 75% total body surface area (TBSA) burns remains high [19], although significant improvement of survival in adults with extensive burns has been reported [20]. Efforts to provide prompt wound closure for patients with insufficient donor sites have included the use of xenograft and allograft skin with the emergence of skin banking techniques, a variety of non-biologic or quasi-biologic skin substitutes including the artificial dermis of Burke and Yannas [21–23], Integra®, Alloderm®, Dermagraft® and others. A great deal of work has been done with keratinocyte sheets grown in tissue culture and the development of bilayered skin equivalents utilizing a Type I collagen matrix seeded with keratinocytes and fibroblasts [24, 25]. Keratinocytes grown in tissue culture can be used to close burn wounds [26, 27]; however, wounds covered with keratinocytes alone remain fragile, are subject to sheer stress for prolonged periods and have generally not achieved closure of significant areas of large TBSA burns. Rue et al, at the U.S. Army Institute of Surgical Research, reported in 16 patients with an average TBSA burn injury of 68 % that, at the time of the patient's discharge, the final burn surface area definitively closed with cultured keratinocytes was less than 5 % TBSA [28].

At the present time, autografting remains the most effective method of obtaining suitable permanent wound coverage in thermal injury. In patients with very large full-thickness TBSA burns, severely restricted donor site availability presents a significant problem for early burn wound coverage. Clearly, anything that would reduce the interval of time required between croppings of available donor site in these patients would shorten the overall time for burn wound closure. A variety of agents is commonly used to hasten donor site reepithelialization, including Opsite®, Biobrane®, Xeroform®, Scarlet Red® and others. Our work with autologous cultured keratinocytes applied to the dermis of burned patients suggested very rapid closure of partial thickness burn wounds as opposed to the poor results seen with application of keratinocytes to subcutaneous fat. As a result, we proceeded to test the hypothesis that allogenic cultured keratinocytes might serve the same purpose.

Methods

Tissue Source

Pregnant middle class women were recruited for this study: none had had previous surgery, blood transfusions or used illicit drugs. The mothers' blood was tested during the last trimester for antibodies to HIV, hepatitis B and herpes virus. At the time of delivery, the infants were circumcised and also had their cord blood similarly tested. Six weeks following delivery, the mothers' blood was again tested for the viral antibodies. The foreskins harvested from the infants were used to produce the allogenic keratinocytes later used for our experiments to determine whether donor site healing could be accelerated by their application. The keratinocytes were not utilized until all of the viral testing had been completed.

Keratinocyte Culture

The details of cell culture are described in previous publications from this laboratory [29–31]. At the time of foreskin harvest, the subcutaneous tissue of the foreskins was removed and the skin was minced and digested with 0.1 % trypsin in 20 % EDTA, pH 7.45. The keratinocytes obtained were grown to confluence. Intact sheets of keratinocytes were obtained by treating confluent cultures in 0.25 % Dispase in Dulbecco-Voigt modified Eagle's media for 45 minutes following the protocols used by Green, Kehinde and Thomas [32]. Keratinocytes from each primary culture flask (approximately 2 million cells) were preserved in liquid nitrogen. Upon final completion of the viral surveillance, these vials of keratinocytes were reconstituted and utilized as first passage wound coverage for selected donor site evaluation.

Patient Population and Study Design

A total of ten patients admitted to the Burn Center at MetroHealth Medical Center were studied. A signed consent form for each pa-

R. Fratianne, I. A. Schafer

tient was obtained prior to participation in the experimental protocol. Patients ranged in age from 21 to 86 years. There were three females and seven males. The average TBSA burn was 35.3 %, range 3 % to 90 %. There were two deaths and eight survivors in the group.

At the time of their split thickness skin grafting procedures, appropriate donor sites were chosen as listed in Table 1. All donor sites for this experiment were from areas used as primary harvest except for two patients whose donor sites had been harvested previously prior to entry into this study. Autogenous skin was harvested using a Zimmer air-driven dermatome, set between .006 and .008 inch thickness. Donor sites from the scalp and back were prepared by subcutaneous injection of Lactated Ringer's solution to elevate the donor skin from underlying bony prominences in order to facilitate the harvest. Hemostasis was achieved using epinephrine soaked telfa pads. A portion of the donor site was chosen by random number assignment for treatment with cultured keratinocytes. The allograft keratinocytes were placed away from the margins and in areas that were indistinguishable from the surrounding donor areas. The keratinocyte sheets were applied to the wound on a vaseline gauze carrier measuring 4 x 7cm which was stapled in place. The entire donor site including the keratinocyte cultures was then covered with Biobrane® and stapled in place. Biobrane® is the most commonly used dressing for donor sites in our Unit. The donor site covered with Biobrane® served as the contiguous control area versus the keratinocyte covered areas.

On the fifth post-operative day the Biobrane® was windowed over the vaseline gauze carrier. The staples were carefully removed and the vaseline gauze was removed from those areas which had separated from the underlying tissue, indicating re-epithelialization. Healing under the Biobrane® was determined by visual inspection, looking for areas of Biobrane® separation from the underlying tissue. Wounds were subsequently inspected on days 7, 9, 11, 14, 17, 20 and 23.

The time of complete healing was documented by photographs. All patients received appropriate antibiotics.

Light and Electron Microscopy

On the seventh post-operative day, 3 mm punch biopsies were obtained on five patients from their donor sites treated with cultured keratinocytes and Biobrane®. Sections were examined by light and electron microscopy. The biopsies in the five patients were representative of all the patients studied.

Each biopsy was divided into two parts. One was fixed in 10 % buffered Formalin, dehydrated through a graded ethanol series (50, 70, 95 and 100 %) and cleaned with Xylene before paraffin embedding. A five micron serial section was made on a glass slide, stained with hematoxylin-eosin and examined under the light microscope [33]. A second biopsy portion was fixed in 2.5 % buffered glutaraldehyde for three hours at room temperature, rinsed in 0.2 M Millonigs phosphate buffer, post-fixed in 1 % osmium tetroxide at 4 °C for one hour, dehydrated through graded acetone series (50, 95, 100 %), infiltrated in 50/50 resin and 100 % acetone, embedded in beem capsule in araldite and polymerized at 60 °C for two days. After the block was trimmed, a thick section (1 micron) was stained with toluidine blue for light microscopic examination to ascertain adequacy of the specimen. This was followed by an ultra-thin section (60 nm) mounted on 200 copper mesh grid which was stained in uranyl acetate and lead citrate solution and viewed in transmission electron microscope Zeiss EM_{10} [34, 35].

Results

The time to complete healing of the donor sites treated with either allograft keratinocytes or Biobrane® are summarized in Table 1. The percent of donor site healing (Table 2) and the time to complete healing were determined by a single observer (pri-

Table 1: Keratinocyte Allografts in Wound Healing

Donor	Anatom-ic Site	Age	Race	Sex	%TBSA	Days to Complete Healing	
						Control	Allograft
1	Scalp	32	W	M	82	7	5
2	Thigh	35	W	M	3	14	5
3*+	Back	48	B	F	46	17**	9**
4*	Back	86	W	F	13	14	11
5+	Back	53	W	M	61	14	5
6	Scalp	21	W	F	3	7	5
7*	Back	43	W	M	13	14	7
8*	Back	59	B	M	35	11	5
9*	Abdomen	29	W	M	90	23**	7**
10	Back	37	B	M	12	11	5
						13.2 Median	6.6

* Patients who were biopsied (Mann-Whitney U-Test) Two Tailed P=< 0.005 + Non-survivors
  Patient #3 – Died on post-burn day 35
  Patient #5 – Died on post-burn day 14
   Biobrane treated donor site 50 % healed at time of death
** Second Harvest

Table 2: % Donor Site Healed

	Biobrane	Allograft
Day 5	33 %	82 %
Day 7	51 %	96 %
Day 14	79 %	100 %

mary author) with extensive experience in skin grafting procedures and wound evaluation. The median time to healing with Biobrane® was 14 days versus 7 days for sites covered with allograft keratinocytes. At the time of complete healing, allografts constituted a re-epithelialized island surrounded by Biobrane® treated control donor site tissue which healed at a later time. As expected, healing of donor sites for both experimental and control areas, taken from the scalp, re-epithelialized sooner than other donor site locations, reflecting the increased numbers of dermal appendages providing increased sources of epithelial cells. Consistent acceleration of re-epithelialization of the keratinocyte treated donor sites was evident in healthy patients with minimal burns, good nutrition and no signs of sepsis, as well as in patients with more extensive burns (#1, #3, #5, #8, #9).

A 27 year-old white male who survived 90 % TBSA burns, with 85 % being full thickness, was entered into the study at the time of the third harvest from his suprapubic area. The healing time for the Biobrane treated donor site was 23 days vs. 7 days for the site covered with keratinocytes.

A 53 year-old white male with chronic alcoholism who failed to survive a 61 % TBSA burn was entered into the study at the time of his initial skin grafting procedure on the third post-burn day. The donor site treated with cultured allograft healed completely in 11 days; however, at the time of his death on the 14th day post-burn, the control donor site was approximately 50 % healed.

A 48 year-old female, who suffered a 46 % total body surface area burn, had a history of severe alcohol and IV drug abuse. At the time of her entry into the study, her serum albumin level was 1.0 gram per dl. Despite her poor nutritional state, the reharvested donor site treated with allograft keratinocytes healed in nine days, whereas the control donor site required 17 days to complete healing.

In three patients, the donor site treated with the cultured keratinocytes was reharvested as the sequential skin grafting procedures continued. In each case, the donor skin

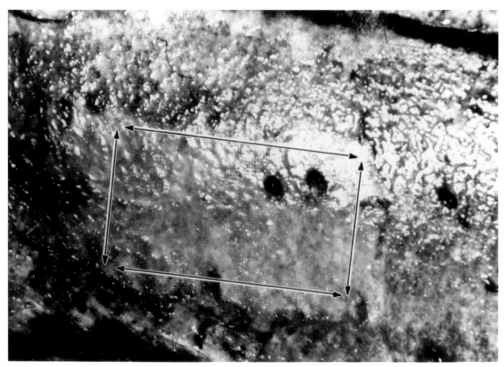

Fig. 1: Donor site covered by allograft keratinocytes (arrows). Two biopsy sites through allograft; two biopsy sites in adjacent donor site.

from the area treated with the cultured keratinocytes took well and was equivalent in every way to the donor skin reharvested from areas treated with the conventional dressing, as well as areas used as donor site for the first time. In our subsequent use of cultured allograft keratinocytes following completion of the study, we found similar results in the ability of those donor sites healed under keratinocyte cells acting as repeat donor sites. We were unable to distinguish the graft take in those patients from graft take in patients with graft sites harvested for the first time.

On clinical examination, the wounds treated with allogenic keratinocytes were covered by a shiny continuous membrane, which was translucent and adherent to the underlying dermis (Fig. 1). We saw no evidence that the cultured keratinocytes grew out from the margins of the keratinocyte grafted donor area. The tissue exhibited good capillary blanching and refill. At the time of complete healing of the Biobrane® treated donor site, it was quite easy to distinguish the area treated with the cultured keratinocytes from the surrounding areas. The epidermis of the areas covered by keratinocytes appeared to be flatter and more homogenous with less redness. In four cases, the Biobrane® covered donor site appeared to be somewhat thickened when compared to the area treated with cultured keratinocytes. The allogenic grafts in the initial two weeks showed a visible difference in the character of the epidermal covering when compared to the healed Biobrane® treated controls. By weeks four to five no differences were noted.

Histologic Studies

Light microscopy of the punch biopsies from the donor sites treated with allograft keratinocytes show re-epithelialization with lay-

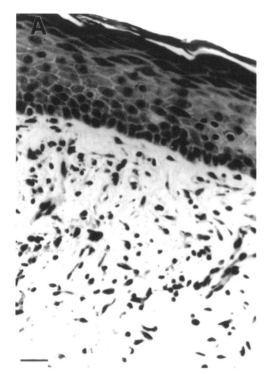

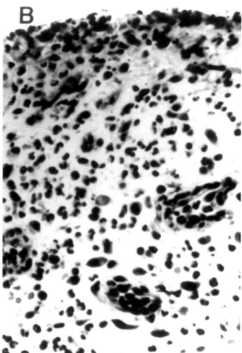

Fig. 2A: Donor site covered with allogenic keratino-cytes at Day 7.

Fig. 2B: Donor site covered by Biobrane®, Day 7.

ers of 8 to 10 cells, a distinct basal cell layer and abundant keratin formation (Fig. 2A). The interface between the epithelium and dermis was smooth and flat without signs of rete pegs. In contrast, the biopsies obtained from adjacent areas treated with Biobrane® showed unhealed dermis without epithelial cell coverage, a moderate chronic inflammatory response (Fig. 2B). Similar tissue histologies were documented at the donor graft sites from four other patients.

The electron microscopic sections from the donor sites treated with allograft keratinocytes showed a distinctive basement membrane with many hemidesmosomes (Fig. 3). The underlying dermal stroma appeared to be well organized with minimal inflammatory changes present. In contrast, electron microscopy of sections taken from adjacent donor sites showed no epidermal cells, but moderate inflammatory changes were present. Since these biopsies were ob-

tained on the seventh post-grafting day, it is clear that donor sites treated with the cultured keratinocytes were ready for reharvesting much sooner than those donor sites treated in a more conventional manner.

Discussion

Our data in this study showed that cultured allogenic keratinocytes accelerate re-epithelization of split thickness donor sites. Similar results were reported by Madden [36] and Faure [37] in an additional 24 patients. In our report and in the two cited studies, wounds covered with keratinocyte allografts healed in 5–8 days as compared to healing in 11–26 days for conventionally treated donor sites. The congruent results obtained in these three experimental studies reduces the probability that the accelerated re-epithelialization in keratinocyte covered areas re-

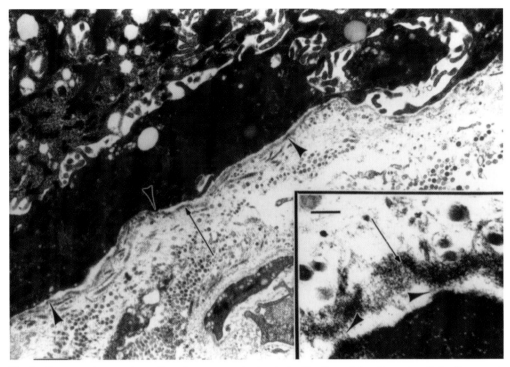

Fig. 3: Electron microscopic sections from donor site treated with allograft keratinocytes. Note: Basement membrane (arrows). Inset: Note formation of hemidesmosomes (arrows).

flects artifacts due to variation in the depth of harvest at the donor site, the location of the donor sites, the presence or absence of infection, or the general health and nutritional status of the patients.

An epidermis attached to the dermis by a basement membrane and hemidesmosomes is seen seven days post-graft placement at the split thickness donor sites in our studies and also in the report of Faure [37]. We do not believe these findings represent persistent allogenic keratinocytes. Accelerated growth of autologous keratinocytes from dermal appendages is more likely. Although increased host tolerance for cultured keratinocyte allografts has been reported, long-term survival has only been documented by DNA fingerprinting with cell of autologous origin [38, 39]. Allogenic keratinocytes have been demonstrated to hasten healing of partial thickness burns, but transplanted allogenic keratinocytes were not found in the wounds following wound healing by using gender chromosomal analyses as a marker of the allogenic cells [39].

The exact molecular mechanisms regulating re-epithelialization of the donor sites by keratinocyte allografts remains to be defined. Cultured human keratinocytes have been shown to produce a variety of growth factors including basic fibroblast growth factor [40], transforming growth factor alpha [41] and cytokines [42]. In addition, they also synthesize and secrete fibronectin [43], laminin [44], thrombospondin [45] and extracellular matrix proteins which promote epithelial cell attachment and spreading [44, 46]. The interaction of these growth factors with extracellular matrix proteins secreted by fibroblast cells into the wounds probably accounts for the increased rates of re-epithelization that we and others have observed. We, therefore, believe that the cultured cells act as a true **"biologic bandage"**. The interaction of the cytokines and growth factors, stimulated by the interaction of the keratinocytes and fibro-

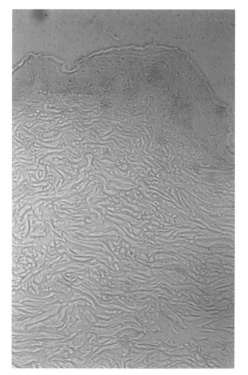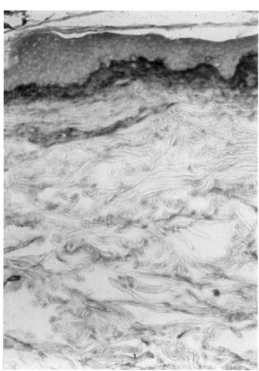

Fig. 4: (Left) Histochemical staining of Type I collagen matrix seeded with fibroblasts and keratinocytes, Day 14. (Right) Histochemical stain of normal epidermis and dermis.

blasts in the native dermis, most likely are responsible for the rapid proliferation of autologous keratinocytes from remaining dermal appendages which close the donor site. Work in our laboratory [25], in which fibroblasts were grown in a Type I collagen matrix and later overseeded with keratinocytes, produced a "skin equivalent." Using monoclonal antibodies and their epitopes, the combination of keratinocytes and fibroblasts reproduced Native Chondroitin SO_4 (4C3, 6C3 and 7D4), Chondroitin $6SO_4$ (3B3) and Dermatan (2B6) (Fig. 4). In those experiments, neither keratinocytes alone nor fibroblasts alone in the Type I collagen matrix reproduced those substances (Fig. 3, 4).

Summary

Donor sites covered with cultured allograft keratinocytes are made available for recropping in a significantly shorter time than donor sites treated by conventional means. Donor sites thus healed can be recropped and take well. They are equivalent to grafts taken from primary donor sites in every respect. Logistically, there are few barriers to the application of this technology. An almost endless supply of cells is available from properly selected male foreskins. These cells can be stored in liquid nitrogen and reconstituted as needed to produce sheets of cells available for donor site grafting in as little as seven days.

The costs of producing sheets of cultured keratinocytes for the rapid re-epithelialization of donor sites restricts the use of this procedure to those patients who require multiple reharvesting of very limited donor sites. In this selected group, we project a positive cost/benefit ratio, since the more rapid re-use of donor sites following treatment with allografts of cultured keratinocytes should lead to earlier wound coverage, may significantly decrease length of hospital stays and decrease morbidity in extensively burned patients as well as improve survival. We continue to examine this modality of treatment using allogenic keratinocytes from human foreskins.

Acknowledgments

Special thanks to Dr. Leroy Dierker, Department of Obstetrics-Gynecology, MetroHealth Medical Center, who recruited the families that contributed skin for these studies.

This work was supported by grants from the NIH – AG-02921 (I.A. Schafer, M.D.) and Cuyahoga County Fire Fighters (R.B. Fratianne, M.D.)

References

[1] Baxter CR, Shires GT: Physiological response to crystalloid resuscitation of severe burns. Ann NY Acad Sci; 150: 874–94, 1968.
[2] Cope O, Moore FD: A study of capillary permeability in experimental burn shock using radioactive dyes in blood and lymph. J Clin Invest; 23: 241–57, 1944.
[3] Cope O, Moore FD: The redistribution of body water and the fluid therapy of the burned patients. Ann Surg; 126: 1010–45, 1947.
[4] Pruitt BA, Jr, Moncrief JA: Current trends in burn research. J Surg Res; 7: 280–93, 1967.
[5] Shires GT, Williams J, Brown F: Simultaneous measurements of plasma volume extracellular fluid volume, and red blood cell mass in utilizing I131, S35O4, and Cr51. J Lab Clin Med; 55: 776–83, 1960.
[6] Moyer CA, Brentano L, Gravens DL, et al.: Treatment of large human burns with 0.5% nitrate solution. Arch Surg 1965; 90: 812–70.
[7] Fox CL, Jr. Silver sulfadiazine: A new topical therapy for pseudomonas in burns. Arch Surg; 96: 184–8, 1968.
[8] Danes RA, Wilmore DW: What is the relationship between the status of a patient's host defense mechanism, his metabolic response, and his ability to respond to injury? J Trauma; 24: S84–S100, 1984.
[9] Odessey R: Effect of various types of injury on proteolysis in normal muscle. Prog Clin Biol Res; 266: 215–288, 1988.
[10] Cynober L: Amino acid metabolism in thermal burns. JPEN; 13: 196–205, 1989.

[11] Jahoor F, Desai M, Herndon DN, Wolfe RR: Dynamics of the protein metabolic response to burn injury. Metabolism; 37: 330–7, 1988.
[12] Hildreth MA, Herndon DN, Desai MH, Duke MA: Reassessing caloric requirements in pediatric burn patients. J Burn Care Rehabil; 9: 616–8, 1988.
[13] Matsuda T, Clark N, Hariyani GD, Bryant RS, Hanumadass ML, Kagan RJ: The effect of burn wound size on resting energy expenditure. J Trauma; 27: 115–8, 1987.
[14] Cunningham JJ, Hegarty MT, Meara PA, Burke JF: Measured and predicted calorie requirements of adults during recovery from severe burn trauma. Am J Clin Nutr 1989; 49: 404–8.
[15] Alexander JW, Gottschlich MM: Nutritional immunodulation in burn patients. Crit Care Med; 18: S149–53, 1990.
[16] Tompkins RG, Burke JF, Schoenfeld DA, et al.: Prompt eschar excision: A treatment system contributing to reduced burn mortality. Ann Surg; 204: 272–81, 1986.
[17] Tompkins RG, Hilton J, Burke JF, et al.: Increased survival after massive thermal injuries in adults: Preliminary report using artificial skin. Crit Care Med; 17: 734–40, 1989.
[18] Tompkins RG, Remensnyder J, Burke JF, et al.: Significant reductions in mortality for children with burn injuries through the use of prompt eschar excision. Ann Surg; 208: 577–85, 1988.
[19] Burke JF: From desperation to skin regeneration: Progress in burn treatment. J Trauma; 30: S36–S40, 1990.
[20] Fratianne RB, Brandt CP: Improved Survival of Adults with Extensive Burns. J Burn Care & Rehabil.; 18 (4): 347–50, 1997.
[21] Burke JF, Yannas IV, Quinby WC, Bondoc CC, Jung WK: Successful use of a physiologically acceptable artificial skin in the treatment of extensive burn injury. Ann Surg; 194: 413–28, 1981.
[22] Hansbrough JF, Boyce ST, Cooper ML, Foreman TJ: Burn wound closure with cultured autologous keratinocytes and fibroblasts attached to a collagen-glycosaminoglycan substrate. JAMA; 262: 2125–30, 1989.
[23] Heimbach D, Luterman A, Burke JF, et al.: Artificial dermis for major burns: A multicenter randomized clinical trial. Ann Surg; 208: 313–20, 1988.
[24] Morykwas MJ, Stevenson TR, Marcelo CL, Thornton JW, Smith DJ: In vitro and in vivo testing of a collagen sheet to support keratinocyte growth for use as a burn wound covering. J Trauma; 29: 1163–7, 1989.
[25] Fratianne RB, Lang C, Schafer I: A biological skin equivalent combining cross-linked type I collagen, human keratinocytes and human dermal fibroblasts. American Burn Association, 1989.

[26] O'Connor NE, Mulliken JB, Banks-Schegel S, Kehinde O, Green H: Grafting of burns with cultured epithelium prepared from autologous epidermal cells. Lancet; 1: 75–8, 1981.

[27] Cooper ML, Hansbrough JF: Use of a composite skin graft composed of cultured human keratinocytes and fibroblasts and a collagen-GAG matrix to cover full-thickness wounds on athymic mice. Surgery; 109: 198–207, 1991.

[28] Rue LW, Cioffi WG, McManus WF, Pruitt BA: Wound closure and outcome in extensively burned patients treated with cultured autologous keratinocytes. J Trauma; 34: 662–8, 1993.

[29] Schafer IA, Silverman L, Sullivan JC, Kofoed J, Svejcar J, Robertson W van B: Ascorbic acid deficiency in cultured human fibroblasts. J Cell Biol; 34: 83–95, 1967.

[30] Schafer IA, Shapiro A, Kovach M, Lang C, Fratianne R: The interaction of human papillary and reticular fibroblasts and human keratinocytes in the contraction of three-dimensional floating collagen lattices. Exp Cell Res; 183: 112–25, 1989.

[31] Schafer IA, Kovach M, Price R, Fratianne R: Human keratinocytes cultured on collagen gels form an epidermis which synthesizes bullous pemphigoid antigens and a2B1 integrins and secretes laminin, Type IV collagen and heparin sulfate proteoglycans at the basal cell surface. Exp Cell Res; 195: 443–461, 1991.

[32] Green H, Kehinde O, Thomas J: Growth of cultured human epidermal cells in multiple epithelia suitable for grafting. Proc Natl Acad Sci USA; 76: 5665–8, 1979.

[33] Sheehan DC: Theory and practice of histotechnology, 2nd ed. Battelle Press, Columbus, Ohio, p 59–78, 1980.

[34] Mackay B: Introduction to diagnostic electron microscopy: Technical procedure. Appleton-Century-Crofts (ACC). New York, p 29–44, 1981.

[35] Jones BR: Electro microscopy: TEM interpretation. Library Research Asso. Inc. New York, p 120–2, 1985.

[36] Madden MR, Finkelstein JL, Staiano-Coico L, et al.: Grafting of cultured allogenic epidermis on second and third-degree burn wounds on 26 patients. J Trauma; 11: 955–62, 1986.

[37] Faure M, Maudiut G, Schmitt D, Kantakis J, Demiden A, Thiovelt J: Growth and differentiation of cultured human epidermal cultures used as auto- and allografts in humans. Br J Dermatol; 116: 161–70, 1987.

[38] Brain A, Purkis P, Hackett M, Navsaria H, Leigh I: Survival of cultured allografts in patients with burns assessed with a probe specific for Y chromosome. Br Med J; 298: 917–9, 1989.

[39] Burt AM, Pallet CD, Sloane JP, et al.: Survival of cultured allografts in patients with burns assessed with a probe specific for Y chromosome. Br Med J; 298: 915–7, 1989.

[40] Landon RC, Haluban R, McGuire J: Cultured human keratinocytes produce mRNA for basic fibroblast growth factor (b FGF) (abstract). J Invest Dermatol; 90: 579A, 1988.

[41] Coffee RJ, Derynck R, Wilcox JN, Bringman TS, Gaustin AS, Moses HL, Pittelkow MR: Production and auto-induction of transforming growth factor- in human keratinocytes. Nature; 328: 817–820, 1987.

[42] Danner M, Luger TA: Human keratinocytes and epidermoid carcinoma lines produce a cytokine with interleukin 3-like activity. J Invest Dermatol; 88: 353–361, 1987.

[43] O'Keefe EJ, Woodley D, Castillo G, Russell N, Payne RE: Production of soluble and cell-associated fibronectin by cultured keratinocyte. J Invest Dermatol; 82: 580–586, 1984.

[44] Alitalo K, Kuismanen E, Myllyla R, Kiistala U, Askoseljavaara S, Vaheri A: Extracellular matrix proteins of human epidermal keratinocytes and feeder 3T3 cells. J Cell Biol; 94: 497–505, 1982.

[45] Wikner NE, Clark RAF: Human keratinocytes synthesize and secrete the extracellular matrix protein thrombospondin (abstract) J Invest Dermatol; 86: 514A, 1986.

[46] Piepkorn M, Fleckman P, Carney H, Linker A: Glycosaminoglycan syntheses by proliferating and differential human keratinocytes in culture. J Invest Dermatol; 88: 215–219, 1987.

Keratinocyte in Fibrin Net: A New Means of Transplantation for Full Thickness Wounds

J. Hunyadi, B. Farkas, A. Dobozy

Summary

Twenty adult individuals with chronic leg ulcers caused by venous insufficiency, and 5 patients with full thickness burns were treated. Twenty of the patients (15 with leg ulcers and 5 with burns) were grafted with separated autologous keratinocytes. In these cases the cells were fixed to the wound by a fibrin net. Five other patients (with leg ulcers) were treated with fibrin without keratinocytes. In 16 of the 20 patients grafted with keratinocytes in a fibrin net, the defect healed completely within 14 to 21 days. On the other hand, the fibrin net without keratinocytes failed to significantly accelerate the process of reepithelialization. Our experience suggests that a rapid healing of full-thickness skin defects can be achieved through keratinocyte grafting.

Introduction

Wound healing is the summation of a complex series of processes beginning with coagulation and ending in remodelling. The sequence of different signals and message substances, such as mediators of inflammation, fulfil a key function in wound repair. Undisturbed wound healing is subject to a fixed time schedule of biochemical and cellular events [10]. The duration of the healing process of full thickness skin defects depends on the spread out of keratinocytes from the edges of the defect. The healing process of full thickness skin defects can be accelerated effectively by auto-transplantation. In that way not only the healing time can be shortened but also a better skin function can be achieved. Frequently the intact skin of the patient is not large enough for auto-transplantation because of the fact that the damaged skin area is too large. To solve the problem, several methods have been applied using cultured keratinocytes [1, 2, 3, 4, 7, 8, 9]. During the eighties we developed a new method, where autologous keratinocytes in fibrin-glue are used for the grafting [5, 6]. The results of our treatment variety and its advantages are summarized in the following paper.

Materials and Methods

Fibrinogen

Fibrin sealant is a highly concentrated fibrinogen preparation made up of two components, for tissue adhesion. One of the components contains fibrinogen, factor XIII, and aprotinin, while thrombin and Ca^{2+} are to be found in the other constituent. A stable fibrin net can be formed by activation of the fibrinogen by the thrombin Ca^{2+}.

Patients

Five patients with full thickness burns (deep third degree) and 20 patients with chronic leg ulcers caused by venous insufficiency were enrolled in the study. Each patient with leg ulcers presented one full thickness skin ulceration for the duration of more than 2 months, that had not responded to conventional treatment modalities. The skin defects of both leg ulcers and burns ranged in size from 9 to 25 cm². Five out of the 20 patients with leg ulcers were treated with fibrin without keratinocytes as a control. Since granulation tissues of several origins were used as a target for keratinocyte grafting, no further controls were involved in the study. None of the patients had relevant underlying diseases such as diabetes, connective tissue diseases etc. that could influence healing. All experiments were carried out with the informed consent of the patients. The Human Investigation Committee in Szeged approved these studies.

Preparation of Epidermal Cell Suspensions

A single epidermal cell (EC) suspension was separated from a full thickness, fresh skin specimen of the patient by the trypsin digestion method described by Eisinger et al. [2]. Briefly, a 2 to 6 cm² biopsy sample was obtained from the patient following local infiltration with 1 % Xylocaine. After removal of the subcutaneous tissue and as much dermis as possible, the tissue was minced and trypsinized (Gibco, 0,25 %, 12 h, 4°C) to produce a single cell suspension. The cells were washed three times n phosphate basal solution (PBS 0,05 Mphosphate buffer, pH 7.2 and 0,1 Msodium chloride). The EC suspension contained 70–80 % viable keratinocytes. Under suitable circumstances 2–30 % of these cells were able to multiply.

Preparation of Fibrin Net for Keratinocyte Grafting

After keratinocytes were suspended in the fibrinogen-containing component (1–8 x 10⁶ cells/ml), the calcium and thrombin containing component was added, and the entire mixture poured onto the wound bed in liquid form. Well-granulated, clean wound beds were prepared by conventional local treat-

ment, for instance with the use of antiseptic solutions and powders. The keratinocyte grafts were covered by sterile paraffin gauze, overlaid with Vaseline gauze and the dressings were changed daily.

Results

In preliminary studies we observed that transplantation with a keratinocyte suspension in PBS failed to significantly accelerate the process of reepithelialization. On the other hand, a complete reepithelialization was seen within 2 weeks in 16 out of the 20 patients (15 leg ulcers, 5 burns) treated by means of keratinocyte grafting. In these cases a thin epithelial layer was already observable on the whole wound surface of the wound bed 8 to 10 days after transplantation. In four patients (all with leg ulcers) treated with keratinocyte grafting, a bacterial infection and or a marked exudation

Table 1: Results of keratinocyte grafting of patients with leg ulcers and full thickness burns

With grafting	No.	Improved Epithelialization
Keratinocytes in fibrin net	20	16
Fibrin sealant (control)	5	0

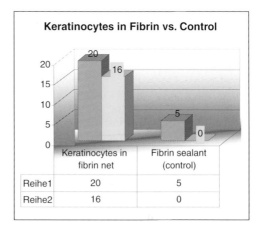

	Keratinocytes in fibrin net	Fibrin sealant (control)
Reihe1	20	5
Reihe2	16	0

caused an early fibrinolytic process even 24 to 48 hours after transplantation.

In these cases the reepithelialization was slow, it occurred only in the peripheral part of the wound, and even after 21 days after the transplantation the major part of the defect (the central one) was still not covered by epithelial tissue. None of the remaining 21 patients (including the controls) encountered similar infections or marked exudation. A slow reepithelialization, predominantly in the outer part of the wound was observed in the five control patients treated with a fibrin net without keratinocytes (Table 1).

Discussion

Nowadays, due to recent efforts and developments in tissue engineering, therapy of chronic wounds may be more efficient. Tissue engineering relies on in vitro cell culture, biocompatible matrix materials and genetic engineering with growth and differentiation factors for guided tissue regeneration. Although the new therapeutic possibilities for wound healing are rather expensive, they reduce overall costs for the treatment of chronic wounds.

Cell culture technology allows expanding keratinocytes up to 6000-fold in vitro after taking a single biopsy from the patient. Today the transplantation of these in vitro cultured keratinocytes in different modifications is an established clinical treatment regimen for the therapy of extensive wounds [1, 2, 4, 5, 6, 7, 8, 9].

Biogenic or semi synthetic biomaterials are alternatives as cell carrirs. The keratinocyte fibrin-glue suspension has been experimentally tested in nude mice and clinically in extensive burns and chronic wounds [7, 9]. In the "in vivo culture" on the wound, the non-confluent keratinocytes formed a differentiated epithelium within a few days [7]. In an athymic mouse model with reproducible standardized full thickness wounds the technique of cultured human keratinocytes suspended as single cells in a fibrin-glue matrix was compared directly to cultured epidermal

sheet grafts. Reepithelialization was similar in both groups, but reconstitution of the dermo-epidermal junction zone, as shown by electron microscopy and immunohistochemistry was significantly enhanced by the fibrin-glue suspension technique [4].

Autologous keratinocytes, cultured in vitro from skin biopsies of patients with deep partial and full skin thickness burns were grafted by burn surgeons onto nine necrectomized wound surfaces between 17 and 25 days after the burn injury. The cells were applied as non confluent single cells suspended in fibrin-glue. In four wounds, this cell-fibrin suspension was used to attach an additional glycerolized allogenic split thickness skin graft (STSG). Re-epithelialization was very rapid as demonstrated clinically and histologically. Keratinocyte grafted areas without overgrafted cadaver skin showed less mechanical stability than when the keratinocyte-fibrin-glue suspension was combined with allogenic STSG. There is clinical and histological evidence that the allodermis may be partially integrated into the new skin [7, 8].

Our results in agreement with other publications prove that grafting with keratinocytes in fibrin-glue is able to transfer actively proliferative single keratinocytes inducing reepithelialization of human skin defects. Using this technique, an earlier healing may be available than with that of standard sheet grafts.

References

[1] Bonnekoh B, Thiele B, Mahrle G, Steigleder GK: [Epidermal cell cultures – significance for wound coverage in the human]. Z Hautkr; 61(20):1433–1442, 1986.
[2] Hefton JM, Caldwell D, Biozes DG, Balin AK, Carter DM: Grafting of skin ulcers with cultured autologous epidermal cells. J Am Acad Dermatol; 14(3):399–405, 1986.
[3] Hefton JM, Madden MR, Finkelstein JL, Shires GT: Grafting of burn patients with allografts of cultured epidermal cells. Lancet; 2(8347):428–430, 1983.
[4] Horch RE, Bannasch H, Kopp J, Andree C, Stark GB: Single-cell suspensions of cultured human keratinocytes in fibrin-glue reconstitute the epidermis. Cell Transplant; 7(3):309–317, 1998.

[5] *Hunyadi J, Farkas B, Bertenyi C, Olah J, Dobozy A:* Keratinocyte grafting: covering of skin defects by separated autologous keratinocytes in a fibrin net [letter]. J Invest Dermatol; 89(1): 119–120, 1987.

[6] *Hunyadi J, Farkas B, Bertenyi C, Olah J, Dobozy A:* Keratinocyte grafting: a new means of transplantation for full-thickness wounds. J Dermatol Surg Oncol; 14(1):75–78, 1988.

[7] *Stark GB, Horch RE, Voigt M, Tanczos E:* [Biological wound tissue glue systems in wound healing]. Langenbecks Arch Chir Suppl Kongressbd; 115:683–8:683–688, 1998.

[8] *Stark GB, Kaiser HW:* Cologne Burn Centre experience with glycerol-preserved allogeneic skin: Part II: Combination with autologous cultured keratinocytes. Burns; 20 Suppl 1:S34–8:S34–S38, 1994.

[9] *Tanczos E, Horch RE, Bannasch H, Andree C, Walgenbach KJ, Voigt M et al.:* [Keratinocyte transplantation and tissue engineering. New approaches in treatment of chronic wounds]. Zentralbl Chir; 124 Suppl 1:81–6: 81–86, 1999.

[10] *Wokalek H, Ruh H:* Time course of wound healing. J Biomater Appl; 5(4):337–362, 1991.

Epidermal Equivalents From Autologous Outer Root Sheath Cells for Chronic Wounds

L. M. Böhlen, A. Limat, T. Hunziker

Summary

During wound healing the outer root sheath cells of hair follicles can substitute for interfollicular epidermal keratinocytes. Using improved culture techniques, we generated highly differentiated epidermal equivalents from cultured outer root sheath cells of patients suffering from chronic leg ulcers. Autologous grafting of such epidermal equivalents in more than 50 recalcitrant leg ulcers of mainly vascular origin resulted in a take rate around 90%, with subsequent complete closure of the ulcers in about 45% and significant size reduction in another 40% within 8 weeks. These positive results are probably due to the large compartment of proliferative cells as well as to the well-developed horny layer which prevents rapid disintegration of the grafts. Practical advantages of this technology are its noninvasiveness and thus repeated availability, the lack of need for surgical facilities, and a short immobilization period after grafting, allowing a strategy of sequential application in an outpatient setting as an alternative to surgical autografting.

Introduction

In the last 20 years, interest has focused on cultured keratinocytes for the treatment of skin wounds (rev. in [1]). Attempts to treat chronic wounds such as chronic leg ulcers using cultured autologous as well as allogeneic keratinocytes yielded controversial results. Allografts do not result in a permanent take [2] and thus may be classified as quite effective, but expensive interactive biological dressings (rev. in [1]). In contrast to acute wounds, a major definitive take of autologous keratinocytes mainly isolated from interfollicular epidermis and grafted by various modalities has not been convincingly demonstrated in chronic wounds (rev. in [1]).

Selection of Keratinocytes

The outer root sheath (ORS) of hair follicles is comprised largely of undifferentiated keratinocytes that encompass the cylindrical structures of the hardened inner root sheath and the hair shaft. ORS cells can substitute for interfollicular epidermal keratinocytes as during healing of superficial wounds, when these cells migrate onto the denuded area and contribute to epidermal regeneration [3]. Populations of ORS cells with a long life span or even stem cell properties have been described in the murine as well as in the human system [4]. Human ORS cells isolated from plucked anagen scalp hair follicles can be expanded extensively in vitro [5, 6]. Under conventional submerged culture conditions, ORS cells resemble interfollicular epidermal keratinocytes by both morphologic and biochemical (e.g. keratin profiles) criteria [6, 7]. In organotypic cocultures with human dermal fibroblasts, i.e., under conditions mimicking the epidermal environment, ORS cells develop a stratified epithelium reminiscent of regenerating epidermis (Fig. 1a) [8, 9, 10].

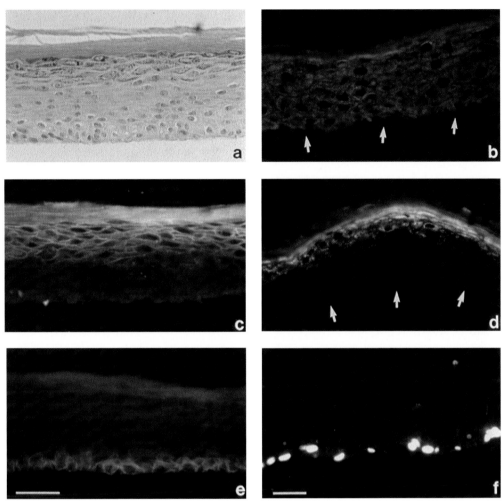

Fig. 1: Tissue organization and immunolocalization of epidermal differentiation products in epidermal equivalents generated from outer root sheath cells. a) Regular stratification with a well developed granular layer and an orthokeratotic horny layer (hematoxylin/eosin). b) Strong expression of keratin 10 in all suprabasal cells. c) Involucrin displaying a typical honey-comb pattern from the mid-stratum spinosum on. d) Granular staining of filaggrin in a continuous band beneath the horny layer. e) Reactivity of the β1-integrin chain distributed over all aspects of the basal cells. f) Proliferative compartment of about 24 % BrdU-positive cells in the basal layer. b–f: indirect immunofluorescence; scale bar, 50 μm (a–e: same magnification). Arrows point to the underside of the basal layer.

Thereby, extensive normalization of tissue differentiation occurs, as illustrated by regular expression of various markers (suprabasal keratins, involucrin, filaggrin, integrins; Fig. 1b–e). If the ORS cells are isolated by explanting the hair follicles, a large compartment of proliferative cells is labeled in the basal layer by BrdU-incorporation (Fig. 1f) [10]. If such organotypic cultures are grafted onto nude mice, ORS cells form a regular neo-epidermis that is under homeostatic control [11]. Comparison of the growth behavior of ORS cells revealed no significant differences between young and old donors [10].

Aware of the advantage that cultures of autologous ORS cells can be established easily and repeatedly from the patient's hair follicles, thus avoiding additional wounding in skin donor sites, we tested organotypic cultures, i.e., epidermal equivalents generated from ORS cells for autologous grafting of recalcitrant chronic leg ulcers.

Generation of Epidermal Equivalents

The epidermal equivalents were prepared essentially as previously described [10]. In brief, about 40 to 60 anagen hair follicles were plucked from the occipital scalp and explanted on the microporous membrane of cell culture inserts (Falcon 3090; Becton Dickinson, Franklin Lanes, NJ) that carried at their undersurface a feeder system of postmitotic human dermal fibroblasts screened for infection [6, 10]. Culture medium consisted of Dulbecco's modified Eagle's medium/Ham's F12 (3:1) supplemented with 10% autologous serum, epidermal growth factor, hydrocortisone, choleratoxin, adenine and triiodothyronine (all from Sigma Chemical Co., St. Louis, MO) [10]. Explanting of anagen hair follicles proved to be an efficient and reproducible technique to establish primary cultures of ORS cells, about 80% of the follicles giving rise to outgrowth of ORS cells with high proliferative capacity, even when derived from individuals aged more than 90 years. After about 14 days, large areas of the insert membranes were usually covered by compactly arranged, small cells, at which time they were harvested and either frozen in liquid nitrogen (KBM [Clonetics Corporation, San Diego, CA] supplemented with 10% autologous serum and 10% dimethylsulfoxide) or immediately used for the preparation of epidermal equivalents. For this purpose, they were seeded at a density of 5 x 10^5/cm² on the microporous membrane of cell culture inserts (Falcon 3095 or 3180, corresponding to surfaces of 0.4 and 0.95 cm², respectively) coated at their undersurface with the postmitotic feeder fibroblasts. Culture medium was the same as for primary cultures. After 36

hours, the ORS cells were exposed to the air-liquid interface and cultured for about 14 days with 3 medium changes per week. About five anagen hair follicles were needed to generate 1 cm² of epidermal equivalents. The period to generate graftable epidermal equivalents usually was 4 weeks, i.e., 2 for the primary culture and 2 for the organotypic culture.

Grafting of Epidermal Equivalents

For grafting, the epidermal equivalents were excised from the cell culture insert together with the insert membrane using a scalpel blade and positioned upside-down on a polyester membrane (Thomapor 95862; Reichelt Chemie, Heidelberg, Germany). Then the insert membrane together with the attached feeder fibroblasts was carefully removed with fine tweezers. Finally, the epidermal equivalents on their supporting polyester membrane were washed in phosphate-buffered saline containing 30% autologous serum and left floating therein until their application on the wound bed.

With the approval of the local Ethics Committees and after obtaining written informed consent more than 50 recalcitrant chronic leg ulcers of mainly vascular origin – many of them failures of surgical autografting – were treated so far, in a few patients repeatedly. The ulcers were prepared conventionally (primarily by repeated debridement and using hydrocolloidal dressings and topical antimicrobial agents) until ready for grafting (Fig. 2a). Then up to 20 autologous epidermal equivalents, 6 or 11 mm in width, were placed, basal layer downward on the surface of the ulcers, and the supporting polyester membranes were carefully removed with fine tweezers (Fig. 2b). The ulcers were then covered with a hydropolymer dressing (Tielle; Johnson & Johnson Medical, Ascot, UK) overlaid by an elastic bandage with compression adapted to the patient's arterial status. This grafting procedure was performed in an outpatient setting, patients remaining immobilized for just about 2 hours. The dressing was

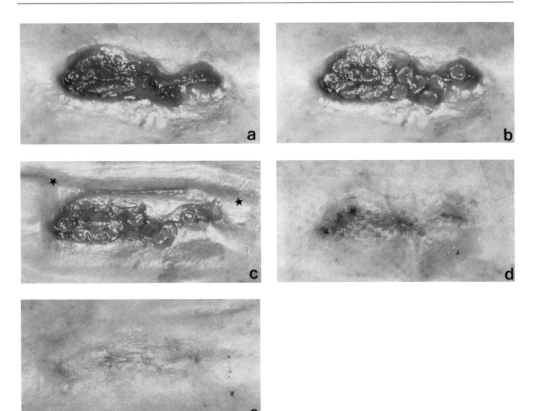

Fig. 2: Grafting of epidermal equivalents from autologous outer root sheath cells on a chronic ulcer with 6/2 cm maximal diameters in a 85-y-old female. a) Cleaned, well granulating ulcer immediately before grafting, and b) after covering about 90 % of the ulcer surface with 18 epidermal equivalents of 6-mm diameter. c) On the first change of the dressing 3 days after grafting, most of the grafts are distinctly visible (* represents pressure marks of the elastic bandage). d) Two weeks after grafting, there is almost complete re-epithelialization. e) 6 weeks after grafting, the former ulcer area exhibits slight scarring.
Reprints of figures 1 and 2 with permission of *The Society for Investigative Dermatology, Inc.*

changed for the first time after 3 days, thereafter twice weekly. After complete re-epithelialization local treatment was switched to topical emollients, and the patients were instructed to adhere to a long-term compression therapy adapted to their arterial status. Take of the grafts and healing of the ulcers was documented by standardized photographs.

On the first change of the dressing, about 90 % of the grafts were visible and adherent to the wound bed (Fig. 2c). Within the following weeks the grafts consolidated and expanded, resulting in re-epithelialization and complete ulcer closure after 8 weeks in about 45 % of the cases (Fig. 1d, e). In another 40 % of the cases, accelerated formation of granulation tissue and re-epithelialization mainly from the wound edges ("edge effect") led to a significant, i.e. more than 50 % reduction of ulcer size within 8 weeks. In the remaining ulcers the grafts were lost primarily because of heavy contamination or even infection of the wound ground, notably with Pseudomonas sp. and Staphylococcus aureus. After re-epithelialization, the epidermis was initially still fragile with some tendency to blistering after minor frictional trauma, occasionally resulting in small erosions. These erosions re-epithelialized rapidly under conventional topical treatment. The first patients have now been followed up for 5 years, apart from a few recurrences most of them showed increasing stabilization of the treated areas. So far there were no adverse events and the development of epidermal tumors was never observed.

Conclusions

These results document that there is no requirement for a dermal substitute to achieve a major take of autologous cultured keratinocytes in chronic wounds. Highly differentiated pure keratinocyte cultures are stable enough for handling when using an appropriate carrier membrane, and they also resist to the hyperproteolytic milieu of the chronic wound, enabling for a definitive take. Furthermore, the suprabasal keratinocytes in the various stages of terminal differentiation present in such cultures may exert promoting effects on adhesion, proliferation and migration of the basal cells as well as stimulate the wound by interactive secretion of growth factor cocktails adapted to the actual healing phase. Compared to interfollicular epidermal keratinocytes, ORS cells bear the advantage that they are successfully cultivated independently of the donor age, a very important aspect when aiming at grafting keratinocytes to chronic wounds, which occur mainly in the elderly. This most probably relates to the presence of keratinocyte stem cells in the ORS. Practical advantages with relevant impact on the costs of this novel treatment modality include its noninvasiveness, so that the cells are available repeatedly, the lack of need for surgical facilities, and a short immobilization period required after grafting, thus allowing a strategy of sequential application in an outpatient setting. From the safety as well as regulatory point of view, all ingredients in the culture media are defined or autologous and contamination of the keratinocyte grafts with feeder fibroblasts is prevented by spatially separating the two cell types. The main indication for grafting of epidermal equivalents generated from autologous ORS cells will be hard-to-heal chronic ulcers, as an alternative to surgical autografting which avoids an additional wound at the donor site.

References

[1] *Hunziker T, Limat A:* Cultured keratinocyte grafts. In Hafner J, Ramelet A-A, Schmeller W, Brunner UV (eds): Management of leg ulcers. Curr Probl Dermatol. Karger, Basel, vol 27, pp57–64, 1999.
[2] *Fabre JW:* Epidermal allografts. Immunol Lett 29:161–166, 1991.
[3] *Eisen AZ, Holyoke JB, Lobitz WC:* Responses of the superficial portion of the human pilosebaceous apparatus to controlled injury. J Invest Dermatol 15:145–156, 1955.
[4] *Fuchs E, Segre JA:* Stem cells: a new lease on life. Cell 100:143–155, 2000.
[5] *Limat A, Noser FK:* Serial cultivation of single keratinocytes from the outer root sheath of human scalp hair follicles. J Invest Dermatol 87:485–488, 1986.
[6] *Limat A, Hunziker T, Boillat C, Bayreuther K, Noser F:* Post-mitotic human dermal fibroblasts efficiently support the growth of human follicular keratinocytes. J Invest Dermatol 92:758–762, 1989.
[7] *Limat A, Breitkreutz D, Stark HJ, Hunziker T, Thikoetter G, Noser F, Fusenig NE:* Experimental modulation of the differentiated phenotype of keratinocytes from epidermis and hair follicle outer root sheath and hair matrix cells. Ann NY Acad Sci 642:125–147, 1991.
[8] *Lenoir MC, Bernard BA, Pautrat G, Darmon M, Shroot B:* Outer root sheath cells of human hair follicles are able to regenerate a fully differentiated epidermis in vitro. Dev Biol 130:610–620, 1988.
[9] *Limat A, Breitkreutz D, Hunziker T, Boillat C, Wiesmann U, Klein E, Noser F, Fusenig NE:* Restoration of the epidermal phenotype by follicular outer root sheath cells in recombinant culture with dermal fibroblasts. Exp Cell Res 194:218–227, 1991.
[10] *Limat A, Mauri D, Hunziker T:* Successful treatment of chronic leg ulcers with epidermal equivalents generated from cultured autologous outer root sheath cells. J Invest Dermatol 107:128–135, 1996.
[11] *Limat A, Breitkreutz D, Thiekoetter G, Klein CE, Braathen LR, Hunziker T, Fusenig NE:* Formation of a regular neo-epidermis by cultured human outer root sheath cells grafted on nude mice. Transplantation 59: 1032–1038, 1995.

The Combination of Cultured Grafts with Artificial Skin

P. K. Lam, E. S. Y. Chan, C. T. Liew, W. W. K. King

Summary

In the process of harvesting cultured epithelial autograft (CEA), the basement proteins such as fibronectin, laminin, of the cultured graft are inevitably damaged by the dispase thus affecting its anchorage on the recipient wound bed. To avid this potential negative aspect of dispase treatment to the cultured epithelium, we investigated the cultivation of kerationocytes directly on a pliable hyaluronate-derived membrane (Laserskin). The preliminary study of combining cultured Laserskin and artificial skin (Integra) was performed on selected small wounds. Apart from infection problems, the application of this combination technique in major burn will be complicated by the unfavorable wound environment associated with a large and open wound. Further research is necessary to overcome these problems.

Introduction

The skin is the largest organ of the body, ranging from 1.2 to 2.0 m² in an adult. The skin consists of epidermis and dermis. The primary functions of the skin are to guard the body from harmful environment and to prevent the excessive loss of body fluid and electrolytes. The loss of skin in thermal injuries breaks the integrity of this biological barrier. Therefore, early coverage of the freshly excised wounds is important in the treatment of burns. Autologous skin is the most efficient and safe biological coverage. The wounds in minor burns can be readily covered by autologous skin graft harvested from healthy donor sites. In case of extensive burns of more than 50% of (total body surface area = TBSA), the donor sites are not sufficient to cover the exposed area although split thickness skin graft can be repeatedly harvested from the same donor site. Allograft and xenograft (pigskin) are temporary biological dressings. The use of allograft is also limited by availability and the risk of hepatitis HIV transmission and other skin diseases [1, 2]. In the past twenty years, tremendous effort has been done in tissue engineering. An ideal human skin substitute should be non-antigenic, biocompatible, durable, adherent, readily available and inexpensive [3, 4, 5]. In this chapter, our preliminary work on the engraftment of cultured Laserskin consisting of autologous keratinocytes on the neodermis of artificial skin (Integra) is discussed.

Cultured Epidermal Substitutes

The epidermis of skin primarily consists of keratinocytes. Other cell types include melanocytes which function to produce pigments for the purpose of ultraviolet radiation protection; Langerhans cells which contribute to immune function and Merkel cells which serve as mechanoreceptors. The outermost layer is the stratum corneum, composed of keratin, along with cellular debris. This is a compact, relatively impervious and protective layer, which eventually desquamates. The basal layer of keratinocytes is epidermis stratum germinativum consisting of stem cells which are mitotically active and provide generation of outwardly migrating epidermal cell layers. In vitro proliferation of keratinocytes can be achieved by using:

(I)   explant technique;
(II) serum free/chemically defined culture medium; and
(III) 3T3 cells feeder layer technique.

In explant technique, the skin biopsy is cut into tiny pieces and placed directly onto culture dish. The keratinocyte outgrowth from the edge of the tissue starts 5 to 7 days after inoculation. The major drawbacks of the explant technique are the contamination of fibroblasts and slow proliferation rate. Keratinocytes harvested from epidermis can be directly seeded on culture flask and cultivated by commercially available serum free/chemically defined culture medium (Gibco/Hyclone) . The former has to be supplemented with bovine pituitary extract and epidermal growth factor [6, 7]. The two culture medium are basically formulated on MCDB 153 (Sigma). According to our own experience, the primary culture of keratinocytes is quite difficult to grow from a small skin tissue of size less than 0.5 cm^2 because a relatively high seeding density is required. The Ca^{+2} level of serum free/chemically defined culture medium is low, 0.02–0.1 mM [8, 9]. Keratinocytes in these culture media can maintain a high proliferation rate without transforming into terminally differentiated cells. Therefore, serum free/chemically defined culture medium is recommended for proliferation of the secondary or tertiary culture. The introduction of 3T3 cell feeder layer technique by Green in 1980s was a breakthrough in tissue engineering [10, 11]. Actually it is the most commonly used method of cultivating keratinocytes for clinical application. A small piece of skin biopsy can be expanded in the laboratory with more than 500 to 1000 times increase in area within 3 to 4 weeks. Keratinocytes can be seeded in a relatively low seeding density $3–10 \times 10^4 \text{ cells/cm}^2$ onto irradiated or mitomycin C-treated 3T3 cells [12]. Apart from enhancing the clonal growth of keratinocytes, the feeder cells also inhibit the outgrowth of fibroblasts. The exact mechanism of the

role(s) of 3T3 cells is not clear. The use of cultured epidermal autograft (CEA) cultivated by Green's method has been extensively used on burn wounds [13–16]. However, the overall graft take rate of CEA is somewhat unpredictable and sometimes disappointing, ranging from 0 to 80 % [17, 18]. CEA is a very fragile sheet consisting of 4–6 layers of cells in thickness. It is vulnerable to bacteria infection. But the application of topical agents onto the wounds grafted with CEA may be cytotoxic to the cultured keratinocytes. The in vitro data of cytotoxicity testing is difficult to interpret for clinical application [19–21]. Shrinkage of the harvested cultured sheet from the flask and blister formation are another two drawbacks of conventional CEA. In the process of harvesting CEA, the basement proteins such as fibronectin, laminin, of the cultured graft are inevitably damaged by the dispase thus affecting the anchorage of the cultured graft on to the recipient wound bed. 3T3 cells were fibroblasts derived from mouse and were transformed by two different viruses, polyoma and SV40 [22]. Although the 3T3 cells in the Green's method are non-mitotic and continuously displaced by the proliferating keratinocytes and washed away by saline, persistent cells has been detected in the grafted CEA by western immunoblotting [23]. This may result in potential xenogenic antigen stimulus and subsequent activation of the recipient's immunologic response, which is a possible factor leading to graft loss [24]. More importantly, there is increasing concern about the potential of transferring oncogenes to the patients [25]. Ideally, the 3T3 cells or their proteins should be completely eliminated in the preparation of cultured graft for clinical application. On the other hand, keratinocytes at their sub-confluent stage can be trypsinized and then either directly sprayed onto the wounds or applied together with fibrin which serves as the glue to immobilize the cells [26–29]. Unlike the CEA sheet, the applied keratinocytes in suspension continue to proliferate and differentiate in vivo. But the clinical efficacy of this approach on major burn wounds has not yet been proven. Moreover, the basement proteins of keratinocytes may also be damaged by trypsin.

Dermal Substitutes

Beside epidermal substitute, dermal analog is also required to replace the dermis lost in full-thickness burns. It is well recognized that meshed allogenic skin enhances the take of CEA [30–32]. After the tangential abrasion of epidermis, the vascularized dermis provides a substantial template for the anchorage of the CEA. Alloderm™ is a commercially available, lyophilized, acellular human dermis prepared from screened cadaver donors. The epidermis is removed by hypertonic saline. Then the cellular components of the dermis such as fibroblasts, endothelial cells are extracted by a patented process. It has been widely used as a dermal replacement, which is overlaid thereafter with an autologuos skin graft [33–35]. The application of CEA sheets onto Alloderm™ has not yet been reported. Bevederm™, an acellular and glycerinised human dermis is currently under investigation by the Euro Skin Bank for clinical application [36]. Bell [37, 38] developed a new living dermal equivalent which is a three-dimensional type I calf – skin collagen lattice modified by human dermal fibroblasts. Transcyte™, is a human fibroblast-derived temporary skin substitute [39–41]. The outer layer is a synthetic epidermal layer, which is semipermeable to water vapor and gaseous exchange. The inner layer consists of allogenic fibroblasts populated on a polygalactin mesh. Upon grafted onto the wounds, the proteins deposited on the mesh from the fibroblasts enhance the formation of neodermis. Presently, the bilayer artificial skin (Integra™) developed by Burke and Yannas is the most commonly used dermal replacement [42, 43]. The outer layer of Integra is a thin layer of silicone (0.009 inch) which allows water vapor loss at approximately 5 mg/cm²/h. The inner dermal analog is prepared from bovine collagen (type I) cold co-precipitated with chrondroitin 6–sulphate (GAG) which is derived from shark. The resultant collagen-GSG is then cross-linkaged with glutaldehyde and freeze-dried. The porous collagen-GAG of Integra is approximately 2 mm thick. The porosity (70–200 μm) is precisely controlled by the proportion of collagen to GAG and the rates of cross-linkage and co-precipitation. The addition of GAG to the collagen can make the latter more resistance to enzymatic degradation by the recipient wounds. The pore size of collagen-GAG is easier to control than collagen alone. Fibrovascular ingrowth is dampened if the pore size of collagen-GAG is too small. The surface area of the scaffolding for the infiltrating cells to proliferate is relatively insufficient when the pore size is too large [44]. Upon complete vascularization, usually 14–21 days, the collagen-GAG is biologically modified into a new neodermis by the cellular components of the host. Thereafter, the silicone sheet is peeled off and replaced by an ultra thin (0.005-inch) autologous split-thickness skin graft (STSG). Before the collagen-GAG is vascularized by the host, Integra is prone to bacteria infection. Research work is now focused on the improvement of the vascularization of collagen – GAG by the recipient host. Similar bilayer artificial skin without GAG cross-linked with the atelocollagen (type I) has been produced in Japan [45, 46]. In multi-center trials around the world, Integra has been well demonstrated as biocompatible dermal replacement in deep and full-thickness wounds in reconstructive and burn surgery although special wound care is required to minimize the infection problem in acute burn application [47, 48]. Scar suppression by Integra has also been reported [49].

Cultivation of Keratinocytes on Dermal Analog

Dermal analog pre-seeded in vitro with proliferating autologous keratinocytes can allow one-stage engraftment. Keratinocytes have been cultivated on allogenic or xenogenic de-epithelialized dermis (DED) in an air-liquid culture system [50, 51]. It is difficult to observe and monitor keratinocytes growing on a DED. A large seeding density is also required. The growth rate can be potentiated with the use of fibrin and proliferating 3T3 cells, which are physically separated from the cultured keratinocytes [52]. The clinical results of keratinocytes-DED application have not been promising [53]. The diffusion of nutrition supply from the recipient wound is critical especially in the first few days when vascularization in the DED has not developed. Hansbrough [54] laminated and seeded the keratinocytes (0.5–$1 \times 10^6 cm^2$) on one side of collagen-GAG whereas the other porous side was seeded with dermal fibroblasts. The preliminary results of graft take were acceptable but further work on this composite graft is required. Carolyn and Orgill [55–57] centrifuged (500 rpm for 15 minutes) keratinocytes (5×10^4 / cm^2) which were freshly harvested, onto the collagen-GAG. This organized skin was evaluated in pig models. Boyce [58] developed a new cultured skin substitute which consisted of dermal fibroblasts and keratinocytes centrifuged on the collagen-GAG. However, this model requires a high seeding density of 1×10^6 keratinoctes/cm^2. Fast fabrication and low reeding density are benefical for a clinically applicable cultured skin graft [59].

Engraftment of CEA and Integra

Attempts have been made to replace the split thickness skin graft (STSG) with conventional CEA sheet. There are several definite advantages. First of all, there may not be STSG sufficient to cover the neodermis in major burns, whereas CEA sheet can be rapidly prepared in the laboratory. The application of CEA sheets can also be simply performed at bedside instead of the operation room. The cost savings is apparent. Ideally, major burn patients can have the wound excised within a few days after injury and covered with Integra. The silicone membranes are peeled off and replaced by the CEAs when ready. If the CEA is not taken because of infection or other reasons, another CEA can be applied again when the wounds are clean. It is observed that when overlaid with CEA, the re-epithelialization by meshed STSG over the neodermis is faster than mesh STSG alone. But

it is difficult to differentiate the origin of the cells of the regenerated epithelium from the CEA or STSG unless specific site markers such as cytokeratin are used [60]. CEA primarily consists of several layers of keratinocytes whose basal proteins may invariably be damaged by the dispase treatment, whereas the STSG (0.005 inch) includes a ultra thin layer of papillary dermis, which consists of some cellular elements such as dermal fibroblasts. Clinically, the STSG anchors readily onto the neodermis of Integra in reconstructive surgery. However, successful engraftment of CEA onto Integra has been inconsistent [61, 62]. According to the latest literature, there has been only one successful trial in resurfacing the neodermis with CEA alone [63].

It is hypothesized that the well-developed rete bridges in the epithelium of the STSG is essential to a firm anchorage on recipient wound. CEA takes months to fully develop after engraftment. Unlike the CEA, the basement proteins of the basal cells of STSG are not exposed to dispase treatment. Moreover, there is an intact basement membrane at epidermal-dermal junction in the STSG. The dermal fibroblasts of the STSG may play biological roles such as deposition of fibronectin, laminin and release of beta-transforming growth factor, and regulation of epidermalization [64, 65]. CEA mainly consists of keratinocytes. These may be the reasons of incompatibility of CEA with the neodermis of collagen-GAG. However, the exact reasons remain unknown.

Re-epitheliazation of Neodermis of Collagen-GAG with Cultured Laserskin

Recently, cultured Laserskin (CLS) (Fig. 1) consisting of autologous keratinocytes has been successfully grafted on the neodermis of Integra in three patients. One of them underwent burn scar release surgery [66]. The other two patients had giant navi excision. Laserskin™ (Fidia) is made of 100 % hyaluronate acid derivative. It is a thin, biocompatible, pliable, transparent membrane. There are laser-perfo-

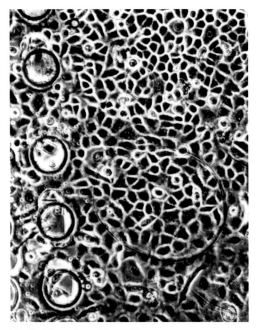

Fig. 1: The cultured Laserskin

Fig. 2: Wound resurfaced by Integra and CLS. Picture taken 3 months after treatment.

rated microholes, 40 μm each, with 6,000 perforations/cm². The micropores allow the migration of the keratinocyte population from the upper surface to the underneath recipient wound bed. There are also some macroholes (0.5 mm) on the Laserskin TM for the drainage of wound exudate. Keratinocytes poorly seed on plain Laserskin. According to the manufacturer's instructions, irrdaiated 3T3 cells are recommended as a feeder layer. As mentioned above, there is a potential risk of oncogenes transmission via 3T3 cells. Non-irradiated human dermal fibroblasts have been demonstrated to enhance the clonal formation of keratinocyte population on Laserskin with seeding density 2–4 x 10⁴ cells/cm² [67]. In an experiment with rat, the take rate of CLS on the neodermis of Integra was 70 % [68]. Clinically a 3 x 5 mm punch skin biopsy was taken from the patient for the fabrication of CLS which consisted of autologous keratinocytes and dermal fibroblasts serving as feeder layer. After complete vascularization into the collagen –GAG, the silicone membrane was removed and replaced by CLS. The initial take of CLS on the neodermis of In-

tegra were 50 %, 70 % and 100 % in these three patients respectively [69]. The initial loss of CLS was due to mild infection. After the wounds were cleansed with saline irrigation, dressing changes and antibiotic, another CLG was applied to expedite the epithelialization. The wounds of the patients completely healed at 12 weeks, 4 weeks and 3 weeks, respectively after the engraftment of the first application of CLS (Fig. 2). Stratified epithelium developed 21 days postgrafting (Fig. 3).

The exact mechanism of combining CLS with neodermis is not fully understood. CLS demonstrates the following advantages: (I) The basement proteins of the CLS are free from dispase exposure because the keratinocytes are directly cultivated on pliable Laserskin; (II) besides acting as feeder layer, the dermal fibroblasts may release some useful proteins such as fibronectin to enhance the anchorage of CLS onto the neodermis; (IV) the preparation time of CLS is 5–7 days sooner than that of conventional CEA because the keratinocytes of CLS are grafted at their sub-confluent stage; (V) CLS is more durable than the more fragile CEA; (VI) CLS requires a relatively low seeding density of 2–4 x 10⁴ cells/cm² which is similar to that of Green's method. It must be empha-

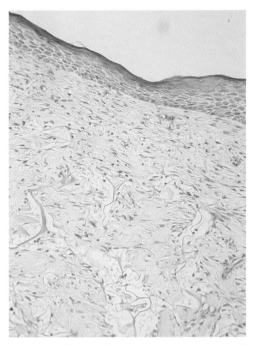

Fig. 3: Histology at day 21 after the application of cultured Laserskin showed complete re-epithelialization by Cultured Laserskin of the neodermis of Integra (H & E x100).

sized that this is only a limited experience including a small number of patients. Further clinical trial is needed. It is recognized that the healing process of clean surgical wounds is quite different from that of burn wounds which are usually infected. The CLS has to be more durable when this combination technique is applied in burns surgery. Moreover, our preliminary study was performed on selected small wounds. Apart from infection problem, the application of this combination technique in major burn will be complicated by the unfavorable wound environment associated with a large and open wound. Further improvement of CLS is reguined to overcome there unfavourable environments.

References

[1] *Spence RJ, Wong L:* The management of wound healing with human skin allograft. Wound healing; 77: 731–745, 1997.

[2] *Clark JA:* HIV transmission and skin (letter). Lancet; 1: 983, 1983.

[3] *Pruitt BA, Levine NS:* Characteristics and uses of biologic dressings and skin substitutes. Arch Surg; 119: 312–322, 1984.

[4] *Pruitt BA:* The evolutionary development of biologic dressings and skin substitutes. J Burn Care Rehabil; 18: S2–5, 1997.

[5] *Tompkins RG, Burke JF:* Burn wound clousure using permanent skin replacement materials. World J Surg; 16: 47–52, 1992.

[6] *Boyce ST, Ham RG:* Calcium-regulated differentiation of normal human epidermal keratinocytes in chemically defined clonal culture and serum-free serial culture. J Invest Dermatol; 81(supplement): 33s–40s, 1983.

[7] *Hennings H, Micheal D, Cheng C, Steinert P, Holbrook K, Yuspa S:* Calcium regulation of growth and differentiation of mouse epidermal cells in culture. Cell; 19: 245–264, 1980.

[8] *Dykes PJ, Marks R:* The effect of calcium on the initiation and growth of human epidermal cells. Arch Dermatol Res; 273: 225–231, 1982.

[9] *Tsao MC, Walthall BJ, Ham RG:* Clonal growth of normal human epidermal keratinocytes in a defined medium. J Cellular Physiology; 110: 219–229, 1982.

[10] *Rheinwald JG, Green H:* Formation of a keratinizing epithelium in culture of a cloned cell line derived from a teratoma cell; 6:317–321, 1975.

[11] *Rheinwald JG, Green H:* Serial cultivation of human epidermal keratinocytes: the formation of keratinizing colonies from single cells. Cell; 6: 331–334, 1975.

[12] *Slacker KL, Williams ML, Goldyne M:* Mitomycin C-treated 3T3 fibroblasts used as feeder layers for human keratinocyte culture retain the capacity to generate eicosanoids. J Invest Dermatol; 89:536–539, 1987.

[13] *Dascome W, Britt LD, Jones GT, Futrell JW, Lind J:* Cultured keratinocytes grafts: A review and clinical update. Current Surgery; 50: 428–438, 1993.

[14] *Carver N, Leigh IM:* Keratinocyte grafts and skin equivalents. Int J Dermat; 30:540–551, 1991.

[15] *Nanchahal J, Ward CM:* New grafts for old? A review of alternatives to autologous skin. Br J Plast Surg; 45: 354–363, 1992.

[16] *O'conner NE, Mulliken JB, Banks-Schlegel S, Kehinde O, Green H:* Grafting of burns with cultured epidelium prepared from autologous epidermal cells. Lancet: 75–76, 1981.

[17] *Munster AM, Weiner SH, Spence RJ:* Cultured epidermis for the coverage of massive burn wounds. Ann Surg; 211: 676–680, 1990.

[18] *Herzog SR, Meyer A, Woodley D, Peterson HD:* Wound coverage with cultured autologous keratinocytes: use after burn wound exci-

sion, including biopsy foloow-up. J Trauma;
28: 195–200, 1991.

[19] *Boyce ST, Warden GD, Hilder IA:* Cytotoxicity
testing of topical antimicrobial agents on
human keratinocytes and fibroblasts for cultured skin grafts. J Burn care Rehabil; 16:
97–103, 1995.

[20] *Lam PK, Chan ESY, Ho WS, King WWK:* In vitro
cytotoxicity of Bactroban as a topical agent
on human keratinocytes and fibroblasts.
Asian J surg; 22: 370–373, 1999.

[21] *Cooper ML, Boyce ST, Hansbrough JF, foreman
TJ, Frank DH:* Cytotoxicity to cultured kerati-
nocytes of topical antimicrobial agents. J Surg
Res; 48: 190–195, 1990.

[22] *Todaro GJ, Habel K, Green H:* Antigenic and cultural of cells doubly transformed by polyoma
virus and SV40. Virology; 179–185, 1965.

[23] *Hultman CS, Brinson GM, Siltharm S, Deserres
S, Cairns BA, Peterson HD, Meyer AA:* Allogeneic fibroblasts used to grow cultured epidermal autografts persist in vivo and sensitize the graft recipient for accelerated second-set rejection. J Trauma; 41: 51–60, 1996.

[24] *Cairns BA, Deserres S, Brady LA, Hutman CS,
Meyer AA:* Exenogeneic mouse fibroblasts
persist in human cultured epidermal grafts:
a possible mechanism of graft loss. J Trauma;
39: 75–79, 1995.

[25] *Breidahl AF, Judson RT, Clunie GJA:* Review of
keratinocyte culture techniques: problems
of growing skin. Aust N Z Surg; 59: 485–497,
1989.

[26] *Lam PK, Chan ESY., Liew CT., Lau CH., Yen S.C.,
King W.W.K.:* Effectiveness of collagen dermis
membrane and fibrin on cultured epidermal
graft using athymic mice model. Annals of
Plastic Surgery; 43: 523–528, 1999.

[27] *Auger FA, Guignard R, Lopez V, Germain L:* Role
and innocuity of Tisseel, a tissue glue, in the
grafting process and in vivo evolution of human cultured epidermis. Br J Plast surg; 46:
136–142, 1993.

[28] *Ronfdard V, Broly H, Mitchell V, Galizia JP,
Hochart D, Chambon E, Pellerin P, Huart JJ:* Use
of human keratinocytes cyltured on fibrin
glue in the treatment of burn wounds. Burns;
17: 181–184, 1991.

[29] *Kaiser HW, Stark GB, Kopp J, Balcerkiewicz A,
Spilker, Kreysel HW:* Cultured autologous keratinocytes in fibrin glue suspension, exclusively and combined with STS-alligraft (preliminary clinical and histological report of a
new technique). Burn; 20: 23–29, 1994.

[30] *Herzog SR, Meyer A, WoodleyD, Peterson HD:*
Wound coverage with cultured autologous
keratinocytes: use after burn wound excision, including biopsy foloow-up. J Trauma;
28: 195–198, 1991.

[31] *Cuono CB, Langdon R, McGuire J:* Use of cultured
epidermal autografts and dermal autografts
and dermal allograft as skin replacement after
burn injury. Lancet; 1: 1123–4, 1986.

[32] *Willaimson JS, Snelling CFT, Clugston P, Macdonald IB, German L:* Cultured epithelial autograft:
five years of clinical experience with twenty-
eight patients. J Trauma; 39: 309–319, 1995.

[33] *Wainwright D, Madden M, Luterman A, Hunt J,
Monafo W, Heimbach D, Kagan R, sittig K, Dimick A, Herndon D:* clinical evaluation of an acellular allograft dermal matrix in full-thickness
burns. J Burn Care Rehabil; 17: 124–136, 1996.

[34] *Sheridan R, Choucair R, Donelan M, Lydon M,
Petras L, Tompkins R:* Acellular allodermis in
burn surgery: 1- year results of a pilot trial. J
Burn Care Rehabil; 19: 528–30

[35] *Wainwright DJ:* Use of an acellular allograft
dermal matrix (Alloderm) in the management of full-thickness burns. Burns; 21: 243–
248, 1995.

[36] *Hoekstra H:* Bevederm: A cellularised glycerinised cadaver dermis. Abstract at The State
of the Art Symposium – Skin Substitutes:
quality and Standard and 5th Central European Burn Conference. 28–30 September, Brno,
Czech Republic, 2000.

[37] *Bell E, Ehrlich HP, Sher S, Merrill C, Sarber R,
Hull B, Nakatsuji, Church D, Buttle D:* Devel-
opment and use of a living skin equivalent.
Plastic Reconst Surg; 67: 386–392, 1981.

[38] *Bell E, Ivarson B, Merrill C:* Production of a tissue-like structure by contraction of collagen
lattices by human fibroblasts of different
proliferative potential in vitro. Proc Natl acad
Sci USA; 76: 1274–78, 1979.

[39] *Purdue GF, Hunt JL, Still JM, Law EJ, et al.:* A
multicenter clinical trial of a biosynthetic
skin replacement, Dermagraft-TC*, compared with cryopreserved human cadaver
skin for temporary coverage of excised burn
wounds. J Burn care Rehab; 18: 52–7, 1997.

[40] *Hansbrough JF, Morgan JL, Greenleaf GE, Bartel
R:* composite grafts of human keratinocytes
grown on a polyglactin mesh-cultured fibroblast dermal substitute function as a bilayer skin
replacement in full-thickness wounds on athymic mice. J Burn care Rehab; 14;465–94, 1993.

[41] *Hansbrough J, Mozingo D, Kealey G, et al.:* Clinical trials of a biosynthetic temporary skin replacement, Dermagraft-Transitional covering,
compared to cyropreserved human cadaver
skin for temporary coverage of excised burn
wounds. J Burn Care Rehabil; 18: 43–51, 1997.

[42] *Yannas IV, Burke JF:* Design of an artificial skin
1. Basic design principles. J Biomed Mat Res;
14: 65–81, 1980.

[43] *Yannas IV, Burke JF, Gordon PL, Huang C, Ru-
bebstein RH:* Design of an artificial skin II.

Control of chemical composition. J Biomed Mater Res; 14: 65–81, 1980

[44] *Dagalaka N, Flink J, Stasikelis P, Burke JF, Yannas IV:* Design of an artificial skin. III . control of pore structure. J Biomed Mater Res; 14: 510–528, 1980.

[45] *Suzuki S, Matsuda K, Isshiki N, Ikada Y:* Experimental study of a newly developed bilayer artificial skin. Biomaterials; 11: 356–360, 1990.

[46] *Matsuda K, Suzuki S, Issihiki N, Yoshioka K, Okada T, Ikada Y:* Influence of glycosaminoglycans on the collagen sponge component of a bilayer skin. Biomaterials; 11: 351–355, 1990.

[47] *Heimbach D, Luterman A, Burke JF, Cram A, Herndon D, Hunt J:* Artificial dermis for major burns: a multi-center randomized clinical trial. Ann Surg; 208: 313–320, 1988.

[48] *Yannas IV, Burk JF, Orgill DP, Skrabut EM:* Wound tissue can utilize a polymeric template to synthesize a functional extension of skin. Science; 215: 174–6, 1982.

[49] *Lorenz C, Hokl HP, Wessel L, Wang KL:* Early wound closure and early reconstruction. Experience with a dermal substitute in a child with 60 per cent surface area burn. Burns; 23: 505–508, 1997.

[50] *Prunieras M, Regier M, Woodley D:* Methods for cultivation of keratinocytes with an air-liquid interface. J Invest Dermatol; 81: 28s–33s, 1983.

[51] *Langdon RC, Cuono CB, Birchall N, et al.:* Reconstitution of structures and cell function in human skin grafts derived from cryopreserved allogenic dermis and autologous cultured keratinocytes J Invest. Dermat.; 91: 478–481, 1988.

[52] *PK Lam, ESY Chan, RSC Yen, HCH Lau, WWK King:* A new system to cultivate keratinocytes on acellular human dermis using fibrin glue and 3T3 feeder cells. J Burn Care Rehab; 21: 1–4, 2000.

[53] *Gao ZR, Hao ZQ, Nie LJ, Liu GF:* Coverage of full skin thickness burns with allograft innocluated with autogenoces epithelials cells. Burns 1986; 12: 220 – thickness burns with allograft innoculated with autogenoces epithelials cells. Burns; 12: 220–222, 1986.

[54] *Hansbrough JF, Boyce ST, Cooper ML, Foreman TJ:* Burn wound closure with cultured autologous keratinocytes and fibroblasts attached to a collagen-glycosaminoglycan substrate. JAMA; 262: 2125–2130, 1989.

[55] *Butler CE, Orgill DP, Yannas IV:* Effect of keratinocytes seeding of collagen-glycosaminoglycan membranes on the regeneration of skin in a porcine model. Plast Reonstr Surg; 101: 1572–79, 1998.

[56] *Orgill DP, Butler C, Regan JF, Barlow MS, Yannas IV, Compton CC:* Vascularized collagen-glycosaminoglycan matrix porides a dermal substrate and improves take of cultured epi-

thelial autografts. Plast Reoconst surg; 102: 423–429, 1998.

[57] *Butler CE, Yannas IV, Compton CC, Correia CA, Orgill DP:* Comparison of cultured and uncultured keratinocytes seeded into a collagen-GAG matrix for skin replacements. Br J Plast Surg; 52: 127–132, 1999.

[58] *Boyce ST, Kagan RG, Meyer NA, Yakuboff KP, Warden GD:* Cultured skin substitutes combined with Integra artificial skin to replace native skin autograft and allograft for the closure of excised full-thickness burns. J Burn Care Rehabil; 20: 453–61, 1999.

[59] *Lam PK, Chan ESY.:* Integra and cultured epithelium. J Burn Care Rehabil; 22:197–188, 2001

[60] *Compton CC, Nadire KB, Regauer S, Simon M, Warland G, Connor NR, Gallico GG, Landry DB:* Cultured human sole-derived keratinocyte grafts re-express site specific differentiation after transplantation. Differentiation; 64: 45–53, 1998.

[61] *Sheridan RL, Tompkins RG:* "Skin substitutes in burns." Burns; 25: 97–103, 1999.

[62] *Tompkins RG, Burke JF:* Alternative wound coverage. In :Total Burn Care. Edited by Herndon DN. Saunders. pp 164–174, 1997.

[63] *Pandya AN, Woodward B, Parkhouse N:* The use of cultured autologous keratinocytes with Integra in the resurfacing of acute burns. Plastic Reconstructive Surgery; 102:825–828, 1998.

[64] *Coulomb B, Lebreton C, Dubertret L:* Influence of human dermal fibroblasts on epidermalization. J Invest Dermatol; 92: 122–125, 1989.

[65] *Demarchez M, Hartmann DJ, Regnier M, Asselineau D:* the role of fibroblasts in dermal vascularization and remodeling of reconstructed human skin after transplantation onto the nude mouse. Transplantation; 54: 317–326, 1992.

[66] *Chan ESY, Lam PK, Liew CT, Yen RSC, Lau WY:* The use of Composite Laserskin graft and artificial skin for burns reconstruction. Plastic & Reconst Surg; 105: 807–8, 2000.

[67] *Lam PK, Chan ESY, To EWH, Lau CH, Yen SC, King WWK:* Development and evaluation of a new composite Laser skin graft. J Trauma; 47: 918–922, 1999.

[68] *Lam PK, Chan PK, Liew CT, Yen RSC, Lau HCH, King WWK:* The combination of a new composite biocompatible skin graft on the neodermis of artificial skin in an animal model. Abstract at the Tissue Engineering Symposium. 5–8 September, Perth, Australia, 2000.

[69] *Chan ESY, Lam PK, Liew CT, Yen RSC, Lau HCH:* A preliminary evaluation of composite biocompatible skin graft(CBSG) on the neodermis of artificial skin. Abstract at the Tissue Engineering Symposium. 5–8 September, Perth, Australia, 2000.

Sub-Atmospheric Pressure Wound Treatment and Cultured Keratinocyte Allografts

M. J. Morykwas, L.C. Argenta

Summary

Cultured keratinocyte auto- and allografts require an optimal wound bed in order to properly adhere to the recipient surface and are prone to infection. In chronic wounds keratinocyte adherence to the surfaces of chronic wounds can be critically hindered by bacterial contamination, poor vascularization, edema, and necrotic material in the wound. The optimal wound bed for keratinocytes should be well vascularized, with a low level of bacterial colonization. The use of sub-atmospheric pressure (Vacuum-assisted-closure, V.A.C.) to prepare the wound bed prior to wound closure, with over 2,500 wounds being treated to date at the Wake Forest Medical center is shown to be an appropriate tool to effectively prepare problem wounds for keratinocyte grafting.

Introduction

This short section will deal with two separate but interdependant topics: preparation of the wound bed prior to placement of cultured keratinocyte grafts; and the cultured keratinocyte graft itself. Both topics are well supported by extensive clinical experience at our institution.

Wound Bed Preparation

An extremely important facet in wound care is to prepare a proper wound bed to maximize the potential for a successful application of a cultured keratinocye graft. While it is an apparently obvious prerequisite, if the wound bed is heavily contaminated and edematous, with necrotic tissue or excessive fibrinous material present, the chance of a successful treatment with either cultured keratinocyte allograft or autograft is greatly diminished. The wound bed should be well vascularized, with a low level of bacterial colonization.

We have over ten years experience in the use of sub-atmospheric pressure (The V.A.C., KCI, San Antonio Texas) to prepare the wound bed prior to wound closure, with over 2,500 wounds being treated to date at our medical center. While its use has greatly expanded to include treatment of acute and traumatic wounds, sub-atmospheric pressure treatment was initially developed for the treatment of chronic wounds, including pressure sores and a variety of lower extremity ulcers [1]. Sub-atmospheric pressure for wound treatment is extremely effective in promoting the formation of granulation tissue and in reducing edema from the periwound tissues [1, 2]. Additionally, studies performed with infected wounds in an animal (swine) model has shown an significant decrease in the number of bacteria in wound tissue during the course of sub-atmospheric pressure treatment [2].

The sub-atmospheric pressure treatment system consists of a sterile, open cell foam dressing with an embedded evacuation tube. No device or treatment is going to restore dead tissue – all necrotic tissue must be debrided. Following debridement, the foam dressing is trimmed to fit to the denuded surface of the wound. The foam dressing should be in contact with all non-epithelialized surfaces. The foam dressing and wound site are covered with a thin film adhesive drape to create an air tight seal. The evacuation tube may exit from the edge of the adhesive drape, in which case a mesentery should be formed by pinching the drape under the tube so it adheres to itself. Alternatively, the tube may be removed from the foam dressing prior to sealing with the adhesive drape. Once the drape is placed, a small incision may be made in the drape and the tubing inserted into the foam dressing and the incision site sealed. The tube is then attached to a micro-processor controlled vacuum pump. As opposed to saline moistened gauze dressings that are changed two or three times per day, the sub-atmospheric pressure dressing is routinely changed at 48 hour intervals. Wounds may be treated to complete closure, closed surgically by suturing, with a muscle flap or with a split thickness skin graft, or treated with cultured keratinocyte allografts after an adequate granulating bed is present.

Chronic lower extremity ulcers, particularly venous stasis ulcers, are frequently painful. A lower, continuous vacuum setting is routinely used at the start of treatment of these wounds than would be used for acute wounds. We routinely will begin treatment of these wounds at 50 mm mercury of vacuum. The normal level of vacuum for treatment of acute or traumatic wounds is 125 mm Hg. While cycled application of the vacuum is more effective in promoting granulation tissue formation [2], the repeated collapse and re-expansion of the foam dressing continually causes pain. Continuous vacuum application is frequently more comfortable for patients with lower extremity ulcers. Continuous vacuum application is painful for 20–30 minutes, then the pain subsides.

In general, the longer a wound has been open, the longer the interval before granulation tissue begins to form. Typically, wounds are treated for 2–4 weeks with sub-atmospheric pressure, although some have been treated significantly longer before the wound bed was covered with granulation tissue. In the event that portions of the wound produce hyperproliferative granulation tissue that projects higher than the surrounding issue, the hyperproliferative growth is removed by chemical cautery with silver nitrate. After production of an adequate layer of granulation tissue, the wound is then treated with cultured keratinocyte allografts.

Keratinocyte Allografts

Fresh tissue samples are obtained from young males undergoing surgical procedures, e.g. hypospadias repair or circumcision. Informed consent is obtained from the parents prior to obtaining the tissue, and all donors undergo the routine battery of tests administered to all organ donors. The epidermis is separated from the dermis by enzymatic digestion. The keratinocytes are plated onto tissue culture dishes and cultured under standard conditions; 37 °C, 5 % CO_2 with humidity. At the third passage, the cells are plated onto an 100 micrometer thick extruded sheet of Type I bovine dermal collagen (Brechteen Corp., Mt Clemens Michigan) in which the cross-linking density has been increased to prevent digestion [3, 4]. Low calcium culture conditions are continued to maximize cellular proliferation. Prior to placement on the wound surface, the allograft is washed twice with a HEPES buffer, placed into a sealed container and transported to the clinic or hospital bed.

The collagen based dermal substrate provides mechanical and dimensional stability to the keratinocyte graft. This stability allows for physical manipulation of the graft prior to placement. The graft may be trimmed, placed and removed and replaced, etc. The graft and wound site is covered with a layer of petrolatum impregnated gauze to prevent dehydration, followed by gauze and then is wrapped. The collagen is resisted degradation and the allograft is changed at weekly intervals until the wound is healed. A wide variety of chronic wounds have been successfully treated, ranging from Buerger's disease to sickle anemia to diabetic ulcers to venous stasis ulcers [5]. Figures 1–3. In addition, the technique and

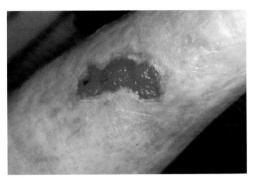

Fig. 1: Chronic leg ulcer on seventy two year old male with sideroblastic anemia. Wound had been open eighteen years. Patient required one unit of blood transfusion per week for last several years.

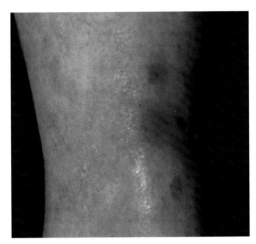

Fig. 3: Closed wound following three placements of cultured keratinocyte allografts. Allografts had been placed at weekly intervals. Wound has been stable for four years.

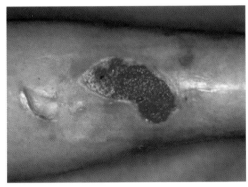

Fig. 2: Wound appearance with abundant granulation tissue present after 2 weeks of sub-atmospheric pressure treatment.

grafts have been used successfully to treat wounds in non-human primates using the human cells as a xenograft [6].

Following successful re-epithelialization, education is extremely important to prevent recurrence of wounds. Patients are advised to wear compression hose or garments, quit smoking, wear proper fitting shoes, etc.

Conclusion

Sub-atmospheric pressure application has been shown to be extremely effective in promoting granulation tissue formation and reducing edema from chronic wounds. Sub-atmospheric pressure foam dressing normally are changed at 48 hour intervals, thus minimizing patient discomfort associated with changing saline moistened gauze every six to eight hours. The highly vascularized, clean wound bed is optimal for accepting a cultured keratinocyte allograft. Plating the keratinocytes on a highly cross-linked collagen sheet provides mechanical and dimensional stability to the allograft, allowing easy manipulation of the graft during placement. The additional stability allows for the graft to be changed at weekly intervals. The patient's own periwound keratinocytes rapidly migrate and proliferate, resulting in a re-epithelialized wound. Long term wound stability is often dependent upon patient education and compliance.

References

[1] *Argenta, LC and Morykwas, MJ:* Vacuum Assisted Closure: A New Method for Wound Control and Treatment – Clinical Experience. Ann Plast Surg 38:563–77, 1997.
[2] *Morykwas, MJ, Argenta, LC, Shelton-Brown EI, McGuirt W:* Vacuum Assisted Closure: A New

Method for Wound Control and Treatment –
Animal Studies and Basic Foundation. Ann
Plast Surg 38:553–62, 1997.

[3] *Morykwas, MJ:* In vitro Properties of Cross-
linked, Reconstituted Collagen Sheets. J Biomed Mater Res 24:1105–10, 1990.

[4] *Morykwas, MJ, Stevenson, TR, Marcelo, CL,
Thornton, JH, Smith DJ:* In vitro and in vivo Test-
ing of a Collagen Sheet to Support Keratinocyte
Growth for Use as a Burn Wound Covering. J
Trauma 29: 1163–67, 1989.

[5] *Morykwas, MJ, Rouchard, RA, Jennings, DA,
Argenta, LC:* One Hundred Fifty Consecu-
tive Chronic Wounds Treated with Cultured Allogenic Keratinocytes on a Collagen
Dermal Substrate. Plast Surg Forum 16:15–
17, 1993.

[6] *Line, AS, Morykwas, MJ, Line, SW:* Use of Cultured Epidermal Xenografts for Wound Treatment in Non-human Primates. J Zoo Wildlife
Med 26:517–24, 1995.

Clinical Results of Cultured Epithelial Cell Grafting in the Oral and Maxillofacial Region

C.-Y. Tsai, M. Ueda, K.-I. Hata, K. Horie, Y. Hibino, Y. Sugimura, K. Toriyama, S. Torii

Summary

Cultured epithelium has proven to be a good grafting material for skin defects. In our experience, two kinds of epithelial cells, skin keratinocytes and mucosal cells, have been used to fabricate cultured epithelial sheets and autografted to the patients. Traumatic scars of the face were treated by cultured epidermal epithelium (CEE). The skin graft in the oral cavity was replaced by mucosa using cultured mucosal epithelium (CME). Also, the CME was applied to the skin defects at the donor sites of split-thickness skin grafts. Postsurgical follow-up showed good results. As a result, CME was useful in improving the biological environment around the abutments of dental implants, and it also promoted the re-epithelialization of skin defects. From our investigations, CEE/CME are promising treatment modalities which can reduce the pain and speed up the healing process in burn patients. Therefore, cultured epithelium banks are worth establishing for auto- and allografting of skin/mucosal defects.

Introduction

The technique of epidermal culture was established by Rheinwald and Green in 1975 [1]. Today, cultured epidermal epithelium (CEE) have been applied widely in the treatment of burn wounds, skin defects and con-genital navies [2, 3, 4]. However, most of these clinical cases have involved the reconstruction of the extremities, in the field of plastic surgery. The Department of Oral Surgery, Nagoya University School of Medicine, has utilized Green's method to fabricate CEE for the treatment of traumatic scars in the maxillofacial region.

Oral cancer patients are always treated by excising extensively a large part of the oral cavity structures, and rehabilitated by autogenous bone graft and/or skin graft. Recently, osseointegrated dental implant modalities have been applied for the reconstruction of occlusal function. However, the thickness of keratinized skin permits it formation of deep peri-implant pockets and results in inflammation around the abutments [5, 6]. Some investigators resolved the inflammation by using a palatal or buccal mucosal grafting [7. 8], but the insufficient mucosa availability at the donor site has been a concomitant problem. Therefore, culture technology was applied to produce abundant mucosal epithelium [9, 10, 11].

In our department, mucosal cells were used to fabricate cultured mucosal epithelium (CME) by a modified Greens' method and applied clinically for intraoral vestibuloplasty related to the implant therapy. Furthermore, it was applied to the repair of skin defects at the donor sites of split-thickness skin grafts. The good results showed that CME is useful in the treatment of oral mucosal and skin defects.

Materials and Methods

The epidermal/mucosal epithelia were fabricated according to Green's method. The skin/mucosal specimens were excised from patients of the Department of Plastic Surgery and the Department of Oral Surgery, Nagoya University Hospital. These tissues were immersed in Dulbecco's modified Eagle's medium (DMEM) containing 1000 PU/ml of dispase for 16 hours at 4° to separate the epithelial layers. The epithelium was treated with 0.25% trypsin for 30 minutes, and stirred with DMEM containing 5% FCS for 30 minutes to isolate the cells. The suspension solution was filtered through a nylon gauze (50 μm) and centrifuged to purified epidermal/mucosal cells, then re-suspended in culture medium.

The 3T3 cells served as the feeder layer, and were treated with 4 μg/ml mitomycin C in DMEM for 2 hours previously. Afterward, epidermal/mucosal cells were inoculated on the feeder layer, and co-cultured at 37° with 10% CO2 incubator. The medium used for culturing epidermal/mucosal cells was composed by DMEM and Ham's F12 medium with the volume ratio of 3:1. Supplements were added with FCS 5%; cholera toxin 1x10-10M; hydrocortisone 0.5 g/ml; transferrin 5 μg/ml; triiodothyronine 2x10-10M, insulin 5 μg/ml and antibiotics. Human recombinant epidermal growth factor (EGF) was added at 10 ng/ml when cell adhesion was complete. After three weeks of culturing, the cultured epidermal/mucosal epithelium was fabricated.

Results

Cultured Epidermal Epithelium Grafting for Treatment of Traumatic Scar

Two cases of traumatic scar were treated by CEE grafting (Table 1). A 21-year-old male patient (case 1) had a pigmented and irregular scar surface on the right side of his face due to a traffic accident (Fig. 1A). A specimen of normal skin near the scar tissue was taken

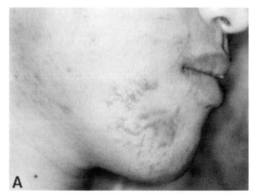

Fig. 1A: Before operation; traumatic tattoo on the face.

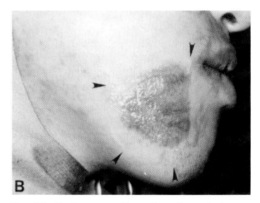

Fig. 1B: During operation; the pigmented scar was debrided off, then the epithelium (arrow) was grafted.

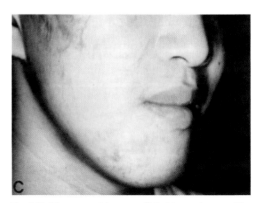

Fig. 1C: The wound became flat skin, and was without pigmented scar after 6 months.

for culturing the CEE. The pigmented scar was debrided to produce a flat grafting bed using a high-speed grinder. The CEE was previously treated with 400 PU/ml dispase in DMEM for 30 minutes to permit peeling off from the culture flask. The detached epithelium was carried by an atelocollagen membrane and grafted to the bed, then the carrier was removed (Fig. 1B). The epithelial grafts were covered with a petrolatum nylon mesh, gauze dressing, then tied over for fixation. The grafted wound rapidly re-epithelialized, and after 6 months became flat skin with no pigmented scar (Fig. 1C).

Cultured Mucosal Epithelium Grafting for Vestibuloplasty Related to Implant Treatment

Four intraoral applications of CME grafting were shown here (Table 2). A 52-year-old male patient (case 1) was diagnosed as squamous cell carcinoma (T2N1M0) and treated by mandibular segmental resection and neck dissection. Rehabilitation of the oral cavity was performed by autografting vascularized fibula bone flap and skin flap and inserting Branemark implants for reconstruction of the occlusion. A small mucosal specimen was obtained in this operation and CME were fabricated three weeks later. They were then kept frozen at – 196° liquid nitrogen until the second implant operation.

After 6 months, the autografted bone and skin survived, but a movable and keratinized skin graft was noted (Fig. 2A). During the second implant operation, the grafted skin was excised as a vestibuloplasty (Fig. 2B), the abutments were connected to the fixtures, then the periosteum was covered by CME (Fig. 2C). Thereafter, CME were compressed by tetracycline gauze and a plastic splint, and fixed by the healing caps of implants (Fig. 2D).

Four months after surgery, all parts of the new mucosal membrane contain translucent capillaries. No keratinized epithelium has developed around the implants. Moveable mu-

cosal membrane was found which showed the grafted skin replacement was successful (Fig. 2E). A small segment was taken from the adjacent of abutment, then examined by H-E staining. Histological findings revealed that CME became stratified squamous epithelium without keratinization and some inflammation cells in the intercellular spaces (Fig. 2F). The adjacent connective tissue contained numerous ectopic capillaries and single inflammatory cells. The histological result underscores the importance of the type of connective tissue for the epithelial differentiation and architecture.

Cultured Mucosal Epithelia Grafting for Applications of Skin Defects

Six extraoral applications of CME grafting are shown here (Table 3). To confirm the usefulness of CME as a skin graft material, CME was applied to the donor site of split-thickness skin grafts. A 64-year-old female patient (case 1) had squamous cell carcinoma (T1N0M0) on the right side of the tongue. An oral mucosal segment was obtained previously for culturing. Hemiglossectomy was performed, and the mucosal defect was autografted with split-thickness skin (18/1000 inches thick) from the right thigh. Cultured mucosal epithelium was then grafted to one half of the donor site, whilst the other half was covered by gentamycin ointment dressing as a control site (Fig. 3A). One week after the operation, CME grafting site had survived completely and exudation had ceased; however, the control site still showed hemorrhage and exudation (Fig. 3B)

Discussion

Cultured epithelial sheets established by Green in 1975 have been widely acknowledged to be a useful and safe material for the transplantation if skin defects. The characteristic of CEE is that epidermal cells are cul-

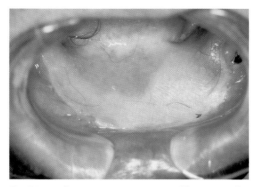

Fig. 2A: Oral cavity was reconstructed by autografting bone and skin, and the Branemark implant fixtures were inserted. Movable and keratinized skin graft remained in the oral cavity.

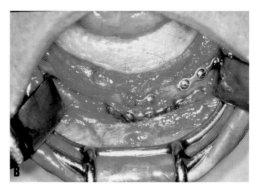

Fig. 2B: The grafted skin was excised as a vestibuloplasty.

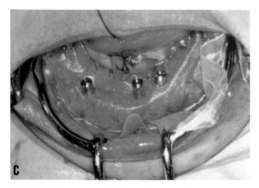

Fig. 2C: CME was grafted on the top of periosteum during vestibuloplasty.

Fig. 2D: CME was retained by a plastic splint and fixed by the healing caps of the implants.

Fig. 2E: Four months after second implant operation, CME replaced the grafted skin.

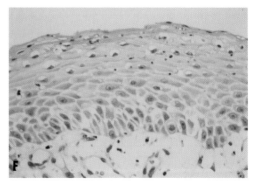

Fig. 2F: Histological examination showed that CME was stratified like typical oral mucosa. (H.E. x400)

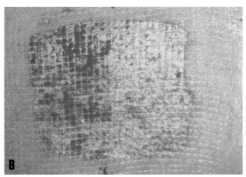

Fig. 3A: CME was grafted to one half of the donor sites of a split-thickness skin graft (arrow).

Fig. 3B: One week after grafting, CME graft on the right donor site survived completely. However, the control site on the left still showed hemorrhage and exudates.

tured with 3T3 feeder-layer cells, and stratified into 6–10 cell layers of epithelium, giving enough strength for grafting.

In our department, the CME was fabricated by mucosal cells and 3T3 feeder-layer cells [12], then temporarily preserved in – 196° liquid nitrogen for several months [13]. Finally, the CME is grafted upon periosteum, when the vestibuloplasty is performed during the second implant operation [14]. As a result, CME could replace the movable and thick grafted skin to diminish the instability and plaque accumulation on the implants. Also, patient no longer experience the uncomfortably rough surface of the keratinized skin surface in the oral cavity.

By applying CME to the donor sites of split-thickness skin grafts, it was demonstrated that CME can promote the re-epithelialization of skin defects. Hata and co-workers (1995) have compared the biological characteristics of CEE and CME, and found the latter had advantages in terms of shorter cell turnover time and long-term maintenance of epithelial viability. These suggest that mucosal cells can fabricate epithelium faster than epidermal cells, which is convenient for clinical grafting. Also, CME are useful grafts when an intact skin segment is difficult to obtain for extensive burn patients [14].

However, there are some disadvantages in this cultured epithelial autograft. Cultured

epithelium possesses only the epithelial layer, and it is too thin in epithelial sheets to resist the mechanical stress of wound contraction. Especially, in patients who suffer from severe skin or mucosal defects and lose the dermal or submucosal layer, cultured epithelium can not assure good results. Also, it takes 3 to 4 weeks to fabricate the cultured epithelium in vitro which is a contraindication in emergency burn patients. This drawback might be overcome by the use of allogenic cultured epithelium.

Several authors have reported the promotion of wound healing of burns by the application of cultured epithelial allografting [15, 16]. Cultured epithelium has also been stored in a frozen state, making long-term use possible [13, 17]. Some other investigators examined the cultured epithelial allografts by a probe specific for the Y chromosome [15], and found that epidermal allografts do not survive permanently. The epidermal regeneration was due to the migration and proliferation of recipient residual keratinocytes [18, 19]. However, it has been proved that the allografted keratinocytes can secrete some cytokine factors which might promote the migration and proliferation of residual keratinocytes [20]. As a result, the main function of cultured epithelium allografts is to serve as a temporary biological dressing, and accelerate the re-epithelialization and wound healing. Decreasing the immunological rejection between the donor and recipient will increase the survival period of the allograft. Therefore, the function of various immunological cells should be further investigated and the rejection mechanisms of cultured epidermal/mucosal epithelial allografts should also be researched.

Cultured epidermal epithelium and cultured mucosal epithelium grafts are novel therapeutic methods for skin or mucosal defects. A new therapeutic modality has been investigated in our department, in which allogenous CEE/CME are preserved in an epithelial bank and allografted to skin or mucosal defects.

References

[1] *Rheinwald JG, H. Green:* Serial cultivation of strains of human epidermal kerationcytes: the formation of keratinizing colonies from single cells. Cell 6, 331–344 (1975)

[2] *O'Connor, NE, JB Mulliken, S Banks-Schlegel, O Kehinde, H Green:* Grafting of burns with cultured epithelium prepared from autologous epidermal cells. Lancet 10, 75–78 (1981)

[3] *Gallico, GG, NE O'Connor, CC Compton, O Kehinde, H Green:* Permanent coverage of large burn wounds with autologous cultured human epithelium. N. Engl. J. Med. 311, 448–451 (1984)

[4] *Kumagai, N, H Nishina, H Tanabe, T Hosaka, H Ishida, Y Ogino:* Clinical application of autologous cultured epithelial for the treatment of burn wounds and burn scars. Plast. Reconstr. Surg. 82, 99–108 (1988)

[5] *Rams, TE, CC Link:* Microbiology of failing dental implants in humans: electron microscopic observations. J. Oral Implantol. 11, 93–100 (1983)

[6] *Krekeler, G, W Schilli, J Diemer:* Should the exit of the artificial abutment tooth be positioned in the region of the attached gingiva? Int. J. Oral Surg. 14, 504–508 (1985)

[7] *Simons, AM, DG Darany, JR Giordano:* The use of free gingival grafts in the treatment of peri-implant soft tissue complications: clinical report. Implant. Dent. 2, 27–30 (1993)

[8] *Hertel, RC, PA Blijdorp, DL Baker:* A preventive mucosal flap technique for use in implantology. Int. J. Oral Maxillofac. Implants 8, 452–458 (1993)

[9] *Langdon, JD, IM Leigh, HA Navsaria, DM Williams:* Autologous oral keratinocyte grafts in the mouth. Lancet 335, 1472–14733 (1990)

[10] *Lauer, G, JE Otten, BU Specht, W Schilli:* Cultured gingival epithelium: A possible suitable material for pre-prosthetic surgery. J. Cranio. Max. Fac. Surg. 19, 21–26 (1991)

[11] *Lauer, G:* Autografting of feeder-cell free cultured gingival epithelium: method and clinical application. J. Cranio. Max. Fac. Surg. 22, 18–22 (1994)

[12] *Hata, K, H Kagami, M Ueda, S Torii, M Matsuyama:* The characteristics of cultured mucosal cell sheet as a material for grafting; comparison with cultured epidermal cell sheet. Ann. Plast. Surg. 34, 530–538 (1995)

[13] *Hibino, Y, K Hata, Y Sugimura, K Horie, M Ueda, S Torii:* A study of freezing methods of cultured mucosal epithelium. Jpn J. Oral Maxillofac. Surg. 41, 616–622 (1995)

[14] *Ueda, M, K Hata, K Horie, S Torii:* The potential of oral mucosal cells for cultured epithelium: A preliminary report. Ann. Plast. Surg. 35, 498–504 (1995)

[15] *Brain, A, P Purkis, P Coates, M Hackett, H Navsaria, I Leigh:* Survival of cultured allogeneic keratinocytes transplanted to deep dermal bed assessed with probe for Y chromosome. BMJ 298, 917–919 (1989)

[16] *Luca, MD, E Albanese:* Multicentre experience in the treatment of burns with autologous and allogenic cultured epithelium fresh or preserved in a frozen state. Burns 15, 303–309 (1989)

[17] *Teepe RGC, EJ Koebrugge, M Ponec, BJ Vermeer:* Fresh versus cryopreserved cultured allografts for the treatment of chronic skin ulcers. Br. J. Dermatol. 122, 81–89 (1990)

[18] *Luca, MD, E Albanese, R Cancedda, A Viacava, A Faggioni, G Zambruno, A Giannetti:* Treatment of leg ulcers with cryopreserved allogenic cultured epithelium: A multicenter study. Arch. Dermatol. 128, 633–638 (1992)

[19] *Rouabhia, M, L Germain, F. Belanger, FA Auger:* Cultured epithelium allografts: Langerhans cell and Thy-1+ dendritic epidermal cell depletion effects on allograft rejection. Transplantation 56, 259–264 (1993)

[20] *Nakano, M, T Yoshida, T Ohura, K Azami, A Senoo, Y Fuse:* Clinicopathologic studies on human epithelial autografts and allografts. Plast. Reconstr. Surg. 90, 899–909 (1992)

Subject Index